62/001-10/1/29

P/PHIS

THE LIFE OF
VERTEBRATES

THE LIFE OF
VERTEBRATES

BY

J. Z. YOUNG
M.A., F.R.S.

PROFESSOR OF ANATOMY
AT UNIVERSITY COLLEGE, LONDON

OXFORD
AT THE CLARENDON PRESS

Oxford University Press, Amen House, London E.C.4

GLASGOW NEW YORK TORONTO MELBOURNE WELLINGTON
BOMBAY CALCUTTA MADRAS KARACHI KUALA LUMPUR
CAPE TOWN IBADAN NAIROBI ACCRA

FIRST PUBLISHED 1950
REPRINTED LITHOGRAPHICALLY IN GREAT BRITAIN
AT THE UNIVERSITY PRESS, OXFORD
FROM CORRECTED SHEETS OF THE FIRST EDITION
1952, 1955, 1958

PREFACE

THE history of text-books is often dismissed by the contemptuous assertion that they all copy each other—and especially each other's mistakes. Inspection of this book will quickly confirm that this is true, but there is nevertheless an interest to be obtained from such a study, because text-books embody an attitude of mind; they show what sort of knowledge the writer thinks can be conveyed about the subject-matter. It may be that they are more important than at first appears in furthering or preventing the change of ideas on any theme.

The results of the studies of scholars on the subject of vertebrates have been summarized in a series of comprehensive text-books during the past hundred years. Most of these works are planned on the lines laid down by the books of Gegenbaur (1859), Owen (1866), and Wiedersheim (1883), lines that derive from a pre-evolutionary tradition. This partly explains the curiosity that in spite of the great importance of evolutionary doctrine for vertebrate studies, and vice versa, vertebrate text-books often do not deal directly with evolution. They derive their order from something even more fundamental than the evolutionary principle. The essential of any good text-book is that it should be both accurate and general. As Owen put it in his Preface: 'In the choice of facts I have been guided by their authenticity and their applicability to general principles.' The chief of the principles he adopted was 'to guide or help in the power of apprehending the unity which underlies the diversity of animal structures, to show in these structures the evidence of a predetermining Will, producing them in reference to a final purpose, and to indicate the direction and degrees in which organisation, in subserving such Will, rises from the general to the particular'. He confessed 'ignorance of the mode of operation of the natural law of their succession on the earth. But that it is an "orderly succession"—and also "progressive" —is evident from actual knowledge of extinct species.'

These principles were essentially sound, and Owen's treatment was to a large extent the basis of the work that appeared after the Darwinian revolution. In English, following the translation of Wiedersheim's book by W. N. Parker (1886) we have H. J. Parker and Haswell's work, now in its 6th edition. The books of Kingsley and Neal and Rand are in essentially the same tradition, though they incorporate much new work, especially from the neurological studies of Johnston and Herrick. Further exact studies on these same general morphological lines made possible the books of Goodrich (1930) and de Beer (1935), which have provided the morphological background for the present work. Throughout these works on Comparative Anatomy the emphasis is on the evolution of the form of each organ system rather than on the change of the organization of the life of the animal as a whole.

Meanwhile many other treatises appeared dealing with the life and habits of the animals, rather than with morphological principles. Among these we may mention Bronn's *Tierreich* (1859 onwards), the *Cambridge Natural History*, and many works dealing with particular groups of vertebrates. The palaeontologists produced their own series of text-books, mainly descriptive, such as those of Zittel and Smith Woodward, culminating in Romer's admirably detailed and concise book, to which the present work owes very much. The results of embryological work have been summarized by Graham Kerr (1919), Korscheldt and Heider (1931), Brachet (1935), Huxley and de Beer (1934), and Weiss (1939), among others. Unfortunately there has been little summarizing of what is commonly called the comparative physiology of vertebrates. Winterstein's great *Handbuch der vergleichenden Physiologie* (1912) covers much detailed evidence, but comes no nearer than do the comparative anatomists to giving us a picture of the evolution of the life of the whole organism.

All of these books deal in some way with the evolution of vertebrates, and yet curiously enough they speak of it very little. It is hardly an exaggeration to say that they leave the student to decide for himself what has been demonstrated by their studies. Huxley's *Anatomy of Vertebrated Animals* (1871) is an exception in that it deals with the animals rather than their parts, and at a more popular level. Brehm's *Thierleben* (1876) gives a picture of the life of the animals, though in this case not of their underlying organization. Kukenthal's great *Handbuch der Zoologie* has the aim of synthesizing a variety of knowledge about each animal-group, and some of the volumes dealing with vertebrates make fascinating reading—notably that of Streseman on birds. But the size of the work and the multiplicity of authors makes it impossible for any general picture of vertebrate life to appear from the mass of details.

The position is, then, that we have good descriptions of the structure, physiology, and development of vertebrates, of the discoveries of the palaeontologists and accounts of vertebrate natural history, but that there is no work that attempts to define the organization of the whole life and its evolution in all its aspects. Indeed, none of these works defines what is being studied or tries to alter the direction of investigation—all authors seem prepared to agree that biological study is adequately expressed through the familiar disciplines of anatomy, physiology, palaeontology, embryology, or natural history. In passing, we may note the extraordinary fact that there are no detailed works on the comparative histology or biochemistry of vertebrates—surely most fascinating fields for the future, as is, indeed, hinted by the attempts that have been made in older works, such as that of Ranvier (1878), and the newer ones of Baldwin (1937 and 1945).

The present book has gradually grown into an attempt to define what is meant by the life of vertebrates and by the evolution of that life. Put in a more old-fashioned way, this represents an attempt to give a combined account of the embryology, anatomy, physiology, biochemistry, palaeontology, and ecology of all vertebrates. One of the results of the work has been to convince me more than ever that these divisions are not acceptable. All of their separate studies are concerned with the central fact of biology, that life goes on, and I have tried to combine their results into a single work on the way in which this continuity is maintained.

A glance through the book will show that I have not been successful in producing anything very novel—others will certainly be able to go much farther, and in particular to introduce to a greater extent facts about the evolution of the chemical and energy interchanges of vertebrates, here almost omitted! However, I have very much enjoyed the attempt, which has provided the stimulus to try to find out many things that I have always wanted to know.

For any one person to cover such a wide field is bound to lead to inexactness and error in many places. I have tried to verify from nature as often as possible, but a large amount has been copied, no doubt often wrongly. Throughout, the aim has been to provide wherever possible an idea of the actual observations that have been made, as well as the interpretations placed upon them. A proper appraisal of general theories can only be reached if there is first a knowledge of the actual materials, which is the characteristic feature of scientific observation. A book such as the present has value only in so far as it leads the reader to make his own observations and helps him to know the world for himself.

Mammalian organization requires more detailed treatment than that of other groups, and in providing this the work grew to beyond the length of a single book. Mammalian structure, function, and development will therefore be dealt with in a separate volume, which will also include a survey of comparative embryology.

The original plan was that the palaeontological parts of the book would be written by J. A. Moy-Thomas. Had he lived this aspect of the work would have been very much better, and his common sense and laughter would have lightened the whole. I have tried to give some compensation at least by the speculation that is possible from a single point of view. To protect the reader against the limitations of my ignorance I have consulted specialists on every part of the work, and my deepest thanks are due to those who have helped in this way. They have done wonders in correcting mistakes, but, of course, are not responsible for any that remain, or for views expressed. Among those who have helped in this way with particular parts are Professor G. R. de Beer, Mr. R. B. Freeman, the late Professor W. Garstang, Dr. A. Graham, Professor J. B. S. Haldane, Professor W. Hollingworth, Dr. W. Holmes, Dr. J. S. Huxley, Dr. D. Lack, Mr. Maynard Smith, Dr. F. S. Russell, Dr. Tyndell Hopwood, Mr. H. G. Vevers, Professor D. M. S. Watson, and Professor S. Westoll. They have been patient and severe critics, and the reader and I owe them very much.

One of the main problems of such a work is its illustration, and here I have been extraordinarily fortunate in having the help of Miss E. R. Turlington, who has not only provided brilliantly clear and beautiful pictures, but has taken extremes of care to ensure their accuracy by drawing from live animals, from dissections, and from skeletons, as well as by research into the illustrations of others. Miss J. de Vere has also given much help with drawing. We have borrowed good pictures unhesitatingly and should like to thank those who have given permission for their reproduction.

I should also like to thank particularly my secretary, Miss P. Codlin, who has played a large part in making the book possible, and my daughter Cordelia for help with the index.

Finally, I have to thank the Secretary and members of Oxford University Press for the care with which the book has been produced, and for their friendly co-operation, which has made the work a pleasure.

J. Z. Y.

1950

ACKNOWLEDGEMENTS

THANKS for permission for reproductions of illustrations are due to:
G. C. Aymar, E. J. W. Barrington, J. Berrill, T. H. Bullock, A. J. E. Cave, W. E.
Le Gros Clark, E. Crosby, F. G. Evans, Helen Goodrich, A. Gorbman, J. Gray,
W. K. Gregory, W. J. Hamilton, J. E. Harris, L. Hogben, A. Holmes, E. Hoskings,
W. W. Howells, J. H. Huxley, F. Knowles, D. Lack, N. A. Mackintosh, G. H.
Parker, A. T. Phillipson, R. J. Pumphrey, E. C. R. Reeve, A. R. Romer, E. S.
Russell, F. K. Sanders, A. H. Schultz, G. G. Simpson, N. Tinbergen, G. L. Walls,
L. Waring, S. Westoll, E. I. White, F. F. Zeuner, Lieut.-Col. W. P. C. Tenison.

and to the following publishers and other bodies:
The American Museum of Natural History; Balliere, Tindall and Cox; E. Benn,
Ltd.; *Biological Reviews*; the *British Medical Journal*; the British Museum; the
Cambridge University Press; the Company of Biologists, Ltd.; Dodd, Mead & Co.;
Editors of the *Ibis*; Longmans, Green & Co., Ltd.; the Physiological Society;
Putnam, Ltd.; the *Scientific Monthly*; the Wilson *Bulletin*; the Wistar Institute;
Zoological Society of London.

CONTENTS

XX. MARSUPIALS

XXI. EVOLUTION OF PLACENTAL MAMMALS

XXII. INSECTIVORES, BATS, AND EDENTATES

XXIII. THE PRIMATES

XXIV. MONKEYS, APES, AND MEN. CATARRHINA

XXV. RODENTS AND RABBITS

XXVI. WHALES   629

XXVII. CARNIVORES

XXVIII. PROTOUNGULATES

XXIX. ELEPHANTS AND RELATED FORMS

NOTE

THE arrangement of this book is systematic, proceeding from the earliest chordates to the mammals. In every group the organization is described in the same way, beginning with the external features and proceeding then to the skeleton, muscles, and locomotion, followed by feeding and digestion, circulation, respiration, excretion, reproduction, the nervous and sensory organization and behaviour. Each system is dealt with in special detail where it is first met with. The index has been arranged so as to make it possible to survey any organ-system, or subject—say, the skull or osmoregulation, throughout the vertebrates.

I

EVOLUTION OF LIFE IN RELATION TO CLIMATIC AND GEOLOGICAL CHANGE

1. The need for generality in zoology

The aim of any zoological study is to know about the life of the animals concerned. Our object in this book is, therefore, to take into mind as much as possible about all the vertebrate animal life that has ever been. Thinking of the great numbers of types that have existed since the first fishes swam in the Palaeozoic seas, one might well be appalled by such a task: to describe all these populations in detail would indeed demand a huge treatise. However, in a well-developed science it should be possible to reduce the varied subject-matter to order, to show that all differences can be understood to have arisen by the influence of specified factors operating to modify an original scheme. Animal and plant life is so varied that it has not yet proved possible to systematize our knowledge of it as thoroughly as we should wish. Thinking, again, of the variety of vertebrate lives, it may seem impossible to imagine any general scheme and simple set of factors that would include so many special circumstances. Yet nothing less should be the aim of a true science of zoology. Too often in the past we have been content to accumulate unrelated particular facts. It is splendid to be aware of many details, but only by the synthesis of these can we obtain either an adequate means of handling so many data or knowledge of the natures we are studying. In order to know life—what it is, what it has been, and what it will be —we must look beyond the details of individual lives and try to find rules governing all. Perhaps we may find the task less difficult than expected. Even an elementary anatomical and physiological study shows that all vertebrates are built upon a common plan and have certain similarities of behaviour. Our object will be to come to know the nature of this plan of life, of structure, and action, to show how it is modified in special cases and how each special case is also an example of a general type of modification.

Since the problem arises from the variety of animals which have lived and live to-day, our central task is obviously to inquire into the reason for the existence of so much difference. If vertebrate life began as one single fish-like type, why has it not continued as such until now? Why, instead of numerous fishes all alike in the seas, are there countless different kinds even in one mass of water, while descendants of most unfish-like form are found living out of the water and even in the air and under the ground?

To put it in a way more familiar, though perhaps less clear: what are the forces that have produced the changes of animal form? Knowing these forces, and the original type, it would be possible to construct a truly general science of zoology, with sure premises and deductions. Even if we cannot reach this end, we should at least try, hoping that after investigation of the biology of vertebrates it will be possible to retain something more than a mass of detailed information. At the end of such a study, if we deal with the subject right, we should surely be better able to answer some of the fundamental biological questions. We should be able to say something about the nature of evolution and of the differences between types, to know the rhythms of change that have been at work to produce these differences, and also—the acid test of any true science—to forecast how these rhythms are likely to operate in the future.

2. What do we mean by the life of an animal?

Much obscurity comes in biology from inconsidered use of analogies in attempting to grasp the nature of life. We have a science of anatomy, which we are told is concerned with the 'structure' of animals, and we feel that we understand what 'structure' means. Physiology is the study of 'function', and this, too, we seem to understand. In both cases we take the implied analogies from our man-made machines; they have what we call 'structure' and they 'function'. But further examination of living things has made these visions of biological science much less clear than they have seemed in past centuries. The whole scheme fails us when we ask what is it, then, that we call the 'life' of the animal, and what is it that is passed on from generation to generation, and that changes through the ages by the process we call evolution? It has gradually become apparent that the body is not a fixed, definite 'structure' as it appears to casual observation or when dissected. In life there is ceaseless activity and change going on within the apparently constant framework of the body. The movement of the blood is one sign of this activity, and since Harvey's discovery of the circulation we have learnt of innumerable others. Everyone knows that the skin is continually being renewed by growth from below, and very many other types of cell are similarly replaced; for instance, red blood-cells last only for a few weeks in man. Even in the cells that are not completely destroyed and replaced, such as the nerve-cells, there is continual very rapid change of the molecules that make up their substance. The full extent of this exchange has been shown by using isotopes to discover for how long individual atoms remain in the body; the work of Schoenheimer (1942), which by this means first clearly established the rapidity of the turnover, is a classic of modern biology.

If the matter of the body is continually changing we cannot expect to be able to describe the characteristics of life in terms of the properties of particular substances. Life is characterized by activities or processes and by the particular molecules that are engaged. Different types of life involve different processes, and each sort of life therefore produces certain types of molecules and certain visible structures. Specification of these chemical and visible units that we can abstract from the living organism is at present our only means of studying the system as a whole. We have to take our science as we find it, and as yet we have no means of grasping the enormously complicated network of activities that constitutes a single life. Throughout this book, however, an attempt will be made to approach that end by use of certain clues to help us to concentrate on significant features, to see the rhythms or patterns common to the lives of the animals, and thus to carry in mind many details. It is possible in this way to bring together information collected by morphologists, geneticists, embryologists, physiologists, biophysicists, and biochemists to give a single view of the life of the organisms concerned. The task is admittedly a hard one and the success achieved only partial. Continually one slips into the discussion and imagination of particular structures, substances, or processes, forgetting the whole life. A detail of form or of chemical composition attracts, and thus distracts, attention; perhaps it can hardly be otherwise if we are to describe exactly. But it is surprising how practice improves the powers of selecting and emphasizing those patterns or details of knowledge that are significant for the study of each life as a whole.

The first difficulty is to force oneself to remember all the time that a living animal or plant system is in a continual state of change. When making any observations, whether by dissection or with the microscope, with a test-tube, oscillograph, or respirometer, it is necessary continually to think back to the time when the tissue was active in the living body, and to frame the observation so that it shall reveal something significant of that activity. *This means that every biologist must know as much as possible of the life of the whole organism with which he deals; indeed, something of the whole population from which the specimen was drawn.*

3. Living things tend to preserve themselves

The clue by which we recognize significant features during any biological study is that living activity tends to ensure the continuance of its own pattern. The processes of life draw materials into the system, organize them there, and then send them out again, all in such a way that the arrangement or pattern of the processes remains almost unchanged as the molecules pass through it. We see analogies in the way that a waterfall or a human institution such as the Catholic Church remains the same, though its components change. Our business is to try to describe this arrangement or pattern of processes that is preserved. It is this pattern that we call the life of the species, and we must realize that the activities which, all together, go to make up one sort of life are not necessarily all to be found in any one individual, still less in any part of an individual. The pattern of life which is preserved is not resident in the cells, the heart, or the brain, any more than in the bones, hair, or nails. The unit of life which tends to preserve the type is a whole interbreeding population, together, in the case of many social forms, with individuals, such as worker-bees, that play a part in the life without participation in reproduction.

A very wide range of activities, therefore, goes to make up any one type of life, and we shall only appreciate these activities properly if we study that whole life as it is normally lived in its proper environment. The way to study animals or men is, first and foremost, to examine them whole, to see how their actions serve to meet the conditions of the environment and to allow preservation of the life of the individual and the race. Then, with this knowledge of how the animal 'uses' its parts we may be able to make more detailed studies down to the molecular level, and show how, together, the activities form a single scheme of action.

The ways of its action constitute the characteristic feature we can observe in each individual animal life and in each sort of animal life, just as action is the characteristic feature of living as compared with lifeless matter. A living animal is continually doing things. Even when it is asleep it is breathing, its heart beating and brain pulsing, while countless chemical changes go on throughout its tissues. The waking life, of course, shows this restless action even more clearly. Animals may indeed sometimes be still, but they are never wholly inactive. It is not difficult to see startling glimpses of this activity if we watch animals alive, especially when they are in groups. A hawk wheeling, a pond full of tadpoles, or a crowd of people moving on a city street will remind us that if we are to see the interesting side of life we have to study activity and not, as is more easy to do and so often done, to spend all our time examining the 'structure' or 'chemistry' of the dead.

The peculiarity of this activity of animals is that much, perhaps most, of it has the effect of maintaining the integrity of the body and, indeed, even of increasing the bulk, or of reproducing more bodies like the first. For example, the search for food provides raw materials which are available to the muscles to give energy for further search. If the situation demands still greater efforts these efforts will themselves lead to 'hypertrophy', or increase in the muscle substance and power. Similarly, the muscular movements of respiration provide the oxygen by which these same movements and others are made possible.

We could go on indefinitely describing how the activity of each part of the body tends, with some exceptions, to ensure the continuation of the whole. The mere statement of the existence of this tendency to self-maintenance does not, perhaps, sufficiently emphasize the power which it represents. It is one of the great 'forces' that control the matter of the earth. It causes huge masses of material to be moved annually to the tops of high trees and millions of wonderfully built animals to roam daily to find and consume uncounted tons of food or, not finding it, to search on and maintain their activity while any calorie remains available. The power of life is sufficient to bring about the incorporation of an appreciable part of the matter of the earth's surface into living things. Within the appropriate range of conditions, found chiefly near the surface of the sea and on the damper parts of the earth, life dominates the lifeless and provides a main influence on the matter present.

4. Awareness of life

A man is aware of this power of life within him. He feels his needs and knows his will to obtain satisfaction of them. It is tempting to think that this which we call consciousness is in some way associated with all life activities. Observation of animals similar to ourselves suggests that they have something which is similar to our awareness, but zoological inquiry has paid so little attention to this problem that it is not profitable to pursue it far at present, though to omit consideration of consciousness altogether in biology is surely likely to produce even greater errors than we may commit through a blundering recognition of its presence.

We cannot, however, in the present state of understanding make a proper synthesis between the consciousness we have of our own lives and the changes in what we call the materials of our own and other bodies. Everyone feels that in the words 'my life' is included some element of awareness, but in describing a given animal life we must be content, until our ideas become clearer, to mean all the activities detectable in that animal, activities that make a certain pattern and serve to maintain that pattern. Thus by the life of a frog we mean, quite simply, all the things that it does. We see these actions not as chaotic and disconnected but grouped into what may be called a pattern. Thus in the frog we can see structures which are concerned with producing movement, and this movement leads the animal to places where it can get food or avoid desiccation or enemies. The clue to recognition of the 'pattern' is to see how the activities of life tend to preserve the organization and make more like it.

5. The influence of environment on life

Growth is the addition of material to that which is already organized into a living pattern. But the pattern is not fixed and invariate, even throughout any one life. Each individual changes through its lifetime, develops, as we say, and moreover is modified by the action upon it of its surroundings. The actions to which its tendencies give rise, bringing an animal against various accidental circumstances, produce in some cases the consequences of use and disuse of its parts. Those parts which are greatly exercised by the product of the animal's tendencies and the surrounding circumstances may increase in amount or hypertrophy, while any disused parts undergo some degree of atrophy or reduction. The pattern is thus able to conform to a considerable extent to the exigencies of change in the external world. It could be imagined that a sufficiently plastic animal organization would be able in this way, if its tendencies to survival were strong enough, to mould itself to all the changes of climate through the millennia, producing a great variety of animal types by use and disuse alone. Only a limited degree of change is possible in this way, however, and it is not such changes either of development or by the direct influence of environment that we call 'evolution'. There is abundant evidence that the result of such interaction between organism and environment is not handed on. Acquired characters are not inherited, and, of course, no individual grows directly into the next generation.

6. What is it that heredity transmits?

That which is passed on is something more subtle, a pattern or plan of organization of the life activities. The material contribution of each generation to the next is infinitesimal and provides only a start, an impetus to develop and to do things in a certain way. The main outlines of the pattern of each life are set by the minute active system it acquires from its parents. The great changes that have produced the variety of vertebrate and other life have been the result of the fact that the activities of life are re-started at regular intervals by reproduction, re-started each time with a slightly different pattern.

In vertebrates reproduction is universally the power not of one but of two individuals. The small fragments which are detached from the parent bodies thus do not perpetuate exactly the characteristics of the previous life but unite those of two lives. The study by geneticists of the way in which this union and transmission takes place has hardly yet passed beyond the formal stage of providing means of identifying the features common to parent and offspring. Indeed, it has hardly even reached this stage, for our knowledge of chromosomes tells us only that the appearance of some character in parent and offspring is associated with the presence of a certain part of a certain chromosome in both. Little has yet been discovered of the nature of the activity which is transmitted. However, it is very important for our study to recognize that bi-parental inheritance provides for the emergence of continually new types of organism.

7. The basis of variation and the origin of species

The obvious means by which variation of any animal or plant species can be secured is the separation of single pieces having the power of developing into creatures not an exact copy of the parent. This process of asexual reproduction and mutation may produce a variety of types, suitable for new environments, *if reproduction is sufficiently rapid.* Probably this is one of the methods by which change is produced among bacteria, which possess relatively simple types of organization. Organizations such as those of vertebrates, in which there are vastly more parts and more complex interactions with their surroundings, cannot divide frequently or rapidly, and changes in them can only be small. The process of sexual reproduction ensures the provision of a series of variants of the organization of each type of life, differing from each other only to a small extent, and hence providing types suitable to meet such new external conditions as may be produced by changes in the climate or the action of other organisms.

Genetical studies have now shown that each characteristic of an animal is influenced by many parts of many chromosomes, not only by a single gene. Certain parts of particular chromosomes have especially strong effects on a character, for instance, height. These are the 'main genes' affecting that character. The interaction of these main genes with others having smaller effects ensures that the characteristics vary continuously throughout a population, not discontinuously, as a superficial study of Mendelism might lead one to expect. For example, it is a commonplace that there are men and women of all sorts of heights, over a wide range. The mechanism of sexual reproduction ensures that the small mutations which occur in the hereditary 'factors' become combined to produce ranges of types out of which some may be suitable to meet the demands of a changing environment.

The organization of life is very rarely identical in any two individuals; there is, therefore, a considerable range of potential patterns resident in all those animals of a population that are capable of mating together. We can speak of the organization of life shown by the individuals of the species (not, of course, all alike), and we can imagine the underlying hereditary activities which make the adult lives possible. The sum of those variants of the hereditary activities constitutes the pattern or mould, as it were, of the life of the whole species. It is this 'genotype' which provides the varied adult animal lives recognized by the zoologist. Evolution consists in a change in the hereditary activity or genotype, producing, of course, a new set of adults. In practice we see the structure of animals as exemplified by a few individuals, and in evolutionary studies we observe that this structure undergoes changes, though usually only slowly. The underlying change is in the as yet unknown characteristic activities resident in the germ-cells of any interbreeding population.

We must therefore direct our studies continually to populations, rather than to single individuals. We must try to think of all the creatures of a kind, spread out wherever a suitable habitat for them occurs. They will not all be alike genetically, and the circumstances of the lives of some members of the group may become sufficiently dissimilar to produce further divergences by use and disuse. Limitations of intermating may occur on account of limitation of movement, accentuated by partial and, perhaps, eventually complete geographical barriers. Such variations in external circumstance become matched by divergences in type, until two new races are produced, at first relatively and then absolutely infertile, so that there are then two separate populations or species instead of one.

So far we can follow the classical Darwinian analysis, but we have not yet fulfilled our aim of showing why varieties of animals arise. We have said that an animal is an active system, tending to maintain and increase itself and to produce others which are like it, though not identical. This provides for the *possibility* of change of type. Whether such change will occur depends on an interaction between the powers of life of the animals and the limitations and opportunities offered by the circumstances in which they find themselves.

8. The increasing complexity of life

The acquisition of new matter, and hence growth and reproduction, occurred in the earliest animals by relatively simple means, as it still does to-day in the bacteria, lower plants, and some protozoa. It would not be profitable here to provide rigid criteria for the definition of 'simple'; perhaps some of the chemical changes involved may be quite complex, but the whole system can, with meaning, be said to be simple. A population of bacteria in a suitable culture medium obtains its raw materials by diffusion; the only special effort which it makes to secure these materials is to provide a large number of spores, so that some may come to rest in suitable surroundings. Such a life can be said to be more simple than that of a vertebrate, whose system includes many special devices for obtaining access to the raw materials that it needs.

It is possible to suggest the conditions under which such an increase in complexity occurs. We have already seen that the system of life of each population shows a range of variation in the activities of its different members, this variation being produced either by rapid asexual reproduction and frequent mutation or, more commonly, by biparental inheritance. The power of growth and multiplication is prodigious, the available raw material limited, the tendency to survival of each unit strong. Some of the extremes of the range of variation may be able to utilize materials not available to the majority, by virtue, say, of some extra chemical powers. The habitable range is thus extended and ultimately a new race produced, living in what is effectively a different environment from the first. Driven by their tendencies to survive and to multiply and by the inexact copying at each act of reproduction, animals have thus continually discovered new ways of life, enabling the colonization of new environments. We can imagine that even if there had been no changes in the earth's surface a whole range of living types might have arisen in this way where there was at first only one type. We shall never know what variety these evolutionary forces of growth, multiplication, self-preservation, and change of type would have produced alone, because the face of the world has not remained the same but has been continually changing, producing new environments for life to occupy.

9. The progression of life from the water to more difficult environments

In general, the new environments colonized have involved ever wider departures from that watery one in which life first arose. This is shown most strikingly if we contrast the simple way in which the means of life are obtained by a marine bacterium with the complicated activities that go to maintain a man alive in a city. Yet all living systems, even those which have changed most markedly since their first origin, are still watery, and must have salt and nitrogenous compounds with which to make proteins and so on. Perhaps, indeed, the basic plan of the living activity differs less in the various types than one might suppose. 'Protoplasm' is certainly not identical in all creatures, but it may be that it differs less than do the outward forms which support it.

In order to provide the necessary conditions for the maintenance of such a watery system, in very different environments, many auxiliary activities have been developed. It is these which give added complexity to the higher animals and plants, enabling them to undertake what can be called more difficult ways of life. It may well be that in doing so their consciousness has also in some way increased, that it is this increased awareness which gives them the ability to make greater use of their activities and to support life under more difficult conditions. In order to do this their activity must also be physically greater than is necessary in more lowly types. It may be presumed that more energy is transferred to maintain a given mass of living matter in the less 'easy' environments, and in this sense the higher animals are less efficient than the lower, if we use only the engineer's criterion of efficiency.

According to this conception, then, evolution has involved a change in the relationship between organism and environment. Life has come to occupy places in which it did not exist before. Perhaps the total mass of living matter has thus been greatly increased. It must not, of course, be supposed that in every case evolutionary change has produced an increase in complexity in this way; examples of 'degeneration' are too well known to need quoting. We have, however, a clear impression that through the centuries there has been, in general, some change in animals and plants and that in some sense some of the later organisms are 'higher' than the earlier. It is hardly possible to deny that there is some meaning in the assertion that man is a higher animal than amoeba. Our thesis attempts to specify more clearly what we can know about this evolutionary change, by saying that it consists of a colonization by life of environments more and more different from that in which life arose, a colonization made possible by the development of special powers, by which the conditions are made supportable.

It is not easy to enumerate the complexity of any animal or to define quantitatively the nature of its relations with its environment, and for this reason it is difficult to prove our thesis rigorously. This book nevertheless makes an attempt to do so, to show how the organization of vertebrate life has become more complex since it first appeared, and that the increasing complexity is related to the adoption of modes of life continually more remote from the simple diffusion of substances from the sea. Of course, even the earliest vertebrates had already departed a long way from the very first conditions of life and were already quite complex organisms. However, in the history of their life through nearly 400 million years since the Silurian period we can trace considerable further changes in complexity. During this time vertebrate life has left the sea to live in fresh water, on swampy land, and finally on dry land and in the air. It has produced special types able to support life by such an astonishing variety of devices that we cannot possibly specify them all but shall only direct attention to a few, and thus attempt to obtain an impression of the scheme of life of the vast hordes of vertebrate animals which in one shape or another have swarmed and still swarm in the waters and over the earth. We shall try to discern whether there is reason to suppose that all this variety is related in some way to changes in the surrounding world. Since many zoologists are unfamiliar with geology, we may finish this introduction by a brief survey of the evidences for climatic and geographical changes such as may have been responsible for the changes in organic life.

10. Cyclical changes of climate and geological periods

10.1. *Changes of level of the continents*

Changes of geography are mostly so slow that they cannot in themselves influence individual lives. On the other hand, certain changes of atmosphere and climate are so rapid and obvious as to be banal, and they operate with rhythmical periodicity throughout the days and years. Nearly all living things must be suited to such short-period cyclical changes, unless they live where no light enters. There is indirect evidence of further cyclical changes in climate and geography, occurring with such long periods that they are without appreciable effect on individual organisms, but may very much affect the history of the race.

The idea of geographical change is made familiar by the fact that coast-lines and river-courses have changed appreciably in historical times. We are familiar with stories of destruction of some houses or of a village by the sea, though it may come as a shock to learn that the sea-level has changed so much that England and France were connected by land 8,000 years ago, and that man-made instruments fished up from the Dogger Bank show that it was an inhabited peat bog 6,000 years B.C. These changes in height of the land are signs of the 'diastrophic movements' which are major features of long-period geological evolution. The action of frost, wind, and rain continually breaks up and carries away the surface of the land, at a rate of the order of 1 ft. per 4,000 years, the processes known as weathering and denudation. The material carried away is deposited in the river-beds and in the lakes and shallow seas around the river mouths (sedimentation) (Fig. 1). Here it builds the sedimentary rocks, which may be many thousand feet in thickness, the whole continental platform continuing in many cases to sink for long periods, perhaps with intervals during which it became raised above the water. Fossil remains are, of course, mainly the result of the preservation of the harder parts of animals in sedimentary deposits, and the most complete series of fossils are likely to be those of animals living in the seas.

The surface crust of the earth is not a layer of uniform thickness and density but consists of certain irregular masses of lighter material, rich in silicon and aluminium (sial), forming the continents, and heavier material, rich in magnesium (sima), under the ocean beds. The reason for this non-uniform distribution is obscure, but it has the effect of making the continents stand higher, floating on the plastic denser medium beneath the crust. When material is removed from the continents by denudation they rise; conversely the addition of millions of tons of ice will depress them. The continents are thus said to rest in isostatic equilibrium, and following the small changes in level the sea leaves more or less of the continental shelf uncovered. Such upward and downward movements profoundly influence the climate, oceanic climatic influences tend to produce a damp, equable climate, with large areas of marsh and forest. When the land stands higher extremes of climate develop, some parts being cold, others forming large, dry interior plains.

Besides changes in the balance produced by denudation and the advance of ice-caps there are also from time to time very marked movements of uplifting or lowering of the land, which may be called

FIG. 1. Curve showing the areas of the earth's solid surface in relation to the sea-level. (From Holmes.)

independent earth movements. Such vertical movements of the continental masses are produced by internal forces, of unknown origin. There are signs that they are rhythmical in nature. They are doubtless related to a second series of major movements of crustal deformation that are due to tangential forces and lead to the formation of new mountain ranges (orogenesis) by compression, or to fracturing by tension. The upwelling of lava from the inside of the earth at these times makes the igneous rocks, usually devoid of fossils.

Changes in geography are, then, mainly changes in the height of the land and the amount of it which is above water. This leads to considerable changes in appearance of the land-masses where the continent is surrounded by a rather shallow continental shelf. The general opinion is that the main outline of the continental masses has remained much as at present, at least since Cambrian times.

10.2. Changes of climate

Evidence of marked changes of climate is the finding in England and other regions now temperate of remains appropriate to warmer or colder conditions (corals and woolly rhinoceros, for instance). There is thus every reason to think that there have been great changes from hot to cold and wet to dry conditions, probably in conjunction with the changes in level of the land already considered.

These fluctuations in geography and climate are obviously of first importance to the biologist. We can hardly expect to treat animals and plants as stable systems if the environment around them is changing. In order to be able to assess the influence of such changes on life we must know more about the rates at which they occur, and careful

FIG. 2. Variation in size of tree-rings and number of sunspots in the nineteenth century. (From Zeuner, after Glock.)

study is now beginning to show many signs that the climatic changes are rhythmic. Rhythmic changes of climate are, of course, very familiar to us in the cycles of days, months, and years, and the immense importance of these short-period changes for animal and plant life must not be forgotten.

Here we are more concerned with changes of longer periodicity, of which the best known are fluctuations of the amount of solar radiation received at any given part of the earth's surface. These are likely to be especially important since plants, and hence ultimately animals, depend for their energy on sunlight. The cycle of number of sunspots (11·4 years) involves a change in amount of radiation, and this is associated with some biological cycles, for instance in the distribution of the rings of growth made by trees (Fig. 2). Longer-period fluctuations in the amount of radiation received on any part of the earth's surface depend on the perturbations of the earth's orbit, particularly on changes in the obliquity of the ecliptic. The effect of these perturbations can be calculated, and the results show that at any one place there are rhythmical variations in the amount of radiation received and in its seasonal distributions. The periodicity of these calculated changes is about 40,000 years, with considerable irregularities and variations in the sizes of the maxima (Fig. 3).

These cycles of radiation received have left their imprint on the structure of the earth's crust. The formation of tree rings is based on the annual cycle, there being more growth in summer than in winter. Signs of the sunspot cycle are clearly superimposed on these annual rings (Fig. 2). The annual periodicity may also appear in the layers of sedimentary deposits, for instance melting glaciers bring down more matter into lakes and seas during summer than winter. The resulting annual layers ('varves') in the clay form a means of dating past history, which has been used extensively, especially by study of the varved clays in countries round the Baltic Sea deposited during

FIG. 3. Curve of solar radiation received at 65° N. lat. in the summer. The radiation is expressed in 'canonic units' (related to the solar constant in calories). Time in thousands of years. (From Zeuner, based on the tables of Milankovitch.)

the retreat of the ice cap. The sunspot cycles can sometimes be recognized in the series of varves, and there are signs of longer cycles, indicating climatic changes corresponding to the longer-period changes in solar radiation received. These cycles are found in varves from Carboniferous times, as well as in the post-glacial Baltic deposits, and the similarity of the periods suggests that the length of the astronomical year has remained constant.

We may expect, also, to find evidence of marked fluctuations of climate with about the periodicity of the slower change in amount of incident solar radiation. During the last 600,000 years (the Pleistocene epoch) there has been a series of waves of glaciation (ice ages); the ice-caps have several times advanced towards the equator and then retreated again. These changes are usually classified into four periods of glaciation, separated by interglacial periods. However, the last (fourth Pleistocene) glaciation, of which we know the most, certainly had three separate climaxes of cold. The correspondence of these with especially marked minima in the curve of solar radiation is not perfect (Fig. 3), but it suggests that the basic periodicity may have been something like 40,000 years, and that the division of the whole Pleistocene period into four periods of glaciation obscures a change with much shorter periodicity. From about 120,000 to 180,000 years B.P. (Before Present) there were no marked minima in the solar radiation curve, and this agrees with other evidence of a long interglacial period (third Pleistocene interglacial). Two marked minima agree with the other signs of a penultimate (third Pleistocene) glaciation, and this was preceded by a very long warmer period, the second interglacial. As we go farther back the study becomes more and more difficult, but the available evidence suggests that fluctuations of climate considerable enough to alter the entire fauna and flora may have taken place at a periodicity of something over 40,000 years. It is a measure of the difficulty of geological science that we cannot yet give a systematic account of the chronology or climatic changes even of the Pleistocene period (estimated 600,000 to 1,000,000 years) during which these glaciations occurred.

As we proceed to study times still more remote our vision becomes increasingly blurred. We can now only rarely distinguish periodicities as short as 40,000 years, though there is evidence that they existed, for instance from varved Cretaceous sediments. All we can see in the study of geological deposits are the very marked changes produced by the major movements of orogenesis and by the isostatic readjustments. The surprising thing is that these immensely slow changes have been sufficiently regular to leave layered deposits, allowing the development of a system of geological classification. The layered appearance of many rocks is due to the fact that the process of sedimentation was interrupted by periods when the continental shelf on which they rest was raised up above the water surface and underwent denudation for a while, before being again lowered below the sea and covered with a new deposit. During the interval, while the shelf was raised above the water, the animals and plants in the sea became changed; thus a rather sharp break will appear in the series of fossils. The occurrence of these breaks has been used by geologists to define the major geological periods, which thus correspond to cycles of elevation and depression of the continents. By comparing the fossils contained in the rocks major geological periods have been recognized in various parts of the world. The times of submergence and emergence differ from region to region, however, and no very close detailed comparison is possible. It is easy to forget that climates and land levels do not always change in the same direction in different parts of the world.

10.3. *Geological time*

The study of the fossils establishes the order in which the rocks were laid down, but other methods have to be used to discover the period of time covered by each stage. This is especially important to the biologist, who wants to know the rate at which animals or plants have evolved. Investigation of the rate of sedimentation itself is one very obvious method of dating rocks. Clearly the thickness of a sedimented layer bears some relation to the length of time of its formation. The amount of matter carried down by rivers at the present day can be calculated, and the rate of deposition in recent years is known approximately. The ages of the various sedimentary rocks can thus be calculated from their thicknesses, if we assume the process of sedimentation to go on at a constant rate. A second method of dating rocks has been the study of the increasing salinity of the seas, due to salt brought down from the land, but this again involves formidable guesses and gives ages now known to be much too short. Reliable knowledge of the ages of the rocks has only begun to accumulate with the discovery of radioactivity. Uranium and thorium disintegrate at rates which are unaffected by any known conditions. The age of any rock since its deposition can therefore be calculated if we can estimate the amount of breakdown products of these elements present in it. This can be done by determining the amounts of helium or lead produced, but since the former is liable to escape, results based on it are suspect. The lead present in a rock is often not all derived from the uranium and thorium there, but separation of the lead isotopes enables those of radioactive origin to be estimated, and the age of the deposit can then be determined, assuming that the breakdown of uranium to lead began when the rock was laid down in its present position.

Here, however, we meet with the difficulty that the few rocks which have suitable radioactive contents are of igneous origin; in the nature of things we cannot hope to determine the dates of sedimentary rocks in this way. Fortunately, there are several points throughout geological history at which the relative ages of radioactive igneous and fossiliferous sedimentary rocks can be compared and from these an approximate time-scale can be drawn up. The oldest known rocks, as dated by the study of radioactive products, are about 1,800 million years old; the Cambrian rocks, when fossils become readily discernible, were laid down about 500 million years ago.

Classical geology divides the time since the Cambrian into eleven major periods, but closer study shows that several of these are double or triple periods of advance and retreat of the sea. Even the most carefully compiled radioactivity data are not yet adequate to provide us with definite estimates of the durations of all of the periods, and reliable authorities differ considerably over parts of the range (Table 1), though there is agreement on a total period of about 500 million

TABLE 1. *Ages in millions of years of geological periods and epochs approximately, as estimated by various workers*

	Zeuner	Bullard	Romer	Holmes	Schuchert and Dunbar	Compromise adopted	Time since beginning of period	Sediment thickness (000 ft.)
Pleistocene	1	5	..	1	..	1	1	4
Pliocene	..	15	..	15	..	9	10	13
Miocene	30	25	..	20	..	15	25	21
Oligocene	..	18	..	15	..	10	35	15
Eocene	..	16	..	20	..	15	50	14
Palaeocene	(40)	..	..	..	..	10	60	..
Tertiary	71	79	70	71	60	60	60	67
Cretaceous	40	76	50	50	80	60	120	64
Jurassic	40	23	35	30	35	30	150	20
Triassic	(40)	30	35	40	25	30	180	25
Permian	35	15	25	30	40	30	210	13
Carboniferous	50	47	85	60	70	60	270	40
Devonian	(35)	44	50	40	40	30	300	37
Silurian	30	18	30	30	40	30	330	15
Ordovician	50	47	90	50	70	90	420	40
Cambrian	60	47	70	100	90	90	510	40

years since the Cambrian. Comparison of the various estimates suggests the probability that there has been a rather regular series of crustal revolutions. A periodicity of 30 million years has been somewhat arbitrarily assumed throughout this book. The extent of the movements has certainly not been equal throughout and some of them, more marked than others, have suggested a major cycle of orogenesis with still longer periodicity, perhaps 200 million years (Fig. 4). Moreover, there have certainly also been many lesser inundations and changes of climate with shorter periods, such as those of about 40,000 years we can detect in the later part of the Pleistocene. It is useful when trying to adjust the mind to periods of 30 million years to remember the frequent changes of level and climate that are known to have occurred in the last 100,000 years. In spite of all that we know about the history of the earth's surface, it is necessary every time that we make statements about the influence of presumed climatic changes on organic evolution to remember how scanty is the evidence.

10.4. *Classification of geological history*

The period isolated as 'Cambrian' by geologists almost certainly included several inundations, and its duration is estimated at between 50 and 100 million years (Fig. 4). There is some evidence for three periods of flood and hence of three cycles, each of 30 million years. The Ordovician also included three floods in North America and may have lasted 90 million years. There were very powerful earth move-

FIG. 4. Diagrams of main changes of areas of land and water and in climatic conditions since the Cambrian. The chief times of mountain-building (orogenesis) in America are also shown. (Redrawn by permission from *Textbook of General Zoology*, 2nd ed. by W. C. Curtis and M. J. Guthrie, John Wiley & Sons, Inc., 1933.)

ments at the end of this period, at any rate in North America, known as the Taconian revolution. The Silurian apparently includes a single main cycle of inundation, ending in an elevation of the land, which, though slight in America, was very marked in Europe as the Caledonian revolution, producing the range of mountains stretching across Scandinavia to Scotland and Ireland. Throughout these early Palaeozoic periods the fossils are entirely those of aquatic animals, except for some traces of land plants and arthropods at the end of the Silurian. The oldest remains of vertebrates are fish-scales from the Ordovician (p. 119). Details of the Palaeozoic climatic changes are not clear, but the fact that corals, which can now live only in warm water, were alive over a considerable part of the earth's surface suggests that conditions were warmer and more uniform than at present.

The Devonian is considered by some to include a single main period, about 30 million years long, with one flood at the middle and more arid conditions at the end, but other authorities divide it into several periods (Fig. 5). The first forests appeared at this time, and here, also, are found the first signs of vertebrate terrestrial life, in the form of fossil lung-fishes and amphibians (p. 281). The period recognized as Carboniferous in Europe is seen in America clearly to include two major periods of about 30 million years each, the Mississippian and Pennsylvanian. Throughout this long time conditions varied

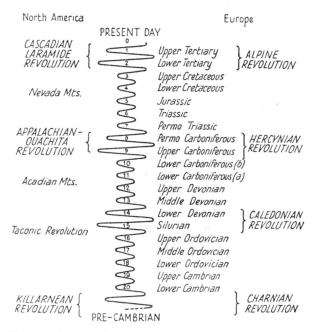

FIG. 5. Diagram of the rhythms of periods of orogenesis (mountain-building). Each cycle lasts for 30 million years. Notice that the arrangement of the periods is different from that suggested in Table 1. (From Holmes.)

widely in different parts of the world. Thus, the early Mississippian included many swamps in North America, whereas in the southern hemisphere there may have been one or more glacial periods at its end. In the northern hemisphere the Pennsylvanian was probably a time of warm, moist conditions, with no cold winters, but there are signs that for part of this time India and Africa were covered with an ice-sheet. The coal measures show us the remains of the forests of spore- and seed-bearing plants that were then produced, and the land conditions evidently favoured the life of the Amphibia.

The Permian probably constitutes a single 30-million-year period with very active orogenesis, leading to a more arid and colder climate, perhaps showing large seasonal changes, with deserts in some parts of the world and glaciation in others. These conditions continued into the Triassic, whose duration is uncertain. The reptiles, first found in the Permian, developed throughout the Triassic and flourished in the succeeding Jurassic, probably lasting 30 million years, with desert conditions in many parts. There is much uncertainty about the duration and conditions during the subsequent Cretaceous period, during which the very thick chalk deposits were laid down. Probably it lasted for rather more than 60 million years, including two major cycles of inundation. The lower Cretaceous certainly included very extensive periods of flooding, when there were large shallow seas in which chalk deposits were produced. Then later, towards the end of the upper Cretaceous there were very extensive orogenic movements, the Laramide revolution, producing the Rockies and the Andes. The temperature was certainly warm until near the end of the Cretaceous, and we do not know what condition it was that led to the very sharp break which is found between the animals of the Cretaceous and Eocene. Some groups of dinosaurian reptiles seem to have died out very suddenly, but it is important to notice that not all disappeared at the same time, for instance, the stegosaurs and pterodactyls (p. 403) disappeared well before the end of the Cretaceous. However, it is probable that great changes went on at the end of this period, and we may guess that the factor leading to the development of the birds and mammals was the great rise of the continents, perhaps accompanied by a fall in temperature over wide areas that had enjoyed warm weather throughout the Mesozoic. As always, when we look closely at such problems, we are appalled by the vast lengths of time involved and the scanty nature of our clues about them. Certainly the land lay very high at this time, and the apparent abruptness of the break between Cretaceous and Eocene fauna may be an artifact due to the scarcity of fossils at the time. In recent years increasing evidence has been collected of terrestrial deposits laid down before the Eocene, during a 'Palaeocene' time of very uncertain duration (? 10 million years).

It is usual to divide the last main geological period, the Tertiary,[1] into epochs, Eocene, Oligocene, Miocene, Pliocene, and Pleistocene, the names originally referring to the percentage of fossil genera surviving to the present day (see p. 547). The duration of these epochs and their relation to the major orogenic cycles already discussed is not very well understood. Probably the whole time since the end of

---

[1] This word is a survival from an old-fashioned classification of rocks, the Tertiary being the period since the Cretaceous.

the Cretaceous has been about 60 million years, including two cycles. During the early part of the Tertiary period the climate was cold, but as erosion of the mountains produced at the end of the Cretaceous proceeded the conditions became warmer, and throughout the Eocene and Oligocene there were large forests and humid conditions. Then during the Miocene there were very marked earth movements, leading to elevation of the land and accompanied by more arid conditions, with wide areas of prairie. The weather probably became gradually colder through the Pliocene, no doubt with many fluctuations, culminating in the ice ages of the Pleistocene. Here we come back to the period of which we have more detailed knowledge, and are reminded that the ice age was not continuous, but interrupted by several, perhaps many, warmer periods.

This very brief survey of geological history can hardly do more than remind us of the depths of our ignorance. We see enough to be sure that climatic conditions have varied throughout the millions of years, but we cannot yet see sufficient details to allow us to trace the rhythm of the major cycles accurately, still less to follow the 'minor' ones, of which we see traces in the last stages of the earth's history. It is easy to talk glibly of 'Carboniferous forests' or 'arid conditions of the Permian', forgetting that these periods lasted for a time which we can roughly record in numbers but not properly imagine in terms of our experience, although we are among the longest lived of animals. The evidence suggests that conditions did not remain stable for such a vast length of time as a whole geological period, but fluctuated markedly with 'shorter' rhythms, perhaps of 40,000 years, which is, after all, an immense time in relation to individual organic lives. We must not forget that very profound 'climatic' changes occur every day, others every year, and some perhaps every 11 years. It is not impossible that these shorter-period changes, necessitating continual readjustment of animal and plant life, have been as important as the slower changes in producing evolution.

11. Summary

To reduce to order our knowledge of vertebrate life we shall try to discover its general organization and then examine the factors which have produced all the varied types. The pattern of organization we have to study is that of the animal as an active system maintaining itself in its environment. This tendency to maintenance and growth is the central 'force' which produces the variety of life. The opportunity for change is provided by the fact that reproduction seldom

produces an exact copy of the parent, and thus a range of types is produced. The tendencies to grow and to vary lead animals to colonize
new environments and produce the variety of life. As evolution has
proceeded animals have come to occupy environments differing ever
more widely from the sea in which life arose. Life in these more
difficult environments is made possible by the development of special
devices making the later animals more complex than the earlier and in
this sense 'higher'. It remains uncertain what influences have been
responsible for producing the changes in organic form. Geological
evidence shows that there have been very many changes in climate and
geography, some of them proceeding at very slow rates in comparison
with the rhythms of individual animal lives. It is uncertain whether
evolutionary changes follow these slow geological changes, or are a
result of the instability imposed on living things by climatic rhythms
with shorter periods, such as those of days, years, and the sunspot
cycles.

II

THE GENERAL PLAN OF
CHORDATE ORGANIZATION: *AMPHIOXUS*

1. The variety of chordate life

The Chordata occupy a greater variety of habitats and show more complicated mechanisms of self-maintenance than any other group in the whole animal kingdom. They and the arthropods and the pulmonate molluscs are the only animals that have fully solved the problem of life on the land—which they now dominate. This domination is achieved by most delicate mechanisms for resisting desiccation, for providing support, and for conducting all those operations which are harder in the air than in water; together with still more wonderful devices by which the body temperature is raised and kept uniform and thus all reactions accelerated. Finally, use is made of this high rate of living for the development of the nervous system into a most delicate instrument, allowing the animal not only to change its response to a given stimulus from moment to moment, but also to store up and act upon the fruits of past experience.

Besides these more developed types of chordate that dominate the land and air there are also great numbers of extremely successful aquatic and amphibious types. The frog is often referred to as a somewhat lowly and unsuccessful animal, but frogs and toads are found all over the world. The sharks and bony fishes share with the squids the culminating ecological position in the food chains of the sea, while the bony fishes are the only animals that have achieved considerable size and variety in fresh water. Among the still more lowly chordates the sea-squirts take a very important, though not dominant, position among the animal and plant communities which occupy the sea bottom, but they have never entered fresh water.

One could continue indefinitely with particulars of the amazing types produced by this most adaptable phylum. Yet through all their variety of structure the chordates show a considerable uniformity of general plan, and there can be no doubt that they have all evolved from a common ancestor of what might be called a 'fish-like' habit. In the very earliest stages only the larva was fish-like, and the life-history probably also included a sessile adult stage, such as the tunicates still show to-day (p. 59). This bottom-living phase was then eliminated by paedomorphosis, the larvae becoming the adults.

Therefore the essential organization of a chordate is that of a long-bodied, free-swimming creature. All the other types can be derived from such an ancestor, though in some cases only by what is often called 'degeneration'. In fact, the chordates are a rather compact group morphologically, and it has therefore been possible for a great amount of analytical work to be done on living and fossil groups, revealing the details of the evolutionary progression. Where details of evolution are well known, classification necessarily becomes correspondingly more difficult, and in the case of the chordates, though major groupings are still used for convenience, it is important not to be misled by the names into opinions about the closeness of affinities. Both crocodiles and snakes are called reptiles, but it does not follow that they are more closely related to each other than either is to a bird.

2. Classification of chordates

We may conveniently divide the Phylum Chordata into four subphyla:

Subphylum 1. Hemichordata
  Balanoglossus, Cephalodiscus, Rhabdopleura
Subphylum 2. Cephalochordata (= Acrania)
  Amphioxus
Subphylum 3. Urochordata
  Ciona, Sea-squirts
Subphylum 4. Vertebrata

The Vertebrata, the largest of these groups, may be subdivided:

Subphylum Vertebrata
  Superclass 1. AGNATHA
    Class 1. Cyclostomata. Lampreys and hag-fishes
    Class 2. *Cephalaspidomorphi *Cephalaspis*
    Class 3. *Pteraspidomorphi *Pteraspis*
    Class 4. *Anaspida *Birkenia*
    Class 5. *Euphanerida *Jaymoytius*

  Superclass 2. GNATHOSTOMATA
    Class 1. *Placodermi *Acanthodes*
    Class 2. Elasmobranchii. Dogfishes, skates, and rays
    Class 3. Actinopterygii. Bony fishes
    Class 4. Choanichthyes. Lung-fishes
    Class 5. Amphibia
    Class 6. Reptilia
    Class 7. Aves
    Class 8. Mammalia.

3. *Amphioxus*, a generalized chordate

It has long been realized that through their great variety all these types show certain common features, often referred to as the *typical chordate characters*. It is better to regard these not as a list of isolated 'characters' but as the signs of a certain pattern of organization which is characteristic of the group. There is every reason to suppose that this basic chordate organization was that of a free-swimming marine animal, probably feeding by the collection of minute particles. We are fortunate in having still alive a little animal *Amphioxus* (the lancelet) that shows nearly all of these features in diagrammatic form. Study of *Amphioxus* will go a long way to show the basic plan on which all later chordates are built, and, indeed, will give us a strong indication of what the early chordates must have been like.

Though it can swim freely through the water, *Amphioxus* is essentially a burrowing animal, and not a few of its special features are connected with this habitat. It lives in the sand, at small depths, and has been found all round the oceans of the world. Evidently, in spite of its simplicity, it is a successful type. It is abundant on British coasts and, indeed, the first individual described was sent (preserved) from Cornwall to the German zoologist Pallas, who supposed it to be a slug and called it *Limax lanceolatus* (1774). It was first figured and given its familiar name *Amphioxus lanceolatus* by Yarrell in 1836. The name *Branchiostoma* was given in 1834 by Costa, but his description was inadequate and without a figure; there is therefore no need to abandon the familiar name. Some eight species of *Amphioxus* are recognized, and in addition there is a group of six species referred to the genus *Asymmetron*. These resemble *Amphioxus* in general organization, but they are very asymmetrical, gonads occurring only on the right side. Certain asymmetrical pelagic forms have been referred to a third genus *Amphioxides*, but no fully adult individuals have been seen, and the specimens are probably larvae of *Asymmetron* that have remained for a long time at the sea surface and failed to undergo metamorphosis.

The adult *Amphioxus lanceolatus* is rather less than 2 in. long and has the typical fish-like organization, whose main external features are related to the methods of locomotion and feeding (Fig. 6). The body is elongated, and flattened from side to side. The skin has no pigment, and the muscles can be easily seen as a series of blocks, the myotomes, serving to bend the body into folds. As the name implies, the body is pointed at both ends; there is no recognizable head separated from the body. Indeed, there are no separate eyes, nose, or ears, and no jaws, so that the fundamental plan of chordate body organization appears in almost its fullest simplicity from one end of the body to the other. The front end is, however, marked by a series of sensory buccal cirri around the opening of an oral hood.

Although the animal is provided with a large number of gill-slits these do not appear externally, being covered by lateral folds of the body, which enclose a ventral space, the atrium, opening posteriorly by an atriopore. The outside edges of the atrium project as a pair of metapleural folds, giving the body a triangular shape in transverse section. The alimentary canal opens posteriorly by an anus, in front of the hind end of the body, thus leaving a definite tail—a region of the body not containing any part of the alimentary canal.

The general arrangement of the organs can best be understood by considering the body as consisting of two tubes, the outer skin (ectoderm) and the inner alimentary canal (endoderm), with a space between (the coelom) lined by a third layer (the mesoderm). This arrangement is actually found during the course of the development (Fig. 20). The mesoderm at first forms thin layers, the somatopleur applied to the outer body-wall and the splanchnopleur to the gut.

Natural Size

FIG. 6. *Amphioxus*, dissected.

The body wall and atrial wall (*at.*) have been removed on the right side, showing the pharynx (*ph.*), mid-gut (*m.g.*) with its diverticulum (*div.*), and intestine (*int.*). The oral hood has been cut away on the right, leaving the left buccal cirri (*b.c.*), wheel organ (*w.o.*), and velum (*v.*). *an.* anus; *at.p.* atriopore; *f.* fin-ray boxes; *g.* gonads; *my.* myotomes; *n.* notochord.

Very soon the inner layer becomes much thickened where it is applied to the nerve-cord and notochord, and here it forms the myotomes, or muscle-blocks. In this dorsal part of the mesoderm the coelom, known here as the myocoel, soon becomes obliterated, leaving the ventral splanchnocoele around the gut. Besides the muscle which forms in the myotomes, non-myotomal muscles develop in the somatopleur and splanchnopleur. These are not divided into segments and are innervated by the dorsal nerve-roots, the ventral roots supplying only the myotomes (p. 145).

4. Movement of *Amphioxus*

The adult myotomes are blocks of striated muscle-fibres, running along the body, separated by sheets of connective tissue, the myocommas. This repetition or segmentation is characteristic of the organization of all chordates. The myocommas do not run straight down the body from dorsal to ventral side but are V-shaped (Fig. 6). However, each muscle-fibre runs straight from before backwards, and the contraction of the whole myotome therefore tends to bend the body. A full discussion of the means by which forward motion is achieved by such a system will be given later. Essentially, contractions of the myotomes result in transverse motion of the body inclined at varying angles in such a way as to result in forward propagation. Each myotome must therefore contract after that in front of it—the effectbeing to produce an S-bend that moves backwards through the water as the fish moves forward.

For our present purpose the essential point is that the contraction is serial, that is to say, it depends on the breaking up of the longitudinal muscle into blocks. Probably the need for this division of the musculature has led to the development of the segmentation, which, affecting primarily the muscles, has come to influence a great part of chordate organization.

Contraction of the longitudinally arranged muscle-fibres will only produce a sharp bending of the body if there is no possibility of shortening of the whole. To prevent telescoping, an incompressible and elastic rod, the notochord, runs down the centre of the body. It is usually stated that this is a 'supporting structure', but, of course, an animal such as a fish in water needs no 'support'. Nor is the notochord a lever to which muscles are attached, as they are to the bones of many higher forms. No muscles pull on it directly, though the myocommas are attached to its sheath. Its function is to prevent the shortening of the body which would otherwise be the result of contraction of longitudinal muscles; in fact, it serves to make that contraction efficient in bending the body; its elasticity may also play an important part.

The notochord has a complex structure, including a fibrous non-

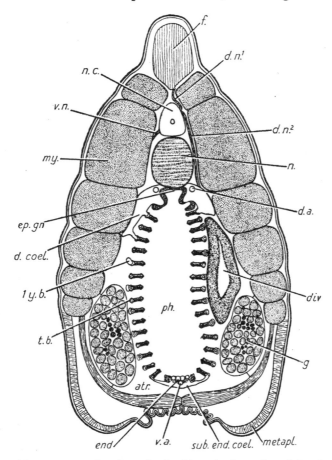

Fig. 7. Transverse section through *Amphioxus* in the region of the pharynx.

atr. atrium; *d.a.* dorsal aorta; *d.coel.* dorsal portion of coelom; *div.* intestinal diverticulum; *d.n.*[1] and *d.n.*[2], branches of the dorsal nerve-root; *end.* endostyle; *ep.gr.* epipharyngeal groove; *f.* fin-ray box; *g.* gonad; *1 y.b.* primary gill bar containing coelom; *my.* myotome; *metapl.* metapleural fold; *n.* notochord; *n.c.* nerve-cord; *ph.* pharynx; *sub.end.coel.* subendostylar coelom; *t.b.* tongue bar; *v.a.* ventral aorta; *v.n.* ventral nerve-root. (After Krause.)

cellular sheath surrounding a series of flattened plates, arranged in a regular manner with their flat surfaces in the transverse plane of the body. These plates are of two sorts, fibrous and homogeneous, which alternate with each other. Each plate develops as a highly vacuolated cell, the nuclei being pushed aside to the dorsal and ventral edges. This structure is well suited by the turgidity of its cells to resist forces tending to shorten the body. The cord of *Amphioxus* is peculiar among all chordates in that it extends from the very tip of the head to the end of the tail, projecting, that is to say, beyond the level of the myotomes, a peculiarity presumably associated with the burrowing habit.

Amphioxus probably does not often swim free in the water and the body is little adapted for fast movements. It has no elaborate fins

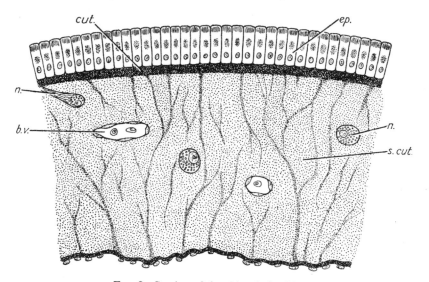

FIG. 8. Section of the skin of *Amphioxus*.
b.v. blood-vessel; *cut.* cutis; *ep.* epidermis; *n.* nerves (containing nerve-cells); *s.cut.* sub-cutis. (After Krause.)

such as those of later fishes, which ensure static stability like the feathers on an arrow, or are movable, to allow active control of the direction of swimming. There is a low dorsal ridge which continues behind as a small caudal fin. There are no definite paired fins, but the metapleural folds might be considered comparable to the lateral fin folds from which all vertebrate limbs are probably derived. They are distended with coelomic fluid and, with the dorsal ridge, probably serve to protect the body during the rapid dives by means of which the creature enters the sand. The habit of swimming, when disturbed, with the front end downwards suggests the presence of a gravitational receptor mechanism. The larvae of lampreys swim in a similar way (p. 107).

5. Skeletal structures of *Amphioxus*

The median ridges, but not the fins, are supported by a series of structures known as fin-ray boxes, though 'connective tissue pockets' would be more appropriate. They are more numerous than the segments and are formed of connective tissue; each contains a central cartilaginous nodule (Fig. 7). The relationship of these structures to

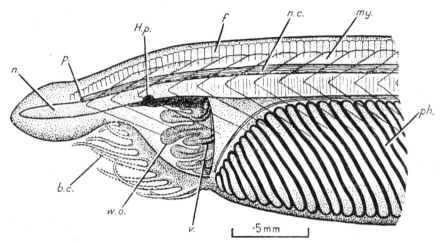

FIG. 9. Anterior end of *Amphioxus*, from a stained and cleared preparation of a young animal.

b.c. buccal cirri; *f.* fin-ray box; *H.p.* Hatschek's pit; *my.* myotome; *n.* notochord; *n.c.* nerve-cord; *p.* pigment spot; *ph.* pharynx; *v.* velar tentacles; *w.o.* wheel organ.

the fin supports of other chordates is obscure. They may perhaps be compared with the lateral folds or 'scutes' found in the earliest agnathous vertebrates (see p. 119).

Other skeletal rods occur in the cirri around the mouth and in the gill bars (see below) and are composed of a tissue resembling that of the notochord, containing large vacuolated cells.

6. Skin of *Amphioxus*

The epidermis differs from that of all higher chordates in being very thin, composed of a single layer of cells, ciliated in the young, and with the outer border slightly cuticularized in the adult (Fig. 8). It is not known whether this cuticle contains a substance similar to the keratin produced by the many-layered skin of later forms. There are no glands or chromatophores in the skin.

Below the epidermis is a fibrous cutis, and below this again a more loosely woven set of fibres, the sub-cutis. The fibres of both these layers are secreted by cells having some similarity to the fibroblasts of higher forms.

7. Mouth and pharynx

Amphioxus obtains its food by extracting small particles from a stream of water, which it draws in by means of cilia. In all animals that use cilia for this purpose a very large surface is provided (e.g. lamellibranchs, ascidians), and the pharynx and gill bars of *Amphioxus* occupy more than one-half of the whole surface area of the body. Special arrangements are made for the support and protection of this ciliated surface, the wall of the pharynx being so greatly subdivided that it needs the protection of an outer layer, the atrium.

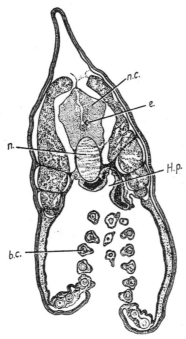

The mouth lies covered by an oral hood whose edges are drawn out into buccal cirri, provided with sense-cells for testing the water (Fig. 9). The sides of the hood can be folded over to cover the mouth as when diving. When feeding the cirri are usually turned inwards to make a funnel excluding the sand particles. Around the mouth itself there is a further ring of sensory tentacles, the velum. The oral hood contains a complex set of ciliated tracts, the 'wheel organ' of Müller, and this plays a part in sweeping the food particles into the mouth (Fig. 10).

Fig. 10. Transverse section through front end of *Amphioxus*.

b.c. buccal cirri; *e.* eyespot; *H.p.* Hatschek's pit; *n.* notochord; *n.c.* nerve-cord.

The main operation of food collection is performed by the pharynx, a large tube, flattened from side to side, whose walls are perforated by nearly 200 oblique vertical slits, the number increasing as the animal gets older. The slits are separated by bars containing skeletal rods and further subdivision is provided by cross-bars (synapticulae). Since the bars slope diagonally many of them are cut in a single transverse section, but it must be remembered that they are essentially the vertical portions of the main walls of body and pharynx, where these have not been perforated by a gill-slit. Such a portion of the body wall must contain a coelomic space and this can in fact be seen in the original or primary gill bars. However, an increase of the ciliary surface is produced by downgrowth of secondary or tongue bars from the upper margin, dividing each primary slit; these secondary bars contain no coelom. The coelomic spaces in the primary bars, of course, communicate above and below with continuous longitudinal coelomic cavities (Fig. 7).

There are cilia on the sides and inner surfaces of the gill bars, the lateral ones being mainly responsible for driving the water outwards through the atrium and thereby drawing the feeding current of water in at the mouth. In the floor of the pharynx lies the endostyle, four

Fig. 11. Currents in the mid-gut of *Amphioxus*, showing the appearance when an animal is placed in a medium containing carmine particles. Arrows show the chief ciliary currents.
div. diverticulum; *f.c.* food cord; *h.g.* hind-gut; *i.c.r.* ilio-colon ring; *m.g.ant.* and *m.g.post.* anterior and posterior parts of mid-gut; *oes.* oesophagus. (After Barrington.)

columns of ciliated cells, alternating with four columns of mucus-secreting cells that produce sticky threads in which food particles become entangled. Various currents then draw the sticky material along until it reaches the mid-gut. The frontal cilia of the gill bars produce an upward current, driving the mucus from the endostyle into a median dorsal epipharyngeal groove, in which it is conducted backwards. The cilia of the endostyle also move mucus along the peripharyngeal ciliated tracts, behind the velum, to join the epipharyngeal groove.

The pharynx narrows at its hind end to open dorsally into a region best known as the mid-gut, the name stomach being inappropriate as the organ contains no gastric glands. A large mid-gut diverticulum reaches forward from this region on the right-hand side of the pharynx. From its position this organ is often called the liver, but Barrington has given reasons for supposing that it is the seat of the production of digestive enzymes. Zymogen cells, similar to those of the mid-gut, are found in its walls. Food does not pass into the diverticulum; indeed, particles placed in it experimentally are swept backwards and join the main food cord that passes through the mid-gut (Fig. 11).

The hind end of the mid-gut is marked by a specially ciliated region, the ilio-colon ring, whose cilia rotate the cord of mucus and food. The movement is transmitted to the portion of the food cord in the mid-gut and presumably assists in the taking up of the enzymes emerging from the diverticulum. Extra-cellular digestion takes place in the mid-gut and the enzymes responsible have been studied by Barrington. The pH of the contents varies from 6·7 to 7·1. An amylase is present in extracts of the diverticulum, mid-gut, and hind-gut, but not in those of the pharynx. Lipase and protease are present in the same regions, the latter having an optimum action at about pH 8·0, being, that is to say, a tryptic type of enzyme. There is no sign of any protease with an acid optimum similar to the pepsin of higher forms.

Behind the ilio-colon ring the intestine runs as a straight hind-gut to the anus. Absorption of food takes place here, and perhaps also in the mid-gut, apparently partly by intra-cellular digestion, since ingested carmine particles are taken into the cells.

FIG. 12. Diagram of the circulation of *Amphioxus*.

aff.d. afferent vessel of diverticulum; *ant. card.* anterior cardinal vein; *br.a.* branchial arch; *d.ao.* dorsal aorta; *d.cuv.* ductus Cuvieri; *eff.d.* efferent vessel of diverticulum; *post.card.* posterior cardinal vein; *sin.* sinus venosus; *subint.* subintestinal vein; *v.a.* ventral aorta. (After Grobben and Zarnik.)

8. Circulation

The blood-vessels of *Amphioxus* show in diagrammatic form the fundamental plan on which the circulation of all chordates is based (Fig. 12). There is no heart but slow waves of contraction pass along the major arterial vessels in such a way as to drive the blood forwards in the ventral vessels, backwards in the dorsal ones. Below the hind end of the pharynx there is a large sac, the sinus venosus, into which blood from all parts of the body is collected. From this there proceeds forwards a large branchial artery (truncus arteriosus or ventral aorta) from which spring vessels carrying blood up the branchial arches. At the base of each primary bar there is a little bulb, presumably functioning as a branchial heart. From the gill bars blood is collected into paired dorsal aortae, which join behind the pharynx. From the paired and median aortae blood is carried to the system of lacunae which supply the tissues. There are no true capillaries. From the lacunae blood is collected into veins, the most important of which are the caudals, cardinals, and a plexus on the gut. The cardinals are a pair of vessels in the dorsal wall of the coelom, and they collect blood from the muscles and body wall. They lead to the sinus venosus by a pair of vessels, ductus Cuvieri, which pass ventrally and across the coelom to join the sinus venosus on the floor of the gut. The caudal veins join the plexus on the gut, from which blood is collected by a large subintestinal vein running on to the liver; from here another plexus leads to the sinus venosus.

The main arteries alone have muscles and show very slow waves of contraction. Only the aorta has an endothelial lining comparable to that of a chordate artery.

The blood is colourless and is not known to contain any respiratory pigment. Presumably the tension of dissolved oxygen acquired by simple solution is sufficient for the small energy needs of the animal, which spends most of its life at rest. It is by no means certain that any oxygenation of the blood takes place in the gills. Orton has suggested that since these, through their cilia, do much of the work of the body, the blood actually leaves the gills less rich in oxygen than when it enters them. Oxygenation probably takes place chiefly in the lacunae close to the skin, perhaps especially those of the metapleural folds.

9. Excretory system of *Amphioxus*

One of the most mysterious features about the organization of *Amphioxus* is that there are flame-cells comparable with those found in platyhelmia, molluscs, and annelids. *The excretory organs, therefore, do not conform to the basic chordate plan,* and are in fact very different from those not only of all other chordates but also from any found in the remote invertebrate allies of the chordates which, as we shall presently see, include the echinoderms, brachiopods, and polyzoa.

The nephridia lie above the pharynx. To each primary gill bar there corresponds a sac, opening by a pore to the atrium and studded with numerous elongated flame-cells (Fig. 13). These flame-cells do not open internally, but are in close contact with special blood-vessels (glomeruli) whose walls separate the flame-cells from the coelomic epithelium. Assuming that there are 200 of these nephridia, each with 500 solenocytes 50 μ long, Goodrich, who has provided the most accurate information about these organs, shows that the total length available for excretion is no less than 5 metres. It is assumed that excretion takes place by diffusion through the flame-cell wall, the

FIG. 13. Solenocytes of *Amphioxus*, showing the nuclei, long flagella, and the openings into the main excretory canal which leads to the atrium. (After Goodrich.)

liquid being driven down the tube by cilia. Coloured particles injected into the blood-stream are not excreted by the nephridia.

In development these remarkable organs arise from groups of cells close to the meeting-place of ectoderm and endoderm; almost certainly they are derived from the former. They have no relation whatever to the mesoderm and this fact alone sufficiently indicates that they are in no way comparable to the pronephros of vertebrates, as is sometimes stated. There is no organ in vertebrates with which they can be compared, nor is there any trace in *Amphioxus* of organs comparable to the vertebrate kidney system. In fact we have here a remarkable case of an isolated feature; evidently separate items of the genotype may vary independently, and the whole bodily organization does not necessarily change together.

There is reason to suppose that some parts of the atrial wall are able to perform excretory functions, and especially the brown tubes or brown funnels, dorsal diverticula of the atrium.

10. Nervous system

Amphioxus possesses a hollow dorsal nerve-cord similar to that of vertebrates. Though this is somewhat modified at the front end, it is

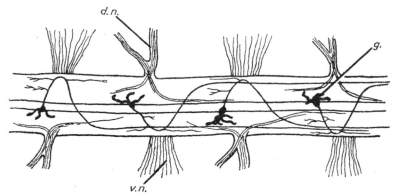

FIG. 14. Nerve-cord of *Amphioxus*.
d.n. dorsal nerve-root; *g.* 'giant' nerve-fibres; *v.n.* ventral nerve-root. (After Retzius.)

not there enlarged into an elaborate brain. The nervous system is connected with the periphery by a remarkably simple set of nerve-roots, a dorsal and a ventral on each side in each segment. The roots do not join (Fig. 14): the ventral roots lie opposite the myotomes, to which they carry motor-fibres, and these end on the muscle-fibres with motor end-plates similar to those of vertebrates. The dorsal root runs out between the myotomes and carries all the sensory fibres of the segment and motor-fibres for the non-myotomal muscles of the ventral part of the body. This is the fundamental pattern of the roots in all vertebrates.

Boeke has shown that in *Amphioxus* the dorsal roots contain fibres running to the wall of the gut, whose movements they presumably control. As in vertebrates there are motor nerve-cells forming a plexus in the gut wall, and the fibres in the dorsal roots therefore correspond to the pre-ganglionic autonomic fibres of vertebrates (p. 168).

The fibres of the peripheral nerves differ from those of vertebrates in that they have no thick myelin sheath which will blacken with osmium tetroxide.

The sensory fibres of the dorsal roots are unique among chordates in that the cell bodies are not collected into spinal ganglia but lie either close below the epidermis or scattered along the course of the nerves (Fig. 8). They thus approach the condition of the neuro-sensory cells which are the typical sense cells of invertebrates, but are found elsewhere in vertebrates only in the olfactory epithelium.

The spinal cord has only a narrow lumen and its elements are arranged as in vertebrates, namely, ependyma close to the canal, cell

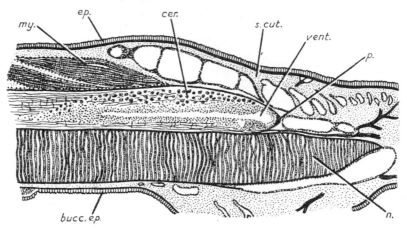

FIG. 15. Sagittal section through the front end of *Amphioxus*.

bucc.ep. buccal epithelium; *cer.* cerebral vesicle, with large nerve-cells; *ep.* epidermis; *my.* myotome; *n.* notochord; *p.* pigment shot; *s.cut.* subcutis; *vent.* ventricle of cerebral vesicle. (After Krause.)

layer ('grey matter'), and outer fibrous layer ('white matter'). The cells are not arranged clearly in horns as they are in vertebrates. The most conspicuous cells are the giant cells which lie dorsally. Each of these has many dendrites, branching in the region of entry of the dorsal root fibres, and a single axon which runs backwards in the front 1/5th of the body, forwards in the remainder, passing in each case for a distance of some segments before breaking up into branches, probably in connexion with the motor neurons from which the ventral root fibres originate. Nothing is known of the connexions of a median giant fibre which runs ventrally for the length of the cord.

Ten Cate has investigated the movements of *Amphioxus* and found that it responds to all stimuli by movements of 'flight'. There are no isolated or local movements; the effect of any stimulus such as touch on the side of the body is to produce waves of myotomal con-traction. These may, however, vary from strong waves going the whole length of the body to single rapid twitches. The giant cells participate in the spread of these waves. It seems likely that the arrangement ensures that touch on the anterior part of the body, normally exposed when feeding, produces backward movement (i.e. withdrawal into the sand) but touch on the hind part the reverse movement of emergence and escape.

At the front end the central cord is enlarged to form a cerebral

FIG. 16. Portion of the wall of the cerebral vesicle of *Amphioxus* to show the infundibular organ, composed of tall cells. (After Boeke.)

FIG. 17. Longitudinal section of the front end of *Amphioxus* to show Kölliker's pit and the nerve that supplies it. (After Krause.)

vesicle (Fig. 15). The whole neural tube is hardly wider here than in the region of the spinal cord and there is very little thickening of the walls, striking indication of the lack of cephalization of the animal. From the region of the cerebral vesicle spring the first two dorsal roots, to which there are no corresponding ventrals. These roots carry impulses from the sense-organs of the oral hood and its tentacles.

The infundibular organ (Fig. 16) is composed of tall cells with long cilia that beat in the opposite direction to those of the rest of the vesicle. The function of this organ is not known.

In young stages the cerebral vesicle opens by an anterior neuropore, and at the point where the closure takes place there develops a depression of the skin, lined by special epithelium and supplied with a nerve (Fig. 17). This is known as Kölliker's pit and is presumed to be a chemoreceptor. The whole of the front end of the cerebral vesicle is covered by a large mass of pigment and there have been attempts to show that this represents an eye. More probably it serves to prevent rather than to receive photic stimulation; there are other cells lying in the spinal cord which are clearly photoreceptors (Fig. 10). In the front part of the body these are unprotected by pigment, whereas more posteriorly they are so pigmented as to be protected asymmetrically from the light (Fig. 18). This asymmetry may

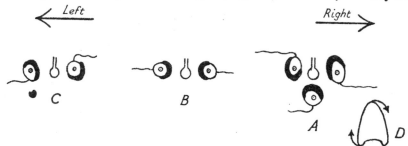

FIG. 18. Diagram to show the direction of the eye-spots of *Amphioxus*.

A, anterior, B, middle, and c, posterior regions of the body. The eyes are shown as if seen from in front. D shows the direction of spiralling of the animal when swimming—as seen from the tail. (After Franz.)

possibly be connected with the fact that when swimming free in the water *Amphioxus* moves spirally about its axis, turning clockwise as seen from behind. It was established by Parker that a small beam of light produces movements of *Amphioxus* only when it is directed on to the region of the body or tail, not when it shines on the head. Since the animal normally lies with the head protruding we may suppose that the pigment spot serves to prevent light which strikes down vertically from stimulating the photoreceptors in the cord.

Amphioxus is therefore provided with sensory and motor systems that serve to keep it in its sedentary position, able to collect its food from the current it makes by the cilia. There are mechanisms which help it to make appropriate movements of escape when it is touched or when its body (but not head) is illuminated. Kölliker's pit and perhaps the tentacles of the oral hood provide chemoreceptors leading to escape from bad water conditions, and the infundibular organ may perhaps be some form of gravity or pressure receptor. By means of these receptor organs and its simple movements of swimming, burrowing, and closing the oral hood the animal is maintained, probably mainly by trial and error (phobotactic) behaviour in an environment suitable for its life.   There are none of those elaborate mechanisms which we find in higher chordates for 'seeking' special environments or for so 'handling' or managing them that they may prove habitable by the animal. *Amphioxus* must take and leave the world very much as it finds it.

11. Gonads and development of *Amphioxus*

The gonads of *Amphioxus* are hollow segmented sacs with no common duct. Each sac develops from cells, perhaps originally from a

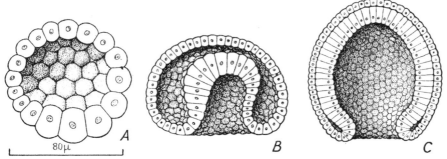

FIG. 19. Three stages in the development of *Amphioxus* as seen in stained preparations.

A, the blastula; B, early, and C, later gastrula.

single cell, at the base of the myotomes in the branchial region, the genital cells themselves developing on the walls (Fig. 7). The sexes are separate and the genital products are shed by dehiscence into the atrium, the aperture by which they escape closing and the gonad developing afresh. Large yellow concretions often develop in the testis, more rarely in the ovary, and it has been suggested that the gonads may thus serve also as excretory organs.

Extrusion of the gametes occurs in spring, on warm days following stormy weather. Fertilization is external, and there is no report of any association of the sexes. Development then occurs free in the water. Numerous eggs are produced and they are small but yolky. Complex flowing movements take place in them after fertilization, and cleavage is then rapid and complete, producing a blastula composed of a dome of somewhat smaller and a floor of rather larger cells (Fig. 19). These latter then invaginate to make the archenteron, opening by a wide blastopore which later becomes the anus. At about this stage the gastrula becomes covered with flagella by which it rotates within the egg case.

The creature now elongates and its dorsal side flattens and eventually sinks in to form the neural tube (Fig. 20 A). At about this time the dorsal side of the inner layer begins to fold near to the front end, in such a way as to make a pair of lateral pouches. The walls of these pouches are the future mesoderm and the cavity is the coelom. As in other early chordates, therefore, the coelom is continuous at first with the archenteron. The roof of the archenteron also arches up

FIG. 20. Further stages in the development of *Amphïoxus* as seen in transverse sections.

A, stage of three somites; B, six somites; C, nine somites; D, eleven somites. *arch.* archenteron; *coel.* coelom; *mes.* mesoderm; *my.* myotome; *my.coel.* myocoele; *n.* notochord; *n.c.* nervecord; *som.pl.* somatopleur; *spl.pl.* splanchnopleur; *spl.coel.* splanchnic coelom. (After Hatschek.)

FIG. 21. Young *Amphïoxus*, soon after hatching.

g. gut; *n.* notochord; *n.c.* nerve-cord; *neur.c.* neurenteric canal; *neur.p.* neuropore.

dorsally and forms the notochord, the gut wall being completed by the approximation of the edges of the remaining portion of the inner layer, which is now the definitive gut wall or endoderm.

The analysis of the processes of development now enables us to say something of the forces by which these formative foldings and cell movements are produced. Here, however, we can only note that the formation of the neural tube, mesoderm, and notochord and the completion of the gut roof all involve an upward movement of cells towards the mid-dorsal line. This process of 'convergence' is a very marked feature of the development of all chordates.

As the animal elongates, further mesodermal pouches are produced, each separating completely from the endoderm and from its neighbours. The cells of each pouch push down ventrally on either side of the gut, the outer ones applying themselves to the body wall to form the somatopleur, the inner to the gut wall as splanchnopleur (Fig. 20 D). The inner wall of the mesoderm on either side of the nerve-cord thickens to form the myotome, and a tongue of cells growing up between this and the nerve-cord forms the sheaths of the latter and probably also the fin-ray boxes and other 'mesenchymal' tissues. The upper part of the coelomic cavity, the myocoele, becomes separated from the ventral splanchnocoele. Whereas the former becomes almost completely obliterated, the latter expands to form the adult coelom, the cavities between the adjacent sacs breaking down.

FIG. 22. Larval *Amphioxus* before metamorphosis.

an. anus; *c.s.g.* club-shaped gland; *end.* endostyle; *g.* gill-slits lying on right side, which will later move over to the left. *H.p.* Hatschek's pit (left first coelomic sac); *m.* lower edge of mouth, lying on left side; *n.* notochord; *p.* pigment spot.

While this differentiation of the mesoderm has been proceeding the animal has elongated into a definitely fish-like form. The neural tube is a small dorsal canal opening by an anterior neuropore and continuous behind through a neurenteric canal with the gut (Fig. 21). The larva hatches when only two segments have been formed and swims at the sea surface by means of its ciliated epidermis, turning on its axis from right to left as it proceeds with the front end forwards.

The mouth now appears as a circular opening in the mid-ventral line and then moves over to the left side and becomes very large. From this time onward the whole development is markedly asymmetrical, presumably in connexion with the spiral movement and method of feeding. The first gill-slit also forms near the midline but moves up on to the right side (Fig. 22). At about the same time the right side of the pharyngeal wall develops into a V-shaped thickening, the endostyle. Behind this there forms a sac, the club-shaped gland, opening to the exterior by a narrow mouth. The significance of this organ is still obscure; it is presumably connected with the feeding-process, which begins at this stage. The morphological status of the club-shaped gland is also uncertain; it has been thought to represent a gill-slit.

The first two coelomic pouches differentiate, asymmetrically, at this time. That on the right becomes the coelomic cavity of the head region, while the left one acquires an opening to the exterior and a heavily ciliated surface. This is no doubt also connected with the feeding-systems and becomes developed into Hatschek's pit and Müller's wheel organ of the adult.

Further gill-slits develop in the mid-ventral line and move over on to the right side until fourteen have been so formed. Meanwhile, a further row of eight slits appears *above* that already formed. These are the definitive slits of the right side and presently the larva proceeds to become symmetrical by movement of eight of the first row of slits over to the left side, the remainder disappearing. Further slits are then gradually added in pairs on both sides. Each slit becomes subdivided, soon after its formation, by the downgrowth of a tongue bar. The atrium is absent from the early larva. Metapleural folds then appear on either side and are united from behind forwards to form a tube below the pharynx. During the latter stages of development the larva sinks and finally rests on the bottom while undergoing the migration of gill-slits, which constitutes its metamorphosis.

The development of *Amphioxus*, like its adult organization, shows us many features of the plan that is typical of all chordates and was presumably present in the earliest of them. Thus the cleavage, invagination, and mesoderm formation proceed in a manner which, while it recalls that of echinoderms and other forms similar to the ancestors of the chordates, also shows a pattern from which all later chordate development can be derived. Unfortunately we cannot pursue this study as far as we should like because of the difficulty of investigating the development of *Amphioxus*. Modern embryologists aim at tracing the morphogenetic movements by which the organism is built, and ultimately at discovering the forces responsible for these processes. The technique used for this purpose has been to make marks with non-toxic dyes on the outside of the developing creatures. Such work requires a plentiful supply of embryos, but no one has yet succeeded in devising a satisfactory method of artificial fertilization by which *Amphioxus* embryos can be obtained. All our knowledge is based on specimens taken from the sea in various stages of development.

Interesting stages are thus revealed, but we still remain ignorant of the details of the morphogenetic movements, and can only guess that the system of cell activities by which an *Amphioxus* is built represents quite closely the original set of morphogenetic processes of vertebrates.

There are, of course, some special features connected with the method of life of the larva, and especially with its asymmetry. The strange sequence of gill formation, the immense left-sided larval mouth, perhaps the club-shaped gland, and Müller's organ, may show considerable modifications of relatively recent date. However, the earliest chordates probably fed by means of cilia and were planktonic, so we must not too hastily assume that even these asymmetrical features are novelties.

The earlier division of the mesoderm of *Amphioxus* into a series of sacs presents an interesting problem. The segmentation of the meso-derm of vertebrates is restricted to the dorsal region. In the lowest chordates (see p. 72), as in their pre-chordate ancestors, there are three coelomic cavities, but it is probable that the many segments of vertebrates arose in order to provide a set of muscles able to contract in a serial manner for the purpose of swimming. Their segmentation would thus be a relatively late development, not related to the segmentation of annelids which divides the whole body into rings. Accordingly the ventral part of the coelom usually remains unseg-mented. But in *Amphioxus* it is subdivided from its first appearance and only becomes continuous later. The best interpretation of this condition is to suppose that in order to provide a series of myotomes a rhythmic process subdividing the mesoderm was adopted. In its earliest stages this affected the whole mesoderm, ventral as well as dorsal, but later became restricted to the dorsal region. New morpho-genetic processes may often pass through stages of refinement and simplification in such ways.

12. *Amphioxus* as a generalized chordate

Amphioxus provides us, then, with a very valuable example of a chordate in all its simplicity, retaining the habit of ciliary feeding which was probably that of the earliest ancestors of our phylum. No doubt in connexion with this, and the bottom-living habit, there are many specializations; the enormously developed pharynx with its atrium, the asymmetry, and so on; but the general arrangement of the body is almost diagrammatically simple, and we cannot doubt that *Amphioxus* shows us a stage very like that through which the ancestors of the true fishes evolved. The closeness with which its organization corresponds to that of later forms might give rise to a suspicion that it is not an ancestral type but a simplified derivative of the vertebrates, perhaps a paedomorphic form. It possesses, however, sufficient peculiar features to make this view very unlikely. Neoteny might explain the regular segmentation, separate dorsal and ventral roots, and other features, but can hardly account for the method of obtaining food, for the condition of the skin, or for the presence of nephridia. We may therefore feel fairly safe in assuming that *Amphioxus* shows us approximately the condition of the early fish-like chordates living in the Silurian some 400 million years ago, and that it has undergone relatively little change in all the time since.

III

THE ORIGIN OF CHORDATES FROM FILTER FEEDING ANIMALS

1. Invertebrate relatives of the chordates

We have seen in the organization of *Amphioxus* the full plan of chordate structure as it may have existed in Palaeozoic times. Before proceeding to discuss the later forms that evolved from animals of this sort we may first look yet farther backwards to discuss the origin of the whole chordate phylum from still earlier ancestors. The great difficulty of such an inquiry is itself a stimulus and a challenge. Typical fish-like chordates were undoubtedly established by the Silurian period, but we have no good fossil record of their earliest form and this must therefore be deduced from study of *Amphioxus* and later animals. No fossils that suggest chordate affinities have been found in the still earlier rocks. There are, however, certain strange animals alive to-day which, though not of fish-like type, show undoubted relationship with our group. These might, of course, be degenerate offshoots from later periods, but careful comparison suggests that they have been separated for a very long time and provide us with relics of some of the very early stages of our history.

The first step in our inquiry, however, before discussing these forms, should be to find out, if possible, which of the main lines of invertebrate animals shows the closest affinity with the chordates. Almost every phylum in the animal kingdom has been suggested. Many still suppose that the annelids and arthropods, because of their metameric segmentation, are related to the chordates, but closer examination shows that the similarities are superficial. The segmentation of these annulate animals is an almost complete division of the whole body into rings, and all the organ systems are affected by it to some extent. In chordates only the dorsal myotomal region is segmented; even the mesoderm is not divided in its ventral region in most cases. Moreover, the whole orientation of the body differs in the two groups. The vertebrate nerve-cord is dorsal to the gut, in annulates the nerve-cord is below: the blood circulates in opposite directions, the limbs are based on quite a different plan, and so on. Attempts have been made to get over these difficulties by turning the invertebrate upside down! Patten and Gaskell carried such theories to extremes in the attempt to show a relationship of chordates with the eurypterids, heavily armoured arachnids of the Cambrian and Silurian. Superficially these animals certainly show a resemblance to the earliest fossil fishes, the cephalaspids of the Devonian (Fig. 81), and these workers, with great ingenuity, claimed to find in them evidence of the presence of a great many chordate organs.

The safest evidence of affinity is a similarity of developmental processes: animals that develop very differently are most unlikely to be closely related. The development of modern annulates is utterly different from that of chordates. The cleavage by which the fertilized egg is divided into blastomeres follows in annulates a 'spiral' plan, in which every blastomere arises in a regular way and the future fate of each can be exactly stated. In later annulates, such as the arthropods, this plan is complicated by the presence of much yolk, but even in these animals the cleavage does not resemble that of chordates, which is radial or 'irregular', the cells not forming any special pattern. This characteristic has been used to divide the whole animal kingdom into two major groups, Spiralia and Irregularia.

The next stage of development, gastrulation, by which the ball of cells is converted into a two-layered creature, also occurs very differently in the two groups. Our knowledge of the mechanics of the processes by which this change is produced is still imperfect, in spite of recent advances, but in early chordates it occurs by invagination, the folding in of one side of the ball of cells to form an archenteric cavity communicating with the exterior. In annulates this never occurs; the cells which will go to form the gut migrate inwards either at one pole or all round the sphere and only later form themselves into a tube, which comes to open secondarily to the outside. It is probable that when we know more of the mechanics of the forces by which the gastrulation is produced the difference will appear even more marked than it does from this crude and formal statement that gastrulation in chordates is by invagination, in annulates by immigration.

The same applies to the method by which the mesoderm and coelom are formed. In earlier chordates the third layer is produced by separation from the endoderm, so that the coelom is continuous with the archenteron and is said to be an *enterocoele*. In annulates cells separate in many ways to form the mesoderm and a coelom then arises within this solid mass as a *schizocoele*. It is true that in some, indeed many, of the higher chordates the coelom is never continuous with the archenteron, but its method of development shows it to be a modified enterocoele.

Thus in many points of development the chordates differ from the annulates but resemble the echinoderms and their allies. Further points support this latter relationship. One of the most important of these is that the echinoderm-like animals, and some of the early chordates, have a larva with longitudinal ciliated bands, very different from the trochophore larva, in which the bands run transversely round the body, which is found in the other line of animals. The nervous system of annulates consists of a system of ganglionated cords, whereas in echinoderm-like animals it is a diffuse sheet of cells and fibres below the epidermis. The nerve-cord of the chordates can be derived from the latter but not easily from the former condition. Many further points could be cited, for instance, the presence of a mesodermal skeleton in both chordates and echinoderms, but not in annulates.

In the study of evolution it is not sufficient merely to make formal comparisons, we must try to find out and compare the plan of development and structure common to all members of two groups, a business often requiring great knowledge and good sense. When this is done in the present case it will be found that the essential plan of development of annulates involves spiral cleavage, gastrulation by immigration, and a coelom formed as a schizocoele, a trochophore-like larva, and full segmentation of the mesoderm. It is exceedingly unlikely that such animals have given rise to chordates with their very different development, which we may crudely define as showing radial cleavage, gastrulation by invagination, and larva of echinoderm type.

Extending this method we may divide the whole world of Metazoa by similar criteria into Spiralia or Polymera and Irregularia or Oligomera. The former include besides the annulates the molluscs and platyhelmia, whereas the latter group contains, in addition to the chordates, the echinoderms, brachiopods, polyzoa (ectoprocta), and *Phoronis*. The animals in this latter group seem at first sight to be very different from the chordates in outward form, but the farther we look into their fundamental organization, the more we become convinced that the ancestors of the fish-like animals are to be found here. By study of the relics of the early chordates it is possible to trace the history of this strange change with some plausibility, though its full details will never be known.

2. Subphylum Hemichordata

Class 1. Enteropneusta
Balanoglossus, Glossobalanus, Ptychodera, Saccoglossus
Class 2. Pterobranchia
Cephalodiscus, Rhabdopleura

In the Hemichordata are placed animals of two types, the worm-like *Balanoglossus* and its allies (Enteropneusta) and two sedentary animals, *Cephalodiscus* and *Rhabdopleura* (Pterobranchia). The Entero-pneusta are burrowing animals (Fig. 23) varying in different species from 2 cm. to over 2 metres long. Several genera are recognized

FIG. 23. *Balanoglossus*, removed from its tube and seen from the dorsal side. *abd.* abdomen; *atr.* atrium; *an.* anus; *c.* collar; *h.c.* hepatic caeca; *p.* proboscis; *ph.* pharynx. (From van der Horst.)

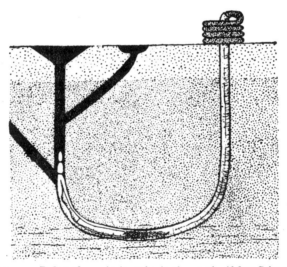

FIG. 24. *Balanoglossus* in its tube in the sand. (After Stiasny.)

(e.g. *Balanoglossus, Saccoglossus, Ptychodera*) and they occur in all seas. *Saccoglossus* occurs around the British coast. The body is soft, without rigid skeletal structures, and divided into proboscis, collar, and trunk. The animals are very soft and fragile and it is difficult to collect specimens in which the hind part of the trunk ('abdomen') is intact. The proboscis, collar, and trunk each contain a coelomic cavity, and the coeloms of the proboscis and collar are distensible by intake of water through a single proboscis pore and paired collar pores. The skin is very richly ciliated all over the body. The epi-thelium is similar to the single-layered skin of *Amphioxus* and unlike the squamous, layered skin of higher forms. It contains numerous gland-cells, whose secretion is very copious, so that the animals are always covered with slime. A characteristic feature is an unpleasant

.FIG. 25. Diagrammatic section of front end of *Balanoglossus*.

c. collar coelom; *card.s.* sac around heart; *div.* pharyngeal diverticulum ('notochord'); *dn.* dorsal nerve-root; *dv.* dorsal vessel; *gl.* glomerulus; *gs.* gill-slit; *lm.* longitudinal muscles of proboscis; *n.c.* nerve-cord; *p.p.* proboscis pore; *sk.* skeletal plate. (Modified after Spengel.)

smell, resembling that of iodoform, which possibly serves, like the mucus, as a protection.

Below the skin are muscles running in various directions. It is said that the animal moves by first pushing the proboscis and collar forward through the sand and then drawing the body after it. Protrusion of the proboscis cannot, however, be very vigorous. It may perhaps be produced by ciliary action distending the coelom as is usually stated—more probably by circular muscles, but these are weak. Numerous longitudinal muscles are present, however, in the proboscis and trunk and are attached to a plate of skeletal tissue in the collar. This tissue contains large cells and bears a considerable resemblance

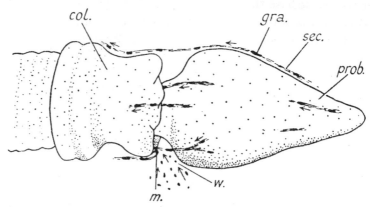

FIG. 26. Feeding-currents on proboscis of *Glossobalanus*, shown by placing the animal in water containing carmine particles. The particles (*gra.*) are either taken directly into the mouth (*m.*) as at w., or are caught up in strands of mucus (*sec.*) and passed backwards. (From Barrington, *Quart. J. Micr. Sci.*, vol. 82, by permission.)

FIG. 27. Transverse section of the pharynx of *Glossobalanus*.

cil. cilia of the gill bars; *dc.* dorsal chamber of pharynx; *es.* epibranchial strip; *gp.* gill pore; *vc.* ventral chamber of pharynx. (From Barrington. With permission as for Fig. 26.)

to a notochord. Moreover, it is formed in development as the wall of a diverticulum of the gut (Fig. 25). A notochord extending throughout the length of the body would clearly be disadvantageous for an animal whose main movements are lengthening and shortening. It is reasonable to suppose that the plate found in the collar is the remains of a notochord, produced by a process similar to that which forms the longer rod in higher forms, and serving as a fixed point by which the body is drawn forward on the proboscis. The cilia probably play a considerable part in locomotion; possibly they are the chief burrowing organs, the muscles serving mainly to perform escape movements.

The mouth lies in a groove between the proboscis and collar (Fig. 26), and food is brought to it mainly by the ciliary currents of the proboscis. In the anterior part of the trunk there is a wide pharynx, opening by a series of gill-slits (Figs. 25, 27). These resemble the

FIG. 28. Diagram of the blood system of *Balanoglossus*.
col. collar; *d.v.* dorsal vessel; *glom.* glomerulus; *hp.* hepatic caeca; *m.* mouth; *not.* notochord; *p.* proboscis; *ph.* pharynx; *v.v.* ventral vessel. (After Bronn.)

gills of *Amphioxus* in the presence of a supporting skeleton in the gill bars; there are also tongue bars dividing the slits from above, and horizontal synapticulae strengthening the gill arches. The slits open in some forms into an atrium formed by lateral folds, usually turned upwards to leave a long mid-dorsal opening. In some species each slit opens to a gill pouch. The whole branchial apparatus perhaps assists in the process of feeding. Relative to the size of the animal it is less extensive than in *Amphioxus*, presumably because ciliary surfaces are provided on the outside and also large masses of sand are forced into the mouth during locomotion.

There is no endostylar apparatus, and the large quantity of matter ingested is passed along the floor of the pharynx to an almost straight intestine opening by a terminal anus. There is no true tail. Numerous hepatic caeca in the anterior part of the intestine can be seen from the outside as folds of the body wall, often highly coloured, and there are various pores leading from the gut to the exterior.

The blood system (Fig. 28) consists of a dorsal vessel ending anteriorly in a sinus and a complex glomerulus at the base of the proboscis. Propulsion of the blood, if it occurs, must be by means of a contractile cardiac sac, which is a closed vesicle above the dorsal sinus. It is said that blood moves forward in the dorsal, backward in the ventral vessel. From the glomerulus a plexus of vessels leads to a ventral vessel below the gut. The functioning of the blood system is not well understood and there is no sign that any parts of the body are specialized for excretion or respiration.

The nervous system is one of the most interesting features of Enteropneusta. It resembles that of echinoderms in consisting of a sheet of nerve-fibres and cells lying beneath the epidermis all over the body. This sheet is thickened in places to make the central nervous system, and in the dorsal part of the collar region it is rolled up as a hollow neural tube, open at both ends (Fig. 25). From this tube 'dorsal roots' proceed to the skin of the back of the collar, and special thickenings of the sub-epithelial plexus run round the base of the proboscis and collar to join a mid-ventral thickening. These unmistakable resemblances not only to the uncentralized sub-epithelial plexus of echinoderms but also to the hollow dorsal nerve-cord of vertebrates are most instructive by showing the affinity of the groups and the origin of the general plan of the vertebrate nervous system. There are no organs of special sense, unless this is the function of a patch of special ciliated cells on the collar. Little is known of

FIG. 29. Diagram of certain tracts in the nervous system of *Balanoglossus*.

com. circular connective; *col.coel.* collar coelom; *col.n.c.* collar nerve-cord; *ep.pl.* nerve plexus in epidermis of trunk; *gp.* gill pore; *tr.coel.* trunk coelom; *tr.n.c.* trunk nerve-cord. (From Bullock, *J. Comp. Neurol.*, vol. 80, by permission.)

the organization of pathways and activities within the system (Fig. 29). It is often stated that the nervous system of these animals has a non-synaptic network, but the evidence of the relationship of the cells to each other is inadequate.

Bullock has investigated the behaviour of the animals and found only one clear-cut reflex, namely, a contraction of the longitudinal muscles in response to tactile stimulation. Isolated pieces of the body are able to show reflex responses, moving away from light or tactile stimuli. Such local actions are an interesting sign of the uncentralized nature of the nervous system, and similar actions are found in echinoderms. A further sign of lack of special conducting pathways is that stimulation of flaps of body wall partly severed from the rest produces generalized contraction, proving that conduction can occur in all directions. The dorsal and ventral nerve-cords do, however, act as quick conduction pathways, and contraction of the trunk following stimulation of the proboscis is delayed or absent if one, and especially if both, cords have been cut.

Perhaps the most interesting behaviour observed was the activity

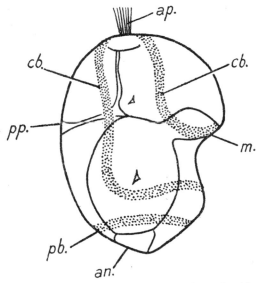

FIG. 30. Young tornaria larva, seen from the side.
an. anus; *ap.* apical organ; *cb.* longitudinal ciliated band; *m.* mouth; *pb.* posterior ciliated band; *pp.* proboscis pore. (After Stiasny.)

shown by an isolated proboscis, collar, trunk, or portion of trunk. These organs may move around vigorously in an exploratory manner; evidently the main nerve-cords are not necessary for the initiation of action, as is the central nervous system of higher chordates.

The sexes are separate in enteropneusts and the gonads resemble those of *Amphioxus* in being a series of sacs in the atrial folds. They open by special pores and fertilization is external. The development is remarkably like that of echinoderms. Cleavage is holoblastic and not spiral, gastrulation is by invagination, and the coelom is formed as an enterocoele, later becoming subdivided into proboscis, collar, and trunk coeloms. Hatching occurs to produce a pelagic tornaria larva with a ciliated band that has exactly the relations found in such a form as the auricularia larva of the sea-cucumbers (echinoderms). The band passes in front of the mouth, down the sides of the body, and in front of the anus (Fig. 30). This arrangement differs essentially from the rings of cilia which pass round the body in the trochophore larva found in the annelids and other spirally cleaving forms. In later tornaria larvae there is, however, in addition to the longitudinal bands always a posterior ring of stout cilia, and in large oceanic forms (which may reach 8 mm. in length) the longitudinal band itself is prolonged into prominent tentacle-like loops (Fig. 31). The cilia of the posterior ring are purely locomotive, while those of the band set up feeding-currents converging to the mouth. As the larva becomes larger the ciliary surface needed for locomotion and feeding has to increase relatively faster than the increasing mass of the body, the latter following the cube but the former only the square of the linear dimensions. Accordingly the cilia of the locomotive ring become broadened and flame-like, while the convolutions of the longitudinal (feeding) band reach fantastic proportions.

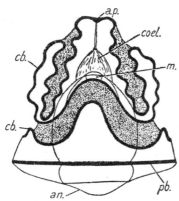

FIG. 31. Older tornaria larva seen from ventral surface.

Letters as Fig. 30. *coel.* proboscis coelom. (After Stiasny.)

Finally the larva sinks, becomes constricted into three parts, and undergoes metamorphosis into the worm-like adult. This development is so like that of an echinoderm that it would be necessary to consider the enteropneusts to be related to that group even if no other clues existed. Such close similarity in the fundamentals of development cannot be due to chance.

These animals thus provide a very remarkable and sure demonstration that the chordates are related to the echinoderms and similar groups. The general arrangement of the nervous system as a sub-epithelial plexus, as well as the whole course of the development, show the affinity with the invertebrate groups, whereas the hollow dorsal nerve-cord and the tongue-barred gill-slits are by themselves sufficient to show affinity with the chordates, this affinity being also suggested by other features, such as the 'notochord'. As we have seen already, affinities are not to be determined by single 'characters' but by the general pattern of organization of animals and especially that of their development. The organization of the enteropneusts is certainly highly specialized for their burrowing life, but showing through the special features we can clearly see a plan that has similarity both with the echinoderms and the chordates. The special value of study of these animals is that it proves decisively that an affinity between these groups exists. Exactly how they are all related is a more speculative matter, which we shall deal with later (see p. 72).

3. Class Pterobranchia

These are small, colonial, marine, sedentary animals, which show

FIG. 32. Longitudinal median section of *Cephalodiscus*.

a. anus; *b.c.* 1, 2, and 3, body cavities; *int.* intestine; *m.* mouth; *nch.* notochord; *n.s.* nervous system; *oes.* oesophagus; *op.* operculum (collar); *ov.* ovary; *ovd.* oviduct; *ph.* pharynx; *p.p.* proboscis pore; *pp.* proboscis; *st.* stomach; *stk.* stalk. (After Harmer, *Cambridge Natural History*, Macmillan.)

some signs of the general echinoderm–chordate plan of organization we have been discussing. *Cephalodiscus* (Fig. 32) has been found on the sea bottom at various depths, mainly in the southern hemisphere: there are several species. The colony consists of a number of zooids held together in a many-chambered gelatinous house. The zooids are formed by a process of budding, but do not maintain continuity with each other. Each zooid has a proboscis, collar, and trunk; there are coeloms in each of these parts, and proboscis and collar pores. The collar is prolonged into a number of ciliated arms, by means of which the animal feeds. There is a large pharynx, opening by a single pair of gill-slits that serve as an outlet for the water drawn in by the cilia of the tentacles for the purpose of bringing food. The intestine is turned upon itself, so that the anus opens near the mouth. A thickening in the roof of the pharynx corresponds exactly in position with the notochord and is prolonged forward like the diverticulum of enteropneusts. The blood system consists of a series of spaces arranged on a plan similar to that in *Balanoglossus*. There is a dorsal ganglion in the collar, but this is not hollow. The gonads are simple sacs and development takes place in the spaces of the gelatinous house. There is some doubt about the details of cleavage and methods of gastrulation, but the larva somewhat resembles the cyphonautes larva of ectoproctous polyzoa, which is not closely similar to the echinoderm larvae, but could be derived from the same plan.

Rhabdopleura occurs in various parts of the world, including the North Atlantic and northern part of the North Sea. The zooids are connected together and have proboscis, collar, and trunk, ciliated arms, coelomic spaces with pores (not 'nephridia' as is sometimes stated) and 'notochord', but no gill-slit. The development is not known. The fossil graptolites are supposed to be related forms, known, of course, only from the shape of their skeleton.

The Pterobranchia thus show undoubted signs of the enteropneust–chordate plan of organization and provide also an interesting suggestion of possible affinities with Polyzoa, Brachiopoda, and *Phoronis*. Like the Pterobranchia the Polyzoa Ectoprocta are sessile, with mouth and anus pointing upwards. They feed by means of the cilia borne on a horseshoe-ring of tentacles (the lophophore); but there is no division into proboscis, collar, and trunk, and no tripartite coelom. The nervous system is in the condition of a sub-epithelial plexus, which is folded, around the base of the lophophore, to form a hollow tube—a remarkable point of similarity to the chordates. Even though it is difficult to compare this tube exactly with the nerve-cord of chordates, it is at least evidence of the organization of the nervous system on a plan that allows of such folding.

Although it would be unwise to suggest close relationship between the polyzoans and the pterobranchs, the similarities are sufficient to suggest that the chordates arose from sedentary creatures, feeding by means of ciliated tentacles. The evidence is sufficiently strong to encourage us to look for the presence somewhere in the line of vertebrate ancestry of an animal with this habit. The difficulties of this view arise when we come to consider how the fish-like organization of a free-swimming animal first appeared, a question better dealt with after consideration of the tunicates.

4. Subphylum Urochordata. Sea squirts

In the adult ascidians or sea squirts there is no obvious trace of the fish-like form at all. The majority of these animals are sack-like creatures living on the sea floor and obtaining their food by ciliary action. Often the separate individuals are grouped together to form large colonies, but in *Ciona intestinalis*, common in British waters, the individuals occur separately, and this is possibly the primitive condition for the group. The whole of the outside of the body is covered by a tunic in which there are only two openings, a terminal mouth and a more or less dorsal atriopore (Fig. 33). The tunic is made mainly of a carbohydrate tunicin, closely related to cellulose, with which is combined about 20 per cent. of nitrogen-containing compounds. It is secreted by special cells which lie in it but have arrived there by migration from the mesoderm. In some tunicates calcareous secretions of various shapes are found in the tunic. The mantle that lines the tunic is covered by a single-layered epidermis, the cells which make the tunic passing through the epidermis. Ascidians are often brightly coloured, the pigment being either in the tunic or the under-lying body, which often shows

Fig. 33. Diagram of structure of *Ciona*.

atr.p. atriopore; *e.* endostyle; *gen.d.* genital duct; *h.* heart; *int.* intestine; *m.* mouth; *mu.* muscle; *oes.* oesophagus; *ph.* pharynx; *st.* stomach. (After Berrill.)

through a transparent tunic. The colour can change, at least over a period of some days. Little is known about the origin of the pigment, but it is sometimes derived from the blood-pigment and may lie in pigment cells.

The mantle is provided with muscle-fibres running in various directions but mainly longitudinally, and serving to draw the animal together, with the production of the jet of water from which the animals derive their common English name.

The greater part of the body is made up of an immense pharynx, beginning below the mouth and forming a huge sack reaching nearly to the base (Fig. 33). The sack is attached to the mantle along one side (ventral) and is surrounded dorsally and laterally by the atrial cavity. This pharynx is, of course, the food-collecting apparatus; its walls are pierced by rows of stigmata (gill-slits) whose cilia set up a food current. The entrance to the pharynx is guarded by a ring of tentacles, which may be compared with the velum of *Amphioxus*. The stigmata are very numerous vertical cracks, all formed by subdivision of three original gill-slits. Tongue bars grow down to divide each slit and then from each tongue bar grow horizontal synapticulae. This arrangement has clear resemblance to that of *Amphioxus* and results in the production of a pharyngeal wall pierced by numerous holes. Just within the stigmata there form a series of folds running longitudinally and provided with muscles and cilia. There is an endostyle, which has three rows of mucus cells on each side, separated by rows of ciliated cells and with a single median set of cells with very long cilia (Fig. 34). The mucus secreted in the endostyle is caught up on the longitudinal folds, whose muscles move them rhythmically, spreading a curtain of mucus over the inside of the pharynx. Food particles are caught in the mucus, which moves upwards and is then passed back to the oesophagus by the cilia of a dorsal lamina or of a series of hook-like 'languets'.

FIG. 34. Transverse section of the endostyle of *Ciona*.

lat.cil. lateral cilia; *mu.* mucous cells; *med.cil.* long median cilia. (After Sokoloska.)

The large ciliated surface of the pharyngeal wall ensures the passage of considerable volumes of water inwards at the mouth and out at the atriopore. It has been calculated that 173 litres pass through a medium-sized individual of *Phallusia nigra* in 24 hours. The pressure of the exhalant current is sufficient to drive the water which has been used well away from the animal.

The oesophagus leads to a large 'stomach' with a folded wall containing gland-cells which produce digestive enzymes. These include an amylase, invertase, small amounts of lipase, and a protease of the tryptic type. The organ is therefore not to be compared with the stomach of vertebrates. From the stomach a rather short intestine leads upwards to open inside the atriopore; this is apparently the absorptive region of the gut.

Between the alimentary canal and the ectoderm lies a peculiar cavity, which is not lined by a continuous epithelium and appears to be derived from the blastocoele of the embryo and is therefore not to be compared with a coelom. In this cavity and its walls mesenchymatous and connective tissue-cells of various types are found.

The heart lies below the pharynx and is a sac, surrounded by a pericardium (see p. 62) and communicating with a system of blood spaces derived from the blastocoele. The larger of these spaces have an endothelial lining; the biggest is a hypobranchial vessel below the endostyle, from which branches pass to the pharynx. From the opposite end of the heart springs a large visceral vessel and others pass to the dorsal side of the pharynx, tunic, body wall, &c. The heart is peculiar in that the beat can proceed in either direction. After passing blood into the hypobranchial vessel and gills for a few beats, its direction reverses, passing the blood to the viscera. It has been shown that this reversal is produced by the presence of two pacemaker centres, each capable of initiating rhythmical contractions, one at either end of the heart. Stimulation of these by warming and cooling allows control of the reversal of the beat. The blood-plasma is colourless but contains corpuscles, some of which are phagocytes, while others contain orange, green, or blue pigment (in different species). The green and other pigments are remarkable in that they contain vanadium, of course in considerably greater concentration than in the sea water. It is uncertain whether these pigments play a part in respiration.

The blood is isotonic with sea water, and ascidians appear to have little or no power of regulating their osmotic pressure; none of them is found in fresh water. They are not even able to colonize brackish waters or those of low salinity. For example, they are rare in the Baltic Sea, from which only six species have been reported. Only one species, *Molgula tubifera*, has been reported from the Zuider Zee (salinity 8·4 per mille).

A possible reason for this inability to regulate the internal composition is that excretion is performed by single mesenchyme cells. These may be aggregated in patches, but do not form definite sac-like organs such as could be used for the maintenance of an osmotic gradient. The cells produce concretions within the cytoplasm and these may in some cases be passed into an excretory sac around which the cells are grouped.

It will be observed that the animal possesses no coelom, but the mode of development of the heart and nearby structures suggests that the ancestors of the tunicates possessed coelomic cavities. The pericardium forms as an evagination from the floor of the pharynx, and the wall of the tube so formed then itself invaginates to form the heart. It might thus be claimed that the pericardium is comparable with a coelom, formed by enterocoely as in other chordates. The situation is complicated by the presence of another pair of outpushings from the pharynx, the epicardia, which are tubes ending blindly on either side of the heart (Fig. 35). Berrill and others have suggested that these epicardia also may be compared with coelomic cavities. Their function in the open condition in which they are found in *Ciona* is perhaps to allow sea water to circulate about the heart and hence to help excretion (and respiration?). In other ascidians the epicardium loses its connexion with the pharynx. The closed sac functions in some cases as an excretory organ, containing concretions, whereas in other animals it becomes the main source of the cells which make the asexual buds.

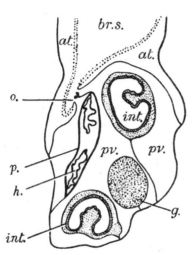

FIG. 35. Section through base of *Ciona*, showing heart (*h.*) in pericardium (*p.*). *pv.* perivisceral sacs (epicardia) opening to pharynx at *o.*

at. atrium; *br.s.* pharynx; *g.* gonad; *int.* intestine. (From Berrill.)

The central nervous system consists of a round, solid ganglion (Fig. 37), lying above the front end of the pharynx. The ganglion consists of a layer of cells around the outside and a central mass of neuropil and is therefore quite unlike the nerve-cord of a vertebrate. From the ganglion nerves proceed to the mouth region, other parts of the mantle, muscles, and viscera. The gut is said to contain a plexus of cells and fibres, whose relation to the autonomic system of higher forms remains uncertain.

Since movement consists mainly of contraction and closure of the apertures, the simplicity of the nervous system is not surprising. It is not even necessary to provide innervation for antagonistic muscles, since the expansion after closure is produced by the elasticity of the walls and not by special muscles. Investigation of the reactions of the species *Ascidia atra* to touch have shown that some local reactions are possible, for instance, one siphon only may contract to light touch in its neighbourhood, whereas stronger stimuli cause contraction of both siphons and of the body. Stimulation just inside either siphon produces closure of the other one and also, if strong enough, contraction of the body, thus ensuring that a jet of water sweeps out the aperture which has received the stimulus.

The surface of the body is sensitive to changes in light intensity, and these are followed by local or total contractions, according to their extent. The local responses, like some of those produced by light touch, continue after removal of the ganglion, suggesting the presence

FIG. 36. Rhythmical 'spontaneous' contractions of *Styela* shown by attaching levers to the two siphons. Branchial siphon above, atrial siphon below. The time-marker shows intervals of 5 minutes. (From Yamaguchi.)

of nerve-cells diffused through the body wall. The various parts of the body are not all equally sensitive to light, the highest sensitivity being in the region of the ganglion. The ocelli are cup-like collections of cells found in various parts of the body, but according to Hecht they are not photoreceptors.

The neuromuscular system thus appears to function mainly as a reflex apparatus for producing protective movements in response to certain stimuli. This is the role which might be expected of it in an animal that remains fixed in one place. The 'initiative' for food-gathering activities comes from the continuous action of the cilia of the pharynx. The nervous system shows little sign of those continuous activities that produce the varied and 'spontaneous' acts of behaviour in higher forms. Nevertheless, it would be unwise to suppose that the nerves are only activated by external stimuli. There are some suggestions that even in these simple animals rhythmical activities are initiated from within. The food-collecting operations of the pharyngeal wall involve rhythmical movement of the longitudinal bars by their muscles. Further, Hecht and others have shown that in some species of ascidians there are regular rhythmical contractions of the siphons and body musculature in rotation, with a frequency of

8–27 per hour (Fig. 36). These contractions are especially marked when the animal is in filtered water and they may be some form of 'hunger' contraction, directed towards the obtaining of food. Their presence is a striking warning of the dangers of assuming that even the simplest nervous system operates only when stimulated from outside.

The subneural gland is a mysterious organ lying between the ganglion and the pharynx and opening in to the latter by a ciliated funnel (Fig. 37). The organ arises in part from the ectoderm of the

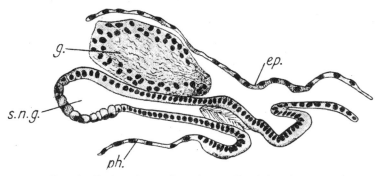

FIG. 37. Longitudinal section to show the ganglion (*g.*) and subneural gland (*s.n.g.*) of an ascidian. *ep.* skin; *ph.* pharyngeal epithelium. (After Metcalf.)

nervous system and in part from the pharynx; this and its position have led to the suggestion that it may be compared with the infundibulum and hypophysis of vertebrates. This seems reasonable on morphological grounds, and it has also been claimed that the gland contains pressor, 'oxytocic', and melanophore-stimulating substances similar to those found in the posterior lobe of the pituitary. However, the nature of these substances and the value of the gland to the animal require further investigation. Attached to the posterior end of the subneural gland is a solid cord of cells, the dorsal strand, derived from the neural canal of the larva; this may reach back to behind the pharynx. In some forms parts of this strand go to make the genital ducts (see below), and this has led to the suggestion that the original opening of the gonads was through the subneural gland, that is to say, close to the mouth, as in the Palaeozoic echinoderms from which the tunicates may have been originally derived. There is not sufficient evidence to allow us to take this suggestion very seriously, but it provides a possible, if speculative, basis for the strong connexion between the functions of the pituitary body and the gonad. It is conceivable that the former first arose as a secretory organ on the genital duct!

5. Development of ascidians

Tunicates are usually hermaphrodite, the ovary and testis being sacs lying close to the intestine and opening by ducts near the atriopore. Fertilization is external in the solitary forms but internal in those which form colonies, the development in the latter case taking place within the parent. The details of cleavage and gastrulation show a remarkable general similarity to those of *Amphioxus*. Indeed, the whole development is so strikingly like that of chordates that it establishes the affinities of the group far more clearly than the vague

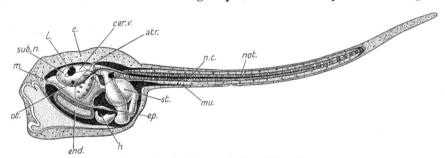

FIG. 38. Ascidian tadpole of *Clavelina*.

atr. atriopore; *c.* mantle; *cer.v.* cerebral vesicle; *e.* eye spot; *end.* endostyle; *ep.* epicardium; *h.* heart; *m.* mouth; *mu.* muscle cells; *n.c.* nerve-cord; *not.* notochord; *ot.* otocyst; *st.* stomach; *sub.n.* subneural gland.

indications of a chordate plan of organization which are seen in the adult. The result of development is to produce a fish-like creature, the *ascidian tadpole*, which is immediately recognizable as a chordate (Fig. 38). The cleavage is total and produces a blastula with few cells, whose future potentialities are already determined. Gastrulation is by invagination and the creature then proceeds to elongate into the fish-like larva. This possesses an oval 'head' and long tail, the latter supported by a notochord formed by cells derived from the endoderm. Some sixty of these cells make up the entire rod, becoming vacuolated and the vacuoles of neighbouring cells then running together to form a central mass, surrounded by a thin protoplasmic layer.

On either side of this notochord run three rows of muscle-cells, derived from a mesoderm, which has separated as a solid strand from the archenteric wall. The muscle-cells contain cross-striated myofibrils. It is not clear how they function in propelling the animal, nor whether they are controlled by the nervous system. Presumably progression by muscle action of this sort would only be possible with some arrangement to ensure serial contraction (see p. 127).

The nervous system is formed by folds essentially similar to those of vertebrates, making a hollow, dorsal tube, extending into the tail and enlarged in front into a cerebral vesicle, within which is an eye-spot and an otocyst.

The larva takes no food and the gut is not well developed. There is a pharynx with usually a single pair of gill-slits opening into an atrium which develops as an ectodermal inpushing. Below or around the mouth various forms of sucker are formed. The heart and peri-cardium arise from the endoderm, but there is little circulation in the young larva.

The whole process of development occupies only one or two days and the larva, in the cases in which it is set free, proceeds to the sea surface. But its life here is also limited. Within a day or two, depend-ing on the conditions, it settles on the bottom by its sucker, develops a large pharynx, and grows into an adult ascidian. Presumably its short life in the chordate stage is sufficient to ensure distribution, but very little is known of the manner of life during this period. The early larva is positively phototropic, the later larva avoids the light. Apart from this we know nothing of its physiology or of the workings of its transitory chordate nervous system.

In addition to the sexual reproduction, tunicates also often multiply by budding. The bud is usually covered with a layer of ectoderm, but the inner organs may be formed either from ectoderm, endoderm, or from the mesenchyme of a strand of cells, the epicardium, near the heart. The fact that a complete new animal is thus formed from one or two layers is often cited as evidence of the untruth of the 'germ-layer theory', but in the absence of details about the way in which realization of the potentialities of the cells is evoked, there seems to be no lesson of great general biological interest to be learned from the process. It leads to the formation of the large colonies of the creatures which are so commonly found.

6. Various forms of tunicate

Besides some 2,000 species of sessile tunicates there are various forms (about 100 species) which have become secondarily modified for a pelagic life. These pelagic animals are probably all related and the whole subphylum may therefore be subdivided into two classes.

Class 1. Ascidiacea.
    Typical bottom-living forms such as *Ciona* (solitary), *Botryllus* (colonial).

Class 2. Thaliacea.
>Order 1. Thaliacea.
>>Pelagic forms, simple or colonial, swimming by means of circular muscle bands. *Salpa, Doliolum, Pyrosoma.*
>Order 2. Appendicularia.
>>Pelagic tunicata without metamorphosis; the adult has a tail and resembles the tadpole of the other groups. *Oikopleura.*

7. Class Ascidiacea

The typical sessile ascidians are often divided into those that live as single individuals (Ascidiae simplices) and those forming colonies (Ascidiae compositae). Both types include many different forms, however, and the division is not along phylogenetic lines. The colonial forms produced by budding may consist simply of a number of neighbouring individuals (*Clavelina*) or of a common gelatinous test in which the individuals are embedded (*Botryllus, Amaroucium*). Different species have differing body form, related to the type of bottom upon which they are found; there has thus been an adaptive radiation within the group; a great variety of habitats is available for bottom-living creatures, and the animals become adapted accordingly.

Most of the species live in the littoral zone, but a few deep-sea forms are known, such as *Hypobythius calycodes*, which are found below 5,000 metres.

Most ascidians probably live only for a short time, becoming mature in their first year and dying thereafter. In some cases the animals live over a second winter, during which they become reduced in size, growing and budding again in the following spring, such as *Clavelina.*

8. Class Thaliacea

These are pelagic tunicates living in warm water. They have circular bands of muscle, enabling the animal to shoot through the water by jet propulsion. In *Doliolum* and its allies the muscle-bands pass right round the body (Cyclomyaria), whereas in *Salpa* the rings are incomplete (Hemimyaria). The mouth and atriopore are at opposite ends of the body. The tunic is thin and, like the rest of the body, transparent.

The life-history of these forms involves a remarkable alternation of generations. In *Doliolum* the ascidian tadpole develops into a mother or nurse zooid (oozooid). This by budding gives rise to a string of daughter zooids, which it propels along by its muscles. The daughter

FIG. 39. *Doliolum*, gonozooid.

1, inhalent aperture; 2, ciliated pit; 3, ganglion and nerves; 4, pharynx; 5, mantle; 6, sense-cells; 7, exhalent aperture; 8, ovary; 9, intestine; 10, heart; 11, endostyle; 12, testis; 13, ciliated groove. (After Neumann.)

FIG. 40. *Salpa*, oozooid.

1, cloacal muscle; 2, ganglion; 3, ciliated pit; 4, ciliated band; 5, longitudinal muscle; 6, inhalent aperture; 7, pharynx; 8, endostyle; 9, stolo prolifer; 10, genital duct; 11, cloacal chamber; 12, heart; 13, stomach; 14, intestine; 15, mantle; 16, exhalent aperture. (After Stiasny, from Kukenthal.)

zooids are of three types: (1) sterile, nutritive, and respiratory individuals, the trophozooids, permanently sessile on the parent; (2) sterile nurse forms, which are eventually set free (phorozooids); (3) sexual forms (gonozooids), nursed and carried by the phorozooids until sexually mature, when they also break loose.

In *Salpa* the sexual form produces only a single egg, which develops within the mother, nourished by a special placenta-like organ whose cells actually migrate into the developing embryo. When fully formed this oozooid is asexual and produces a long chain of buds (blastozooids) which it tows about. The older groups of these break away by sections and ultimately develop gonads.

The pelagic colonial *Pyrosoma* of warm seas consists of a number of individuals associated to form an elongated barrel-shaped colony so that the mouths open outwards and the atria inwards into a single cavity with a terminal outlet. The mode of budding from the epicardium and other features suggest an affinity with *Doliolum* and *Salpa*, but *Pyrosoma* also resembles the ascidians in that its zooids are all sexual and capable of budding; the pharynx has internal bars. The outstanding characteristic of the creatures is the powerful light which they shine. This is produced by symbiotic bacteria, living in special cells in various parts of the body (Fig. 41). These bacteria infect the eggs, and light is thus produced at all stages. The light is so powerful that when large masses of *Pyrosoma* occur together the whole sea is illuminated sufficiently to allow of reading a book. A remarkable feature of the phenomenon is that the light is not produced continuously but only when the animal is stimulated, as by the waves of a rough sea. If one individual is stimulated others throughout the colony may show their lights, but the mechanism of this effect is not known and the groups of cells which form the luminescent organs receive no nerves. The sudden flashes of light probably serve as a protection against enemies, producing a flight-reaction in the same way as do sudden manifestations of colour or black spots by other animals. It has been observed in the laboratory that colonies of *Pyrosoma* which are dying and do not light up may be eaten by fishes, whereas those which light up when seized may then be dropped.

FIG. 41. Cell of *Pyrosoma* filled with luminescent bacteria. (After Kukenthal.)

9. Order Appendicularia

The Appendicularia or Larvacea (Figs. 42 and 43) are neotenous tunicates that live in the plankton. Instead of the test, each individual builds a 'house', by secretion from a special part of the skin, the 'oikoplastic epithelium'. The tail is a broad structure held at an angle to the rest of the body; its movement produces a current in which the food is carried and caught by a most elaborate filter arrangement in the house (Fig. 43). Water enters the house by a pair of posterior 'filtering windows' and is passed through a system of filter pipes in the part of the house in front of the mouth. The very minute flagellates of the nanoplankton are stopped by these pipes and sucked back to the mouth. The pharynx has two gill-slits, also an endostyle and peripharyngeal bands. The general organization is that of a typical ascidian tadpole, and there can be no doubt that these forms have arisen from tunicates by the acceleration of the rate of development of the alimentary organs and gonads so that the metamorphosis and normal adult stage are eliminated. This may, of course, have happened long ago, so that the modern Larvacea are not closely related to any living forms, but the fact that they differ in many ways from known ascidian tadpoles does not invalidate the hypothesis; it would be expected that many special features would be developed during evolution after the paedomorphosis. Garstang, however, believes that there is sufficient evidence to show that the Larvacea are related to the Doliolidae and suggests an ingenious hypothesis by which the appendicularian home could be derived from the doliolid test, the animal itself remaining attached at the front end by gelatinous threads which come to make the filter tubes (Fig. 44).

FIG. 42. *Appendicularia* seen from the side and from below. (After Lehmann.)

The tail is a highly developed organ, serving for locomotion, nutrition, and in the building of the house. It has a wide, continuous fin and is supported by a notochord. A band of 7–12 large striped muscle-cells extends down each side, giving an appearance which has been compared with that of metameric segmentation. The small

FIG. 43. *Oikopleura*, one of the Larvacea, in its house, showing the feeding-currents.

e. exhalent aperture; *e.e.* entrance; *f.p.* filter pipes; *f.w.* filter window; *g.* gill-slit; *m.* mouth; *t.* trough; *ta.* tail. (After Garstang; this and Figs. 44 and 45 by permission of the Editors of the *Quarterly Journal of Microscopical Science*.)

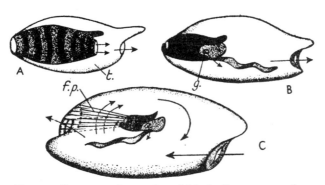

FIG. 44. Sequence of stages by which the Larvacea may have been evolved from a doliolid type.

A, Thaliacean type of individual in its test (*t.*). B, Paedomorphosis has occurred so that a tailed creature is found in the test; *g.* gill-slit. C, The tadpole has moved away from the inhalent aperture, leaving a series of threads that become the filter pipes (*f.p.*), the inhalent aperture becoming exhalent and vice versa. (After Garstang.)

number of the cells makes any such comparison very difficult. Moreover, the muscles are not developed from anything resembling a myotome. The muscle-cells are supplied by a series of 'segmental' nerve-fibres. The nerve-cord forms a hollow tube with ganglionic thickenings, each containing a few (1–4) nerve-cells. From these cells fibres proceed to the muscle-cells, some being apparently motor and others perhaps sensory (? proprioceptive).

10. The formation of the chordates

We can now recapitulate the points which we have established about the origin of the chordates and attempt to piece together the evidence to show the sequence of events that led to the production of a free-swimming, fish-like animal. The chordates are related to the echinoderms and their allies. This is established by the similarities in early development (cleavage, gastrulation, mesoderm formation); by the presence in early members of both groups of three separate coelomic cavities, some with pores; by the similarity of the larva of enteropneusts to the auricularia, and by other points of general morphological similarity between early chordates and echinoderms, especially the arrangement of the nervous system and presence of a mesodermal skeleton.

The echinoderms we have to consider are not the modern star-fishes and sea-urchins, which are relatively active animals, but their sessile Palaeozoic ancestors. These were sedentary, often stalked animals, the cystoids, blastoids, and crinoids, feeding by ciliary action. Surviving animals of related phyla, such as the Polyzoa Ectoprocta and *Phoronis* suggest that the ancestor for which we are looking may have possessed a ciliated lophophore for food-collecting. For purposes of dispersal its life-history presumably included a larval stage with a longitudinal ciliated band, similar in plan to that of the auricularia.

One might well ask how such an animal could possibly become converted into a motile, metameric fish, feeding with its pharynx. Yet the evidence of the early chordates is sufficient to establish that this change has occurred, and even provides us with an outline of the main stages in the process of the change. *Cephalodiscus*, which is in some ways the most primitive of these early chordates, with its lophophore also possesses gill-slits. This suggests that the pharyngeal mechanism was substituted for the lophophore as a means of feeding in the adult stage. Ciliary mechanisms must have been present in the pharynx to deal with the food collected by the tentacles and it is reasonable to suppose that these might have become developed into a self-contained feeding mechanism, making unnecessary the tentacles, which provide a tempting morsel for predators. The adoral band of cilia of the auricularia probably serves to carry food into the mouth, and for this purpose it is actually turned in to the floor of the pharynx. Garstang suggests that the endostyle has been derived from this loop of the adoral band.

The pharyngeal method of food-collecting thus replaced the tentacles in the adult and the whole apparatus of an endostyle and an atrium to protect the gills became developed. We may notice here the remarkable similarity of this arrangement of the pharynx in tunicates, *Amphioxus* and cyclostome larvae, and the partial similarity in *Balanoglossus*.

The tunicates show us a stage in which branchial feeding has fully replaced tentacle feeding in a sessile adult. But they have a larva

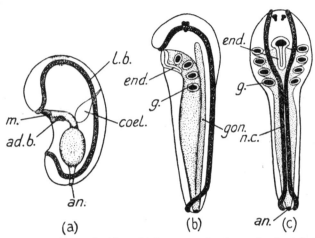

FIG. 45. To show the method by which a protochordate animal might have been derived from an echinoderm larva such as the auricularia.

a. Auricularia in side view; *b.* protochordate in side view; *c.* same, dorsal view. *ad.b.* adoral band; *an.* anus; *coel.* coelom; *end.* endostyle; *g.* gill-slit; *gon.* gonad; *l.b.* longitudinal ciliated band; *m.* mouth; *n.c.* nerve-cord. (After Garstang.)

which is beyond all question a fish-like chordate. If the adult tunicate has evolved from a modified lophophore-feeding creature, how has the ascidian tadpole arisen from the auricularia larva? Garstang's auricularia theory, first propounded in 1894, provides an answer. As a ciliated larva grows its means of locomotion becomes inadequate because the ciliated surface increases only as the square of the linear dimensions, the weight as the cube. Muscular locomotion is not subject to this difficulty, and some of the star-fish larvae actually show flapping of the elongated processes, movements which presumably assist them to remain at the surface. Garstang suggests that the fish-like form arose by development of muscles along the sides of the elongated body, the ciliated bands being pushed upwards and eventually rolled up with their underlying sheets of nerve plexus to form the neural tube. The adoral ciliated band might then well be the endostyle (Fig. 45).

This theory may seem at first sight fantastic. It is necessarily speculative, but it has certain strong marks of inherent probability. It violates no established morphological principles and certainly enables us to see how a ciliated auricularia-like larva could be converted by progressive stages into a fish-like creature with muscular locomotion, while the adults, at first sedentary, substituted gill-slits and endostyle for the original lophophore.

We may, therefore, plausibly regard the adult tunicate organization as directly derived from that of sessile lophophore-feeding creatures, and the larval organization as descended from an echinoderm-like larva. There is no need, on this view, to regard the sessile adult tunicate as a 'degenerate' chordate. The problem which remains is in fact not 'How have sea-squirts been formed from vertebrates?' but 'How have vertebrates eliminated the sea-squirt stage from their life-history?' It is wholly reasonable to consider that this has been accomplished by paedomorphosis. Advance of the time of development of the gonads relative to that of the soma is well known to occur in certain special cases such as the axolotl. There are strong grounds for supposing that a similar process has been responsible for the production of several of the main animal phyla, for instance the molluscs and insects. Finally the example of the Appendicularia shows that a similar process can happen among tunicates! Various workers have stressed the differences between the ascidian tadpole and the adult appendicularian, in attempts to show that the two are not comparable. But the differences, though considerable, are superficial: the similarity of organization is profound. Any sensible biologist with an understanding of the way in which the characteristic forms of animals arise by change in the rate and degree of development of features can see how the Appendicularia may represent modified ascidian larvae.

The appendicularians do, indeed, carry certain characters of the 'adult' sea-squirt, in particular they have gill-slits, though of simple form. Nothing is more likely, however, than that some features of the sessile adult would be adumbrated in its larva and capable of fuller development therein if advantageous. Larva and adult, it must be remembered, possess the same genotype; the remarkable feature in all animals with metamorphosis is the difference between the two stages, not the similarity. Any characteristic may appear at either larval or adult stage or be transferred by evolutionary selection from one to the other. There is no serious objection to the view that the early adult free-swimming chordates arose by paedomorphosis of some tunicate-like metamorphosing form. If the creatures abandoned the habit of fixation it would be possible for characters previously present

Fig. 46. Table to show the probable times of origin and affinities of the chordates and related groups of animal.

separately in larva and adult to become combined in a single stage. This is indeed what has happened in the Appendicularia.

Strangely enough, one of the chief difficulties of this theory is to find the position of the enteropneusts. Since the larva is still in the ciliated-band stage there should be no sign of organs characteristic of the muscle-swimming, fish-like pro-chordate. Yet such signs are present in the adult *Balanoglossus*; there is a hollow nerve-cord and some sign of a notochord. These features almost compel us to suppose that the group has at one time possessed a free-swimming, fish-like stage. The only escape from this conclusion would be by supposing the hollow nerve-tube to be a case of convergence, for which a parallel might be cited in the hollow nervous system of Polyzoa. But there is no clear reason why the nerve-cord should become rolled up in the collar, and it is easier to suppose it a vestige. This imposes two further hypotheses on us. First that a fish-like stage once *followed* an advanced ciliated-band stage in ontogeny, and secondly that this fish-like stage later became adapted to a burrowing life, in fact that *Balanoglossus* is a 'degenerate' chordate. Neither of these propositions is impossible, but it must be admitted that the position of the enteropneusts is not clear. Showing a combination of ciliated larva and chordate characters they provide a valuable proof of the affinity of chordates and echinoderm-like creatures, but these very chordate characters become an embarrassment when we try to explain in detail how they have arisen!

There is strong reason to suppose that what we may call the Bateson–Garstang theory of the origin of chordates is correct. There is no doubt that chordates are related to the sessile lophophore-feeding type of creature rather than to any annulate, and we can reconstruct the course of events by which the lophophore-feeder may have come to have a pharynx with gill-slits and its larva to have muscles, a notochord, and a nerve-tube. Then by paedomorphosis the sessile stage disappeared and the free chordates began their course of evolution. There are some reasons for supposing that a type such as *Amphioxus* could have been derived from a creature not distantly related to the simpler Appendicularia and this in turn from a neotenous doliolid or some similar ancestral type.

We need not, however, follow the theory into its details, which are speculative. The whole treatment provides a conspicuous example of close morphological reasoning, allied with proper consideration of general biological principles, and establishes with some probability the main outlines of the origin of our great phylum of active creatures from such humble sedentary beginnings.

Can we see in the production of the first fish-like creatures clear signs of an 'advance' in evolution? In acquiring the power of active muscular locomotion the animals became able to live and feed in a variety of habitats, either at the sea surface or on the bottom. Forms with a sedentary adult stage are limited by the necessity for the presence of a sea bottom of suitable character. The larvae were no doubt developed in order to make sure of reaching such conditions. But whereas suitable situations on the bottom are not common, and are liable to change, the sea surface provides a generalized habitat in which there is always abundant food, though no doubt also strenuous competition for it. Paedomorphosis in this case, as in others, allows the race to eliminate from its life-history the stage passed in a 'special' environment which is difficult to find. Although the fish-form which was thus produced proved to have great possibilities for further evolution, the change was not at first a strikingly progressive one. The surface of the sea is perhaps the most general of all environments; probably it was the seat of the origin of life. Races which have devised means of living on the sea bottom may therefore be said to have advanced, because they have invaded a more difficult habitat. To abandon the sedentary life might in this sense be regarded as a retrograde step. The peculiar feature of the early fishes, however, was that they developed powers of active movement in a relatively large organism, and by making use of the feeding mechanism developed at first by the bottom-living adult were able to live successfully at the sea surface. They acquired their dominance at this stage not by invading new habitats but by developing effective means of living in the richly populated plankton.

THE VERTEBRATES WITHOUT JAWS. LAMPREYS

1. Classification

Phylum Chordata
Subphylum 4. Vertebrata (= Craniata)
  Superclass 1. Agnatha
    Class 1. Cyclostomata
      Order 1. Petromyzontia
        Petromyzon, Lampetra, Entosphenus, Geotria, Mordacia
      Order 2. Myxinoidea
        Myxine, Bdellostoma
    Class 2. *Cephalaspida. Silurian–Devonian
      *Cephalaspis, *Tremataspis*
    Class 3. *Pteraspida. Ordovician–Devonian
      *Astraspis, *Pteraspis, *Drepanaspis*
    Class 4. *Anaspida. Silurian–Devonian
      Birkenia
    Class 5. *Euphanerida. Silurian *Jamoytius*
  Superclass 2. Gnathostomata

2. General features of vertebrates

All the remaining chordates are alike in possessing some form of cranium and some trace of vertebrae; they make up the great sub-phylum Vertebrata, also called Craniata. The organization of a vertebrate is similar to that of *Amphioxus*, but with the addition of certain special features. A few of these novelties may now be surveyed, with emphasis on those that provide the basis for the independence of the environment which is so characteristic of the vertebrates. Firstly the front end of the nervous system is differentiated in to an elaborate brain, associated with special sense-organs, the nose, eye, and ear. Through these sense-organs the vertebrates are able to respond to more varied aspects of the environment than are any other animals. Some of them have the ability to discriminate between visual shapes and colours, and in the auditory field between patterns of tones, not to mention between a host of chemical vapours. The motor organization allows the performance of delicate movements, to suit the situations which the sense-organ reveals. The swimming process, by the passage of waves down the body, is itself perfected by improvements in the shape of the fish, allowing very rapid movements and turns. Besides the median fins there develop lateral paired ones, playing at first only a small part in locomotion, but made use of, when the land animals arose, first as organs of locomotion on the ground or in the air and finally, in the shape of the hands, as a means of altering the environment to suit the individual.

The brain itself, at first mostly devoted to the details of sensory and motor function, comes increasingly to preside, as it were, over all the bodily functions, and to give to the vertebrates that 'drive' which is one of their most characteristic features. The skull is developed as a skeletal thickening around the brain, probably at first mainly for protection, but later serving for the attachment of elaborate muscle systems. The study of vertebrates is especially identified with study of the skull, because in so many fossils this is the only organ which has been preserved.

The food of the earliest vertebrates was collected by ciliary action, but this habit has long been abandoned and only in rare cases to-day does the food consist of minute organisms. The pharynx of most vertebrates is small, there are relatively few gill-slits and these are respiratory. In all except the most ancient forms the more anterior of the arches between the gills became modified to form jaws, serving not only to seize and hold the food but also to 'manipulate' the environment.

The blood system shows two of the most characteristic vertebrate features, namely, the presence of a heart that has at least three chambers and thus provides a rapid circulation, and of haemoglobin carried in corpuscles, serving to carry large amounts of oxygen to the tissues. The efficiency of this system must have been a major factor in producing the dominance of the vertebrate animals. In the air-breathing forms, and especially the warm-blooded birds and mammals, the respiratory and circulatory systems allow the expenditure of great amounts of energy per unit mass of animal, so that quite extravagant devices can be used, allowing survival under conditions which would otherwise not support life.

The excretory system is based on a plan quite different from that of *Amphioxus*, namely, of mesodermal funnels, leading primarily from the coelom to the exterior, though closed later in ontogeny, and phylogeny. It may be that this type of kidney arose in connexion with the abandoning of the sea for fresh water. Probably all existing

vertebrates have passed through a freshwater stage, and it is significant that all, so far as is known, have less salt in their blood than there
is in sea water. Elaborate devices for regulation of osmotic pressure
have been developed, and the mesodermal kidneys play a large part in
this regulation.

This outline only gives a few suggestive features of vertebrate
organization. The details differ bewilderingly in the different types
and it is our business now to survey them. In the earliest forms the
more special mechanisms are absent or at least function only crudely,
and passing through the vertebrate series we find more and more
special devices adopted, along with more and more delicate co-ordination between the various parts, culminating in the extremely highly
centralized control of almost every aspect of life exercised by the
mammalian cerebral cortex.

3. Agnatha

The earliest vertebrates, while showing most of the characteristic
features of the group, differ from the rest in the absence of jaws and
are therefore grouped together in a superclass Agnatha, distinguished
from the remaining vertebrates, which have jaws, and are therefore
called Gnathostomata. The only living agnathous animals are the
Cyclostomata, lampreys and hag-fishes, but the first vertebrates to
appear in the fossil series, the cephalaspids and pteraspids from the
Silurian and Devonian strata, also show the agnathous condition, and
have some other features in common with the Cyclostomata. This
group of agnathous vertebrates shows a most interesting condition of
experimentation in methods of feeding, before the jaw-method became
adopted. The modern cyclostomes are parasites or scavengers, in the
adult state, but as larvae the lampreys still feed on microscopic
material, using an endostyle resembling that of *Amphioxus* in many
ways, but making use of muscular contraction rather than ciliary
action to produce a feeding current. The method of feeding of the
Devonian forms is not known for certain, but probably it included
shovelling detritus from the bottom.

The Cyclostomata are therefore worth special study as likely to
show us some of the characteristics possessed by the earliest vertebrate populations.

4. Lampreys

The most familiar cyclostomes are the lampreys, of which there
are various sorts found in the temperate zones of both hemispheres.

All lampreys have a life-history that includes two very distinct stages: the ammocoete larva lives in fresh water, buried in the mud, and is microphagous: the adult lamprey has a sucking mouth, and usually lives in the sea, where it feeds on other fishes. *Lampetra fluviatilis* (Linn.), the river lamprey (Fig. 47), is a typical example, common in Great Britain. The adult is an eel-like animal about 30 cm. long, black on the back, and white below. The surface is smooth, with no scales. The skin is many-layered, as in all vertebrates, and is therefore very different from the skin of the *Amphioxus*. The

FIG. 47. Brook lampreys, *Lampetra planeri*.
A, ripe female, with anal fin; B, ripe male; note shape of dorsal fin and presence of copulatory papilla. (Curves due to fixation.)

cells of the inner layers of the epidermis are protoplasmic and become progressively cornified by production of keratin as they pass out-wards (Fig. 48). A protective layer of this sort is characteristic of all vertebrates from cyclostomes to mammals. Mixed with these epithelial cells the lamprey, like most aquatic vertebrates, has many gland-cells for producing slime. Below the epidermis lies the cutis, a layer of bundles of collagen and elastin fibres, running mostly in a circular direction. This tissue is sharply marked off from a layer of sub-cutaneous tissue containing blood-vessels and fat, as well as con-nective tissue. There are pigment cells in the cutis and a thick layer of them at the boundary of cutis and subcutaneous tissue. The chromatophores are star-shaped cells whose pigment is able to migrate, making the animal dark or pale. This change is especially marked in the larva and is produced by variation in the amount of a pituitary secretion (p. 103).

The head of the lamprey bears a pair of eyes and a conspicuous round sucker. On the dorsal side is a single nasal opening, and behind this there is a gap in the pigment layers of the skin through which the third or pineal eye can be seen as a yellow spot. There are seven pairs of round gill openings, which, with the true eyes (and some miscounting), are responsible for the familiar name 'nine eyes'. There is no trace of any paired fins, but the tail bears a median fin, which is expanded in front as a dorsal fin. There are sex differences in the

FIG. 48. Section of skin of lamprey.
c. club cells; *cut.* cutis; *ep.* epidermis; *gr.* granular gland-cells; *m.* myotomal muscle; *pig.* pigment cells; *s.cut.* subcutis. (After Krause.)

shape of the dorsal fins of mature individuals and the female has a considerable anal fin (Fig. 47).

The lamprey swims by an eel-like motion, using its myotomes in the serial manner, which has been mentioned in *Amphioxus* and will be later discussed (p. 127). The waves that pass down the body are of short period relative to the length of the body, so that the swimming is mechanically inefficient; lampreys show great activity, but their progress is not rapid. The animal often comes to rest, attaching itself with the sucker to stones (hence the name, 'suck-stone') or to its prey. In this position water cannot of course pass in through the mouth, but both enters and leaves by the gill openings. When swimming the backward jet of water may assist in locomotion.

The trunk musculature consists of a series of myotomes separated by myocommas. Each myotome has a W-shape, instead of the simple V of *Amphioxus*. The muscle-fibres run longitudinally and they are striped, but of a somewhat peculiar fenestrated type.

5. Skeleton of lampreys

The skeleton of lampreys consists of the notochord and various collections of cartilage. This latter is partly of the typical vertebrate

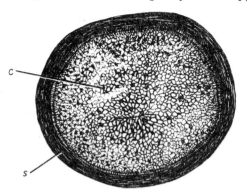

FIG. 49. Transverse section through notochord of lamprey.
c. cells; *s.* sheath. (After Krause.)

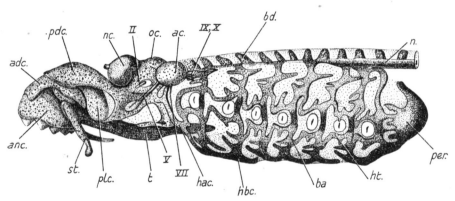

FIG. 50. Lateral view of skeleton of head and branchial arches of *Petromyzon*.
ac. auditory capsule; *adc.* antero-dorsal cartilage; *anc.* annular cartilage; *ba.* branchial arch; *bd.* basidorsal; *hac.* hyoid cartilage; *hbc.* hypo-branchial rod; *ht.* horizontal bar; *n.* notochord; *nc.* nasal capsule; *oc.* orbital cartilage; *per.* pericardial cartilage; *pdc.* postero-dorsal cartilage; *plc.* posterolateral cartilage; *st.* styliform cartilage; *t.* tendon of tongue; *II–X*, cranial nerves. (After Parker.)

type, that is to say, consists of large cells in groups, separated by a matrix of the protein chondrin which they secrete. In other regions a tissue containing more cells and less matrix is found, the so-called fibro-cartilage, and this more nearly resembles fibrous connective tissue and serves to emphasize that no sharp line can be drawn between these tissues. There is also, in the larva, a tissue known as muco-cartilage, forming the earliest skeleton.

The notochord remains well developed throughout life as a rod below the nerve-cord. It consists of a mass of large vacuolated cells, enclosed in a thick fibrous sheath (Fig. 49). The rigidity of the whole rod depends on the turgor of the cells and it often collapses completely in fixed and dehydrated material (Fig. 59). No doubt in life it serves, like the notochord of *Amphioxus*, to prevent shortening of the body when the myotomes contract.

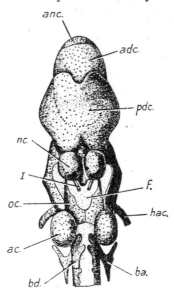

FIG. 51. Dorsal view of skull of *Petromyzon*.
Lettering as Fig. 50. *I*, olfactory nerve; *f*. hole in roof of cranium.
(After Parker.)

The notochordal sheath is continuous with a layer of connective tissue, which also surrounds the spinal cord and joins the myocommas and thus eventually the subcutaneous connective tissue. Within this connective tissue there develop certain cartilaginous thickenings that are of special interest because they may be compared with vertebrae. They lie on either side of the spinal cord (Fig. 50), that is to say, above the notochord, and consist either of one nodule on each side of the segment, through the middle of which the ventral nerve-root emerges, or of two separate nodules, with the nerve between them. In the tail region the 'vertebrae' are fused to form a continuous plate, which also supports rods of cartilage extending dorsally and ventrally into the fins.

The skull consists of a series of incomplete cartilaginous boxes surrounding the brain and organs of special sense (Fig. 51). To this skull is attached the skeleton that supports the sucker and gills. The arrangement of the skull differs considerably from that of later vertebrates. The cranium has a floor around the end of the notochord, and in front of this there is a hole containing the pituitary gland. The side walls are strong but the roof is composed only of a tough membranous fibro-cartilage. The auditory capsules are compact boxes surrounding the auditory organs at the sides. The olfactory capsule, imperfectly paired, is also almost detached from the cranium. Other ridges of cartilage lie below the eyes and there is a complex support for the sucker.

The skeleton of the branchial region consists of a system of vertical plates between the gill-slits, joined by horizontal bars above and below them. This cartilage lies in the body wall and is therefore difficult to compare with the branchial skeleton of higher fishes, which lies in the wall of the pharynx. A backward extension of the branchial basket forms a box surrounding the heart.

6. Alimentary canal of lampreys

The sucker is bounded at the edges by a series of lips, which besides

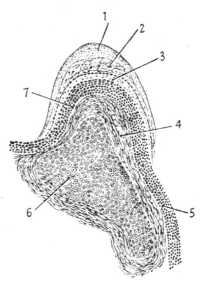

FIG. 52. Sucker of *Petromyzon* show-ing outer circular lip, teeth, and tongue, with special teeth, at the centre.

(After Parker.)

FIG. 53. Section through tooth of lamprey.

1, horny cap; 2, stellate tissue; 3, cap to re-place 1; 4, connective tissue; 5, epidermis of mouth; 6, cartilage; 7, proliferative layers of epidermis that produce the horny cells.
(After Hansen, from Kukenthal.)

being sensory serve also to make a tight attachment when the lamprey sucks (Fig. 52). In the sucker are numerous teeth, whose arrangement varies in the different types of lamprey. These teeth are horny epi-dermal thickenings, supported by cartilaginous pads, and are there-fore not comparable with the teeth of vertebrates, which are derived mainly from mesodermal tissues (Fig. 53). The sharper and larger teeth are borne on a movable tongue, which is used as a rasp (Fig. 54).

The muscles of the sucker are complicated and will only be described briefly. An annular muscle runs round just above the lips and presumably serves to narrow the margin and hence to release the fish. The remaining muscles are mostly attached to the tongue and base of the sucker. The largest of these muscles, the m. cardio-apicalis, is attached posteriorly to the cartilage surrounding the heart and in front is prolonged into a conspicuous lingual tendon, which is attached to the tongue and serves to pull it backwards. Presumably the action of this muscle deepens the oral cavity and is thus the main agent securing attachment of the sucker. There is a collar of circular fibres around the front end of the cardio-apical muscle, serving perhaps to lock the tendon and maintain the suction. Dorsal and ventral to the main tendon are groups of muscles that rock the tongue up and down to produce a rasping action. The muscles of the sucker are all

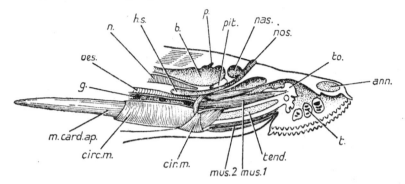

FIG. 54. Longitudinal section through head of lamprey.

ann. annular muscle of sucker; *b.* brain; *circ.m.* circular fibres of tongue-muscles; *oes.* oeso-phagus; *g.* gill aperture; *h.s.* hypophysial sac; *m.card.ap.* cardio-apical muscle; *mus. 1* and *2*, muscles that rock the tongue; *n.* notochord; *nas.* nasal sac; *nos.* nostril; *p.* pineal; *pit.* pituitary gland; *t.tend.* tendon of tongue, pulled back by *m.card.ap.*; *to.* tongue. (Partly after Tretjakoff.)

derived from the lateral plate and are innervated from the trigeminal nerve; their fibres are striated.

The mouth is a small opening above the tongue and leads into a large buccal cavity. At the hind end this divides into a dorsal passage, the oesophagus, for the food, and a ventral respiratory tube, which leads to the gill pouches but is closed behind. At the mouth of the respiratory tube is a series of velar tentacles, corresponding exactly in position to those of *Amphioxus*, and presumably sensory. The seven branchial sacs are lined by a folded respiratory epithelium and sur-rounded by muscles and these, together with appropriate valves, ensure the pumping in and out of the water. In front of the first sac is the remains of an eighth pouch, whose surface is not respiratory.

The 'salivary' glands are curious organs of which little is known. They are a pair of pigmented sacs, embedded in the hypobranchial muscles. Each has a folded wall, from which a duct proceeds forward to open below the tongue. The salivary glands produce a secretion that prevents coagulation of the blood of the fishes on which the lam-prey feeds. The nature of this secretion is not known, but it rapidly turns black on exposure to the air and the glands for this reason appear to be pigmented. Salivary glands are not found in other vertebrates below the mammals; this gland in the lamprey is a special development. It has been observed that in lampreys taken from other fishes the intestine is filled with red corpuscles, and there is therefore no doubt that they feed mainly on the blood of their prey. Little is known of the habits of lampreys in the sea, but in North America there are races of *Lampetra* that are land-locked and feed on the fishes in the lakes (Fig. 55).

The oesophagus (fore-gut) leads directly into a straight intestine

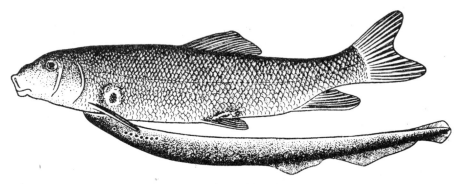

FIG. 55. Lake lamprey attached to a bony fish, which also shows the scars of the attacks of other lampreys. (After Gage.)

(mid-gut); there is no true stomach in lampreys (Fig. 56). The surface of the intestine is increased by a typhlosole, running a somewhat spiral course. There is a liver, gall-bladder, and bile-duct of typical vertebrate plan, but no separate pancreas. However, in the wall of the anterior part of the intestine there are large patches of cells that resemble those of the acini of the pancreas of higher forms and contain secretory granules. Barrington has shown that extracts of this region have a high proteolytic power, the enzyme being of the tryptic type, with its optimum between pH 7·5 and 7·8. In the Australian lampreys (*Geotria* and *Mordacia*) this tissue is collected in the walls of blind diverticula, reaching forwards. The situation is therefore essentially similar to that found in *Amphioxus*, and we may regard these patches of zymogen cells, or the diverticuli, as the forerunners of the exocrine portions of the pancreas. In the lampreys the endocrine portion, not yet identified in *Amphioxus*, also appears. Around the junction of the fore-gut and intestine are groups of follicles which do not communicate with the lumen of the intestine. These 'follicles of Langerhans' were, appropriately enough, first seen by the discoverer of the islets in higher forms, and Barrington has now shown that following destruction of this tissue by cautery there is a rise in blood-sugar. Moreover, after injection of glucose, vacuolation of the cells occurs. We may safely conclude that these cells are involved in carbohydrate metabolism, though they cannot definitely be identified

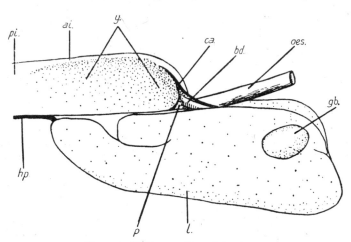

FIG. 56. Mid-gut of larval lamprey.

ai. anterior region of intestine; *bd.* bile-duct; *ca.* coeliac artery; *gb.* gall-bladder; *hp.* hepatic portal vein; *l.* liver; *oes.* oesophagus; *p.* position of 'pancreas', containing islet tissue; *pi.* posterior intestine; *y.* yellow area where wall of intestine contains zymogen cells. (From Barrington.)

by their appearance as similar to any of the types of islet cell found in mammals.

7. Blood system of lampreys

The blood vascular system is arranged on the same general plan as in *Amphioxus* but approaches that of higher forms in the possession of a heart. This lies behind the gills and can be considered as a portion of the sub-intestinal vessel, folded into an S-shape and divided into three chambers. The heart is suspended in a special portion of the coelom, the pericardium, whose walls are supported by cartilage. In the larva the heart first appears as a straight tube and owing to an abnormality of development it sometimes fails to develop its S-shape. Contractions can nevertheless be seen in these abnormal hearts, passing from behind forwards along the straight tube. Similarly in the normal heart contraction proceeds in the chambers from behind forwards. The most posterior chamber is a thin-walled sinus venosus, into which the veins pour blood. This leads to an auricle, or atrium, also thin-walled, lying above the sinus. The atrium passes blood into the ventricle below it, a thick-walled chamber, providing the main force for sending the blood round the body.

Blood leaves the ventricle by a large ventral aorta, running forwards between the gill pouches, to which it sends a series of eight afferent branchial arteries. These break up into capillaries in the gills, and efferent branchial arteries collect to a pair of dorsal aortae, running backwards, which join and form the main dorsal aorta. This passes down the trunk and carries blood to all the parts of the body by means of series of segmental arteries and special vessels to the gut, gonads, and excretory organs. A curious feature is that many of these arteries are provided with valves at the point at which they leave the main trunks (Fig. 57). It may be significant that such valves are not found where the efferent branchials join the dorsal aorta, nor at the points of exit of the renal arteries, so that perhaps the valves serve to reduce the pressure in the majority of the arteries, while leaving it high in those to the kidneys. The removal of large quantities of water is an important problem in all freshwater animals and is facilitated by a high pressure in the kidneys. This must be difficult to maintain in an animal with a branchial circulation and hence a double set of capillaries.

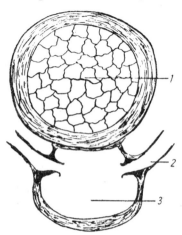

FIG. 57. Valves at the origin of segmental arteries of a lamprey.

1, notochord; 2, segmental artery; 3, aorta. (From Kukenthal, after Keibal.)

The venous system consists of a large caudal vein dividing where it enters the abdomen into two posterior cardinals. These run forward in the dorsal wall of the coelom, collecting blood from the kidneys, gonads, &c., and opening into the heart by a single ductus Cuvieri on the right-hand side, this being the remains of a pair found in the larva. Anterior cardinals collect blood from the front part of the body, and there is also a conspicuous ventral jugular vein draining venous blood from the muscles of the sucker and gill pouches. Besides the veins proper there is a large system of venous sinuses, especially in the head. Blood from the gut passes by a hepatic portal vein to the liver, from which hepatic veins proceed to the heart.

The blood of lampreys, like that of all vertebrates, contains the respiratory pigment haemoglobin, enclosed in corpuscles, here nucleated. This arrangement immensely increases the oxygen-carrying power of the blood. A curious feature of lampreys is the absence of any spleen. Very little is known of the production and destruction of corpuscles. White corpuscles resembling lymphocytes and polymorphonuclear cells occur, apparently produced by lymphoid tissue in the kidneys and elsewhere.

8. Urinogenital system of lampreys

The excretory and genital systems of vertebrates consist of a series of tubes opening from the coelom to the exterior and serving to carry away both excretory and genital products. This plan of organization is quite different from that found in *Amphioxus* and represents a new acquisition by the vertebrates. It is not clear whether the excretory or genital component of the complex is the primary one, nor indeed why they are associated. The gonads develop from the walls of the coelom in all animals possessing that cavity; some hold that the coelom represents an enlargement of a sac which at first served purely as a gonad. Genital ducts leading from the coelom to the exterior are common in invertebrates, and we may guess that at their first appearance the urinogenital tubules of vertebrates served only for genital products.

The conversion of these tubules to excretory purposes may have been a result of the adoption of the freshwater habit. Any animal in fresh water is bound to suffer from an inflow of water, on account of the osmotic pressure of the salts in its blood and tissues. This water must be removed without losing salt; accordingly in most freshwater animals, including vertebrates, we find some system by which the separation can be achieved.

The region that gives rise to the kidney during development lies between the dorsal scleromyotome and the more ventral lateral plate mesoderm; it is known as the nephrotome. This tissue differentiates during development from in front backwards, making a series of segmental funnels, opening into a common archinephric duct (Fig. 58). The most anterior funnels open into the pericardium; usually there are four of these in a freshly hatched larva, opening into a single duct, which reaches back to an aperture near the anus. Close to each funnel there develops a tangle of blood-vessels, the glomerulus (Figs. 59 and 60). Presumably the osmotic flow of water into the body is relieved by the pressure of the heart-beat forcing water out from the glomeruli into the coelomic fluid, whence it is removed by the funnels, with the aid of their cilia. The tubules become longer and twisted after hatching and may perhaps serve for salt-reabsorption.

These anterior funnels constitute the pronephros; as the animal

FIG. 58. Diagram to show arrangement of the pronephros in a freshly hatched
lamprey.

g. gonad; *pr.* pronephros; *prd.* pronephric duct. (After Wheeler.)

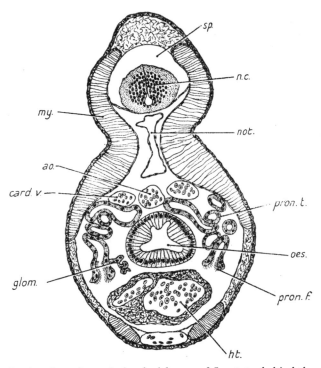

FIG. 59. Section through newly hatched larvae of *Lampetra* behind the pharynx.

ao. aorta; *card.v.* cardinal vein; *glom.* glomerulus; *ht.* heart; *my.* myotome; *n.c.* nerve-cord;
not. notochord, which has collapsed because of lack of turgidity after fixation; *oes.* oesophagus; *pron.f.* ciliated funnel of pronephros; *pron.t.* twisted pronephric tubule; *sp.* space
around nerve-cord.

grows they are replaced by a more posterior set, the mesonephros. There is, however, a gap of several segments in which no tubules appear (Fig. 60), a strange and unexplained discontinuity, common to all vertebrates. The pronephric tubules gradually disappear and

FIG. 60. Kidney system of a 22-millimetre larva of *Lampetra*.

mes. mesonephric tubules; *mesgl.* mesonephric glomeruli; *pr.* pronephric funnels; *prd.* pronephric duct; *prgl.* pronephric glomeruli. (After Wheeler.)

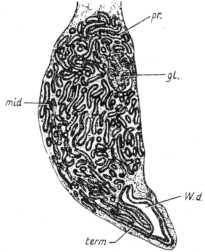

FIG. 61. Transverse section of kidney of *Lampetra*.

gl. glomerulus; *mid.* middle section of tubule; *pr.* proximal region of tubule; *term.* terminal region, opening into *W.d.* Wolffian duct. (After Krause.)

finally in the adult all that remains of the organ is a mass of lymphoid tissue. Meanwhile the mesonephros develops as a much larger fold, hanging into the coelom and containing very extensive winding tubules. These do not open to the coelom (at least in the adult) but each to a small sac, the Malphigian corpuscle, which contains a portion of the coelom and the glomerulus. This is obviously a more efficient method for allowing the heart to pump excess water out of the blood and down the tubules. The latter themselves have become greatly elongated and make up the main bulk of the organ (Fig.61). The segmental arrangement is therefore much obscured and as extra glomeruli are added it disappears completely. The mesonephros extends at its hind end as the animal grows, until it forms the adult kidney, a continuous ridge of tissue reaching back to the hind end of the coelom. Besides the excretory apparatus the kidney also contains much lymphoid tissue and fat, and it probably plays a part in the formation and destruction of red and white corpuscles.

The gonads develop from ridges of tissue lying medial to the mesonephros on each side. Primordial germ-cells, set aside very early in development, migrate into these ridges and develop into eggs or sperms. The differentiation of the gonad occurs relatively late in lampreys, so that in young animals the organ is 'hermaphrodite', containing developing oocytes and spermatocytes together. The ripe ovary consists of ova each surrounded by single-layered, follicular epithelium, which finally ruptures and liberates the egg into the coelom, whence it escapes by a pore, to be described presently. The

FIG. 62. Cloacal region of fully adult *Lampetra*.

C. coelom; *Cl.* lips of cloaca; *Ct.* connective tissue; *D.* duct leading from coelom to the mesonephric duct; *Df.* dorsal fin; *M.* muscle; *Md.* mesonephric ducts; *N.* notochord; *R.* rectum; *Ug.* urinogenital papilla. (From Knowles.)

testis consists of a number of follicles containing sperms; it is unique among vertebrates in that the follicles have no ducts; when ripe they rupture into the coelom, which becomes filled with spermatozoa and these escape, like the ova, by a single pore developed just before mating.

These apertures by which the gametes escape are similar in the two sexes and consist of short channels, one on each side, leading from the coelom to the lower end of the kidney duct (Fig. 62). These normally become open only a few weeks before spawning, but Knowles has shown that injections of oestrone or anterior pituitary extract will cause perforations of the ducts in young lampreys, indeed even in the ammocoete larve.

Fertilization is external, but there are modifications of the cloaca in

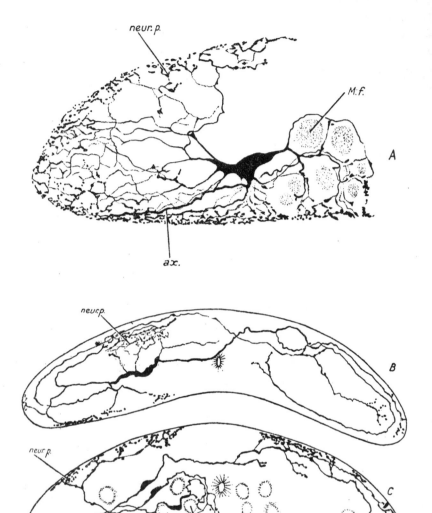

FIG. 63. Cells of the spinal cord of the larva of *Lampetra*.

A and *B*, large motor-cells, with dendrites reaching to the opposite side; *C*, small cells with widespread dendrites, but no axon; *ax.* axon; *M.f.* Müller's fibres; *neur.p.* neuropil at periphery of spinal cord. (After Tretjakoff.)

the two sexes to assist in ensuring fertilization and proper placing of
the eggs in the 'nest' (p. 109). The lips of the cloaca of the ripe male
are united to form a narrow penis-like tube. The cloacal lips of the
female are enlarged and often red; in addition she has an anal fin,
probably used, as in salmon and trout, to make a nest (p. 103). These
sex differences, which develop shortly before spawning, can also be
initiated by injection of anterior pituitary extracts (p. 115).

9. Nervous system of lampreys

The nervous system of the cyclostomes is very much better
developed than that of *Amphioxus* and shows the characteristic plan
that is present in all vertebrates. The essence of the vertebrate
nervous organization may be said to be that it consists of large amounts
of tissue and is highly centralized. The brains of vertebrates contain
much larger aggregates of nervous tissue than are to be found in any
other animals, and this tissue produces by its actions the most characteristic features of vertebrate life. Vertebrates are active, exploratory
creatures, and their behaviour is much influenced by past experience.

We shall return later to detailed discussion of the organization of
the central nervous system; now we may look briefly at the plan
found in the lamprey, as an introduction to that of other vertebrates.
As compared with *Amphioxus* there has been a very high degree of
cephalization. The front end of the spinal cord is enlarged into a
complicated brain, and the nerves connected with a number of the
more anterior segments have become modified to form special cranial
nerves.

The spinal nerves, however, still show the plan found in *Amphioxus*
in that the dorsal and ventral roots do not join. In *Amphioxus* the
ventral roots contain only motor-fibres for the myotomes, while the
dorsal contain sensory fibres and motor-fibres for the lateral plate
musculature (p. 37). The details of the composition of the nerves
of lampreys are still unknown, but there are hints of considerable
deviations from this plan. The ventral roots contain many large
fibres passing to the myotomes and also smaller ones, which run in the
septa between the muscle-blocks and may well serve as muscle sense-
organs. The dorsal roots consist largely of sensory fibres with bipolar
cell bodies collected into dorsal root ganglia: it is not known whether
the dorsal roots also contain any efferent fibres.

It would be very interesting in an animal with separate dorsal and
ventral roots to know the condition of the visceral nerves and sympathetic nerve system, but here again the available information is

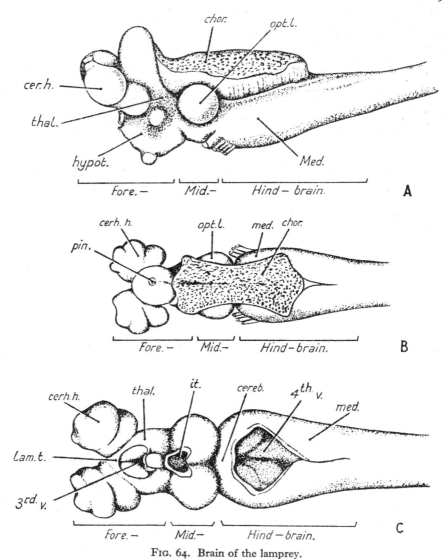

FIG. 64. Brain of the lamprey.

A, side view; B, dorsal view with choroid plexus intact; C, after removal of choroid. *cereb.*
cerebellum; *cer.h.* cerebral hemisphere; *chor.* choroid plexus; *hypot.* hypothalamus; *it.* iter
between third and fourth ventricles; *lam.t.* lamina terminalis (thickened anterior wall of
third ventricle); *med.* medulla oblongata; *opt.l.* optic lobe; *pin.* pineal eye; *thal.* thalamus;
3rd v., *4th v.*, third and fourth ventricles. (After Sterzi.)

unsatisfactory. There is probably no chain of sympathetic ganglia
(though some authors describe one in the head); scattered nerve-cells
occur along the cardinal veins. Nothing is known of how these cells
are connected with the nerve-roots. There is an elaborate plexus of
nerve-cells and fibres in the gut and heart, but the only information

about its connexions is that the visceral branches of the vagus reach only a short distance backwards in lampreys, farther in *Myxine*, and that some of the hinder motor roots send branches to join the gut plexus.

The nerve-fibres in the nervous system of cyclostomes are not provided with myelin sheaths; in this they resemble the nerves of *Amphioxus*, but differ from those of all other chordates. Conduction is slow in such non-medullated fibres, the only case actually investigated in cyclostomes being the lateral line nerve of *Bdellostoma*, found by Carlson to conduct at the low rate of 5 metres a second (frog about 50 m./sec., mammals up to 100 m./sec.).

The spinal cord is of a uniform transparent grey colour and is flattened dorso-ventrally, apparently to allow access of oxygen, and metabolites, no blood-vessels being present within the cord. The nerve-cell bodies lie, as in higher vertebrates, around the central canal, but the synaptic contacts are not made in this 'grey' matter but at the periphery, in what would correspond to the white matter of higher forms. The outer part of the cord is thus made up of a neuropil or nerve feltwork, formed of the terminations of the incoming sensory fibres and the dendrites of the motor-cells. These cells (Fig. 63) lie in the ventral part of the cord, their axons running out to make the large fibres of the ventral roots and their dendrites passing to all parts of the peripheral regions of both the same and the opposite sides of the cord. They are thus presumably able to be stimulated directly by impulses in the processes of the afferent fibres that end in these regions.

Direct control of the spinal cord from the brain is obtained through a number of very large Müller's fibres, originating from giant cells in the midbrain and hind-brain (Fig. 65). There is some difference of opinion as to whether any branches of these large fibres proceed directly into the ventral roots; probably they do not do so but the dendrites of the motor-cells branch around them and thus receive stimulation (Fig. 63).

Other nerve-cells in the more dorsal parts of the cord have no long axon and apparently serve to connect the neuropil of the various regions. It is not easy to obtain a clear idea of the function of a system of this sort in terms simply of connexions and synaptic contacts. There is need for a great deal more information about the activities of such small cells and masses of neuropil; this peripheral part of the cord of the lamprey might well be suitable for such investigation. The afferent fibres reaching the cord in the dorsal roots give off branches that ascend towards the brain. It is not certain, however, whether there is any considerable direct upward projection pathway, such as is found in higher vertebrates.

The brain itself (Fig. 64) is built on the typical vertebrate plan, as an enlargement of the front end of the spinal cord, with thickenings and evaginations corresponding to the various organs of special sense. Although we know little of its internal functional organization in lampreys, it is probably not far wrong to regard it as chiefly consisting of a series of hypertrophied special sensory centres; thus the forebrain is connected with smell, midbrain with sight, hind-brain with acustico-lateral and taste-bud systems. The forebrain and olfactory sense are well developed in adult lampreys, as is the visual sense, with its chief centre in the midbrain. The auditory and acustico-lateral systems are not very well marked, and the cerebellum is small. Taste is also much less developed than in the higher fishes (p. 210).

Parts of the Brain

Forebrain (prosencephalon)	Cerebral hemispheres (telencephalon)
	Between-brain (diencephalon)
Midbrain (mesencephalon)	Optic lobes
Hind-brain (rhombencephalon)	Cerebellum (myelencephalon)
	Medulla oblongata (metencephalon)

The upper surface of the brain is covered by an extensive vascular pad, the choroid plexus or tela choroidea (Fig. 64). This extends into the ventricles of the brain at three points—into the third ventricle of the diencephalon, into the iter (duct) leading through the midbrain from third to fourth ventricles, and into the fourth ventricle itself. The roof of the brain is therefore non-nervous in these regions. In later vertebrates the choroid extends only into the third and fourth ventricles. It is not known why the vascular membranes of the brain are so highly developed in lampreys.

From the lower part of the mid- and hind-brain arise all the cranial nerves except the olfactory and optic. The details of these nerves are difficult to make out by dissection in the lamprey and will be left for consideration in connexion with the dogfish, in which they can easily be dissected. The cranial nerves represent nerves similar to the dorsal and ventral nerve-roots of the trunk, much modified as a result of the special development of the head (p. 144). They carry afferent fibres from the skin of the head and gills and motor-fibres for moving the eyes, sucker, and branchial apparatus.

From the relative sizes of the parts of the brain it can be seen that the various special sensory centres are still small. The largest part of the brain is the medulla oblongata, which is well developed because

Fig. 65. Sagittal section through head of lamprey.

cereb. cerebellum; *cer.h.* cerebral hemisphere; *chor.pl. 3 & 4,* choroid plexuses of the 3rd and 4th ventricle, extending also into the midbrain; *h.s.* hypophysial sac; *hab.* habenular region; *hyp.* hypothalamus; *interped.* interpeduncular region; *med.* medulla oblongata; *Mull.* Müller's cell; *not.* notochord; *o.* glandular organ of nasal sac; *olf.ep.* olfactory epithelium; *olf.n.* olfactory nerve; *p.ant., p.int.,* and *p.nerv.* partes anterior, intermedia, and nervosa of the pituitary gland; *parap.* parapineal; *pin.* pineal; *tect.opt.* tectum opticum.

of the extensive sucking apparatus, innervated from the trigeminal nerve.

The forebrain consists of a pair of large cerebral hemispheres and these open by the foramina of Munro into a median third ventricle, whose walls constitute the diencephalon or between-brain (Fig. 65). This diencephalon, besides connecting the forebrain with the midbrain, includes the thalamus and serves important functions of its own. Its ventral part, the hypothalamus, is well developed in all vertebrates as a central organ controlling visceral activities and the internal life of the organism.

10. The pineal eyes

The diencephalon is also the region of the brain from which the eyes are formed. In lampreys, besides the usual pair of eyes, there is also, attached to the roof of the between-brain, the so-called third,

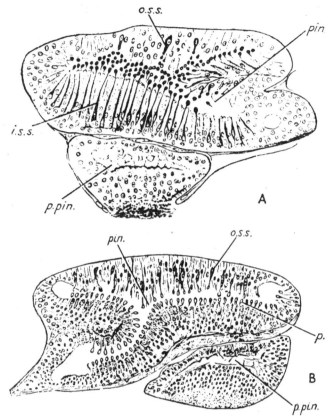

FIG. 66. Pineal and parapineal organs of adult *Lampetra fluviatilis*
A. larva, B. adult. Sagittal section.

i.s.s., *o.s.s.*, inner and outer sensory cells; *pin.* pineal; *p.pin.* parapineal. (After Tretjakoff.)

epiphysial or median eye, better developed in these animals than in any other living vertebrate except perhaps certain reptiles.

This organ is actually not median but consists of an unequally developed pair of sacs, that on the right, the pineal, being larger and placed dorsal to the morphologically left parapineal (Fig. 66). The sacs form by evagination from the brain and remain connected with the dorsal epithalamic or habenular region of the between-brain by stalks. The two organs are similar in structure, consisting of irregular flattened sacs with a narrow lumen. Both upper and lower walls of each organ contain sensory cells, ending in processes that project into the lumen; the cells have centrally directed nerve-fibres. These fibres apparently mostly end within the organ, and the connexion with the brain is made by the processes of ganglion cells, which are also found in the pineal. In addition there are supporting and pigment cells present. Knowles has shown that the retinal cells of the pineal

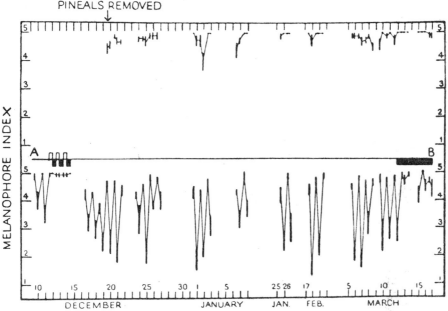

FIG. 67. Colour-changes of larval lampreys, measured by the melanophore index. Animals kept out of doors except as shown along the line AB, where rectangles above the line show illumination with electric light and below the line total darkness. Normal animals show a regular daily rhythm, becoming pale at night. Reversal of normal day and night illumination stops the change. On 19 December the pineal eyes were removed from five out of the ten individuals and these thereafter remained dark (upper chart); the other five continued to show the normal rhythm, until placed in total darkness. (After Young.)

make movements, being arranged differently under conditions of illumination and darkness. The significance of these photomechanical changes is unknown; they demonstrate that the pineal cells are sensitive to light.

The structure of these pineal organs shows that they are eyes, based on the same general plan as the paired eyes, but with little special differentiation. In recent years it has been possible to find out something of the part which these organs play in the life of the lamprey. When a bright spot of light is directed upon the pineal region of a stationary ammocoete larva movement is usually initiated, but only after illumination for many seconds. Moreover, these movements

can be elicited even after the pineal organs have been removed!
In the larval lamprey the paired eyes are deeply buried below pigmented skin, so the movement is not likely to be due to them; indeed
it continues when they too have been taken out! Evidently there must
be still other receptors, able to respond to changes of light intensity in
the wall of the diencephalon. This recalls the fact that photoreceptors
are found within the substance of the nervous system of *Amphioxus*.
This power of response to changes of illumination has been retained

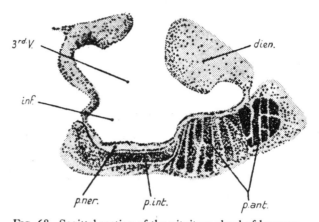

FIG. 68. Sagittal section of the pituitary gland of lamprey.
dien. diencephalon; *inf*. infundibulum; *p.ant.*, *p.int.*, and *p.ner*. partes anterior, intermedia, and nervosa, there are two types of cell in the pars anterior; *3rd V*. third ventricle.
(After Stendell.)

in the vertebrates, and persists in some as yet unknown cells in the
brain, even after the paired and pineal eyes have become specialized
for light reception. The whole study is of special interest as showing
the stages by which the eyes have been evolved. Higher fishes also
show the power of responding to changes of illumination after the
paired eyes and epiphysis have been removed (p. 200).

   If the pineal eyes are not essential for the initiation of movement,
what is then their function? In the ammocoete larva there is a daily
rhythm of change of colour, the animals becoming dark in the day-
time and pale at night. After removal of the pineal eyes this change
no longer occurs: the animals remain continually dark (Fig. 67).
This effect on the colour is produced by the action of nerve-impulses
from the pineal, passing to the pituitary gland (see p. 103). It seems
that the pineal apparatus is an organ concerned with adjustment of
the internal activities of the animal to correspond to the changing
conditions of illumination. The control may be effected by impulses
carried in the large tract that proceeds from the habenular ganglion

to the hypothalamus, in the floor of the diencephalon. The latter is known to be concerned, throughout the vertebrate series, with the integration of the internal activities of the animal.

11. Pituitary body and hypophysial sack

The lower portion of the diencephalon, the hypothalamus, forms a prominent pair of sacs, the lobi inferiores, containing a partly separated diverticulum of the third ventricle and ending below in the infundibulum (Fig. 65). The pituitary gland (hypophysis) is pressed

Fig. 69. Onset of pallor in a larval lamprey after removal of the pituitary gland, as shown by the decline in the melanophore index. (From Young.)

against the underside of the hypothalamus (Fig. 68). The lower wall of the brain in this region consists not of nerve-cells but of a single epithelial layer, corresponding to the pars nervosa of the pituitary of higher forms. The major portion of the pituitary gland is a mass of secreting cells in which two parts can be recognized, the partes anterior and intermedia. After experimental removal of the intermediate portion of the pituitary lampreys become permanently pale in colour (Fig. 69), showing that, as in other vertebrates (p. 285), a melanophore-expanding substance is liberated into the blood by this gland, the secretion being presumably under the control of the pineal eyes (p. 102). No detailed evidence is yet available about other functions of the pituitary in lampreys, but injections of mammalian anterior pituitary extracts induce appearance of the secondary sexual characters. Evidently the functions of the pituitary have remained essentially the same through the whole chordate series.

The pituitary of lampreys is peculiar because of great development of the naso-hypophysial sac (Fig. 70). Characteristically in vertebrates the pituitary body develops by the formation of a pocket of buccal ectoderm whose walls then become folded so that the part in front of the lumen becomes the pars anterior, that behind the pars intermedia. In nearly all vertebrates the lumen then loses its connexion with the exterior. However, in adult lampreys the sac becomes extraordinarily developed and opens with the nostril on to the dorsal surface of the head. Just inside the main aperture are openings into the nasal sacs, which are cavities with folded walls. Some of the cells of these walls are the olfactory receptors and give off the axons which make up the olfactory nerve, entering the olfactory bulbs on the anterior end of the hemisphere (Fig. 65).

FIG. 70. Dissection of lamprey from the ventral surface after injection of coloured gelatine to show the outline of the hypophysial sac (*s*) and its duct (*d*), which is shown dotted where it runs upwards between the nasal sacs (*n*): *g* shows the gill pouches. Contraction of the branchial apparatus squeezes the sac *s*, so that water is drawn in at each relaxation.

The hypophysial tube proceeds back below the brain, its dorsal wall being thickened below the diencephalon, making, as already described, the secreting portion of the pituitary. A further continuation of the tube behind the pituitary then leads back to a closed sac lying just above the dorsal wall of the pharynx, between the first pair of gill pouches (Fig. 70).

During the movements of respiration this sac is squeezed and water is expelled with some force through the nostril. When the gills relax water flows in at the nostril, and in this way the olfactory organ is provided with samples. If the naso-hypophysial opening is closed with a plug of plasticine the lamprey no longer reacts to solutions, for instance, of alcohol, to which it normally responds by freeing its sucker and swimming away.

In the hag-fish, *Myxine*, the naso-hypophysial duct opens to the pharynx. When it feeds, this animal buries the head in its prey, and the only opportunity for intake and output of water is then through the branchial openings, which lie far back for this purpose. Probably the communication between the nose and the pharynx enables the hag-fish to 'smell' even when its head is embedded in the prey. A similar condition can be produced experimentally in a lamprey by making an operation which opens the blind end of its hypophysial sac. Particles of carmine introduced at the gill openings then emerge at the nostril, and the animal swims away when small quantities of noxious substance are placed near the gills.

12. Lateral line organs of lampreys

The lateral line sense-organs, peculiar to fish-like vertebrates, are

Fig. 71. Section of lateral line organ of tail of adult *Lampetra*.
p. pigmented cells around the pit; *s.c.* receptor cells. (After Young.)

little patches of sensory cells found along certain lines on the head and on one main line extending down the trunk. They are all inner-vated by cranial nerves, those on the body and tail being served by a special backward branch of the vagus nerve. In the lamprey the lateral line organs are very simple (Fig. 71), being open to the exterior and not sunk in a canal as in higher forms. The rows are somewhat irregular, especially those on the body.

13. Auditory organs of lampreys

The auditory sacs may be considered as a specialized portion of the lateral line system. They develop by an inpushing of the wall of the head, and this then becomes closed off from the exterior. Internal foldings then divide up the sac into a number of chambers, namely, two tubes, the semicircular canals (in most vertebrates there are three) set at right angles to each other, and two pockets, the sacculus and utriculus. Sense-organs develop in the walls of these organs. They provide the discharges of nerve-impulses by which the animal maintains its orientation and rights itself when disturbed.

14. Paired eyes of lampreys

The structure of the paired eyes is similar to that in other vertebrates. They are formed, like the pineal eyes, by evaginations of the wall of the diencephalon; the so-called optic nerve is therefore not really a peripheral nerve but a portion of the brain; it should strictly be called the optic tract. The eyes are moved by six extrinsic muscles as in other vertebrates, but these are arranged in a somewhat unusual

FIG. 72. Horizontal section of the eye of a lamprey.

er., ir., sr., external, internal, and superior rectus muscles; *v.v.* venous sinuses which cushion the eye. (From Walls, *The Vertebrate Eye,* Cranbrook Institute of Science.)

manner and there is some uncertainty about their innervation. Evidently the arrangement of the head organs in cyclostomes, though similar in general plan to that of later forms, has diverged along its own lines during the hundreds of millions of years of separate evolution. Accommodation is effected by a process found in no other vertebrates. Two anterior myotomes are modified to make a cornealis muscle which pulls on the cornea, flattening it and pushing the lens closer to the retina (Fig. 72). The cornea does not move with the rest of the eye. There is an iris, outlining a round pupil, which changes little, if at all, in diameter under different illuminations. Nothing is known of the use made of the eyes by the animals, nor whether they find their prey by this means or by smell. In the ammocoete larva the paired eyes are buried below the pigmented skin and the animal makes no movements when light is shone on to this region.

The optic tracts of adult lampreys end in the roof of the midbrain (tectum opticum) which is a highly differentiated, stratified region.

Besides the optic fibres it receives also impulses from sensory fibres ascending from the spinal cord and others from the auditory and lateral line centres. The midbrain is therefore undoubtedly one of the most important parts of the brain in lampreys, though nothing is known in detail of its functions. Its cells control movements of the animal, by means of fibres which run to make connexion with the dendrites of the large Müller's cells, whose axons pass down the spinal cord; other fibres from the tectum opticum reach to various parts of

FIG. 73. Experiment to show behaviour of larval lampreys when illuminated. The tank is left in total darkness and the larvae settle in all parts. When the light is switched on those in the illuminated part begin to swim and continue to do so until by chance they arrive in the darkened part, where they settle down. (From Young.)

the brain, and it is probable that its activities are closely correlated with those of many other regions.

15. Skin photoreceptors

Like many lower vertebrates the lamprey has light-sensitive cells in the skin, as well as those in the eyes. These receptors are abundant in the tail and if a light is shone on to this region the animal rapidly moves away (Figs. 73 and 75). If the spinal cord is cut just behind the head and a light then shone on to the tail, the *head* will be seen to move. This suggests that the impulses are carried forwards by means of the lateral line nerves, which is confirmed by the fact that if these latter are sectioned, leaving the spinal cord intact, then no movements follow when the tail is illuminated. This sensitivity of the lateral line organs to light is not found in other fish-like vertebrates.

16. Habits and life-history of lampreys

We have very little information about the mode of life of lampreys during the time that they are in the sea. They are caught in considerable number attached to other fishes. It is not known how many years a lamprey spends in the sea, but it returns only once to the river for spawning and dies after this act. The up-river migration of *L. fluviatilis* occurs in the autumn, for instance large numbers come up the River Severn and are caught in traps on the way, for use as food. The

FIG. 74. Spawning lampreys seen in their nest. (From Gage.)

spawning migrations of lampreys may take them for hundreds of miles, for example those of the eastern Pacific ascend to the head-waters of the Columbia River. They are said to perform remarkable feats of climbing, leaping from stone to stone and hanging on by their suckers. During this period of migration some lampreys assume brilliant orange and black colour patterns. On the other hand, lampreys land-locked in the lakes of New York (*Petromyzon marinus unicolor*) feed in fresh water and ascend only a few miles up streams to breed.

Once in the river the lampreys do not feed again but live over the winter on the reserves accumulated in the form of fat, especially under the skin and in the muscles. During the winter the gonads ripen progressively and the secondary sexual characters begin to become apparent only in February. The females then develop a large anal fin, while in the male a penis-like organ appears (Fig. 47) and the base of the dorsal fin becomes thickened.

Spawning occurs in the spring and is preceded by a form of nest-building. Numerous lampreys collect together, usually at a place below a weir where the water is shallow and rather swift, and the bottom both stony and sandy. Stones are then dragged by the mouth

FIG. 75. Ammocoete larva of *Lampetra planeri*, showing the effect of shining a narrow beam of light on to various parts of the body. Illumination of 1, 2, or 8 is followed by movement after a few seconds, but no movement follows illumination at points 3–7. (From Young.)

in such a way as to make a small depression. Fertilization is secured by a process of copulation in which the male fixes by the sucker on to the fore-part of the female and the two then become intertwined and undergo rapid contortions, the eggs being squeezed into the water, while sperms are ejected through the 'penis' (Fig. 74). Fertilization is therefore external, but the sperms must be placed very close to the eggs, for they remain active only for about one minute after entering the fresh water, which provides the stimulus that activates them. Probably not all the eggs and sperms are laid at once; mating is repeated several times until all the products have been shed, after which the animals are exhausted and soon die. The movements of the animals stir up the sand in the nest (this is probably the function of the anal fin of the female) ensuring that the eggs are covered up as they are carried away by the current.

17. The ammocoete larva

The eggs contain a considerable quantity of yolk, but their cleavage is total and proceeds in a manner not unlike that of the frog. After about three weeks the young hatches as the ammocoete larva, about 10 mm. long. At first this is a tiny transparent creature, but its larval life lasts for a long time, during which it grows into an opaque eel-like fish, up to 170 mm. long (Fig. 75).

This portion of life is spent buried in the mud, the animals emerging only occasionally to change their feeding-ground, presumably if the mud is not sufficiently nutritious. There is no sucker, the mouth being surrounded by an oral hood very like that of *Amphioxus* (Fig. 76). The paired eyes are covered by muscles and skin. The head at this stage is little sensitive to light, but the animal quickly begins to swim if the tail is illuminated. We have seen already (p. 107) that in lampreys there are photoreceptors in the tail, connected with the

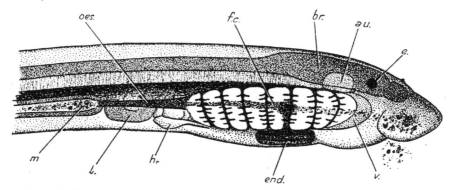

Fig. 76. Freshly hatched ammocoete larva of lamprey fixed while feeding on green flagellates and detritus and then stained and cleared.

au. auditory sac; *br.* brain (covered by meninges); *e.* eye; *end.* endostyle; *f.c.* food cord in pharynx; *h.* heart; *l.* liver; *m.* mid-gut; *oes.* oesophagus; *v.* velar fold.

lateral line nerves. In the larva these are the main photoreceptors, and they ensure that the animal lies completely buried.

If a number of larvae are left in a vessel with a layer of mud on the bottom they rapidly disappear and remain hidden indefinitely, the heads perhaps just visible in small depressions made by the rhythmic gill movements. When disturbed they always swim with the head downwards and in contact when possible with the ground. This habit leads them to burrow rapidly. It is not known whether they have other senses by which they seek mud rich in possible food organisms. The nasal and hypophysial sacs are very poorly developed, and the sense of smell can hardly serve this purpose.

Feeding takes place by the intake of water through the mouth and the separation of small food particles from it in the pharynx (Fig. 76). For this purpose there is used a great quantity of mucus, which is secreted by the endostyle and gathered into a strand by the cilia of the pharynx. This endostyle is a most remarkable organ, forming early in development as a sac below the pharynx (Fig. 77). It consists of a pair of tubes, on the floor of which there are four rows of secretory cells (Fig. 78). There is a single opening to the pharynx, by a slit at about the middle of the length. As development proceeds the inner

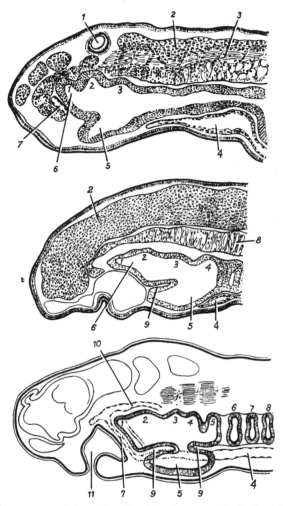

Fig. 77. Development of the endostyle of the lamprey. Sagittal sections through the head at three stages.

1, auditory sac; 2, medullary tube; 3, myotome; 4, conus arteriosus; 5, endostyle; 6, first gill-slit; 7, first arterial arch; 8, notochord; 9, inpushings which cut off the endostyle from the pharynx; 10, aorta; 11, stomodaeum. (After Dohrn, from Kukenthal.)

rows of cells at the hind part of the organ become coiled upwards, and at the end of larval life the endostyle therefore forms a very large mass below the pharynx, composed of tubes lined partly by secretory and partly by ciliated cells. No enzymes have been discovered in the endostyle, and its function is probably only to produce mucus in which the food particles become entangled. Although it resembles the endostyle of *Amphioxus* in the arrangement of the secretory columns, there is a difference in that the organ in the ammocoete larva is not an open groove along which the food current passes. There is, however,

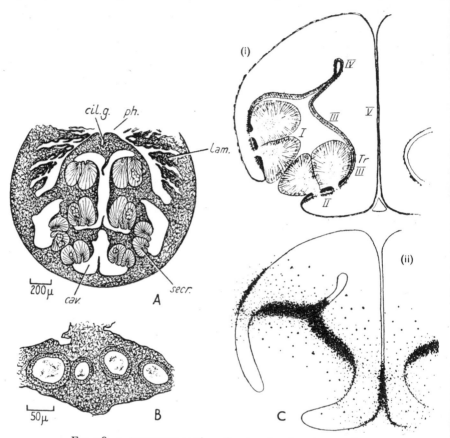

FIG. 78. A, transverse section of endostyle of ammocoete larva.

cav. cavity of the gland; *cil.g.* ciliated groove in floor of pharynx; *lam.* lamellae of gills; *ph.* cavity of pharynx; *secr.* mucus-secreting cells of the gland.

B, transverse section of thyroid follicles of adult. (After Young and Bellerby.)

C, distribution of radio-active iodine in the endostyle of the ammocoete larva.

(i) shows the various cell types (I–V) as seen in cross-section. (ii) is the autoradiograph produced when an animal is left for 45 hours in a litre of water containing 200 microcuries of radio-active iodine, then fixed in formol, sectioned, and a section placed in contact with X-ray film. The iodine is found mainly in the type III cells, to some extent in those of type V. It is usually considered that the adult thyroid develops from the cell types II and IV of the larva. (From original of Fig. 1 by A. Gorbman and C. W. Creaser, *J. of Exp. Zool.* **89**, 395.)

a ciliated groove in the floor of the pharynx, that is to say, on the roof of the endostyle (Fig. 78).

The details of the feeding-currents of the ammocoete larva are not understood. An important difference from the arrangement in *Amphioxus* is that the current is produced by muscular rather than ciliary action. The whole branchial basket is repeatedly expanded and contracted by an elaborate system of muscles, drawing water in at the mouth and expelling it at the gill-slits. The velum forms a pair of muscular flaps which also assist the current. It is not easy to observe how the food particles are taken up from the current, but apparently a strand of mucus shoots from the endostyle and occupies the whole of the centre of the pharynx (Fig. 76). This strand probably rotates and as it passes backwards into the oesophagus it catches the particles.

Evidently the system enables the animals to feed efficiently on the small unicellular algae and bacteria of the mud. In *Amphioxus* the ciliated pharynx, occupying a considerable proportion of the whole surface, is only able to support a tiny creature, but the muscular feeding-system of the ammocoete allows a relatively small pharynx to feed a fish 170 mm. long and weighing up to 10 grams. This use of muscles for moving the gills was evidently an important step in chordate evolution. It allowed the animals to escape from the limitation of size imposed by the ciliary method of feeding. After the development of jaws to form a still more efficient feeding mechanism the rhythmic movement of the branchial apparatus persisted for the purpose of respiration. We cannot be certain about changes which occurred so long ago, but it seems likely that the respiratory movements of a fish were first introduced to provide food rather than oxygen.

The endostyle therefore shows the survival of the primitive feeding-methods of chordates, but it also undergoes at metamorphosis an astonishing change into a thyroid gland. The mucus-secreting columns shrink and the whole organ becomes reduced to a row of closed sacs, lying below the pharynx (Fig. 78 B). Each of these sacs is lined by an epithelium, contains a structureless 'colloid' substance, and is therefore closely similar to a thyroid vesicle. Moreover, experiments have shown that extracts of this organ contain iodine and exert an accelerating effect on the metamorphosis of frog tadpoles. Although nothing is known of the part played by the secretion of this gland in the life of the adult lamprey, we may safely conclude that we have here the conversion of an externally secreting feeding-organ into a gland, of internal secretion. The actual mucus-secreting cells are not transformed into those of the thyroid follicles, these latter are derived from epithelial cells in the wall of the larval organ. One cannot avoid speculating on this extraordinary change of function. It may perhaps be significant that the endocrine gland that regulates basal metabolism (the thyroid) is derived from that part of the feeding-system which in the earliest chordates was responsible for providing the raw materials of metabolism. Experiments with radio-active iodine show that this element is concentrated in certain cells of the larval endostyle (Fig. 78 c).

The great change in the endostyle is only part of the very complete metamorphosis by which the ammocoete larva becomes an adult lamprey. The mouth becomes rounded and its teeth, tongue, and complex musculature develop. The paired eyes appear, the olfactory organ becomes internally folded, and the olfactory nerve and tracts much enlarged. The hypophysial sac, very narrow in the ammocoete and terminating at the level of the pituitary, becomes widened and extended backwards to the gills. In the pharynx the gills develop into sacs opening to the branchial chamber. Changes also take place in the intestine. The yellow-brown colour of the larva gives place to the black with silver underside of the adult. The animal more and more frequently leaves the mud and finally migrates to the sea to begin its parasitic life.

18. Races of lampreys, a problem in systematics

Besides the river lampreys, such as *L. fluviatilis* (Linnaeus), which show this characteristic migratory life-history, there are also in various parts of the northern hemisphere small brook lampreys ('prides'), such as *Lampetra planeri* Bloch, which remain throughout their life in fresh water. These prides are very abundant in many English rivers and streams, but since the greater part of their life is passed in the ammocoete stage they are not often seen. The larvae remain in the mud probably for three years and undergo metamorphosis in late summer and autumn. The characteristic of this type of lamprey is that the adults never migrate and never feed. The gonads are already well developed at metamorphosis and ripen during the winter. Spawning takes place in March or April and the animals then die.

There has been much dispute about the status of these freshwater races. In structure the adult *L. planeri* is very nearly if not quite identical with an adult *L. fluviatilis*, except that the latter is very much the larger. Certain small differences in the mouth and teeth may well result from the effects of use in feeding. Crossing of the two sorts could presumably never take place in nature, on account of the size difference, but by artificial stripping of the adults cross-fertilization in both directions can easily be achieved. Unfortunately the hybrid larvae have never been reared to maturity; we cannot therefore be sure whether the small size and failure to migrate of the *planeri* forms are inherited characters or are produced by the influence of the environment. The effect of the non-migratory condition is to enable the lampreys to colonize very fully rivers that, because of effluents, they would be unable to occupy if a migration to the sea was necessary. By this process of acceleration of the development of the gonads a dangerous stage in the life-history has been avoided.

Similar pairs of migratory and non-migratory forms of lamprey are found in Japan and in North America. Indeed, the condition appears to be developing independently in several river systems in the United States. Since it may be difficult for the brook lampreys to spread from one river system to another it is possible that many of the *planeri* forms have evolved separately, perhaps quite recently. If so, this is a remarkable example of a similar response produced in different parts of a population by a similar environmental stimulus, in this case the effluents. This process of alteration in the relative times of metamorphosis and sexual maturity is called paedomorphosis and it has occurred also in certain amphibians (the axolotl) and in ascidians (Larvacea). It is believed that similar changes in rates of development have been essential factors in the development of some major groups of animals, probably of the whole chordate phylum (p. 74).

In the lampreys the paedomorphosis is only partial: metamorphosis does take place, but is immediately followed by maturity. Since in mammals injections of anterior pituitary extracts accelerate development of the gonads, it was thought possible that complete neoteny might be produced by making such injections into larvae of *L. planeri*. No completely sexually mature ammocoetes have yet been produced by this method, but following the injections the larvae assumed the secondary sexual characters, which are normally shown only at maturity, namely, swelling of the cloaca, opening of the pore from coelom to exterior, and the changes in body form. No signs of metamorphosis were produced by these injections and we are left without information as to the cause of that change in the lamprey. In Amphibia even very young larvae undergo metamorphosis when treated with thyroid extracts, but similar treatment of ammocoete larvae has failed to produce any change. Further investigation of the problem should be very interesting, since it seems likely that the differences between the *fluviatilis* and *planeri* forms are the result of an endocrine factor accelerating the onset of sexual maturity in the latter. The fact that the change is occurring in various parts of the world adds further interest to this example of evolution in progress.

Besides all these relatively small lampreys, there is a much larger form, the sea lamprey, *Petromyzon marinus* Linnaeus, reaching a metre in length. This animal differs from *Lampetra* in body form, structure of the sucker, and other features, as well as in size. Like most other groups of animals lampreys therefore present several problems of nomenclature. Linnaeus included the three types that occur in Europe in the one genus *Petromyzon*; since they are all rather alike in shape this is in some ways a reasonable procedure. But are we then also to include in the same genus forms that differ more widely, such as the lampreys of North America? Those of the southern hemisphere differ still more. As so often happens, systematists have chosen the course of splitting up the Linnaean genus, even though several of the resulting genera have only one species. Thus Gray suggested the genus *Lampetra* for the brook and river lampreys, keeping *Petromyzon* for the larger species of sea lamprey. Other genera have been added, such as *Entosphenus* Gill for some of the North American forms and *Geotria* Gray and *Mordacia* Gray for the forms from the southern hemisphere (Chile, Australia, and New Zealand). Such distinctions, though they may seem irritating at first sight, are an advantage in that they call attention to the differences which exist. For instance, it is a striking fact that lampreys are found in temperate waters of both hemispheres, but not in the tropics, and it is interesting to learn that the forms from New Zealand, Australia, and South America (there is none in South Africa) show distinct peculiarities. Thus *Geotria* possesses a large sac behind the sucker.

A special problem of nomenclature arises from the fact that the river and brook lampreys are almost identical in structure and differ only in size, time of sexual maturity, and habits. A further complication is that the germ-cells of the two races allow cross-fertilization, although this probably never occurs in nature! We may take Dobhzansky's definition of species as 'groups of populations which are reproductively isolated to the extent that the exchange of genes between them is absent or so slow that the genetic differences are not diminished or swamped', and in this sense we may retain the specific names *L. fluviatilis* and *L. planeri* for the two populations.

19. Hag-fishes, order Myxinoidea

The hag-fishes, *Myxine* and *Bdellostoma*, are animals still more modified for sucking than are the lampreys (Fig. 79). The eyes are very small, and are covered by pigmented skin in *Myxine*; the animals however, are sensitive to changes of illumination. There are sensory tentacles around the mouth, and in both hag-fishes the teeth and sucking apparatus are well developed. The animals live by burrowing into the bodies of dead or dying fishes. As many as 123 *Myxine* have been taken from a single fish. Since the introduction of trawling they have become less common in the North Sea, where they used to be a

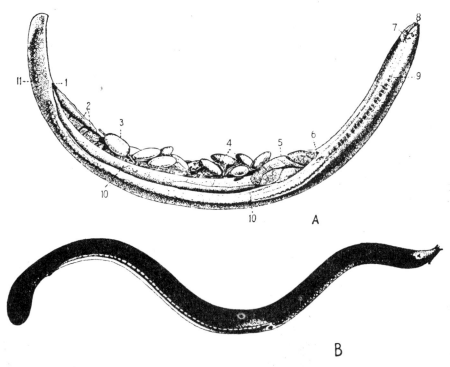

FIG. 79. A, *Myxine*, partly dissected.

1, cloaca; 2, testis; 3 and 4, ovary with eggs; 5, liver; 6, branchial opening; 7, mouth; 8, nostril; 9 and 11, slime glands; 10, intestine. (After Retzius, from Kukenthal.)

B, *Myxine*. (After Smith.)

serious source of loss to fishermen by their attacks on fishes caught in drift nets or on lines. They seem to find fish when they are dying or just dead, and entering by the mouth of their prey eat out the whole contents of the body, leaving a sack of skin and bones. When they are themselves caught on lines (for instance, with a salted herring bait) the hook is swallowed so deeply that it may be found near the anus!

The gills are modified into pouches (6–14 in *Bdellostoma*, 6 in *Myxine*), opening by tubes into the pharynx, and to the exterior (Fig. 80). In *Myxine* all of the tubes are joined and open by a single posterior aperture on each side. In both species there is also a separate posterior oesophago-cutaneous duct, that of the left only being developed in *Bdellostoma*. The naso-hypophysial sac opens to the pharynx, presumably allowing the animal to smell even when its head is deeply embedded in the body of its prey (p. 104).

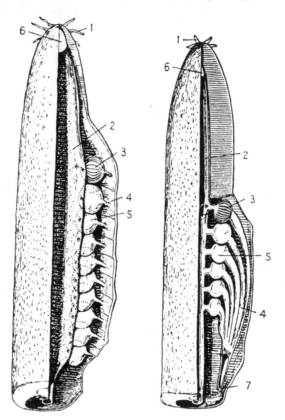

FIG. 80. Arrangement of gills in *Bdellostoma* and *Myxine*.

1, tentacles; 2, wall of pharynx; 3, branchial sac opened to show gill lamellae; 4, branchial duct; 5, branchial sac; 6, mouth; 7, common branchial aperture in *Myxine*.
(From Kukenthal after Dean.)

Down the sides of the body are pairs of slime glands, able to produce immense amounts of mucus, which may be protective and is said also to be produced under the operculum to hasten the end of a dying fish which the hag-fish has attacked.

A curious difference from the nervous system of lampreys is that the dorsal and ventral roots join, though in a manner that suggests that the union is not similar to that found in gnathostome vertebrates. The brain shows several features of reduction and simplification and no well-developed pineal eyes are present. There is only one semicircular canal in the ear. The kidneys show a more generalized condition than in any other chordate in that the pronephros persists in the adult and is hardly marked off from the mesonephros, so that an almost continuous series of funnels and Malphigian bodies can be recognized. There are, however, certain peculiar secondary developments, such as the multiplication of funnels in the pronephros.

The hag-fishes are entirely marine. The development is known only in *Bdellostoma*, where the egg is yolky and cleavage partial, leading to the formation of an embryo perched on a mass of yolk. It is often stated that *Myxine* is a protandric hermaphrodite, because individuals are found in which the front end of the gonad contains eggs, whereas the hind part is testis-like (Fig. 79 A). No ripe sperms have ever been found in this region, however, and, moreover, individuals with fully testicular gonads do occur. Since it is known that in other vertebrates (including the lampreys) the gonads go through a hermaphrodite stage during development it seems likely that *Myxine* is not a functional hermaphrodite but that the double-sexed gonad shows a rather late persistence of the indeterminate stage.

These animals are evidently highly modified scavengers, closely related to each other and rather more distantly to the lampreys. In this connexion it is interesting that they, like lampreys, are found in the temperate seas of both hemispheres, but not in the tropics. The organization of the lampreys and hag-fishes shows that they preserve many characteristics from a very early stage of chordate evolution, probably that of about the Silurian period. The two types have probably diverged fairly recently, though an early separation has been suggested (p. 124). Their special interest for us is in giving an insight into the organization possessed by the vertebrates before jaws were evolved. However, no doubt very many changes have gone on during cyclostome evolution and we must not suppose that all Silurian vertebrates were like lampreys. Indeed, we must now complete our picture of this stage of evolution by examining the fossil fishes known to have existed at that period. We shall find them superficially so different from modern cyclostomes that only careful morphological comparison reveals the similarities. The inquiry will show us once again how a common plan of organization can be found in animals of very different superficial form and habits.

20. Fossil Agnatha, the earliest-known vertebrates

The cephalaspids, pteraspids, and anaspids are fossil forms from freshwater Silurian and Devonian deposits. They are therefore the oldest fossil veterbrates known to us (except for a few Ordovician fragments), and this makes it specially interesting that they show several signs of affinity with the cyclostomes. These are rare fossils,

FIG. 81. A cephalaspid restored (*Hemicyclaspis*).

d. dorsal fin; *lsf.* lateral electric field; *pec.* pectoral fin; *p.* pineal; *sclr.* sclerotic ring.
(From Stensiö.)

FIG. 82. Head of a cephalaspid, seen from below.

aort.V. passage for ventral aorta; *br.1* equivalent of first branchial arch in fishes; *h.* equivalent of hyoid arch; *M.* mouth; *md.* equivalent of mandibular arch; *oes.* passage for oesophagus; *p.md.* equivalent of premandibular arch; V_1, V_2, *VII, IX, X,* foramina for cranial nerves; *1–10,* external openings of gill pouches. (From Westoll.)

but several specimens may be found together, for instance, a quarry in Herefordshire yielded numerous specimens of *Cephalaspis* and *Pteraspis* of Old Red Sandstone age, probably all from a single dried-up pool.

Stensiö has made a very careful investigation of the cephalaspids (Osteostraci), which are specially favourable for study because the whole upper surface of the body was encased in a bony shield, whose under surface bears an imprint of the brain, nerves, and branchial apparatus (Figs. 81 and 82). The rest of the body was fish-like, with an upturned tail (heterocercal; see p. 135) and covered with heavy bony scales (p. 182). A pair of flaps behind the gills probably represent pectoral fins, but there is no trace of pelvic fins.

On the dorsal surface of the shield are two median apertures, one

Fig. 83. Three views of a restoration of *Pteraspis*.
d.sp. dorsal spine; *e.* eye; *m.* mouth; *r.* rostrum. (From White.)

behind the other, which are supposed to have served for a naso-hypophysial aperture and a pineal spot: there were also paired eyes. The head shield carried areas of a strange tissue, provisionally considered to have been an electric or perhaps sensory organ. The brain shows some similarities to that of cyclostomes and there is evidence that the dorsal and ventral nerve-roots remained separate. There were only two semicircular canals. There were 9 or 10 pairs of sac-like gills and from the relation of the nerve-roots to these it appears that the first cranial dorsal root (nervus ophthalmicus profundus; p. 149) lay in relation to the first gill pouch (Fig. 82). In gnathostomes we shall find that this and the succeeding arch are modified to make the jaws, and therefore the presence of a complete series of unmodified gill-slits in cephalaspids shows that in spite of their specializations (head shield, 'electric organ', &c.) they have departed relatively little from the early craniate condition.

There are many other points in which Stensiö claims that these forms show affinity with the modern cyclostomes and there can be

FIG. 84. *Pteraspis* restored to show the mouth closed in A, open in B. The dotted lines show the lateral line canals. (From White.)

little doubt that the groups are related, though perhaps not quite so closely as he supposes. If this view is correct, it follows that many features of the modern lampreys and hag-fishes, such as the absence of bone and of paired fins, are secondary.

In the pteraspids (Heterostraci) of the Silurian and Devonian there was a carapace over the front part of the body and a covering of rhomboid scales on the tail (Fig. 83). The plates of the carapace did not contain bone-cells; presumably they were of the nature of dentine, whose cells lie outside the hard substance. There are no signs of paired fins. There was a pineal eye but no clear sign of a nostril. The mouth was at the very front end, surrounded by bony plates, which suggests that it consisted of a protrusible apparatus which could be pushed out to form 'a kind of scoop or shovel (Fig. 84) whereby mud and decaying refuse could have been taken off the bottom, for it seems most likely that such were their food and habit' (White).

The tail shows a lower lobe longer than the upper (a condition known as 'hypocercal'; this shape would presumably serve to drive the head end upwards. The opposite ('heterocercal') condition found in many fishes (for instance, the dogfish) is associated with the presence of pectoral fins and produces a tendency to negative pitch (p. 135).

The Anaspida, mostly from the Silurian, are also usually placed with the Agnatha, but there is little clear evidence of their affinities. They were small fishes (3–4 in. long) covered with rows of bony scales but without the large plates found in cephalaspids and ptera-

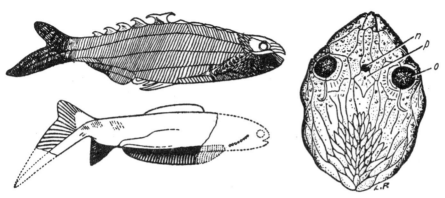

FIG. 85. Various anaspids. Upper left, *Birkenia*; lower left, *Endeiolepis*; right, dorsal view of head plates of *Pharyngolepis*.

n. nostril; *o.* lateral eye; *p.* pineal eye. (From Romer, *Vertebrate Paleontology*, University of Chicago Press, after Stetson, Stensiö, and Kiaer.)

spids (Fig. 85). The tail was hypocercal like that of pteraspids, and some forms possessed a very interesting series of several pairs of fins. There were paired eyes, openings on the top of the head presumed to be pineal and nasal apertures, and a series of round gill openings. The general shape of the head seems to have resembled that of later gnathostome fishes, but no jaws have been discovered.

White has recently described an unarmoured agnathan, **Jamoytius* from the Silurian. The notochord was persistent and there was no calcified endoskeleton. There were long, continuous lateral fin folds. The myotomes have been preserved and show a simple arrangement, like that of *Amphioxus*. The earliest chordates may well have resembled this creature.

The affinities of these early fossils with each other and with the cyclostomes have been much disputed. Lankester claimed that pteraspids were related to cephalaspids 'because they are found in the same beds, because they have a large head shield and because there is nothing else with which to associate them'. At the other extreme Stensiö holds that we have sufficient evidence to assert that the pteraspids have given rise to the myxinoids, and the cephalaspids to the lampreys. Except for the absence of jaws there is indeed little in common among the fossil forms. The differences in the shape of the tail are especially baffling. As White points out, an animal with a heterocercal tail and pectoral fins can hardly have lost either of these organs independently. He suggests that the earliest vertebrates possessed straight ('diphycercal') tails and from these were evolved on the one hand the pteraspids with hypocercal tails and on the other the cephalaspids with upturned heterocercal tails. The modern cyclostomes are perhaps derived from the latter, but which, if either, group gave rise to the earliest gnathostomes is unknown.

In fact we have too little evidence to be able to say much that is definite about the course of vertebrate evolution at this early stage. These were the first animals of the chordate type to become large, and they apparently all did so by feeding on the detritus at the bottom of rivers and lakes. They seem to have evolved into various types, most of which were rather heavily armoured and perhaps slow-moving forms. The lampreys and hag-fishes have been derived from early Agnatha by the evolution of a sucking mouth, perhaps with loss of the bony skeleton and paired limbs. However, it was the unknown forms that evolved a biting mouth that made the next great advance in vertebrate evolution.

V

THE APPEARANCE OF JAWS.
THE ORGANIZATION OF THE HEAD

1. The elasmobranchs: introduction

In all parts of the sea there are to be found members of the class of the elasmobranchs (literally 'plate-gilled' fishes), including sharks ranging from monsters of 30 ft. long to the common dogfish *Scyliorhinus canicula* of 1–2 ft. Nearly all fishes in the group are carnivorous or scavengers: the skates and rays are bottom-living relatives, feeding mostly on invertebrates. Shark-like animals are among the most numerous and important members of the community of the sea. Although they are not quite so fully masters of the water as are the bony fishes, they are yet well enough suited to that element to survive in great numbers in all oceans. Perhaps the skill and cunning of a shark is exaggerated by the frightened boatman or bather, who is apt to mistake a keen nose and the persistence of hunger for intelligence, especially when he is faced at intervals with a well-armed mouth; but the sharks have a large brain and their active, predacious habits enable many of them to live by eating the more elaborately organized bony fishes.

Evidently such active creatures have changed considerably if they have been evolved from the heavily armoured and probably slow-moving agnathous vertebrates that shovelled up food from the bottom of Palaeozoic seas. It used to be supposed that these elasmobranch or cartilage fishes represent a very primitive stock, but we now realize that there have been very great changes since the biting mouth was first evolved; we cannot be sure that any features we find in the elasmobranchs were possessed by the earliest gnathostomes.

The typical shark is a long-bodied fish, swimming by the passage of waves of contraction along the metamerically arranged muscles. As in the lampreys and eels, the wave that passes down the body is of short period, relative to the length of the fish, and is therefore evident as it travels along. This is probably a less efficient system than is provided by the longer period waves of the most highly developed bony fishes; the sharks are good swimmers, but not among the swiftest. Stability and control of direction are ensured by the upturned tail and the fins. The tail, with its dorsal lobe larger than the ventral, is said to be heterocercal, and tends to drive the head downwards. This is corrected by the flattened shape of the head itself and by the pectoral fins, which act as 'aerofoils', allowing steering in the horizontal plane (p. 135). There are two dorsal fins, which secure stability against rolling, and also assist in making possible the vertical turning movements, which are accomplished by passing a wave of contraction down one side of the body only (for further details see p. 133).

FIG. 86. A, side view of precaudal vertebrae of *Scyliorhinus canicula*; B, similar view of caudal vertebrae.

b.d. basidorsal; *c.* centrum; *h.* basiventral; *h.s.* haemal spine; *i.d.* interdorsal; *p.* parapophysis; *r.* rib; *s.d.* supradorsals. The vertical dotted lines indicate the limits of neuromeres and myotomes. The small circles represent the exits of the dorsal and ventral roots of spinal nerves. (After Ridewood, from *Cambridge Natural History*, Macmillan & Co.)

The muscles for the production of these movements are a serial metameric set, with longitudinal fibres, essentially like those of the lamprey or *Amphioxus*. The central axis is no longer simply a rod; the notochord has become surrounded and partly replaced by a series of vertebrae (Figs. 86 and 87). These develop as two pairs of cartilaginous nodules in each segment, the basidorsals and basiventrals behind, and smaller elements, the interdorsals and interventrals, in the front. The basiventrals, lying on either side of the notochord, form the centrum of each vertebra, constricting and almost interrupting the notochord, which widens again, however, between the vertebrae. The vertebrae are held together by ligaments, but are not articulated by complex facets as they are in land animals. The basidorsals form neural arches above the nerve-cord, the interdorsals intercalary arches. The interventrals partly separate the centra. Attached to each basiventral is a pair of transverse processes, which in the anterior region bear short ribs and in the tail are fused in the midline to make the haemal arches.

The median and paired fins are supported by cartilaginous rods, the radials, and their edges are further strengthened by special horny rays, the ceratotrichia. The radials of the paired fins form a series attached to larger rods at the base. These more basal rods are attached

FIG. 87. Diagram of the organization of a vertebrate.

ac. wall of abdominal coelom; *bd.* basidorsal; *bv.* basiventral; *bw.* body wall; *dr.* dorsal rib; *i.* intestine; *iv.* interventral; *m.* myocomma; *ms.* mesentery; *msd.* median dorsal septum; *nes.* neural tube; *ns.* notochordal sheath; *pr.* ventral (pleural) rib; *sp.* neural spine; *ts.* horizontal septum. (From Goodrich.)

to a 'girdle' of cartilage embedded in the body wall. The pectoral girdle is a hoop extending some way round the body, but the pelvic girdle is simply a transverse rod in the abdominal wall. The origin of these girdles and of the fins will be discussed later (p. 174).

2. The swimming of fishes

The propulsive forces that move a fish through the water are produced by the longitudinal muscle-fibres of the myotomes. Only in exceptional and aberrant forms is the propulsion produced by movement of the fins, whose function is usually rather to give the fish its stability, enabling it to keep on a constant course, and also to change its course.

The myotomes consist of blocks of longitudinal muscle-fibres, placed on either side of an incompressible central axis, the notochord or vertebral column. The effect of contraction of the muscle-fibres in any myotome is therefore to bend the body. In forward swimming the contraction of each myotome takes place after that in front of it. In this way waves of curvature are passed down the body, alternately on each side. This can be illustrated by a series of photographs of a

FIG. 88. Successive positions of a swimming dogfish at intervals of o·1 sec. The lines are 3 in. apart. The passage of a wave is marked by dots. (After Gray.)

FIG. 89. Successive positions of a swimming eel at intervals of o·05 sec. Scale 3 in. The wave-crests are marked. (After Gray.)

fish such as the dogfish or eel in which the amplitude of the waves is large (Figs. 88 and 89).

In other fishes the waves are not so immediately obvious, but serial photographs show that even in such forms as the mackerel and whiting there is a backward movement of waves. The number of waves per minute in steady swimming varies from 54 in the dogfish to 170 in the mackerel, the corresponding velocities of the waves being 55 and 77 and of the whole fish 29 and 42·5 cm./sec.

Gray has shown how the muscle contractions produce movements of the parts of the body, related to one another in such a way as to transmit a backward momentum to the water. Fig. 90 shows superposed drawings of an eel, made from successive photographs. The region marked XY is moving from right to left and that X_1Y_1 from left to right and evidently, as Gray puts it,

'all parts of the fish's body which are in transverse motion have their leading surfaces directed backwards and towards the direction of transverse movement, but the angle of inclination is most pronounced when the segment is crossing the axis of longitudinal motion, and at this point the segment of the body is travelling at its maximum speed. Each point of the body is travelling along a figure 8 curve relative to a transverse line which is moving forward at the average forward velocity of the whole fish. The track of any point on the body (relative to the earth) is a sinusoidal curve whose pitch or wave length is less than that of a curve which defines the body of the fish. There is therefore a definite angle between the surface of the fish and its path of motion.'

Each portion of the side of the fish can thus be considered as moving like the blade of an oar used for sculling at the back of a boat. The principle used, that of an inclined plane, is the same as in screw propulsion, the essential feature being that the moving surface is inclined at an angle to its line of motion.

The magnitude of the forward thrust which is thus generated depends 'among other things on (a) the angle which the

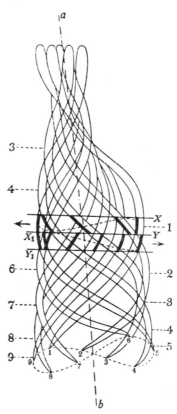

FIG. 90. Enlarged drawings of successive photographs of a young eel superimposed on each other so that the tips of the head on the same transverse axis and the longitudinal axes of motion (ab) are made to coincide. As the wave passes the section XY it first moves to the left and is directed backwards and to the left, whereas X_1, Y_1, moves in the opposite direction. The tip of the tail follows a figure of 8. (From Gray.)

surface of the fish makes with its own path of motion, (b) the angle between the surface of the fish and the axis of forward movement of the whole fish, and (c) the velocity of transverse movement of the body' (Gray). These are evidently factors that will vary with the shape of the body and the action of its muscles. The body form of the faster-moving types of bony fishes provides substantial advantages for swimming over that of the more elongated types. The essential differences are that the bony fishes have (1) large caudal fins, (2) a much smaller length of the body relative to its depth, (3) less flexibility.

The role of the large caudal fin is to resist transverse movements; its effect is, again quoting Gray, 'to keep the leading surface of the body directed obliquely backwards during both phases of its transverse movements and thereby to exert a steady pressure on the water'. Since, however, the tail does execute transverse movements, and at the same time is being rotated towards and away from the axis of motion, it exerts a very large propulsive effect, probably as much as 40 per cent. of the total thrust.

The effect of the caudal fin, combined with the shortness of body and reduced flexibility, is that the front part of the fish makes only small transverse movements; the track of the head is therefore nearly straight and the whole front of the body presents a streamlined surface with little resistance. Further, the muscles just in front of the tail exert their tension with very little change in length.

No doubt the shape of the body also has a very important influence on the effect of the fish on the water and hence on the turbulence in the flow of water and the resistance which has to be overcome. Gray has shown that in the case of a dolphin the resistance to be overcome cannot be that of a rigid model towed at the speed at which the animal moves, since this would require that the muscles generate energy at a rate at least seven times greater than that known in the muscles of other mammals. By watching the flow of particles past the body of fish-like models he showed that movements such as those produced in swimming accelerate the water in the direction of the posterior end, and this would greatly reduce the turbulence.

Something is known of the nervous mechanism responsible for the production of the swimming waves. An eel can swim if its whole skin has been removed. If a region of the body is immobilized by a clamp, swimming waves can pass along. Therefore the rhythm is determined by some intrinsic activity of the spinal cord and not by any mechanism such as proprioceptor impulses arising in active muscles and causing others to contract.

Experiments in which the spinal cord was cut across show that in the eel the rhythm is only produced when suitable impulses reach the cord either from spinal afferents or from the brain. Thus the spinal eel can be made to swim either by fixing a clip onto its caudal fin or by electrical stimulation of the cut end of the spinal cord. Though the cord requires such afferent stimuli for its functioning, they do not determine the frequency of the rhythm, which bears no relationship to that of the applied stimuli.

In the dogfish the isolated spinal cord is able to initiate rhythmic swimming. After transection behind the brain the posterior portion of the fish exhibits continuous swimming movements for many days.

Fig. 91. Diagram of model of the dogfish *Mustelus*, showing the conventional terms for describing deviations of motion. The longitudinal axis X is that of the wind tunnel and Y (horizontal) and Z (vertical) are at right angles to it. The arrows show the directions known as positive rolling, pitching, and yawing, which occur about the X, Y, and Z axes respectively. α is the angle of attack between the axis of the model and the X axis. (From Harris, *J. exp. Biol.* 13.)

Light touch on the sides of the body inhibits these movements, but some sensory impulses are necessary for their initiation; after complete de-afferentation, by section of all the dorsal roots, the movements cease.

The information available does not yet enable us to understand fully how the swimming rhythm is initiated and maintained, nor how it is influenced by the brain. It would be very interesting to have further knowledge on these topics, especially because the locomotor rhythms of land animals are probably based on the serial contractions of their fish ancestors.

3. Equilibrium of fishes in water; the functions of the fins

Making use of the methods of investigation of aeronautical engineers, very interesting studies have been made of the forces that operate to keep such a body as a fish stable as it moves through the water, or allow it to become temporarily unstable and hence to change direction.

Instead of attempting to study a living or dead fish moving in water, Harris made models of fishes and supported them in a wind tunnel in an apparatus suitable for measuring the forces at work in the various directions. Such a method, in which no compensating movements of the fins are allowed, makes it possible to investigate the so-called 'static stability' of the fish, that is to say, to see whether the body and fins are so shaped as to provide forces that tend to bring the fish back into its previous line of movement after it has deviated in any direction. Any body such as a fish or aeroplane is said to be in stable

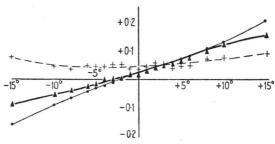

FIG. 92. Results of yawing test on model of *Mustelus* without fins. The lateral force is plotted as a light full line, drag force as a light broken line; yawing moment about centre of gravity as full heavy line. Abscissae show the angle of attack in degrees, ordinates the lateral force and drag in pounds weight, yawing moment in in.-lb. $\times \frac{1}{16}$. (From Harris.)

motion if when it veers slightly from its line of progress the new forces produced upon its planes tend to restore the original direction of motion.

The forces acting on the fish are measured along three primary axes, longitudinal, horizontal, and vertical. Deviation from the line of motion about the longitudinal axis is known as rolling, about the transverse axis as pitching, and about the vertical axis as yawing (Fig. 91). The forces along these three axes are known as drag, lateral force, and lift.

In order to discover the effect of the median fins and tail on the stability, these fins were removed, the heterocercal tail being replaced by a cone having the same taper as the actual caudal fin. The model was then placed in the wind tunnel with a wind at 40 m.p.h., which corresponds to a motion of 3 m.p.h. in water. The lateral force was measured when the body was made to yaw at various angles. The results showed that 'the equilibrium in this plane is quite unstable; a slight turn off the direct course would produce a turning moment tending to increase still further the deflection (Fig. 92). This is a well-known property of all airship hulls, and is known as the "unstable moment" of the hull. It is corrected in the airship by the addition of suitable horizontal and vertical fin surfaces at the rear end, when the airship becomes in effect a feathered arrow.' The forces operating on the fins tend to bring the body back into the original line of motion.

The fins of the fish operate in a similar manner. If the experiment is performed with a model to which all the fins behind the centre of gravity have been added, namely, the caudal, anal, and second dorsal

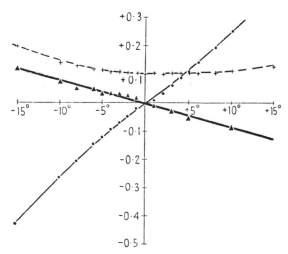

FIG. 93. Yawing test similar to Fig. 92 but with the fins behind the centre of gravity in place. (From Harris.)

fins, it is found that the curve for the yawing moment now has a steep negative slope (Fig. 93), that is to say, every deviation produces forces which tend to give directional stability. With the dorsal fin also in position the model possesses a remarkable neutral equilibrium (Fig. 94). Deviations by as much as 10° produce no resultant yawing moment about the centre of gravity. The form of the dorsal fins is therefore definitely such as to maintain stable swimming and prevent yawing.

Turning of a fish is produced either by the propagation of a wave down one side only of the body or by asymmetrical braking with the pectoral fins (see below). The former type of turn has been investigated by Gray in the whiting, where there is a large caudal fin. This gives great lateral resistance, so that the first part of the turn is executed by bending the front part of the fish on the tail as a fulcrum. This enables the animal to turn through 180° within a circle of the diameter of its own length. After removal of the caudal fin the turns are much less effective.

In both elasmobranchs and teleosts the dorsal fins are well developed in the active swimmers. In most elasmobranchs they are fixed, but in many teleosts the dorsal fin can be folded up and down, and it is observed that the fin is raised during turning. This would have the effect of increasing the yawing moment produced by asymmetrical action of the body muscles or unilateral braking with the pectoral fins.

Since the body is so markedly flexible in the lateral plane and there are powerful muscles available for turning it in this direction, the part

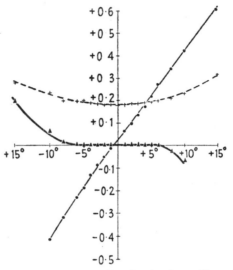

FIG. 94. Yawing test with all median fins in place. (From Harris.)

played by the fins in determining the stability is important mainly when the body is held straight. The fish thus has the double advantage of great stability (by keeping the body straight) and great controlability (by bending it). In a body that cannot change its shape in this way, stability and controlability would be inversely related. This is the case for the stability of the fish in the vertical plane, in which the body is little flexible. Fig. 95 shows the positive slope of the curve for the pitching moment and clearly the equilibrium in this plane is quite unstable. The pectoral fins contribute more than any others to movement in this plane, and since they lie in front of the centre of gravity they greatly increase the instability. Since the fish must be able to alter direction in the vertical plane, it has apparently sacrificed static stability for controlability. The equilibrium in this plane is a dynamic one, controlled by the highly movable pectoral fins, and it is so unstable that only a small movement of these fins is necessary to produce a deflecting force that restores the original direction of motion.

The pectoral fins, lying in front of the centre of gravity, tend to produce a movement of positive pitch, that is to say, they force the head upwards. This effect is normally compensated by a component which is produced by the heterocercal tail. Since the upper lobe of this is rigid and the lower more flexible, the lateral motion given by the

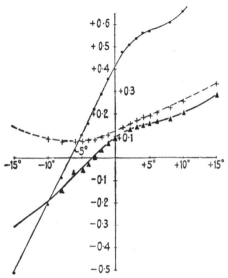

FIG. 95. Pitching test on model of *Mustelus* with all fins intact and pectoral fins set at an angle of incidence of 8°. Lift force is shown as a light full line, drag force as a light broken line, pitching moment about the centre of gravity as a heavy full line. Axes and units as Fig. 92. (From Harris.)

swimming movements of the body produces a vertical lift force on the tail, giving, of course, negative pitch. After amputation of the hypocaudal lobe and anal fin a dogfish swims continually along the bottom of the tank: in order to compensate for the absence of negative pitch the pectoral fins are held horizontally and hence there is no moment to counteract the weight of the fish. After removal of the pectoral fins the anterior end of the body is pointed upwards, often so much so as to cause the fish to swim with its head out of the water. This is the result of an over-strenuous attempt to compensate, by raising the head, for the negative pitch produced by the tail. The system is not suitable for making the continuous adjustments necessary to ensure stability.

This analysis makes it clear why a heterocercal tail is found in almost all the primitive swimming chordates; it is almost a necessity for an animal with a specific gravity in excess of the medium and little flexibility in the vertical plane. The component of positive pitch could be provided by the flattened head or by a continuous fin fold, such as may have been present in early fishes, and adjusted by the limited flexibility which is possible in the fin. The development of movable pectoral fins confers much greater control. Since the useful portions of a fin fold for this purpose would be those well in front and behind the centre of gravity, we can perhaps see the reason why the intervening portion has become lost. In the modern sharks the pelvic fins have little influence on the stability and are perhaps retained only for their modification as claspers.

It is not surprising that races of fishes with stability ensured by systems of this sort should tend to adopt a bottom-living habit and dorso-ventral flattening, such as is found in the skates and rays. Expansion of the front end is necessary at first to compensate the effect of the tail, but the pectoral fin becomes expanded to allow vertical adjustments and then reduction of the hypocaudal lobe of the tail accompanies the adoption of life on the sea bottom. Eventually all locomotion is produced by undulatory movements of the fins, which were at first used only to raise the fish off the bottom.

4. Skin of elasmobranchs

Being swift and predatory animals, more attackers than attacked, the sharks do not possess a very heavy external armament. The skin itself is very tough, being formed of many layers of the inert protein keratin. Scattered over it are a number of characteristic denticles or placoid scales (Fig. 96). Each of these consists of a pulp cavity, around the edge of which lies a layer of odontoblasts secreting the calcareous matter of the scale, known as dentine. This has a characteristic structure resulting from the fact that the odontoblasts send fine processes throughout its substance. The outside of the dentine is covered by a layer of enamel, secreted by the overlying ectoderm. Usually the denticles pierce through the ectoderm, after which no further enamel can be added to their surface. Obviously the scales are very similar to teeth, which are indeed to be considered as specialized denticles developed on the skin of the jaws. It has often been supposed that the denticle is the primitive type of fish scale, from which others have been derived, but it now seems more likely that the earliest covering was a continuous layer, later broken into large scales from which the denticle was ultimately derived (p. 183).

The skin also gives protection to the fish by its colour. Most sharks have a spotted or wavy pattern, which breaks up their visible outline as they move in the water, especially near the surface. They are able to change their colour, though only slowly, becoming darker on a dark background (see p. 160).

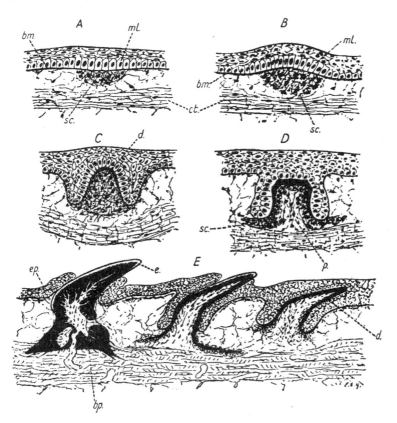

Fig. 96. Development of denticles in the dogfish.

A and B, first gathering of scleroblasts (*sc.*) below the basement membrane (*bm.*); *ml.* are the epidermal cells that will become modified. C, first deposition of dentine (*d.*). In D there is more dentine and a pulp cavity (*p.*) is seen. In E are shown stages in the formation of enamel (*e.*) and of the basal plate (*bp.*) while the denticle cuts the skin. (From Goodrich, *Vertebrata*, A. & C. Black, Ltd.)

5. Morphology of the head

In general organization a dogfish follows closely the fish plan which we have already considered (p. 78). Most of its special new features are in the head, and we may now turn to a consideration of the organization of the head and jaws of a gnathostome vertebrate.

5.1. *Origin of the mouth*

The jawless vertebrates of the Silurian and Devonian included freshwater animals of various sorts, but the vertebrate type began to flourish and increase more abundantly with the appearance of creatures with jaws in the late Silurian. From this stage onwards we have to follow the parallel history of numerous orders and families, as the vertebrate plan of structure became adapted for various habitats. It seems likely that the development of a biting mouth very greatly increased the range of possibilities of vertebrate life. The most obvious use of a mouth is for attacking other animals, allowing a predacious habit; but it may also have been used to collect plant food from all sorts of situations where it would not be available to the microphagous or sucking Agnatha. Probably the mouth was also early used for defence, and in this way influenced the whole bodily organization, making unnecessary the heavy armature so characteristic of many early vertebrates. Modern research has shown very strikingly how the armament has become progressively reduced along various lines of fish evolution. Older ideas of comparative anatomy regarded the 'cartilage fishes' as showing a primitive stage, preceding the appearance of bone. We now realize that this is the opposite of the truth and that the dogfish and its relatives represent a higher type, able to defend themselves by mobility, by biting, and by efficient sensory and nervous organization. Heavy defensive armament is a primitive form of protection for animals, as for man.

Besides its use in feeding and defence, the mouth can also be used as a means of 'handling' the environment, for instance in the nest-building activities of many fishes. Indeed, it is difficult for us to realize the utility of the jaws for an animal not provided with any other means of seizing hold of objects.

The development of the mouth to a point at which it could be used in these varied ways was, therefore, a very important stage in evolution. Recognition of the Gnathostomata as a separate group of animals is far more than a matter of classificatory convenience, it marks the achievement of the possibility of life in a greatly increased range of environments.

5.2. *The skull and branchial arches*

Morphological analysis now enables us to give some account of the way in which this biting mouth was produced, by modification of one or more of the gill-slits. The main differences that separate the gnathostome from cyclostome vertebrates are therefore in the head and its skeleton. Although the modern elasmobranchs show the skull and jaws in a modified and reduced condition, they provide by their simplicity a good starting-point for discussion. The 'skull' of a dogfish consists of a series of cartilaginous boxes surrounding the brain and sense-organs (Fig. 97). The nasal capsules, orbital ridges, and auditory capsules are largely fused with the main cranium, producing a single continuous structure, the chondrocranium. It is interesting to consider how this structure has arisen during the process of cephalization.

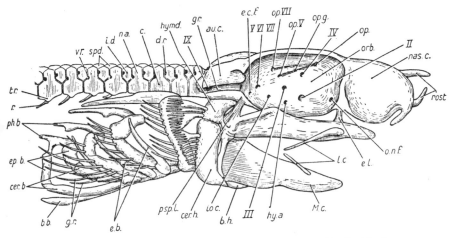

FIG. 97. Skull and branchial arches of the dogfish (*Scyliorhinus*).

au.c. auditory capsule; *b.b.* basibranchial; *b.h.* basihyal; *c.* centrum; *cer.b.* ceratobranchials; *cer.h.* ceratohyal; *d.r.* foramen for dorsal root; *e.b.* extrabranchials; *e.c.f.* external carotid foramen; *e.l.* ethmoid ligament; *ep.b.* epibranchials; *gr.* groove for anterior cardinal sinus; *g.r.* gill rays; *hy.a.* foramen for hyoid artery; *hymd.* hyomandibula; *i.d.* interdorsal; *io.c.* interorbital canal; *l.c.* labial cartilages; *M.c.* Meckel's cartilage; *na.* neural arch; *nas.c.* nasal capsule; *o.n.f.* orbito-nasal foramen; *op.* foramen for ophthalmic nerve; *op.g.* groove for *op.V.*; *op.V*, *op.VII* ophthalmic branches of *V* and *VII*; *orb.* orbit; *ph.b.* pharyngobranchials; *p.sp.l.* prespiracular ligament; *r.* rib; *rost.* rostral cartilages; *spd.* supradorsals; *tr.* transverse process; *vr.* foramen for ventral root; *II–IX*, foramina for cranial nerves. (After Borradaile.)

Presumably parts of it represent in some way the modified sclerotomes of trunk regions. We shall see presently that there is strong evidence that the head has arisen by modification of a segmental arrangement such as is seen in the trunk; the processes that build the skull must therefore be related in some way to those of the vertebrae. The first rudiment of the skull in the embryo consists of two pairs of cartilaginous rods, the parachordals and trabeculae (Fig. 98). The former lie on either side of the notochord, the trabeculae in front of the notochord. These first rods fuse up to make a continuous plate; from this grow sides and roof, completing the cartilaginous neurocranium around the brain. Meanwhile cartilaginous capsules form around the nose, eyes, and ears, and become joined to the neurocranium. Posteriorly, behind the auditory capsules, the cranium is completed by the addition of a number of segmented elements, evidently modified vertebrae.

The problem is, therefore, to determine the nature of the pro-otic part of the skull. Before we can settle this we must consider the visceral or branchial arches. These are pairs of rods of cartilage developed in the walls of the mouth and pharynx, between the gill-slits. In the dogfish each typical branchial arch (Fig. 97) consists of a series of four pieces, the pharyngo-, epi-, cerato-, and hypo-branchials. Ventrally some of the arches join a median basibranchial plate. These rods lie in the pharynx wall and on their outer sides carry a series of

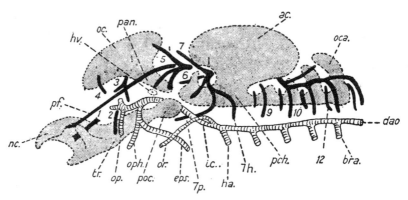

Fig. 98. Diagram of skull of selachian embryo before fusion of the main cartilages; cranial nerves black, numbered; arteries cross-lined.

ac. auditory capsule; *bra.* epibranchial; *dao.* dorsal aorta; *eps.* efferent pseudobranchial; *ha.* efferent hyoid; *hv.* hypophysial vein; *i.c.* internal carotid; *nc.* nasal cartilage; *oc.* orbital cartilage; *oca.* occipital arch; *op.* optic; *oph.* ophthalmic; *or.* orbital; *pan.* pila antotica; *pf.* profundus nerve; *pch.* parachordal; *poc.* polar cartilage; *tr.* trabecula. (From Goodrich.)

projecting rods, the branchial rays and extrabranchial cartilages, whose function is to support the lamellae of the gills.

There are five such branchial arches, differing only slightly from each other. In front of these lie two arches, the hyoid and mandibular, which, though modified, are obviously of the same series. The hyoid the more nearly resembles a typical branchial arch. Its most dorsal element, the hyomandibular cartilage, is a thick rod attached dorsally to the skull by ligaments and at its lower end forming the support for the hind end of the jaw. It apparently corresponds to the epibranchials. The more ventral elements, cerato- and basihyal, resemble the corresponding members of more posterior arches. The jaws themselves (mandibular arches) depart more widely from the form of a typical branchial arch, but the two thick rods of which each is composed, the upper palato-pterygo-quadrate bar and the lower Meckel's cartilage, are recognizably members of the branchial series. Looking at the whole apparatus with a thought to the embryological processes which have produced it, with as it were a manufacturer's eye, we can see at once that the jaws and hyoid arch have been produced by a modification of the processes that make the branchial arches.

The function of the branchial arches is not merely to support the gills but to allow the movements of the pharynx wall by which the respiratory current of water is produced. It is for this reason that the jointed system of rods is present. The respiratory movements consist in a lowering of the floor of the mouth by means of the hypoglossal muscles, with at the same time an expansion of the walls of the pharynx. This causes an inrush of water through the mouth, which is then closed and the floor raised, forcing the water out through the gill-slits. The whole movement is worked by the 'visceral' (lateral plate) muscles of the pharynx wall, innervated by the glossopharyngeal and vagus nerves, in co-operation with the myotomal hypoglossal muscles, innervated by the hypoglossal nerve (p. 152).

5.3. *The jaws*

Study of the serial relationship of the jaws and branchial arches gives us an understanding of the course of evolution of the mouth. We may suppose that the ancestors of the gnathostomes possessed a nearly terminal mouth, either on the front end of the body or on the ventral surface. The pharynx was pierced by a series of gill-slits, beginning shortly behind the mouth and separated by arches, each containing a set of cartilaginous bars (Fig. 97). There is some evidence that this condition persisted in the cephalaspids (p. 121), where there is found to be a series of ten pairs of gill-slits, beginning far forward on either side of the mouth. The muscles moving the more anterior parts of the pharynx wall and the anterior arches could be called into play to help in the collection of food. In this way the mouth came to be used for prehension, and the grasping jaws of the gnathostomes appeared as the more anterior arches became modified to allow more efficient seizing, and the skin over them was modified to form the teeth. The mouth probably shifted backwards during this process and its lateral edges joined the first gill-slit. The rods supporting the posterior wall of that slit thus became bent over into the characteristic position of the vertebrate jaws.

There is some uncertainty as to the means of support of the jaws in the earlier stages of their evolution. The upper end of the mandibular arch would, of course, be attached to the axial skeleton (cranium), and the front end of the palato-pterygo-quadrate bar is so attached in the dogfish by the ethmo-palatine 'ligament'. In most elasmobranchs the hind end of the upper jaw is not fixed to the cranium but is slung from the latter by the hyomandibula and by a prespiracular ligament. This means of support, known as hyostylic, was for long supposed to have been the original one. But the earliest gnathostomes (the acanthodians) do not have this arrangement (p. 181), indeed, their hyoid arch is a typical branchial arch, not modified to support the jaw. In the primitive condition one would not expect the hyoid arch to have any connexion with the mandibular. In the acanthodians the jaw is supported by direct attachments to the cranium at its hind as well as front end, a condition known as autostylic.

FIG. 99. Diagrams to show the condition of the visceral arches and jaws in early vertebrates.

A. cephalaspid; *B.* acanthodian; *C.* elasmobranch; *ac.* auditory capsule; *br.a.* 1, 3, 4 branchial arches; *c.n.c.* nerve-cord; *e.* eye; *gs.l.* first gill-slit; *h.* hypophysis; *ha.* hyomandibular arch; *ma.* mandibular arch; *m.* mouth; *pma.* premandibular arch; *sp.* spiracle; *V1,* profundus nerve; *V2, 3,* trigeminal nerve; *VII,* facial; *IX,* glossopharyngeal; *X,* vagus. (From Westoll.)

The early elasmobranchs themselves do not have a hyostylic jaw support, but an arrangement in which the upper jaw is both attached to the cranium and also supported by the hyomandibula. This amphistylic condition persists to-day in the shark *Hexanchus.* Apparently the jaws, which at first swung from the skull, later became fixed at the hind end to the hyoid, and this finally became the only means of support posteriorly. The advantage of this last arrangement is presumably that it allows a very wide gape for swallowing the prey whole. As the sharks sought to eat larger and larger fishes, those in which the hind end of the upper jaw was less firmly fixed to the skull were the more successful and so the hyostylic condition was achieved.

If this theory of the origin of the jaws is correct we may expect to find some trace of a cartilaginous support for the side wall of the pharynx in front of the original first gill-slit, a premandibular visceral arch. There are very strong grounds for believing that this is repre-

sented by the trabeculae cranii, the rods lying on each side in front of
the parachordals and contributing to the floor of the skull (Fig. 99).
Many points indicate that these rods are not part of the axial skeleton.
The main axis of the body presumably ends at the front end of the
notochord, that is to say, at the level of the
front ends of the parachordals. Indeed there
is much confirmatory evidence to show that
this level represents the end of the segmented
part of the body, everything in front of this
level being as it were pushed forward from
above or below. The trabeculae have exactly
the relations to the most anterior nerves and
blood-vessels that would be expected of
visceral arches. A most convincing confirma-
tion of the theory comes from the discovery
that the cartilage of the visceral arches is
formed by material streaming down from the
neural crest, that is to say, from ectoderm.
The neural crest cells contain a characteristic
pigment, which is not found in the meso-
blastic cells; the cells of the visceral arches
show this pigment (Fig. 100)—and so do
those of the trabeculae. More convincing
still, if the neural crest be removed the
embryo develops without visceral arches, *and
also without the anterior part of the trabeculae.*

FIG. 100. Transverse section
of developing axolotl to show
formation of Meckel's cartilage
from neural crest. Derivatives
of the ectoderm contain pigment (small granules), those of
the mesoderm and endoderm
have large yolk granules.

e.m. ectomesenchyme; *en.* endoderm; *h.b.* hind-brain; *M.c.* Meckel's cartilage; *m.s.* mesodermal
somite; *n.c.* neural crest; *v.m.*
visceral muscle. (After deBeer.)

The view that the branchial arches, hyoid,
jaws, and trabeculae all constitute a single
series may seem fantastic at first, but it is
important to realize the very strong ground
on which it stands, since it gives us our clue
to the understanding of the whole organization of the vertebrate head. The resem-
blance between the cartilages of the jaws and arches goes far by
itself to prove the thesis. It is obvious by inspection that the cartilages are all formed by modifications of the same process (Fig. 97).
What matters for our understanding is to realize that these structures of the head are the result of the working of a repetitive or
rhythmic process, appropriately modified at each level.

6. Segmentation of the vertebrate head

The rhythmicity or metamerism that we have seen in the study of the cartilages can be traced throughout the structure of the head. Although in higher vertebrates the head appears as a very distinct structure, separated from the body by a neck, yet there is every reason to think that it has arrived at that state by gradual modification of the anterior members of an originally complete metameric series. The activities which have led to the modification of the front end of the body in this way are those of the jaws, the receptor-organs, and the brain. The organs connected with these activities have become developed at the front end of the body, disturbing the original metamerism and producing what zoologists conveniently if pretentiously call cephalization.

The fundamental segmentation of the head is not very easily apparent to superficial observation; the working out of its details is an excellent exercise in morphological understanding. Recognition of the segmental value of the various structures also makes them the more easily remembered. For instance, the nerves found in the head have been named and numbered for centuries by anatomists in an arbitrary series:

I. Olfactorius
II. Opticus
III. Oculomotorius
IV. Trochlearis (patheticus)
V. Trigeminus
VI. Abducens
VII. Facialis
VIII. Acusticus
IX. Glossopharyngeus
X. Vagus
XI. Accessorius
XII. Hypoglossus

Morphological study has shown that these nerves are not isolated structures, each developed independently, but that they represent a regular series of segmental dorsal and ventral roots of the head somites. The satisfaction and simplification given by this generalization is one of the clearest advantages of morphological insight. Only a savage would wish to continue to memorize an arbitrary series when given the opportunity of understanding its underlying rhythmicity.

More important still, such understanding of the morphology of a structure shows us how to look for the morphogenetic processes that produce it; such knowledge of how organs are made is an essential step in mending or remaking them.

The idea of the essential similarity of structure of the head and trunk was early developed by Goethe, who tried to show the mammalian skull to be composed of a series of modified vertebrae. Unfortunately this view cannot be maintained in detail and the theory was brought to ridicule by T. H. Huxley and others. As we have seen, the segmental value of the skull floor and sides is not at all easy to determine; the parachordals arise as a pair of unsegmented rods on either side of the notochord.

7. The pro-otic somites and eye-muscles

Ideas about the segmentation of the head were first correctly formulated by F. Balfour. In his studies of the development of elasmobranchs (1875) he showed that in the region of the head in front of the auditory capsule three myotomes, the pro-otic somites, can be recognized during development (Fig. 101). The auditory sac, pushing inwards and becoming surrounded by cartilage, then breaks the series of myotomes, so that several are missing in the adult, though the series is complete in the embryo.

If this analysis is correct we should be able to recognize that the nerves of the head belong to a series of dorsal and ventral roots, similar to that in the trunk, the ventral roots being those for the myotomes and the dorsal roots, running between the myotomes, carrying sensory fibres for the segment and motor-fibres for any non-myotomal musculature present (p. 147). In the spinal region the dorsal and ventral roots join, but this is not the primitive condition (witness *Amphioxus* and the lampreys), and in the head region the earlier state of affairs is retained, the dorsal and ventral roots remain separate. Presumably the arrangement we find in the head to-day was laid down in the very early times, in the Silurian period or earlier, when the dorsal and ventral roots were still separate. The head, in spite of its specializations, preserves for us a relic of that ancient condition.

There has been some controversy as to whether there is a strict relationship between the segmental arrangement of the myotomes and nerves (the myomeric or mesomeric segmentation) and that of the gill-slits (sometimes known as branchiomeric). Since the lateral plate mesoderm is not segmented there is no necessary reason for any close relationship. In tunicates and *Amphioxus* the gill-slit repetition may occur much more frequently than that of myotomes. However, in the craniates, where the number of gill-slits is never very large and is usually limited to five, plus the spiracle and one slit incorporated in the mouth, there is reason to believe that there is a slit corresponding to each myotomal segment. The dorsal roots send regular segmental

Fig. 101. Diagram of the segmentation of the head of a dogfish.

cr. limit of neurocranium; *vr.* limit of visceral arch skeleton; *a.* auditory nerve; *aa.1,* pre-occipital arch; *aa.2,* occipital arch; *ab.* abducens nerve; *ac.* auditory capsule; *ah.* anterior head cavity; *c.* coelom; *f.* facial nerve; *gl.* glossopharyngeal nerve; *ha.* hyoid arch; *hm.* hypoglossal muscles; *hy.* hypoglossal nerve; *la.* pila antotica; *m.* mouth; *m.2–6,* myomere 2–6; *ma.* mandibular arch; *mb.* muscle-bud; *nc.* nasal capsule; *om.* oculomotor nerve; *prf.* profundus nerve; *scl.* sclerotome of segment 10; *sp.1–2,* ganglion of spinal nerve 1–2; *t.* trochlear nerve; *tr.* trigeminal nerve; *v.* vagus nerve; *vgl.* vestigial ganglion of segment 7; *vc.* ventral coelom; *vr.* ventral root of segment 6. (From Goodrich.)

branches to the gill-slits, and the glossopharyngeal nerve gives a complete picture of the arrangement of such a branchial nerve. It shows a small pre-trematic branch in front of the slit, a larger post-trematic branch behind it, and a pharyngeal branch to the wall of the pharynx. The pre-trematic branch usually contains mostly sensory fibres from the skin, the pharyngeal branch visceral sensory fibres, including those from taste buds. The post-trematic branch contains both motor and sensory fibres. In addition to these more ventral branches the branchial nerves also usually provide dorsal rami to the skin of the back.

The three pro-otic somites become completely taken up in the formation of the extrinsic muscles of the eye. There are six of these muscles, arranged similarly in all gnathostome vertebrates. The four recti roll the eye straight upwards, downwards, forwards, or backwards, and the two obliques, lying farther forward, turn it, as their name suggests, upward or downward and forward (Fig. 102). Of these muscles the superior, anterior, and inferior rectus and inferior oblique are all derived from the first myotome and are innervated by the oculomotor (third cranial) nerve. The superior oblique, innervated by the trochlear nerve (fourth cranial), is the derivative of the second and the posterior rectus (external rectus of man), innervated by the abducens (sixth cranial), of the third somite. These three nerves are evidently the ventral roots of the three pro-otic somites. This arrangement is an extremely ancient and constant one. At some very early stage of vertebrate evolution all the myotomal musculature of the front part of the head became devoted to the movement of the eyes. This change occurred so long ago that it is not possible to reconstruct the stages by which the muscles originally forming part of the swimming series became attached to a cup-like outgrowth from the brain. It is interesting that in lampreys myotomal muscles are attached to the cornea (p. 106).

Most of the rest of the musculature of the head, including that of jaws and branchial arches, is derived from the somatopleure wall of the coelom and is therefore lateral plate or visceral musculature. This lateral plate muscle is indeed better developed in the head than in the trunk, where, as we have seen, all of the muscles, even of the more ventral parts of the body, are formed by downward tongues from the myotomes. The lateral plate origin of the jaw-muscles at once gives us the clue to the nature of some more of the cranial nerves, the fifth, seventh, ninth, and tenth. These nerves all carry ganglia containing the cell bodies of sensory fibres and these are comparable to the spinal dorsal root ganglia. But the nerves also transmit motor-fibres to the muscles of the jaws and branchial arches. They are in fact mixed roots, just as we have seen that the primitive dorsal roots should be, carrying the sensory fibres for the segment and motor-fibres for the non-myotomal muscles.

8. The cranial nerves of elasmobranchs

These nerves are more easily studied in elasmobranchs than in any other vertebrates, because of the relatively soft and transparent cartilage through which they run. We may therefore take this opportunity to examine the whole series of cranial nerves in some detail in the dogfish, beginning with the oculomotor nerve, the first ventral root. Examination after removal of the brain will show quite clearly in any vertebrate, including man, that this nerve arises from the ventral surface, at the level of the hind end of the midbrain (optic lobes). This is not true of the trochlear or pathetic nerve, which

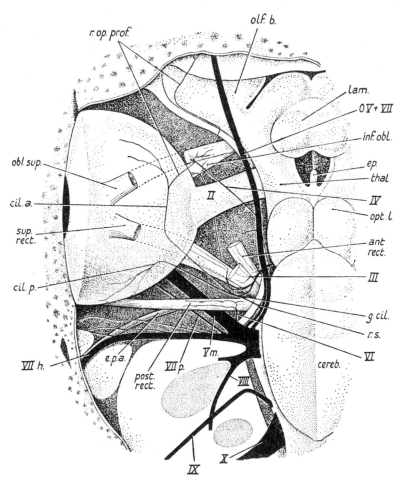

FIG. 102. Orbit of the dogfish.

ant.rect. anterior rectus; *cereb.* cerebellum; *cil.a.*, *cil.p.* anterior and posterior ciliary nerves; *epa.* efferent pseudobranchial artery; *ep.* epiphysis; *g.cil.* ciliary ganglion; *inf.obl.* inferior oblique; *lam.* lamina terminalis of cerebrum; *O.V.* and *VII*, superficial ophthalmic branch of trigeminal and facial; *obl.sup.* superior oblique; *olf.b.* olfactory bulb; *opt.l.* optic lobe; *post.rect.* posterior rectus; *r.op.prof.* ramus ophthalmicus profundus of trigeminal; *rs.* sensory root of ciliary ganglion; *sup. rect.* superior rectus; *thal.* thalamus; *II* to *X*, cranial nerves. (After Young, *Quart. J. Micr. Sci.* 75.)

emerges from the dorso-lateral surface of the brain but nevertheless is the ventral root of the second segment. Its cells of origin lie close behind those of the oculomotor nerve, in the ventral part of the brain. The reason for the dorsal emergence is that the muscle lies dorsally and the nerve has been modified so as to reach its muscle by running partly within the tissues of the brain. The third ventral root (abducens), which is very short, is clearly ventral.

In looking for the dorsal roots that correspond to these three segments we have to examine the trigeminal, facial, and auditory nerves. The trigeminal of the dogfish, like that of man, has ophthalmic, maxillary, and mandibular branches (Fig. 102). The first of these is a sensory nerve carrying fibres for the skin sensation from the snout. The maxillary branch supplies sensory fibres to the upper jaw, whereas the mandibular is a mixed nerve to the skin and muscles of the lower jaw. Besides these main branches there is also a small but important sensory branch from the trigeminal to the eyeball (Fig. 102). This joins a motor root from the oculomotor nerve where the latter swells slightly to form a ciliary ganglion. Two ciliary nerves then carry motor and sensory fibres to the eyeball. In some specimens a branch of the more anterior ciliary nerve leaves the eyeball anteriorly, runs between the oblique muscles, and out of the orbit again to end in the skin of the snout (Fig. 102). Though this branch is small and inconstant in the dogfish, its course corresponds exactly with that of a much larger nerve in the related shark *Mustelus* and in skates and rays. In these animals there are *two* ophthalmic branches of the trigeminal nerve; one, having a course similar to that of the main nerve in the dogfish, is the ramus ophthalmicus superficialis; the second, the ramus ophthalmicus profundus, runs across within the orbit, gives off the long ciliary nerve to the eyeball, passes between the oblique muscles, and leaves the orbit for the skin of the snout. In higher vertebrates the ophthalmic branch apparently corresponds to the ramus ophthalmicus superficialis of the elasmobranchs, but the profundus is always represented by the long ciliary nerve, which runs to the eyeball.

The relations of these nerves to other structures shows that the so-called trigeminal nerve really includes the dorsal roots of two segments combined. The profundus can be traced back in development to a nerve that is obviously the dorsal root of the first somite, of which the oculomotor nerve is the ventral root. Indeed it may be noticed that the profundus and oculomotor are nerves that partly join, at the ciliary ganglion. The ramus ophthalmicus profundus and the oculomotor nerve thus constitute the dorsal and ventral roots of the first or pre-mandibular somite, whose corresponding branchial arch is presumably the trabecula cranii (p. 143). The dorsal root shows no sign of the full structure of a branchial nerve, presumably because there is no gill-slit. The profundus represents only the dorsal branch of a typical branchial nerve, innervating the skin.

The ramus ophthalmicus superficialis, the maxillary and mandibular branches together constitute the dorsal root of the second pro-otic somite, whose ventral root is the trochlear nerve. The corresponding gill arch is the mandibular (palato-pterygo-quadrate bar and Meckel's cartilage) and the gill-slit is that which we have suggested as incorporated with the edge of the mouth. The trigeminal nerve shows considerable similarity to a branchial nerve, its maxillary branch represents the pre-trematic and the mandibular the post-trematic ramus, while the ophthalmicus superficialis is the dorsal branch to the skin. There is no pharyngeal branch and the maxillary branch differs in composition from a typical pre-trematic branch, but such divergences from the main plan might be expected and can be easily accounted for.

The dorsal root of the third segment, whose ventral root is the abducens, includes the whole of the facial and also the auditory nerve. The facial is a large mixed nerve in the dogfish. Its ophthalmic branch runs to the snout, carrying mainly fibres for the organs of the lateral line system which lie there. A large buccal branch supplies sensory fibres to the mouth; a small prespiracular branch carries sensory fibres from the skin in front of the spiracle, and the main portion of the nerve continues behind the spiracle as the hyomandibular nerve, dividing up into motor branches for muscles of the hyoid arch and sensory ones for the skin of that region.

This nerve is obviously the branchial nerve to the spiracle; we can safely say that the facial and abducens are the dorsal and ventral roots of the third or hyoid segment. The auditory nerve is included as part of the dorsal root of the third somite because the auditory sac is formed by sinking in of a portion of the ectoderm within the territory of the facial nerve. The labyrinth still communicates with the surface of the head in the adult dogfish by a canal, the aquaeductus vestibuli. The nerve that innervates the auditory sac, whatever complexities it may acquire, is to be regarded morphologically as a portion of the dorsal root of the segment in which it occurs, and it can be seen to develop as such.

The segmental nature of the structures in the pro-otic region can therefore be made out without very serious difficulty. The disturbance introduced by the auditory capsule makes the segmental arrangement of the more posterior region of the head somewhat confused. The series of dorsal roots is uninterrupted; the ninth (glossopharyngeal) nerve is the dorsal root of the fourth segment of the series and runs out through the cartilage of the auditory capsule.

The dorsal roots of the succeeding segments are then fused to form that very puzzling nerve the vagus. The branches it sends to the gills are clearly typical branchial nerves, but why should they all come off together from the medulla oblongata, and if there is any advantage in this union, why is the ninth nerve not also so incorporated? Above all, why does the vagus send two branches far outside the segments of its origin, the lateral line branch carrying fibres to the organs right to the tip of the tail and the visceral branch fibres to the heart, stomach, and probably small intestine?

Evidently these 'wanderings', from which the vagus gets its name, began very long ago. The nerve reaches as far back in cyclostomes as in any other vertebrates. It is easy to understand that if visceral functions are to be directed from the medulla oblongata there is an advantage in having sensory impulses sent direct to that region of the brain and motor impulses sent out direct to the viscera. It may be that these advantages allowed the centralization of these visceral functions, while the need for serial contraction of the swimming muscles led to the retention of the segmental arrangement of the spinal cord. It is an interesting thought that but for the swimming habits of our ancestors our nervous system might by now consist of a central ganglion with nerves passing from it direct to all the organs. Indeed we are tending in that direction, as the spinal cord shortens and becomes more and more nearly a simple pathway between the brain and the periphery.

However this may be, the vagus is certainly a nerve compounded of the dorsal roots of several segments and it is a mixed nerve, containing both receptor and motor-fibres. Some of the more posterior rootlets of this series are separated off in higher animals (not the dogfish) to form the eleventh cranial nerve, the accessorius or spinal accessory, which in mammals sends motor-fibres to certain muscles of the neck, the sternomastoid, and part of the trapezius. Its motor nature has led some to suppose that this nerve is a ventral root, but these muscles are derived from lateral plate musculature and the accessorius represents the motor portion of the hinder dorsal roots of the vagus series. Its dorsal attachment to the medulla oblongata suggests that it is not a ventral root and the cells of origin of its fibres are not strictly part of the somatic motor column of cells, which gives rise to the ventral roots.

The ventral roots of this post-otic region have become very much reduced. Several myotomes are always missing completely, so that there are no ventral roots corresponding to the glossopharyngeal and first three or four vagal segments. The more anterior of the surviving post-otic somites are to be found not in the dorsal region but ventrally, as the hypoglossal musculature of the tongue. The muscle-buds have grown round into this portion behind the gill-slits, and the nerve (hypoglossal) which innervates them represents the ventral roots of the more posterior segments of the vagus–accessorius series (Fig. 106). The origin of this nerve from the floor of the medulla is a clear sign that it is a ventral root.

Thus the entire series of cranial nerves is:

Segment	Arch	Dorsal root	Ventral root
Pre-mandibular	Trabecula	R. op. profundus V	Oculomotorius III
Mandibular	Palato - pterygo - quad - rate bar and Meckel's cartilage	Rr. op. superficialis, maxillaris, and mandibularis V	Trochlearis IV
Hyoid	Hyoid	Facialis VII Acusticus VIII	Abducens VI
1st Branchial	1st Branchial	Glossopharyngeus IX	(absent)
2nd Branchial	2nd Branchial ⎫	Vagus X	
3rd Branchial	3rd Branchial ⎪	+	Hypoglossus XII
4th Branchial	4th Branchial ⎬	Accessorius XI	
5th Branchial	5th Branchial ⎭		

We can have no doubt that the connexions between the central nervous system and the periphery are arranged in the head, as in the spinal region, on the plan of a series of dorsal and ventral roots. The fundamental rhythmicity of the nerves is quite clear, though its manifestation has been obscured by the development of the jaws and special sense-organs. The detection of this fundamental plan, besides immensely simplifying our outlook on the complicated structure of the head, gives us a hope of achieving a real understanding of the processes by which the head has been built up and the changes in these processes that have constituted its evolution.

Two cranial nerves have not yet been considered, the first, olfactory, and second, optic. Our thesis is that all connexions between centre and periphery are made by means of a segmental series of dorsal and ventral roots and therefore these nerves, too, should be fitted into the series. No embryological or other studies have enabled this to be done and the reason in the case of the optic nerve is quite clear. It is not morphologically a peripheral nerve at all. The eye is formed as a vesicle attached to the brain; the optic 'nerve' therefore develops as a bundle of fibres joining two portions of the central nervous system; in fact it is now usually called the optic tract, not the optic nerve.

This reasoning will not apply to that very peculiar and interesting structure the olfactory nerve. This is unique among all craniate nerves in consisting of bundles of fibres whose cell bodies lie *at the periphery*. The cells of the olfactory epithelium, like the sensory cells in invertebrates and some of those of *Amphioxus*, are neurosensory cells, that is to say, their inner ends are prolonged to make the actual nerve-fibres that pass into the brain. This fact does not by itself solve the problem of fitting the nerve into the series of dorsal and ventral roots, but it reminds us that the nerve is very ancient, and suggests that it does not fall into the rhythm of the rest of the series because it precedes the other cranial nerves either in time or space, or perhaps even both. The olfactory nerve may have existed before any segmental structure appeared, possibly as the nerve of sense-organs on the front end of the ciliated larva which we suppose gave rise to our stock (p. 55). Alternatively we can say that the olfactory nerve is as it is because it lies in front of the region over which the segmenting process operates; it is, as it were, 'prostomial'. If we wish we can hold both these views together.

There are one or two other exceptions to the rhythmic arrangement of nerves, perhaps more difficult to account for than the first and second cranial nerves. If all connexions between centre and periphery are made by dorsal and ventral roots what is the status of the fibres that run down the infundibular stalk to reach the cells of the pituitary body? This glandular tissue, derived from the epithelium of the hypophysial folding of the roof of the mouth, is undoubtedly a peripheral organ. Why then does it receive its nerve-fibres direct from the brain? Presumably we must say that the pituitary, like the nose, is prostomial, lying in front of the segmental region, and this is reasonable enough from its position.

A still more puzzling exception is the nervus terminalis, a small bundle of fibres that leaves the front end of the diencephalon and runs forward across the olfactory capsule. It is present in many vertebrates from elasmobranchs to man, but its exact connexions, either central or peripheral, are still unknown and its significance remains a mystery.

A further puzzle of some importance which may be mentioned here is the course of the proprioceptor fibres for those muscles which are supplied purely by ventral roots. The eye-muscles contain proprioceptor organs and Sherrington and others have shown that the afferent fibres connected with these run to the brain through the third, fourth, and sixth nerves, that is to say, through ventral roots. Similarly it has been shown that there are afferent fibres in the hypoglossal nerves in mammals. To pursue this question farther would lead us into discussion of the factors that control the making of connexions within the nervous system. Here we are concerned only with analysis of the plan that produces the main outlines of the structures in the head, a plan which, with all its modifications, is essentially segmental.

9. The gut of elasmobranchs

The digestive system of sharks shows several changes from the plan

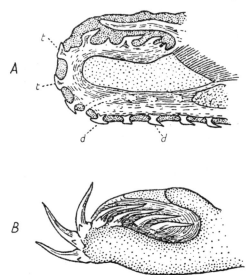

FIG. 103. Sections through the jaws of A, dogfish (*Scyliorhinus*), and B, sand-shark (*Odontaspis*), showing the transitions between dermal denticles (*d*) and teeth (*t*). (From Norman, partly after Gegenbaur.)

found in lampreys, especially the presence of a true stomach, characteristic of all gnathostomes. Apparently little or no digestion goes on in the mouth and pharynx. The teeth, consisting of rows of backwardly directed denticles (Fig. 103), serve rather to prevent the escape of the prey than to bite. If the food needs subdivision this is probably achieved by tearing. The teeth are carried on special folds of skin lining the jaws and are continually being replaced as they are worn away on the edge. The replacement of milk by permanent teeth in mammals is a relic of such serial replacement in a fish. Teeth are often found attached to the branchial cartilages and these also serve to prevent the escape of prey. The basihyal supports a short non-protrusible tongue.

The wall of the pharynx is lined by a stratified type of epithelium on to which numerous mucus glands open. This mucus serves to assist the passage of the food, but probably has no strictly digestive function, though the salivary glands of higher vertebrates no doubt originate from a modification of these mucus glands.

The pharynx narrows to an oesophagus with thick muscular walls, leading without sharp transition to the stomach. We have seen that in cyclostomes the oesophagus opens directly into that region of the gut which receives the bile and pancreatic secretion. The stomach, which we now meet for the first time, has probably been formed as a special portion of the oesophagus. Barrington suggests that it served originally as a receptacle for the large pieces of food, or even whole fishes, swallowed by a carnivore. The mucus glands became modified to produce acid, since this prevents bacterial decay. Finally, an enzyme, pepsin, was evolved able to digest proteins in acid solution. In the dogfish this condition has been fully established and the stomach has essentially the structure and functions found in all higher vertebrates. It is, however, peculiar in being divided into two parts, a descending cardiac and ascending pyloric limb, the significance of the division being unknown.

The region where the stomach joins the intestine is guarded by a powerful pyloric sphincter, immediately beyond which open the bile and pancreatic ducts. The liver is a large two-lobed organ; little is known of the details of its function in fishes but we may suppose them to be similar to those of higher forms, that is to say, to receive the food as it passes in the hepatic portal blood from the gut, and to perform the necessary chemical operations. It no doubt serves as a storage organ and probably also plays a part in destruction of red blood corpuscles. Bile is carried away to a gall-bladder, from which a bile-duct leads to open at the front end of the spiral intestine.

The pancreas, hardly recognizable as a distinct organ in the lamprey, forms in the dogfish an elongated white body between the stomach and intestine. Its duct enters the intestine shortly below the pylorus. The 'small' intestine of elasmobranchs is of a very peculiar form, being short but with surface greatly increased by the presence of a spiral ridge or 'valve'. Absorption presumably takes place wholly in this organ, for the remaining length of gut consists only of a short rectum, to which is attached an organ of unknown function, the rectal gland.

10. The circulatory system

The heart and blood vascular system of elasmobranchs is built on the lines which we have already seen in lampreys, and can therefore be dealt with briefly. The heart consists of a single series of three main chambers, sinus venosus, auricle, and ventricle, all of which are muscular, and there is also a muscular base to the ventral aorta, the conus arteriosus, provided with valves (Fig. 104). The beat originates in the sinus, where there is a very abundant plexus of nerves, connected with the cardiac branch of the vagus (Fig. 106). The action of this nerve, like vagal cardiac branches in all animals, is to slow the

FIG. 104. Diagram of the branchial circulation of an elasmobranch fish.

a.a. median anterior prolongation of aorta; *a.c.* anterior carotid; *afa.* efferent vessel of spiracular gill (pseudobranch); *a.ef.* efferent vessel from last hemibranch; *a.f.* anterior efferent vessel; *a.f.*[2-6], five afferent vessels from ventral aorta; *af.a.* afferent artery of spiracular gill; *c.* conus leading to ventral aorta; *cl.* coeliac artery; *d.* ductus Cuvieri; *d.a.* dorsal aorta; *ef.* epibranchial artery; *h.a.* hyoid efferent vessel; *hp.* hepatic veins; *ht.* heart; *p.c.* posterior carotid; *p.ef.* posterior efferent vessel; *s.* spiracle; *v.a.* ventral artery; I–V, branchial slits.
(From Goodrich, *Vertebrata*, A. & C. Black, Ltd., after Parker.)

heart, and there is no sign of any branch from the sympathetic, comparable to the accelerator nerve of higher forms.

The four afferent branchial arteries carry blood to the gill lamellae, whence it is collected by a system of four efferents and connecting vessels into a median dorsal aorta, carrying blood to all parts of the body. Oxygenated blood is supplied to the head from three sources. (1) From the top of the first gill a carotid artery leaves the efferent branchial and runs forwards and towards the midline: it then divides into an external carotid to the upper jaw and internal carotid to the brain. (2) The dorsal aorta divides at its front end into branches, which join the carotids before their division. (3) From the vessel which collects blood from the first gill arises a hyoidean artery, carrying oxygenated blood to the pseudobranch, a leaf-like structure in the spiracle, presumably with some receptor function. From here the hyoidean artery runs on as the efferent pseudobranchial (Fig. 102) across the floor of the orbit to join the internal carotid within the brain-case.

The pressure in the dorsal aorta is of course lowered by the passage of the blood through the gills, and presumably for this reason the venous return of the fishes is ensured by a system of very large sinuses. The return of blood to the heart is perhaps also assisted by a suction process, the pericardium being almost completely enclosed in a cartilaginous framework by the basibranchial plate above and pectoral girdle below it. There is a passage, the pericardio-peritoneal canal, leading from the pericardium to the abdominal coelom and the hinder end of this is very narrow. Possibly it operates as a valve, allowing fluid to pass backwards but not forwards and thus maintain the negative pressure on the veins.

A caudal sinus from the tail opens into a renal portal system above the kidneys. From the latter, and from the muscles of the back, blood is collected into the pair of very large posterior cardinal sinuses, lying on the dorsal wall of the abdomen. Above the heart these receive the openings of other large sinuses, such as the anterior cardinal sinus, running above the gills and collecting blood from the head by way of an orbital sinus, and the jugular, lateral cardinal, subclavian, and other sinuses from the body wall. Blood then passes round the oesophagus in the ductus Cuvieri into the sinus venosus, where hepatic sinuses also open.

Since the resistance offered by a vessel to flow within it decreases with approximately the fourth power of the diameter, we may suppose that the presence of these large vessels substantially assists in the maintenance of a return pressure to the heart, necessary for proper functioning. The heart-muscles, like any others, require antagonists; they can contract in one direction only, and each chamber therefore needs to be actively dilated. It will be noted that the fish heart consists of a series of three muscular chambers, presumably because the low venous pressure is able to dilate only a chamber with very thin walls, such as the sinus venosus. Contraction of the sinus then inflates the auricle, and the auricle inflates the ventricle, which thus constitutes the third step in this serial pressure-raising system. In the land animals, where most of the blood only passes through a single set of capillaries, a two-step system (auricle and ventricle) is sufficient for each part of the circulation.

11. Urinogenital system

The blood of the elasmobranchs differs from that of all other vertebrates in its very high content of urea. As measured by the depression of the freezing-point the blood is isotonic with the surrounding sea water (say, 3·5 per cent. NaCl); it may even be slightly hypertonic. But there is far less salt in the blood than in the sea, in fact only about

1·7 per cent. NaCl; there is also a high concentration of urea. This arrangement is apparently a legacy of the fact that all the vertebrates were originally freshwater animals. The return passage to the sea has been accomplished by the elasmobranchs through the device of urea retention. The gill surfaces, in which alone the blood comes into close contact with sea water, are not permeable to urea, but this substance penetrates freely into the tissues, as it does in other animals. Elasmobranch tissues if placed in sea water are therefore in contact with a strongly hypertonic medium. They are so habituated to the presence of urea that they are unable to function unless it is present in a concentration that would be toxic to most animals.

This arrangement has presumably been responsible for the failure of the elasmobranchs to return again to fresh water. In the case of the saw-fish *Pristis*, which is found some hundreds of miles up the Mississippi and various rivers in China, Smith found that a considerable concentration of urea is still maintained in the blood, thus further increasing the work which these fishes, like any freshwater animal, must do in order to maintain an osmotic concentration above that of the surrounding water. One shark (*Carcharodon nicaraguensis*) and some rays, *Trygon*, also live in fresh water.

In the ordinary marine elasmobranchs the high urea concentration is maintained by the presence of a special urea-absorbing section of the kidney tubules. The urinary apparatus is a mesonephros and these fishes show a considerable specialization in that the urinary functions of this organ are separated from its generative ones in the male. The hinder part of the kidney (sometimes call opisthonephros, the term metanephros should be used only for the definitive kidney of amniotes, which has a different method of development) consists of a mass of tubules ending in glomeruli, and a section of each tubule has the function of urea absorption. All the tubules join to form a series of five urinary ducts and these enter a urinary sinus, opening to the cloaca. The sinus can be compared functionally with a bladder, but it is a mesodermal structure, derived from the main kidney duct, and not strictly comparable to the endodermal bladder of tetrapods. The urinary sinus is a small organ and the volume of liquid excreted is small, as would be expected since the blood is isotonic with the surrounding sea water.

The genital system is highly specialized to allow internal fertilization and the production of a few very yolky and well-protected eggs. There is a single large ovary, from which the eggs find their way to a pair of funnels lying on either side of the liver behind the heart (Fig.

105). These are apparently formed from pronephric funnels and the Müllerian duct (oviduct) separates from the original nephric duct. In the adult it becomes a thick-walled muscular tube, bearing a swelling, the shell-gland, in which the egg-coverings are produced.

FIG. 105. A. Urinogenital system of the female, B, of the male dogfish.

ab.p. abdominal pores; *cl.* cloaca; *cp.* claspers of the male; *F.* rudiment of the oviducal opening in the male; *Md.* urinary ducts; *mtn.* hinder (excretory) part of mesonephros; *od.* oviduct; *oe.* cut end of oesophagus; *o.f.* oviducal funnel; *o.g.* oviducal gland; *ov.* ovary; *P.f.* pelvic fins; *R.* rectum; *s.s.* sperm-sacs; *T.* testis; *u.p.* urinary papilla in the female; *ug.p.* urogenital papilla in the male; *u.s.* urinary sinus; *v.c.* vasa efferentia; *v.s.* vesicula seminalis; *W.D.* Wolffian duct; *W.g.* Wolffian gland or mesonephros. (After Bourne, from Goodrich, *Vertebrata*, A. & C.Black, Ltd.)

The testes are paired and sperms are collected at their front ends by vasa efferentia leading into the anterior or reproductive portion of the mesonephros. This consists of a very much coiled, thick-walled, vas deferens, expanding below into a broader ampulla (seminal vesicle) which, at its lower end, gives off a forwardly directed blind diverticulum, the sperm sac, developmentally the lower end of the Müllerian duct, reduced of course in the male; small funnels are still visible at the upper end.

Transmission of the sperms is produced by a very large and

complicated pair of claspers. These are the modified pelvic fins of the male, developed into scroll-like organs and containing erectile tissue; they are inserted into the female cloaca. The mechanism of erection is apparently operated by the liberation of adrenalin; experimental injection of that substance will produce erection, and it is perhaps significant that the male possesses a reserve of adrenalin-producing tissue (see p. 162).

Development of elasmobranchs is by partial cleavage, producing a blastoderm, perched on the top of a large mass of yolk. The egg is protected by an elaborate egg-case, the 'mermaids purse', within which development proceeds until the yolk has been used up.

In several elasmobranchs (*Acanthias*, *Trygon*) development is viviparous, the oviduct forming a 'uterus' whose walls carry vascular and secretory ridges and papillae (trophonemata) that supply nourishment to the young.

12. Endocrine glands of elasmobranchs

Elasmobranch fishes possess the full complement of endocrine glands, but these show some interesting differences from the glands of higher vertebrates. The pituitary body lies in the usual place below the diencephalon and anterior, intermediate, tuberal, and neural divisions can be recognized. Little is known of the functions of the gland. The colour change is controlled by it and the neuro-intermediate lobe contains a substance that produces the expansion of melanophores. Hogben and Waring have also produced evidence that the pars anterior produces a substance causing contraction of the melanophores, but this has not yet been isolated and the evidence for its existence is indirect.

The thyroid is formed by a downgrowth from the floor of the pharynx, to which it often remains attached by a narrow stalk containing a small ciliated pit, a reminder that the organ was once a ciliated mucus-secreting gland.

The adrenal tissue is especially interesting because the two parts, so closely associated in mammals, are here found widely separated. The adrenalin-producing tissue consists of a segmental series of glands, the suprarenals, projecting into the dorsal wall of the posterior cardinal sinus (Fig. 106). In the region immediately behind the heart these can be seen very clearly by opening the sinus. The more anterior ones are fused to form an elongated structure on either side of the oesophagus. The sympathetic ganglia are closely associated with these suprarenal bodies, as would be expected from their common

FIG. 106. Dissection of suprarenal bodies and sympathetic nervous system of the dogfish.

ba. brachial artery; *ca.* coeliac artery; *da.* dorsal aorta; *g.* first sympathetic ganglion; *hyp.* hypoglossal nerve; *l.c.* longitudinal sympathetic 'chain'; *n.card.* cardiac branch of vagus; *pbp.* post-branchial plexus; *rc.* ramus communicans; *s.* sensory fibre; *sa.* segmental artery; *sg.* sympathetic ganglion; *spa.* anterior splanchnic nerve; *spm.* middle splanchnic nerve; *spn.* spinal nerve; *sup.* suprarenal body; *v.* ventricle; *vd.* vas deferens; *vs.* vago-sympathetic anastomosis; *X.* vagus; *Xbr.* branchial branch of vagus; *X.visc.* visceral branch of vagus. (After Young, *Quart. J. Micr. Sci.* 75.)

origin from cells of the neural crest. The segmental series continues along the whole length of the abdomen, the more posterior members being embedded in the kidney tissue (Fig. 107). These posterior suprarenal bodies are larger in the male than in the female, but only the central part of the male glands shows the reaction with chrome salts, which indicates the presence of adrenalin. The peripheral portion of each gland appears to consist of non-functioning cells, possibly a reserve used only during reproduction (see p. 160).

The part of the adrenal corresponding to the cortex of mammals is represented in elasmobranchs by the interrenal bodies, lying medially in some species, paired in others, in the kidney region (Figs. 107 and 108). The cells of these organs resemble cortical adrenal cells and their removal is said to produce fatal results. Since they are not in contact with the suprarenals at any point, it would seem that the association of the two parts is not necessary for their functioning, at least in these animals.

Little is known about the sex hormones produced by the gonads of elasmobranchs, nor of other possible endocrine organs such as the thymus. The pineal body is reduced to a small mass of tissue, not obviously secretory, and with no trace of eye-like structure.

13. Nervous system

The brain is large and well developed in elasmobranchs, having a structure characteristically different from that of both the cyclostomes and bony fishes (Fig. 102). The forebrain is very large and has cerebral hemispheres thickened both in floor and roof, whereas in teleosts the roof is thin. The hemispheres are wide relative to their length and the end of the unpaired portion of the forebrain between the hemispheres, the lamina terminalis, is also much thickened. Attached to the ends of the cerebral hemispheres are large olfactory bulbs and there are also large nasal sacs. Evidently the olfactory sense is very well developed in these animals and they probably use it largely in hunting.

All parts of the cerebral hemispheres receive fibres from the olfactory bulbs and it is probable that the forebrain serves mainly as an apparatus for analysing the olfactory impulses. However, it is stated that there are fibres reaching forward to one area at the back of the roof of the hemispheres from other sensory centres. Johnston therefore called this region the 'general somatic area' and suggested that it represents the beginnings of that development so characteristic of mammals by which all the senses are centred on the cerebral

FIG. 107. Diagram of transverse section through hind region of mesonephros of dogfish.

cv. cardinal vein; *da.* dorsal aorta; *int.* interrenal body; *k.* mesonephros; *l.c.* longitudinal sympathetic connective; *n.c.* sympathetic nerve-cells scattered in suprarenal body; *nv.* sympathetic nerves; *rc.* ramus communicans; *sg.* sympathetic ganglion; *sv.* subcardinal vein; *sup.* suprarenal body. (From Young, *Quart. J. Micr. Sci.* 75.)

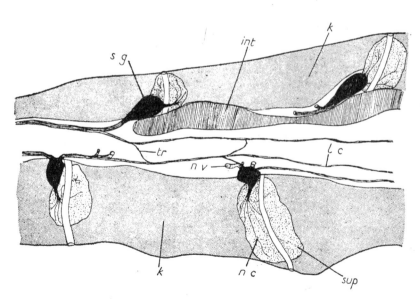

FIG. 108. Diagram of arrangement in hinder mesonephric region of dogfish.

Lettering as Fig. 107. *tr.* transverse sympathetic nerve. (From Young, *Quart. J. Micr. Sci.* 75.)

hemispheres. Further work is needed to confirm the existence of this pathway, and even if present its significance must not be exaggerated. There is of course no cortical arrangement of tissue in the hemispheres. The cells form thick masses around the ventricle (Fig. 109). The roof is quite thick and contains decussating fibres in the midline. The sides and floor make up the main bulk of the organ, the lateral wall being known as the striatum, its upper part the epistriatum. The medial wall is known as the septum and its upper portion is often referred to

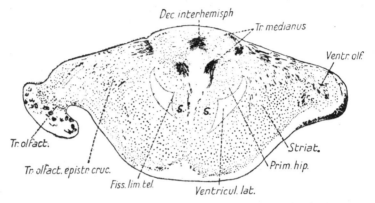

FIG. 109. A cross-section through the forebrain of a shark.

Dec.interhemisph. decussatio interhemispherica; *Fiss.lim.tel.* fissura limitans telencephali; *Prim.hip.* primordium hippocampi; *S.* septum; *Striat.* striatum; *Tr.medianus.* tractus medianus; *Tr.olfact.* tractus olfactorius; *Tr.olfact.epistr.cruc.* tractus olfacto-epistriaticus cruciatus; *Ventricul.lat.* ventriculus lateralis; *Ventr.olf.* ventriculus olfactorius.
(From Kappers, Huber, and Crosby.)

as the primordium hippocampi, having a position similar to that of the hippocampus of mammals. The functioning of the whole system is very obscure. Its main efferent pathways appear to be tracts leading to the hypothalamus and to the optic lobes (mid-brain).

The diencephalon is a narrow band of tissue, there are no extensive tracts leading forward through it, and the optic and other pathways do not end here as they do in higher animals. The lower part of the between-brain, the hypothalamus, is, however, as well developed (relatively) in these animals as in mammals. There are no data about its functioning in fishes, but in higher forms it acts as a regulator of many activities such as sleep and various visceral functions. Attached to the hind end of the hypothalamus of fishes is a peculiar organ, the saccus vasculosus, with folded, pigmented walls. It has been suggested that this acts as a pressure receptor, since it is well developed in deep-sea fishes. It is one of the characteristic features which the sharks and bony fishes have in common.

The midbrain, as in cyclostomes and teleosteans, is very large and is perhaps the dominant centre of the brain. The optic tracts end in its roof (tectum opticum) after complete decussation below the brain. The cells of the tectum are arranged in a complicated pattern of layers. Other sensory centres that send tracts to the optic lobes are the olfactory (cerebral hemispheres), acustico-lateral, cerebellar, gustatory, and probably also the general cutaneous centres of the spinal cord. Efferent tracts leave the midbrain roof to the base of the midbrain and extend backwards into the medulla, perhaps into the spinal cord. The efferent midbrain fibres have direct influence on the spinal cord, and electrical stimulation of points on the tectum opticum produces various movements of the fins, suggesting a system of control similar to that exercised over spinal centres by the cerebral cortex of mammals through the pyramidal tract. Various forced movements follow injury to the midbrain.

The cerebellum is a very large organ in elasmobranchs, as in all animals that move freely in space. Its main source of sensory fibres is from the ear and from the organs of the lateral line system, whose afferent fibres enter through the seventh, ninth, and tenth cranial nerves. The internal structure of the cerebellum is very uniform and essentially similar in all vertebrates. Removal of portions of it from dogfishes produces aberrations of swimming.

The medulla oblongata is the region from which most of the cranial nerves spring and especially those which regulate the respiration and visceral functions. Whereas in mammals this control is indirect, in fishes the nerves which spring from the medulla directly innervate the respiratory muscles of the gills and floor of the mouth. It is no doubt for this reason that the centre for the initiation of the respiratory rhythm developed in the medulla.

14. Sense-organs of elasmobranchs

Besides its highly developed nose the dogfish has other chemical sense-organs in the taste-buds scattered over the wall of the pharynx. It has been shown experimentally that, as in higher animals, these are receptors for sampling the food after it has been brought close to the animal, whereas the nose acts as a distance receptor. Smell and taste are therefore different senses for a dogfish, as for us. It is claimed that by training animals to discriminate between various substances it can be shown that those which we should smell are detected by the nose in the dogfish, but its organs of taste, like ours, can discriminate only between the qualities of salt, sweet, sour, and bitter.

The eyes are quite well developed in sharks and no doubt serve as an important means of finding the prey and avoiding enemies. However, the retina contains only rods, and visual discrimination is probably poor. Unfortunately details as to the power of performance, of the eyes, ability to discriminate shapes, &c., are scanty. The lens is spherical and very hard, as in all fishes, since it must perform the whole work of refraction. It is provided with a protractor-lentis muscle, presumed to produce active accommodation for near vision by swinging the lens forward. The iris is peculiar in those elasmobranchs which hunt by day in that when it narrows it divides the pupil

FIG. 110. Movements of margin of pupil of isolated iris of the shark *Mustelus*, followed by plotting with a camera lucida and here shown magnified 53 ×. Addition of adrenaline causes slight dilation of the already dilated pupil and illumination then causes closure. Acetyl choline even in concentrations of 1 in 10,000 has a similar *dilatory* effect. (From Young, *Proc. Roy. Soc. B.* 112.)

into two slits by the descent of an upper flap or operculum. It can be shown that the two slits may produce a single image. The muscles of the iris are better developed in elasmobranchs than in most bony fishes and the pupil makes wide excursions. The sphincter iridis muscle, which narrows the pupil, works as an independent effector. It is stimulated to contract by light, but its movements are not controlled by any nervous mechanism. The radial dilatator fibres, which open the pupil, receive motor-fibres from the oculomotor nerve. The closure of the iris when illuminated is relatively slow. If the whole eye is cut out from the head, in the dark, the iris, being an independent effector, still closes when illuminated. The muscle, being without nerves, is not affected by any of the usual drugs that mimic action of the autonomic nervous system, though some of these affect the innervated dilatator muscle. We have therefore the curious situation that no 'autonomic' drugs applied to the isolated dark adapted eye cause closure of the pupil; this can only be produced by illumination (Fig. 110).

The ear of elasmobranchs is mainly an organ for the control of balance and position. Besides semicircular canals, set in three planes, it possesses a sacculus and utriculus, but nothing corresponding to the lagena. There appear to be no experiments indicating that the animals respond to sound, but it cannot be excluded that they do so. Sand has analysed in some detail the functions of the semicircular canals and the organs of the lateral line with which they are related. The receptors of all these organs tend to discharge impulses continually and the effect of movement of fluid in the canals is to slow or stop the discharge of impulses, thus presumably affecting the centres

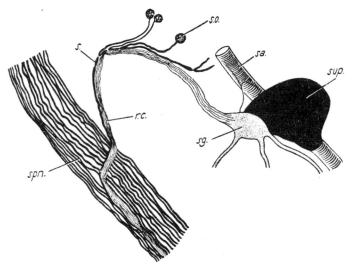

Fig. 111. Drawing of a sympathetic ganglion and related structures in a dogfish. Lettering as in Figs. 106 and 107. *so.* sense-organs. (After Young, *Quart. J. Micr. Sci.* 75.)

which they were reaching. We shall return to the functions of the lateral line organs later (p. 209).

The organs of this system on the head are highly modified in elasmobranchs to form the ampullae of Lorenzini, very deep canals filled with mucus. Sand showed that these organs alter their discharge of nerve-impulses with very slight changes of temperature, and he suggests that their function is to detect such differences.

No doubt elasmobranchs, like other animals, have many senses referred to the skin, such as we call touch, pain, and the like, but no studies of these exist. Sand has shown the presence of volleys of impulses in the nerves connected with muscles when the latter are stretched, but we have no further details of the existence of proprioceptors in these animals.

15. Autonomic nervous system

The sympathetic system of elasmobranchs consists of an irregular series of ganglia, approximately segmental, lying dorsal to the posterior cardinal sinus and extending back above the kidneys. These ganglia contain motor nerve-cells (post-ganglionic cells) whose processes proceed to end in the smooth muscles either of the arterial walls or of the viscera. The cells themselves are controlled by pre-ganglionic nerve-fibres whose cell bodies lie in the spinal cord and whose processes run out in the ventral spinal roots and rami communicantes (Fig. 111). In higher animals the sympathetic ganglia send post-ganglionic fibres back to the spinal nerves for distribution to the skin ('grey rami communicantes') but these are absent in elasmobranchs and correspondingly there is no evidence of sympathetic control of skin functions (e.g. chromatophores); a very different condition is found in bony fishes (p. 211). Another peculiarity of the sympathetic system of elasmobranchs is that it does not extend into the head. This condition is unique among vertebrates, but it is not clear whether it is primary or the result of a secondary loss.

In mammals it is usual to recognize a parasympathetic system acting in antagonism to the sympathetic, but this is not easy to define in the elasmobranchs (Fig. 112). The vagus, it is true, is well developed, with branches

FIG. 112. Diagram of the autonomic nervous system of the dogfish.

art. artery; *card.n.* cardiac nerve; *cil.g.* ciliary ganglion; *h.* heart; *in.* intestine; *k.* mesonephros; *ov.* oviduct; *ph.* pharynx; *pr.* profundus nerve; *py.* pylorus; *st.* stomach; *symp.* sympathetic ganglion (with suprarenal near it); *u.s.* urinogenital sinus; *III, V, VII, IX, X*, cranial nerves. (From Young, *Quart. J. Micr. Sci.* 75.)

to the heart and gut, but little is known of autonomic fibres in the other cranial nerves, or of a special 'sacral' parasympathetic system. The ciliary system is approximately as in other animals, but there is no sense in which it can be called antagonistic to the sympathetic system, since the latter does not extend into the head. The post-branchial plexus is a peculiar network of fibres and cells connected with the vagus but stretching back above the posterior cardinal sinus (Fig. 106).

FIG. 113. The early evolution of Vertebrates.

VI

EVOLUTION AND ADAPTIVE RADIATION OF ELASMOBRANCHS

1. Characteristics of elasmobranchs

The organization of a shark used to be considered to show the earlier stages of fish evolution, but we have seen evidence that this is a mistake (p. 138). The sharks and skates and rays are highly developed creatures; in particular the absence of bone is a secondary feature; they have been able to give up their defensive armour because of the development of other means of protection, swift swimming, good sense-organs and brain, and powerful jaws. We can now examine the history of these changes and study the varied creatures that can be classified as elasmobranchs. As usual in examining such histories we must try to discover evidence about the forces that have operated to produce the changes of type, and look for signs of any consistent trends, persisting for long periods of years.

2. Classification

Superclass Gnathostomata
  Class Elasmobranchii (= Chondrichthyes)
  Subclass 1. Selachii
    *Order 1. Cladoselachii. Devonian–Permian
      (*Cladoselache, *Goodrichia*)
    *Order 2. Pleuracanthodii. Devonian–Trias
      (*Pleuracanthus*)
    Order 3. Protoselachii. Devonian–Recent
      (*Hybodus*, *Heterodontus*)
    Order 4. Euselachii. Jurassic–Recent
      Suborder 1. Pleurotremata. Jurassic–Recent
        Superfamily 1. Notidanoidea. Jurassic–Recent
          (*Hexanchus*)
        Superfamily 2. Scylloidea. Jurassic–Recent
          (*Scyliorhinus, Mustelus, Cetorhinus, Carcharodon*)
        Superfamily 3. Squaloidea. Jurassic–Recent
          (*Squalus, Squatina, Pristiophorus, Alopias*)
      Suborder 2. Hypotremata. Jurassic–Recent
        (*Raja, Rhinobatis, Pristis, Torpedo, Trygon*)

Superclass Gnathostomata (*continued*)
   Subclass 2. Bradyodonti. Devonian–Recent
      *Order 1. Eubradyodonti. Devonian–Permian
         (*Helodus*)
      Order 2. Holocephali. Jurassic–Recent
         (*Chimaera*)

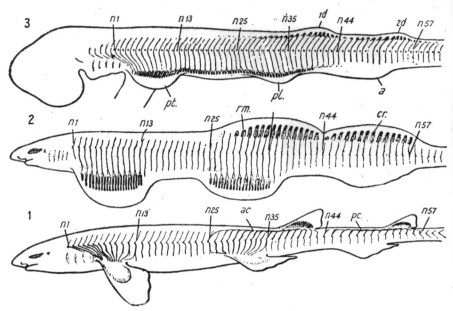

FIG. 114. Development of the fins of the dogfish. 1, Adult showing the nerve-supply of the fins; 2, adult with the fins shown expanded and their nerves and muscles shown as if concentration had not taken place; 3, a 19-mm. embryo, showing the actual condition.

a. anal fin; *ac.* anterior collector nerve of first dorsal fin; *cr.* (black) cartilaginous radial partially hidden by the radial muscle; *n.* 1–57, spinal nerves and ganglia; *pc.* collector nerve of second dorsal fin; *pl.* pelvic fin; *pt.* pectoral fin; *rm.* radial muscle; *1d.* and *2d.* first and second dorsal fins. (From Goodrich, *Vertebrata*, A. & C. Black, Ltd.)

The elasmobranchs form a very compact group of fishes, nearly always marine and of predaceous habit, having a great quantity of urea in the blood, with no bone in the skeleton, no operculum over the gills, and no air-bladder. The tail is usually heterocercal. The pectoral fin is anterior to the pelvic and the latter is usually provided with claspers, fertilization being internal. The body is more or less completely covered with placoid scales (denticles) and these are specialized in the mouth to form rows of teeth. The intestine is short and provided with a spiral valve. The typical cartilage-fishes with these characters may be placed in the subclass Selachii, to distinguish them from an early aberrant offshoot the Bradyodonti, represented to-day by the peculiar creature *Chimaera* (p. 179).

3. Palaeozoic elasmobranchs

The selachians are among the most numerous of the various predatory animals in the sea. There have, however, been many side-

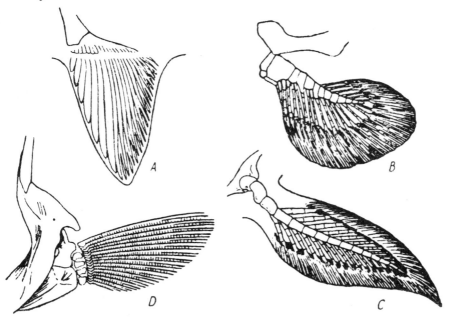

FIG. 115. Pectoral fins of various fishes.

A, *Cladoselache*; B, *Pleuracanthus*; C, *Neoceratodus*; D, *Gadus*. (From Norman.)

branches of the main shark line and we may now survey the history of the group from its first appearance. The characters we have used in our definition mark the elasmobranchs off from the earliest-known gnathostomes, the acanthodians and other placoderm types (Fig. 113), which we shall consider later (p. 181). Presumably the elasmobranchs were derived from some placoderm, but the earliest evidence of the existence of true sharks is in the form of isolated teeth and scales from Middle Devonian deposits, and the earliest type about which full information exists is *Diademodus* from the Upper Devonian. These fishes were similar to modern sharks in their general form, but the fins were remarkable in having a broad base, not sharply marked off from the body wall. It has been suggested by Goodrich and others that this was the earliest condition of the pectoral fin, perhaps showing its derivation from a continuous or at least extended fin-fold (Fig. 115).

This theory has the advantage that it agrees with the embryological development of the fin by concentration of a series of segments (Fig. 114). It also seems likely that anterior and posterior fins expanded in the horizontal plane would be necessary for stabilization (p. 135). Moreover, this theory of the origin of paired fins has the great advantage that it compares them with the median fins, which are also continuous folds. It has been argued, however, that the cladoselachians are very far from the earliest known fishes and that in both ostracoderms (p. 120) and placoderms (p. 182) fins are known which have a narrowly constricted base. We cannot yet say for certain what has been the course of evolution of the paired fins, but the fin-fold theory has much plausibility, in spite of the difficulties raised by palaeontologists.

The radials of the cladoselachian fin extended to the edge, and the pectoral girdle consisted simply of the enlarged basal plates to which these radials were attached; the two halves of the girdle did not fuse in the middle line. The jaw suspension was amphistylic (p. 142) and the vertebrae did not constrict the notochord.

The cladoselachians represent the ancestral Devonian sharks, from which all later forms have been derived. Animals of similar type were fairly common in late Devonian and Carboniferous seas. The ctenacanths, such as *Goodrichia*, reached a length of 8 ft. Later radiation of the selachians took place along three different lines, represented by the three remaining orders shown in the classification. The pleuracanthodians (*Pleuracanthus*) were a specialized group of freshwater carnivores. The tail was straight (diphycercal) and the paired fins had become modified accordingly (see p. 135). The axis was completely freed from the body wall to give a paddle-like fin, with pre- and post-axial rays, a type known as archipterygial, because it was once supposed to be ancestral to all others. A large spine on the head gives the group its name. Claspers were present. These animals were common in the Carboniferous and Lower Permian, but in subsequent times when they disappeared they did not leave descendants.

4. Mesozoic sharks

After flourishing in Palaeozoic seas the shark line seems to have become nearly extinct during the Permian and Trias. During this period there was indeed very little fish life in the sea and the stock seems only to have survived by adopting a varied diet, including invertebrate food. The protoselachian or heterodont sharks of this period had two types of tooth, pointed ones in front and flattened ones, for crushing molluscs, behind. *Heterodontus*, the Port Jackson shark of the Pacific, is a surviving form having amphistylic jaws and a dentition of this type. Then in the later Triassic sharks again

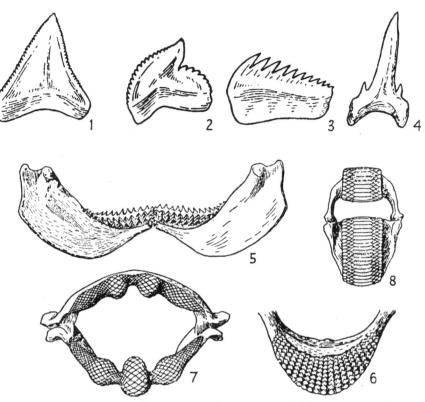

FIG. 116. Teeth of various elasmobranch fishes.

1, Man-eater (*Carcharodon*); 2, tiger shark (*Galeocerdo*); 3, comb-toothed shark (*Hexanchus*); 4, sand-shark (*Odontaspis*); 5, blue shark (*Carcharinus*); 6, nurse shark (*Ginglymostoma*); 7, guitar fish (*Rhina*); 8, eagle-ray (*Myliobatis*). (After Norman.)

became more abundant, and this agrees with the presence of numerous bony fish types, on which they presumably fed. Some of the Triassic sharks still possessed a heterodont dentition (**Hybodus*), though otherwise much like the modern forms.

In Jurassic times or earlier, however, the sharks divided into the main types that exist to-day. In the sub-order Pleurotremata or true sharks the teeth all became sharp and the animals swift swimmers. In the sub-order Hypotremata, on the other hand, the teeth remained flattened and sometimes became highly specialized for a mollusc-eating diet (Fig. 116), producing the flattened bottom-living creatures,

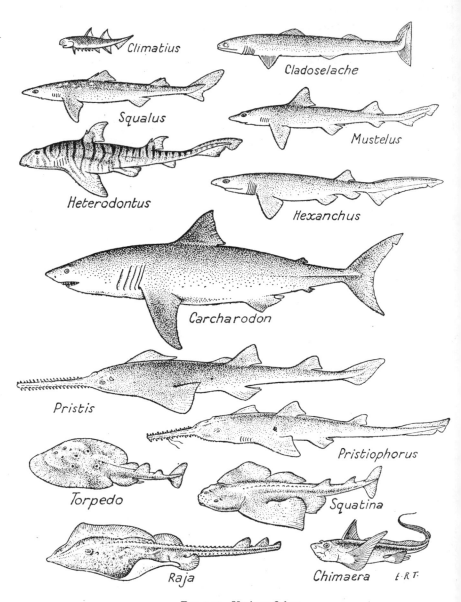

FIG. 117. Various fishes.

the skates and rays. The stages of this transition can be followed, and some of the intermediate types still exist. Thus in *Rhinobatis*, the banjo-ray (Fig. 117), the pectoral fins are enlarged but still distinct from the body. Almost identical creatures have been found in Jurassic rocks. It is probable that several separate lines showed this flattening of the body.

5. Modern sharks

The Pleurotremata may be divided into three superfamilies all dating from the Jurassic. The Notidanoidea show many primitive features, such as an amphistylic jaw, the presence of six or seven gill-slits, and an unconstricted notochord. These are widespread but not common forms; *Chlamydoselache*, *Hexanchus*, and *Heptanchus* are found in the Mediterranean, Atlantic, and Pacific. The superfamily Scylloidea is much larger and includes the dogfishes with two dorsal fins, not supported by spines. Here belong the true dogfishes (*Scyliorhinus*) and nurse-hounds (*Mustelus*), the latter sluggish, bottom-living animals feeding on a mixed diet, including crustaceans and molluscs; for this diet they have flattened grinding teeth. Related to these animals is *Cetorhinus*, the basking shark, in which the predaceous habit of the group has been abandoned in favour of straining small food directly from the plankton by means of special combs on the gills, an arrangement recalling that of the whalebone whales. The great effectiveness of this method of feeding may be seen in the length of 35 ft. or more attained by some of these, the largest of living sharks. In this group there are also many of the fiercest man-eating sharks, such as *Carcharodon*, often 30 ft. long, found in many seas. Some fossil forms of this genus are estimated to have reached a much greater length, possibly of 90 ft.

The superfamily Squaloidea includes those sharks in which there is a spine in front of each dorsal fin. They are not, however, otherwise different in habits from the other sharks. The spiny dogfish (*Squalus*) is a well-known type and here belong also the saw-sharks (*Pristiophorus*) and a group of bottom-living forms, the angel-fishes or monks (*Squatina*), which acquire a superficial similarity to the skates and rays. *Alopias*, the thresher, is said to differ from most sharks in that instead of seizing the prey as it is presented, it hunts systematically, several sharks working together and using their whip-like tails to drive smaller fishes such as mackerel into shoals, where they are then seized.

6. Skates and rays

The Hypotremata, skates and rays, have become specialized for life on the bottom of the ocean in shallow waters, feeding mainly on invertebrates. Locomotion is no longer by transverse movements of the body but by waves that pass backwards along the fins. In the earlier stages, such as *Rhinobatis*, the banjo-ray, which has existed from the Jurassic period to the present, the edges of the fins are still free and the tail is well developed. In *Pristis*, another saw-fish type, outwardly similar to *Pristiophorus* and known since the Cretaceous, the head is drawn out into a long rostrum armed with denticles. There are species in India, China, and the Gulf of Mexico that live in fresh water. In *Raja*, first found in the Cretaceous, the pectoral fins are attached to the sides of the body and the median fins are very small, whereas in the more recent *Trygon* and other sting-rays the tail is reduced to a defensive lash, the dorsal fin persisting as a poison spine. In *Torpedo*, the electric ray, the fins extend so far forward that the front of the animal presents a rounded outline. The animal is protected by a powerful electric organ, formed by modified lateral plate muscle, innervated by cranial nerves.

Life on the bottom has produced many further modifications in the skates and rays. In those that live in shallow and hence well-illuminated waters the colour of the upper surface is often elaborate, the under side being white. In *Raja*, for example, there is a pattern of black and white marks, which probably serves to break up the outline of the fish.

The eyes of the skates and rays have moved on to the upper surface of the head and are protected by well-developed lids. In most forms the pupil is able to vary widely in diameter and often has an operculum able to reduce the aperture to two small slits.

There is a special modification of the respiratory system so that water is drawn in not through the mouth but by the spiracle, which is provided with a special valve that shuts at expiration, as the water is forced out over the gills. The Hypotremata have therefore developed many special features for their bottom-living habits and have diverged among themselves into many varied lines. They have been very successful and are among the commonest fishes in the sea.

7. Chimaera and the bradyodonts

Finally we must consider an aberrant group, the bradyodonts, which diverged from the main stock at least as early as the Carboniferous and remains to-day in the form of a few types, such as the strange *Chimaera* or king of the herrings, found in various seas, including those of the European coasts (Fig. 117). Instead of the usual large, toothed mouth these Holocephali have a small aperture surrounded by lips, giving the head a parrot-like appearance. The teeth are large plates firmly attached to jaws, and the upper jaw is remarkable in being firmly attached to the skull ('holostylic'), the hyoid arch being free. These peculiarities of the mouth are associated with a capacity to eat plant food, though other foods such as worms, molluscs, crustaceans, and other invertebrates and even fishes may be eaten. The Holocephali differ further from the Selachii in the presence of an opercular flap attached to the hyoid arch. There are also extra claspers in front of the usual pelvic ones and an organ on the head of the male which is known as the cephalic clasper, although its function is obscure.

Many of the internal features resemble those of selachians, for instance, the presence of a spiral intestine, conus arteriosus, and urinogenitals in which there are separate urinary and spermatic ducts. The brain has a very peculiar shape on account of the large size of the eyes, which almost meet above the brain, the diencephalon being therefore long and thin.

These strange creatures appear in the Jurassic, apparently descended from the somewhat similar bradyodonts (such as *Helodus*), which were very common in the Carboniferous and Permian. They presumably represent an offshoot from the early elasmobranch stock, with specializations for a mixed diet.

8. Tendencies in elasmobranch evolution

The elasmobranchs have been in existence ever since the Devonian, and for much of this long period of nearly 300 million years we can follow their changes with some accuracy. This type of fish was first formed by loss of the heavy bony armature of the earliest gnathostomes, associated with the adoption of a rapidly moving and carnivorous habit. The resulting shark-like form has remained with relatively little change through the whole history of the group; cladoselachians from the Devonian are remarkably like modern sharks, and it would be difficult to assert that the latter show clear signs of being in any way of a 'higher' type. Both are in fact suited to the same type of life.

If our interpretation of the evidence is right, however, the modern shark type has been evolved from the Devonian type through a heterodont stage. During the late Permian and Trias there was little fish food for the sharks and they appear to have taken to living on invertebrates. Eating this diet was presumably easier for animals possessing the two types of teeth described on p. 175, and the animals also became rather flattened with their life on the bottom. On the reappearance of numerous fishes in the sea, in the Jurassic, some of these heterodonts resumed the shark-like habit, lost the crushing teeth, and developed into the varied fish-eating types alive to-day. Others of the heterodonts, however, became still more specialized for bottom life, as the modern skates and rays.

It is difficult to see any persistent tendency in all this, except to eat other animals of some sort. When fishes are available sharks will eat them, and the bodily organization for doing so seems to have been evolved at least twice. Similarly other members of the same stock ate molluscs and crustacea and became modified for this. The tendency is for survival or continuance of the animals and this leads them to adopt whatever habits are possible given their surroundings. In meeting the circumstances certain types will be suitable at one time, others at another. We know that genetic variations will produce fluctuations of type—at a time when circumstances force the animals to strive in one direction those with a particular bodily type, say, broad, 'heterodont' teeth will be selected. When fish food again becomes available those animals born with quicker habits and sharper teeth will be able to eat the fish and the shark type returns.

The method of ensuring stability in the pitching plane adopted by elasmobranchs (p. 135) necessitates a certain flattening of the front end of the animal. It is not therefore surprising that this tendency is often exaggerated and has several times produced flattened bottom-living creatures, such as the skates and rays. The Actinopterygii show the opposite tendency, to lateral flattening (p. 235). We might imagine that most of the modern skates and rays had become so modified in structure that only life on the bottom is possible for them and that there could be no return to a free-swimming, fish-eating habit, but it would not be true to say that this is certain or that the past history of the group shows undoubted evidence of such irreversible specialization.

The only general conclusion from our study of elasmobranchs since the Devonian, then, is that they have tended to keep alive by eating fish or invertebrates, that some have changed little during this time but that, judging especially from the modern forms, the group tends to produce varied types at any one time, each able to find its food in a special manner. It is not clear that the group has advanced, in any sense, since the Devonian. The type has always been a successful one, able to produce specialized carnivores. We do not know enough to be sure whether the number of creatures with this organization has changed greatly, but it seems that, except for a reduction in numbers in the Triassic, they have always been moderately abundant and are perhaps at present on the increase.

9. The earliest Gnathostomes, Placoderms

*Class Placodermi (= Aphetohyoidea)
    *Order 1. Acanthodii. Silurian–Permian (*Climatius*)
    *Order 2. Arthrodira. Silurian–Devonian (*Coccosteus*)
    *Order 3. Macropetalichthyida. Devonian (*Lunaspis*)
    *Order 4. Antiarchi (= Pterichthyomorphi). Devonian (*Bothriolepis*)
    *Order 5. Stegoselachii. Devonian–Carboniferous (*Gemundina*)
    *Order 6. Palaeospondyli. Devonian (*Palaeospondylus*)

It has already been mentioned that the earliest gnathostome vertebrates to be found in the rocks do not have the shark-like form, and present so many peculiarities that they are placed in a distinct class. In the past the fossils included here have been referred to various groups, usually either to the agnatha or the elasmobranchs, and there is still some doubt as to their position. In many respects they are highly specialized, but they all have one feature that may be presumed to have existed in the ancestral gnathostome, namely, that the hyoid arch played no part in the support of the jaws and the spiracle was therefore a typical gill-slit. For this reason they are often given the name Aphetohyoidea, but we shall prefer to call them Placodermi, to emphasize that they all have a heavy armour of bone. The class contains several orders, not obviously very closely related to each other; all are fossil forms, none of which is known to have survived the Permian.

The best-known, earliest, and perhaps most interesting group is the acanthodians, found in freshwater deposits extending from the Upper Silurian to the Permian but chiefly in the Devonian. These were small fishes with a fusiform body (Fig. 117), with heterocercal

tail and two, or later one, dorsal fins. The lateral fins consisted of a
series of pairs, often as many as seven in all, down the sides of the
body. The effect of these in stabilizing the fish would presumably be
different from that of a continuous fold, and the problem of the form
and function of the earliest paired fins remains obscure (see p. 174).
The fins were all supported by the large spines from which the group
derives its name.

The whole surface of the body was covered with a layer of small
rhomboidal scales, composed of layers of bone (see p. 218), covered
with a shiny material similar to the ganoin of early Actinopterygii.
On the head these scales were enlarged to make a definite pattern of
dermal bones, numerous at first but fewer in the later forms. The
pattern of the bones has no close similarity to that of later fishes. The
reduced bones of the later acanthodians are related to the lateral line
canals, which have an arrangement similar to that in other fishes, but
run between and not through the scales and bones of the head. The
teeth are formed as a series of modified scales. The skull is partly
ossified—important evidence that the boneless condition of elasmobranchs was not typical of all early gnathostomes.

The jaws of acanthodians were attached by their own processes to
the skull (autostyly) and are remarkable in that four separate ossifications take place in them (two in the upper and two in the lower jaw),
making a series of elements similar to that found in the typical
branchial arches. The hyoid was an unmodified branchial arch. At
first the mandibular, hyoid, and each of the branchial arches were provided with small flap-like opercula, but in later forms the mandibular
operculum became especially developed and covered all the gills.

These animals might well represent the ancestors of many if not all
other groups of gnathostomes. They have not the peculiar features
that we characterize as shark-like, and though they may well have
been carnivorous they are not very highly specialized for that mode of
life; but they could have given rise to the elasmobranchs. It is possible
to imagine that the bony fishes and lung-fishes could also have been
derived from an acanthodian. Whether or not the known acanthodians
represent the actual ancestors of the other gnathostome groups, it is
clear that knowledge of their anatomy forces us to discard two conclusions which have often been accepted in the past, namely, that lack
of bone and amphistylic jaw support are primitive gnathostome
features. Here already in the Silurian we find animals that possessed
both endochondral bone and scales composed of bony substance.
Moreover, some of them have no trace of denticles and we must

therefore regard with suspicion any theory that considers the placoid scale as the original type of all scales. It is at least as likely that scales composed of simple layers of bone in the dermis were the ancestral type and that placoid forms with a pulp cavity were a later specialization.

Several other types of placoderm fish are known, mostly from the Devonian strata. The Arthrodira, Macropetalichthyida, and Antiarchi (Fig. 113) were mostly heavily armoured fishes with dermal bones on the head and often a large shield over the body. There was usually a heterocercal tail and a covering of scales. The earlier fishes were mostly from fresh water, the later from the sea. Many were rather flattened, probably bottom-living and invertebrate-eating forms. The bony plates on the head were often arranged in characteristic patterns, none of which, however, shows close similarity to the pattern of bones on the head of bony fishes or tetrapods. Lateral line canals of typical arrangement were present and the 'bones' follow these to some extent.

Gemundina was a flattened animal, superficially similar to a skate, from marine Lower Devonian deposits. The skin was covered with denticles, but under these were large plates, apparently of bone. This fish is placed in a special order Stegoselachii and its affinities are unknown, but it shows again that the tendency to develop a flattened form has been present from the earliest appearance of fishes. *Palaeospondylus* from the Devonian is another isolated form, in the past often classed with the cyclostomes. Moy-Thomas has shown, however, that jaws were present and that probably the hyomandibula was not suspensory. He therefore classes the fish with the placoderms, in spite of the absence of any dermal skeleton. So far as can be discovered, all these placoderm fishes except the acanthodians were specialized types and have not left any later descendants. Indeed it may well be that they have been preserved only because of the great extent of their armour; less heavily protected relatives may have existed but have not survived as fossils. The remains which are known are sufficient to establish the fact that there were, in the Devonian period, numerous types of fish possessing a bony skeleton.

VII

THE MASTERY OF THE WATER. BONY FISHES

1. Introduction: the success of the bony fishes

The acanthodians and some other of the late Silurian and Devonian gnathostome fishes possessed bony skeletons; from these, or some placoderm animals like them, may have been derived not only the elasmobranchs but also the bony fishes and the lung-fishes, which gave rise to the land animals. These presumed descendants of the placoderms can be divided into three groups: first the elasmobranchs, secondly, the crossopterygians, the lobed-fin or lung-fishes, including the Devonian forms which led to the amphibia, and thirdly, the actinopterygian or rayed-fin fishes, culminating in the modern bony fishes. In Devonian times the Crossopterygii and Actinopterygii were very alike and both, like the placoderms, contained bone. The term bony fishes or Osteichthyes is often applied to these two groups together, since they have some features in common and distinct from the elasmobranchs.

The great group of Actinopterygii, which, for all the importance of the elasmobranchs, must be reckoned as the dominant fish type at the present time, includes most of our familiar fishes, perch, pike, trout, herring, and many other types of 'modern' fish. In addition there are placed here some surviving relics of the stages which have been passed before reaching this condition, such as the sturgeons, bichir, bow-fin, and many fossil forms.

Many groups of animals have been successful in the water; crustacea, for instance, are very numerous and so are cephalopod molluscs and echinoderms, but the success of the bony fishes surpasses that of all others. From a roach or perch in a stream, to a huge tunny or a vast shoal of herrings in the sea, they all have the marks of mastery of the water. They can stay almost still, as if suspended, dart suddenly at their prey or away from danger. They can avoid their enemies by quick and subtle changes of colour. Elaborate eyes, ears, and chemical sense-organs give news of the surrounding world and complex behaviour has been evolved to meet many emergencies. Reproductive mechanisms may be very complex, involving elaborate nest-building and care of the young; social behaviour is shown in swarming movements, which may be accompanied by interchange of sounds (p. 216).

Bony fishes abound not only in the sea but also in fresh water, which has never been effectively colonized by cephalopods or elasmobranchs. They can exist under all sorts of unfavourable or foul-water conditions and a considerable number of them breathe air and live for a time on land. Perhaps the majority are carnivorous, but others feed on every imaginable type of food, from plankton to seaweeds.

To whatever features of fish life we turn we find that the bony fishes excel in it, and probably do so in several different ways in different species. It is small wonder that with all these advantages they are excessively numerous. There are some 3,000 species of living elasmobranchs, but more than 20,000 species of bony fish have been described.

The number of individuals of some of the species must be really astronomical. For instance, at least 3,000 million herrings are caught in the Atlantic Ocean each year, so that the whole population there can hardly be less than a million million. Again, it is estimated that a thousand million blue-fish collect every summer off the Atlantic coast of the United States and, being very voracious carnivores, they consume at least a thousand million million of other fishes during the season of four months. This gives some idea of the tremendous productivity of the sea, and of the way the bony fishes have made use of it. Needless to say, man has also made considerable use of the bony fishes, which indeed provide, with the elasmobranchs, a not inconsiderable portion of the total of human food.

2. The trout

Salmo fario, the brown trout, may be taken as an example of a bony fish; we shall also refer at intervals to conditions in other common freshwater fish such as the dace, *Leuciscus*, (fig. 119) and perch (*Perca fluviatilis*). There is considerable confusion about the various types of trout and their close relatives the salmon. The brown trout is abundant in rivers and streams throughout Europe and is commonly about 20 cm. long at maturity, though it may grow larger. It is grey above and yellowish below, with a number of dark spots scattered down the sides of the body (Fig. 118).

The body form is typical of that of teleostean fishes in being short, narrow in the lateral plane but deep dorso-ventrally, in fact more obviously streamlined than the shape of elasmobranchs. The movements of a trout do not at first sight obviously involve the bending of the body into an S; nevertheless, the method of swimming is essentially by the propagation of waves along the body by the serial contraction of the longitudinally directed fibres of the myotomes (p. 128).

The tail differs from that of elasmobranchs in being outwardly

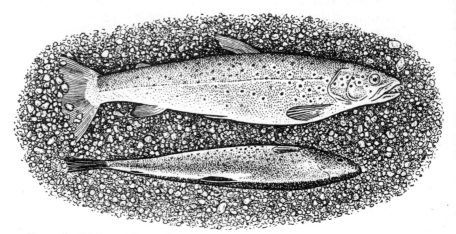

FIG. 118. Male and female brown trout (*Salmo fario*) spawning; the female is on her side, 'cutting' with the tail, thus digging a hole in the gravel. (From a photograph by Mallock.)

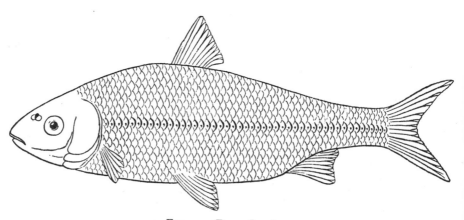

FIG. 119. Dace, *Leuciscus*.

symmetrical, though internally there are still traces of the upturned tip of the vertebral column (Fig. 121). Besides the typical caudal 'fish-tail', supported by bony rays, there are two dorsal fins and a ventral fin, but the hinder dorsal fin differs from the others in having no rays to support it and is called an adipose fin, because of its flabby structure. The paired fins are rather small and it is from their structure that the whole group derives the name Actinopterygii or rayed-fin fishes. There is no lobe projecting from the body and containing basal fin supports, as there is in the fin of lung-fishes. All the basal apparatus of the fin is contained within the body wall and only the fin rays project outwards, as a fan. The pelvic fin of bony fishes often lies relatively far forward; in the trout, however, it is unusually far back, just in front of the anus; in other types it may be found level with the pectoral fin, or even anterior to it (Fig. 121). The significance of the shape of the body and fins in swimming will be discussed later (p. 235).

The skin all over the body contains glands, opening between the epithelial cells, and is usually said to be soft. It must be remembered, however, that the squamous epithelium of the epidermis provides the animal with a covering of keratin and this is inert and presumably not permeable to water or dissolved substances. Indeed it is important for the osmotic regulation of the fish that the skin should be waterproofed in this manner and it does not therefore seem likely that oxygen can be taken in through the surface to any great extent.

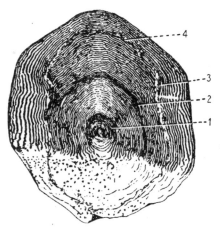

FIG. 120. Scale of salmon.

1 marks the edge of the smolt scale; 2 the first winter zone formed in the sea; 3 the spawning mark; 4 the second winter zone formed after return to the sea. (After Regan, *B.M. Guide.*)

In the mesodermal dermis, just beneath the skin, lie the scales, thin overlapping bony plates. The scales are internal structures, covered by skin, that is to say, they do not 'cut the gum' as do placoid denticles. The exposed part of each scale bears the pigment cells, which control the colour of the animal, in a manner presently to be described. The bone of the scales is deposited in a series of rings, which, like the growth-rings on a tree, are due to the fact that growth is not constant but occurs fast in the spring and summer and hardly at all in the winter. The age of the fish can therefore be determined from these rings (Fig. 120), or from the similar markings on the ear stones (p. 207). While a salmon is in fresh water no growth occurs, leaving a spawning mark on the scale.

The head of the trout shows some of the most specialized and typical teleostean features (Fig. 122). There are two nostrils on each side, but no external sign of ears. The mouth is very large and its

FIG. 121. Skeleton of the perch.

A. anal fin; AG. angular; B+R. basal and radial cartilages; BS. branchiostegal rays; C. caudal fin; CH. ceratohyal; D. dentary; D'. dermal rays of fins; E. ethmoid; EPO. epiotic; FR. frontal; GH. glossohyal (hypobranchial); HM. hyomandibula; HS. haemal spine; IO. interoperculum; MX. maxillary; NC. notochord; NS. neural spine; O. operculum; P. pectoral fin; PA. parietal; PF. prefrontal; PMX. premaxillary; PO. pre-operculum; PS. supporting processes of ribs; PT, PT', and PT''. ecto-, ento-, meta-pterygoid; PTF. post-frontal; PTO. pterotic; Q. quadrate; R. ribs; SG. shoulder-girdle; SG'. dorsal process of SG. SG''; outer rim of SG; SG', SG'''. posterior processes of SG; SM. symplectic; SO. suboperculum; SOC. crest of supra-occipital; SOR. suborbital ring; SQ. squamosal; UH. urohyal. (After Zittel, from Dean, *Fishes, Living & Fossil*, The Macmillan Co.)

edges are supported by movable bones, to be described below. Behind the edge of the jaw is the operculum, a flap covering the gills and also supported by bony plates. In connexion with these special developments of jaws and gills the skull has become very much modified and has developed complex and characteristic features (Fig. 121).

FIG. 122. Arrangement of organs of head and gills in A, a shark, and, B, a teleostean fish.

GB. gill bar; GC. outer opening of gill cleft; GF. gill filament; GR. gill-rakers; GV. gill vessels; J, J′. upper and lower jaw; M. mouth; N, N′. openings of nasal chamber; OP. operculum; SP. spiracle; ST. septum between gill filaments. (From Dean, *Fishes, Living & Fossil*, The Macmillan Co.)

3. The skull of bony fishes

The main basis for the skull is a chondrocranium and set of branchial arches, exactly comparable to those of the elasmobranchs. In the early stages of development there is a set of cartilaginous boxes around the nasal and auditory capsules, brain, and eyes, and a series of cartilaginous rods in the gill arches. Bones are then added in two ways: either (1) as cartilage bones (endochondral bones) by the replacement of some parts of the original chondrocranium, or (2) as membrane or dermal bones, laid down as more superficial coverings and considered to be derived from a layer of scales in the skin. This outer position of the bones can be clearly seen in many cases by the readiness with which the membrane bones can be pulled away from the rest of the skull.

The arrangement of the numerous bones of the skull is made less difficult to understand and remember if they are considered in the following order. First the endochondral ossifications in the original neurocranium, then the dermal bones that cover this above and below; next the endochondral bones formed within the original cartilaginous jaws, then the dermal bones that cover the edges of the jaws, and finally the ossifications in the branchial arches and pectoral girdle, which latter is in bony fishes attached to the skull.

The endochondral ossifications may be considered by beginning at the hind end of the skull: here the floor ossifies as the basioccipital, the sides as the exoccipitals, and the roof, over the spinal cord, as the supra-occipital bone; these posterior bones are not well marked off from each other in the adult skull. In the auditory capsule are five separate ossifications, and these can be seen in Fig. 121, as far as they appear externally.

The floor in front of the basioccipital is occupied by a basisphenoid bone and the walls above this by alisphenoids. The eyes nearly meet in the midline and the orbits are here separated only by a thin orbito-sphenoid. The only more anterior part of the chondrocranium to ossify is the region between the nasal capsule and the orbit, forming the ectethmoid.

The dermal bones that cover this partly ossified neurocranium are: on top and in front a pair of nasals and a median supra-ethmoid, behind these, large paired frontals and small paired parietals. Around the eyes a ring of circum-orbitals, and on the floor of the skull two median bones, the parasphenoid and vomer.

The jaw bones are numerous, including both endochondral and dermal elements, and the relation of the method of support to that found in other animals is not clear. In the embryo clear palato-pterygo-quadrate bars and Meckel's cartilages are seen. The upper jaw bears inward projections which extend towards the chondro-cranium and probably represent the traces of an autostylic means of support (see p. 142). But the effective support in the adult is achieved by the ossified hyomandibular cartilage. The palato-pterygo-quadrate bar ossifies in several parts and palatine, pterygoid, mesopterygoid, metapteryoid, and quadrate bones appear, some of them partly formed in membrane. The only part of Meckel's cartilage to ossify is the articular bone, at the hind end. The actual edges of the jaws are supported by membrane bones, the premaxilla, maxilla, and jugal, covering the upper jaw. The dentary covers most of the lower jaw, except for a small bone, the angular, which lies on the inner side at the posterior end.

The hyomandibular bone runs from an articulation with the otic capsule to the upper end of the quadrate. The symplectic is a small separate ossification at the lower end of the hyomandibula. The rest of the hyoid arch is present as epi-, cerato-, and hypohyals, which support a large toothed tongue. Bony fishes only rarely possess an open spiracle and immediately behind the hyoid are attached the bones supporting the operculum that covers the gills. The branchial arches are formed of several pieces, as in elasmobranchs, each being ossified separately.

The effect of this complicated set of bones is to provide a very efficient apparatus for the protection of the brain and sense-organs, support of the jaws and teeth and of the respiratory apparatus. Teeth are found on the vomers, palatines, premaxillae, maxillae, dentary, and on the tongue. They are spikes pointing in a backwards direction, used to prevent the escape of the food and not usually for biting or crushing.

Respiration is produced by a current passing in the same direction as in elasmobranchs, namely, in at the mouth and out over the gill lamellae, but the mechanism by which the current is produced is somewhat different. The pumping action is mainly a sideways movement of the operculum, enlarging the branchial cavity. The branchiostegal folds, below the operculum, prevent inflow of water from behind. When the operculum moves inward dorsal and ventral flaps in the throat prevent the exit of water forwards.

The actual gill lamellae differ from those of elasmobranchs in the great reduction of the septum between the respiratory surfaces (Fig. 122). This has the effect of leaving the gill lamellae as free flaps, no doubt increasing the surface available for respiration.

4. Vertebral column and fins of bony fishes

The vertebral column of bony fishes performs the same function as in other fishes, namely, to prevent shortening of the body when the longitudinal muscles contract. It has, however, become very complicated and with the ribs and neural and haemal arches forms an elaborate system serving to maintain the body form under the stresses of fast swimming. Like other parts of the skeleton it is extensively ossified, and the necessary lateral flexion is obtained by division of the column into a series of sections jointed together. Typically there

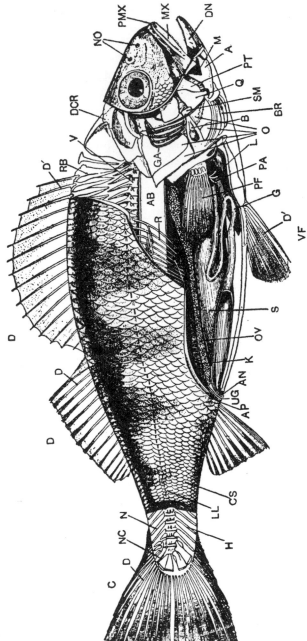

Fig. 123. The general anatomy of a teleostean fish.

A. angular; AB. air-bladder; AN. anus; AP. abdominal pore; B. bulbus arteriosus; BR. branchiostegal rays; C. caudal fin; CS. cycloidal scales; D. dorsal fin; D′. dermal supports of fins; DN. dentary bone; DCR. dermal bones roofing cranium; G. intestine; GA. gill arches; H. haemal arch and spine; K. kidney (mesonephros); L. liver; LL. lateral line; N. neural arch and spine; NO. anterior and posterior nares; O. opercula; OV. ovary; PA. pyloric appendices; PF. pectoral fin; PMX. premaxillae; PT. pterygoid; Q. quadrate; R. ribs, showing accessory supports; RB. radial and basal fin supports; S. stomach; UG. urinogenital opening; V. vertebra (centrum); VF. ventral fin. (From Dean, *Fishes, Living & Fossil*, The Macmillan Co.)

is one such section (vertebra) corresponding to each segment, but in the tail region of *Amia* there are twice as many vertebrae as segments.

Each vertebra consists of a centrum, neural arch and neural spine, and in the tail region, in addition, haemal arch and haemal spine. These parts are formed partly by ossification of cartilaginous masses, the basidorsal and basiventral, interdorsal and interventral, such as we saw in elasmobranchs, and partly by extra ossification in the sclero-genous tissue around the notochord and nerve-cord and between the muscles. The vertebrae are inter-segmental, the middle of each lying opposite the myocomma that separates two muscle segments.

The centra are concave both in front and behind (amphicoelous), and in the hollows between them are pads made of the remains of the notochord, an arrangement which allows the column to resist longitudinal compression and yet remain flexible; similar flat or concave articulations of the centra are found in other aquatic vertebrates from the elasmobranchs to the whales. Extra processes on the front and back of the vertebrae ensure the articulation and are comparable to the zygopophyses found in tetrapods. The ribs, which are so prominent in the backbone of many fishes, are of two sorts; pleural ribs between the muscles and the lining of the abdominal cavity, and more dorsal intramuscular ribs. Both sorts are attached to the centrum. The bony rods attached above the neural and below the haemal arches are often called neural and haemal spines, though it is doubtful whether they correspond to the neural spines of land vertebrates. They form the supporting rods or radials of the median fins and are usually divided into two or three separate bones in each segment. In addition to these radials the fins are also supported by a more superficial set of bony rods, the dermal fin rays (dermotrichia or lepidotrichia), which may be considered as modified scales and therefore lie superficial to the radials. These dermal fin rays are usually forked at their tips. They make an extra support for the fin margin and to them are attached the muscles that serve to throw the fin into folds (see p. 172).

In the tail region the internal skeleton is not quite symmetrical and shows signs of origin from an animal with a heterocercal tail. The notochord turns up sharply at the tip, so that the neural spines are very much shorter than the haemal spines, known here as hippural bones. The final portion of the notochord is often surrounded by a single ossification, the urostyle, and the whole makes a rigid support for the dermotrichia of the tail. Such a tail with internal asymmetry but external symmetry is said to be homocercal.

The paired fins are similarly supported by ossified radials, covered by dermal fin rays. At the base the radials are connected with 'girdles' lying in the body wall. The pectoral girdle (Fig. 121) consists of a cartilaginous endo-skeletal portion in which there form three ossifications, the scapula, coracoid, and mesocoracoid, while dermal bones, large cleithrum, and one or more small clavicles, become attached superficially. Above these a further series of dermal bones, the supra-

Fig. 123a. Muscles of a teleostean fish, mainly based on *Mullus*.

ad-mand. adductor mandibuli; *ep.* epaxonic muscles; *h.* horizontal myoseptum; *hy.* hypobranchial muscles; *hyp.* hypaxonic muscles; *lev.max.* levator maxillae; *my.* myocomma; *op.* operculum. (From Ihle.)

clavicle and post-temporal, attach the pectoral girdle to the otic region of the skull.

The pelvic girdle is very simple, consisting only of a single bone, the basipterygium.

5. Alimentary canal

The food of the trout consists mainly of small invertebrates such as *Gammarus*, *Cyclops*, and other crustaceans, and aquatic insects and their larvae, together with the fry of other fishes and perhaps sometimes larger pieces of 'meat'. The food is mostly swallowed whole, being helped down the pharynx by the mucous secretions which, as in elasmobranchs, contain no enzymes. The entrance to the stomach is guarded by a powerful oesophageal sphincter, no doubt serving to prevent the entry of the water of the respiratory stream. The stomach is divided into cardiac and pyloric portions, though the distinction is less clear than in elasmobranchs. The duodenum in all teleosts is beset by a number of wide-mouthed hepatic caeca (Fig. 123). The intestine is relatively longer than in elasmobranchs and often coiled;

its internal surface may be increased by folds, but there is no true spiral valve, though this was present in the ancestors of the Teleostei (p. 222). There is no gland attached to the rectum.

6. Air-bladder

Dorsal to the gut is a very large sac with shiny, whitish walls, the air-bladder, filled with oxygen. A narrow pneumatic duct connects

FIG. 124. Diagram of the branchial circulation of a teleostean fish.

ab. artery to air-bladder; *af*$^{3-6}$. four afferent vessels from ventral aorta; *ca.* carotid artery; *cc.* circulus cephalicus; *cl.* coeliac artery; *d.* ductus Cuvieri; *da.* dorsal aorta; *ef*^{3}. efferent vessel of first branchial arch; *ep.* epibranchial artery; *ha.* hyoidean artery (afferent vessel of pseudobranch); *hp.* hepatic vein; *ht.* heart; *mis.* mesenteric artery; *oa.* ophthalmic artery (efferent vessel of pseudobranch); *ps.* pseudobranch (hyoidean gill, possibly with spiracular gill); *s.* position of spiracle (closed); *va.* ventral artery; *I–V.* five branchial slits. (From Goodrich, *Vertebrata*, A. & C. Black, Ltd., after Parker.)

this with the pharynx. The origin and functions of the air-bladder will be discussed below (p. 248); it serves as a hydrostatic organ, enabling the animal to remain suspended in the water at any depth.

7. Circulatory system

The general plan of the circulation is similar to that of an elasmobranch (Fig. 124), that is to say, there is a single circuit and all the blood passes through at least two sets of capillaries. The heart contains a series of three chambers, sinus, auricle, and ventricle, but the muscular conus arteriosus is absent, there being only a thin-walled bulbus arteriosus at the base of the ventral aorta. The walls of the bulbus are elastic but not muscular, and study of its action by means of X-rays shows that it is dilated by the ventricular beat and then contracts, thus maintaining the pressure against the capillaries of the gills. The ventral aorta is short, but the arrangement of the afferent and efferent branchial vessels is essentially as in elasmobranchs. The circulatory system presumably works at the disadvantage of a low venous return pressure, but it is not clear how this has been overcome. The main veins are large in diameter, but not so big as in elasmobranchs. The heart is not enclosed in a rigid box and there is no communication between the pericardial and peritoneal chambers. The bony fish, therefore, seems to have overcome the difficulty of a single-circuit system without these devices used by selachians, but it is not clear how this is done, perhaps by more efficient use of the power of the ventricle or lower resistance in the gill capillaries. The matter would repay further study. There is a vagal cardiac depressor nerve, but no sympathetic nerve to the heart.

8. Urinogenital system and osmoregulation

The kidneys are mesonephric in the adult and consist of an elongated brown mass above the air-bladder. The ducts of the two kidneys join posteriorly and are swollen to form a bladder which, being mesodermal, must be distinguished from the endodermal cloacal bladder of tetrapods. The urinary duct opens separately behind the anus, there being no common cloaca.

One of the most striking features of the life of bony fishes is that they occur both in fresh water and the sea, and many, such as the trout itself, can move from one to the other. There is every reason to suppose that the earliest gnathostomes were freshwater animals, and the bony fishes show evidence of this in that the concentration of salt in their blood is always less than in the sea, in the neighbourhood of 1·4 per cent. NaCl against 3·5 per cent. outside. In fishes in fresh water the blood is more dilute, about 0·6 per cent. NaCl, but is, of course, more concentrated than the surrounding medium, which contains only traces of inorganic ions.

The kidney apparatus, with its filtration system of glomeruli and tubules for salt re-absorption, was developed for life in fresh water and still serves in this way in the freshwater forms. Various special devices are adopted in fresh water for minimizing the tendency to gain water and lose salt. The skin is little vascularized and probably makes an almost waterproof layer. The production of mucus assists in this waterproofing, and abundant mucus is secreted when an eel is transferred from salt to fresh water: the full change cannot be made suddenly without killing the fish.

In marine teleosts the problem is the opposite one of keeping water in, or keeping out salt. The usual kidney mechanism is clearly ill suited for this and it is found that the glomeruli are few or often completely absent from the kidneys. This no doubt reduces the loss of water, but is not enough by itself to solve the problem, which is met by taking in water and salts and excreting the salts. For this purpose special chloride-secreting cells are present in the gills and it has been shown that the amount of oxygen they use, and hence the work they do in diluting the blood, is proportional to the difference of concentration between the inside and the outside. A marine fish is able to drink and absorb sea water in spite of the fact that this is more concentrated than its blood. The chloride-secreting cells dispose of the excess salts. It remains to explain the means by which a solution passes against the os- motic gradient from the cavity of the gut to the blood; the mem- branes here must have some special properties of which we are ignorant.

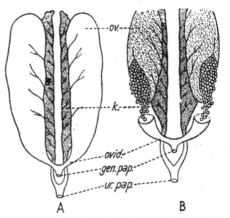

Fig. 125. Ovaries and kidneys of A, typical teleostean fish, B, trout and some other fishes where the eggs are shed into the coelom. (From Norman, after Rey.)

The genital system is nearly completely separated from the excretory in both sexes. The testes (soft roes) are a large pair of sacs opening into the base of the urinary ducts. The ovaries (hard roes) are also elongated in the trout and the eggs are shed free into the coelom (Fig. 125) and passed to the exterior by abdominal pores. This condition is unusual among teleosts, whose ovaries in most cases form closed sacs, continuous with the oviducts.

Fertilization is external and the eggs of the trout are shed in small pits or depressions in the sand; being sticky, they become attached to small stones. The eggs are very yolky and cleavage is therefore only partial, forming a cap of cells, the blastoderm, which eventually differentiates into the embryo. After hatching, the young fish may still carry the yolk sac and obtain food from it for some time, while beginning to eat the small crustaceans and other animals which are its first food.

9. Races of trout and salmon and their breeding habits

There is considerable confusion about the various races of trout and their allies the salmon. In both trout and salmon the adult originally spent the great part of its life in the sea but returned to the rivers to breed. Trout and salmon which do this are still abundant on the West Atlantic coasts and ascend all suitable rivers to breed, the process being known as the 'run'. But the trout has produced very many races of purely fluviatile animals, living either in lakes (where they often become very large) or rivers, and never returning to the sea to breed. These freshwater races differ in small points from each other and are given various common names (phinock, severn, Loch Levern trout, brook trout, &c.). There can be no doubt that interesting genetic differences between these forms exist, but they have not yet been fully studied. The salmon are much less prone to form purely freshwater races, though such are known, e.g. in the land-locked Lake Wenern in Sweden.

FIG. 126. Three stages in the development of the salmon. I and II are alevins; III, parr. (From Norman.)

During the breeding-season characteristic changes take place in the fishes and differences between the sexes appear. In the salmon the jaws become long, thin, and hooked, especially in the male. The animals make pairs and the males fight with others which approach the female. As the gonads ripen, the other parts of the fish, which were well supplied with fat at the beginning of the run, become progressively more watery. Finally, spawning takes place, the female laying the eggs in a shallow trough (redd), which she has 'cut' in the gravel by movements of her tail, while the male sheds sperms over them. She then covers the eggs with gravel by further cutting movements. In some rivers the young male salmon (parr), which have not yet been to the sea, may become sexually mature. They accompany the fully grown fish, hanging around the cloacal region and shedding their sperms at the same time as the large male. It is possible that this development of a kind of third sex serves to increase the variability of the population. The spent parr have been shown to eat some of the eggs and they then proceed to grow, migrate to the sea, and return later.

It is interesting that male trout will follow a spawning salmon and fertilize her eggs if her own male is not looking. Hybrids formed in this way can develop, but are said to be less fertile than the normal types; indeed, the males are wholly sterile.

After fertilization the salmon are very exhausted (known as kelts); the males never return to the sea. The females, however, may recover and after a period in the sea return to breed again, and this process may be repeated several times.

Very young trout or salmon are known as alevins or fry and remain mostly among the stones (Fig. 126). When they emerge they are called parr and have a number of characteristic parr-marks along their sides. After about two years spent as parr in fresh water salmon acquire a silver colour and pass to the sea as smolts. Young salmon

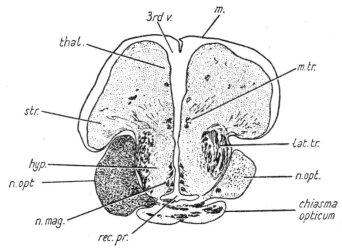

FIG. 127. Cross-section of the forebrain of the cod.

lat.tr. and *m.tr.* lateral and medial tracts between olfactory region and hypothalamus; *hyp.* hypothalamus; *m.* membranous roof of forebrain; *n.mag.* nucleus magnocellularis preopticus; *n.opt.* optic tracts (that on the right has atrophied in this specimen); *rec.pr.* preoptic recess; *str.* hind end of striatum; *thal.* thalamus; *3rd v.* third ventricle. (From Kappers, Huber, and Crosby.)

(about 3½ years) returning for the first time to breed are called grilse and they then return again to the sea as grilse-kelts. Fish ascending for the first time at four years old are small spring salmon and still older ones are maidens.

It is well established that salmon nearly always return to breed in the river in which they were born, but it is not certain that they journey for considerable distances in the sea. It may be that they remain throughout their life in the area fed by water descending from their native river.

10. Brain of bony fishes

The brain of bony fishes is built on the same general functional and structural plan as that of elasmobranchs, namely, the development of a number of separate centres, one concerned with each of the main sense-organs. The forebrain is often large, but it is characterized by great development of its ventral regions (the 'corpus striatum'), the roof being wholly membranous (Fig. 127). This condition is known as 'eversion' and is the very opposite to the inverted or thick-roofed forebrains which are found in the lung-fishes, close to the line of tetrapod descent (p. 255). The whole of this forebrain is reached by olfactory fibres, and there is little evidence that fibres from other sensory sources reach forward to it; it is mostly a smell brain.

FIG. 127a. Transverse sections of forebrain in various vertebrates to show the condition of inversion (thick roof) in A, B, and C and eversion (thin roof) in D, E, and F.

A, lamprey; B, frog; C, chelonian; D, chimaera; E, sturgeon; F, teleostean; *pall.* pallium; *sep.* septum; *str.* striatum. (From Kappers, Huber, and Crosby.)

The diencephalon is not well developed, since most of the optic fibres end not here, but in the midbrain. The roof is everted to form a pineal body, but this has not an eye-like structure. Nevertheless the diencephalon is sensitive to light. The minnow *Phoxinus* has a transparent patch on the head in this region, and it has been found possible to train the fish to give appropriate responses to changes of illumination even after removal of the paired eyes and the pineal body. Evidently there are light-sensitive cells in other parts of the walls of the diencephalon, besides those which become evaginated to form the eyes. Experiments on lampreys also showed the presence of such cells (p. 107). The hypothalamus is well developed and receives large tracts from the forebrain. Below and behind it is a large saccus vasculosus in some forms (p. 164).

The midbrain is very well developed and is often the largest part of the brain. The cells spread out over its roof (tectum opticum) are not all collected round the ventricle but have migrated away to make an elaborately layered system. Into this midbrain cortex there pass not only the great optic tracts but also ascending tracts from the sensory regions of the spinal cord, lateral line system, gustatory systems, and cerebellum. Large motor tracts pass back towards the spinal cord;

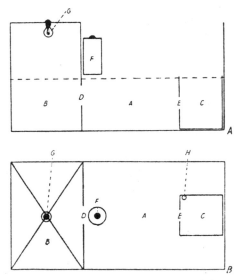

FIG. 128. Diagram of experimental tank used for training goldfish: (*A*) elevation, (*B*) plan. Explanation in text. (From Sanders, *J. exp. Biol.* 17.)

the details of their endings have not been traced, but they certainly exercise control over motor functions. Electrical stimulation of the optic lobes produces movements of local groups of muscles, for instance those of the fins. It can hardly be doubted that this well-developed midbrain apparatus controls much of the behaviour of the fish and is able to mediate quite elaborate acts of learning and other forms of more complex behaviour. For instance, Sanders showed that a goldfish placed in one compartment of a tank (A, Fig. 128) will learn to react to the shining of a light at F by passing through the hole D into the compartment B, in which it is fed with ant pupae. Fig. 129 shows the decrease in the time taken to pass through the hole by four fishes.

It can be shown that when a goldfish is trained to respond to some visual stimulus the learning process occurs in the midbrain and continues unaffected after removal of the forebrain. Conversely, olfactory learning takes place in the latter and is undisturbed by injury to the

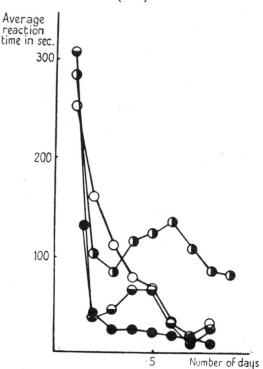

FIG. 129. Times taken by four goldfishes to pass through from chamber A to chamber B on presentation of a light at F. (Sanders.)

FIG. 130. Times taken by goldfishes to pass from chamber C on presentation of an olfactory stimulus at H. After partial removal of the optic tectum in animals V, X, Y, and Z this second-order learned reaction was discontinued. AA was a control animal in which the skull was opened but no incision made into the brain. N before operation, O after operation. (Sanders.)

tectum opticum. Sanders showed, however, that in spite of the existence of separate centres for the two processes it is possible to teach the animals second-order conditioned reflexes in which first an optic and then an olfactory stimulus is used. He first trained the animals

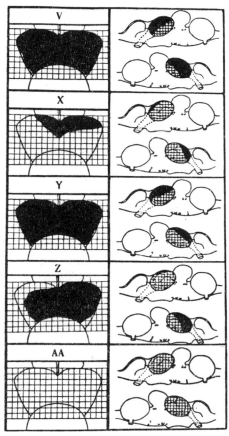

FIG. 131. Portions of the brain removed from the goldfishes whose learning curves are shown in Fig. 130. (From Sanders.)

to pass through the hole D (Fig. 128) when the light F was shone. Then he placed them in the dark in an inner tank C whose glass front also possessed a hole E. By means of a pipette H he then gave an *olfactory* stimulus in the form of a few drops of amyl acetate. When the fishes passed through the hole E they were 'rewarded' by switching on the light, but were caught before being allowed to pass through the hole D. Under these conditions the time taken to pass out of the inner tank after presentation of the 'smell' showed a steady decline (Fig. 130), indicating what can only be called second-order learning.

Operative removal of parts of the optic lobes then caused the animals to lose this association, which they were unable to re-learn (Fig. 131).

These and similar experiments show that the teleostean brain is capable of quite elaborate acts of association and that these powers are probably resident mainly in the optic lobes.

The cerebellum is very large in all teleosts and a special forwardly directed lobe of it, the valvula cerebelli, extends under the midbrain. The medulla oblongata is also well developed, having special ridges connected with the entry of the lateral line nerves and

FIG. 132. Sagittal section of brain of the gurnard, showing the swellings in the spinal cord at the point of entry of the nerves from the fin.

c. cerebral hemisphere; ce. cerebellum; hy. hypothalamus; m. midbrain; sw. swellings of spinal cord. (From Scharrer, Z. verg. Physiol. 22.)

gustatory fibres of the cranial nerves. In the gurnard, *Trigla*, there are special chemical receptors in the elongated fins. These are innervated from spinal nerves, and there are special swellings of the dorsal part of the spinal cord at the points where these nerves enter (Fig. 132).

11. Nose

The sense-organs are very highly developed in teleosts. The nose is provided with two nostrils to allow for the sampling of a stream of water; both nostrils open on the surface of the head (Fig. 122) so that there is no communication between the nasal cavity and the mouth. The nose certainly functions as a distance receptor for the finding of food, but we have little detailed evidence of its powers (p. 165).

12. Eyes

The eyes are characterized by a very large, dense, round lens (Fig. 133). There is a muscle, the retractor lentis or campanula Halleri, attached to the back of this lens and able by its contraction to pull the

latter somewhat nearer to the retina and thus to act as a focusing
device. It is not certain how far this action is used in life; presumably
the fixed focus is already sufficiently deep and the campanula perhaps
serves mainly to steady the lens.

It would be unwise, however, to generalize about all teleostean
eyes, for they are very varied. Whereas the trout, like most, has a

FIG. 133. Diagramatic vertical section of a typical teleostean eye. Not all the structures here shown are found in all species. (From Walls, *The Vertebrate Eye.*)

round pupil, which varies very little if at all in size, other fishes, whose
eyes are more exposed to light from above, have a more mobile iris.
In the angler-fishes, such as *Lophius*, and the Mediterranean *Uranoscopus*, the star gazer, the iris has an 'operculum' (p. 166) and is very
muscular; its movements are controlled by nerves and not, as in
selachians, by the direct effect of light. The sympathetic system
sends branches into the head in these animals (Fig. 141) and its fibres
cause contraction of the sphincter of the iris, whereas fibres in the
oculomotor nerve cause contraction of the dilatator, the opposite
arrangement to that in mammals. In the eel the pupil is also capable
of wide changes of diameter, but here the control is mainly by the
direct response of the circular sphincter iridis muscle to light incident
upon it. The pupil of the isolated eye of an eel closes when illuminated and reopens again in darkness (Fig. 134). Presumably because
of its lack of nervous control this iris is not affected by many of the
usual 'autonomic' drugs. For instance, closure will occur in the presence of atropine and the dark-adapted pupil remains unchanged

FIG. 134. Closure of the pupil of the isolated eel's eye, followed by plotting the movement of its margin with a camera lucida. The movements are shown magnified 54×. Time in minutes.

FIG. 135. Changes of diameter of isolated eel's iris in Ringer's solution with the addition of various drugs. Acetyl choline produces some closure, atropine some opening. Light still produces closure after application of atropine.

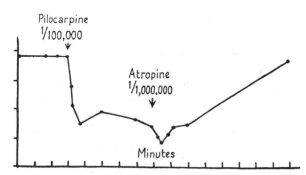

FIG. 136. Movements of margin of pupil in isolated iris of *Uranoscopus* in isotonic solution. Pilocarpine produces closure and atropine opening of this pupil whose sphincter muscle is innervated by *sympathetic* nerve-fibres. (From Young, *Proc. Roy. Soc. B.* 107.)

when placed in a solution of 1 per cent. pilocarpine, but then closes immediately on illumination (Fig. 135). The isolated pupil of *Uranoscopus*, however, closes when pilocarpine is applied (Fig. 136), and in this case the sphincter muscle is innervated by sympathetic nerve-fibres (p. 212). Adrenaline also causes the sphincter to contract and acetyl choline in moderate concentrations causes dilatation.

13. Ear and hearing of fishes

The ear of teleosts receives all its vibrations direct through the

FIG. 137. Diagram of ear of the minnow *Phoxinus*.
Ast. asteriscus; *L.* lagena; *N.l.*, *N.s.* nerves of lagena and saccule; *S.* saccule; *Sag.* sagitta; *U.* utricle. (From V. Frisch, *Z. vergl. Physiol.* 25.)

body of the fish, there being no ear-drum or outer ear, although in some cases the air-bladder may help in receiving sound (p. 251). The ear apparatus consists, therefore, only of the inner ear, enclosed in the otic bones. Each ear sac becomes subdivided into three semicircular canals and three other chambers, the utriculus, sacculus, and lagena (Fig. 137). In each chamber is carried an ear stone or otolith and these are given special names, the lapillus, sagitta, and asteriscus, occupying the above three chambers respectively.

Some fishes have been shown to be capable of responding to sounds and of learning to make different responses to notes separated by only small differences of wave-length. Moreover, these powers have been shown by suitable extirpation experiments to be resident in the lagena. The fact that tones can be discriminated without the presence of the elaborate organ of Corti found in higher vertebrates has an interesting bearing on theories of the functioning of the human ear. The lagena includes no basement membrane with fibres of different lengths such as is supposed by the Helmholtz theory to allow discrimination of pitch by acting as a differential resonator. The power of discriminating tones therefore depends on different peripheral analysers in fishes and mammals. These powers of hearing are very unequally developed in different teleosts. Most of the cyprinoids and siluroids hear well, but some other groups seem to be almost or completely deaf. It may be significant that the Weberian ossicles, modifications of the vertebrae linking the air-bladder with the ear, are well developed in cyprinoids and siluroids.

Fig. 138. Position of ear in Ostariophysi and its relation to the Weberian ossicles, which are shown in black.

C.tr. transverse canal between the two sacculi; *H.* brain; *I.* 'incus'; *L.* lagena; *M.* 'malleus'; *S.* sacculus; *Sch.* swim-bladder; *S.i.* sinus impar (perilymphatic space); *St.* 'stapes'; *U.* utriculus. (From V. Frisch.)

14. The lateral line organs of fishes

The lateral line system is more highly developed in bony fishes than in any others. The organs concerned do not lie on the surface but are sunk into pits, the pits communicating with each other by a canal and this with the surface by pores, which pierce the scales. Besides the main canal running down the body and served by the lateral line branch of the tenth cranial nerve, there are also lines following a definite pattern on the head, namely, supra- and sub-orbital lines, a line on the lower jaw, and a temporal line across the back of the skull.

There has been much speculation and some careful experimentation about the function of the lateral line organs. Sand has shown that in the ray they discharge impulses all the time, even when not under the influence of any external stimulation (Fig. 139). By forcing currents of water along the tubes he showed that a tailward flow of water is able to check and a headward flow to accelerate this 'spontaneous' discharge of impulses. Such changes in the streams of impulses arriving at the brain could, no doubt, form the basis for initiation of movements of the fish. This, however, still leaves open the question of what agency initiates movement of the fluid in the canals during life. It has been shown that when small streams of water are directed against the side of the tail some fish make escaping movements, but

FIG. 139. Responses of a single end organ in a lateral canal of a ray, shown with an oscillograph after amplification. Time signal 0·2 sec. intervals. The movements of the continuous white line show A, the beginning of a headward flow, increasing the frequency of discharge; B, the end of this flow; C, return of spontaneous discharge after an interval of 28 sec.; D, spontaneous discharge 60 sec. later; E, beginning of a tailward perfusion, inhibiting the discharge; F, the end of this perfusion; G, the spontaneous discharge 10 sec. later. (From Sand, *Proc. Roy. Soc. B.* 123.)

that these no longer appear when the lateral line nerve has been cut. These careful experiments leave little doubt that the lateral line organs enable the animal to respond when agitation of the water causes pressure against the side of the body. In fact the lateral line organs provide the animal with a kind of water touch, though it is not certain whether this is their only function. Why this type of receptor should need such a peculiar apparatus of canals, rather than a system of nerve-fibres in the skin, innervated by the spinal dorsal roots is not clear, nor do we know the significance of the pattern of lines on the head. The lateral line system must certainly be of great significance for aquatic life, for it is found in all types of fishes and also in the early Amphibia and in the aquatic larvae of modern members of that group.

15. Taste-buds in fishes

Another sensory system very well developed in bony fishes is that for taste. Taste is a sensation produced by stimulation of special papillae, the taste-buds, and in ourselves is restricted to certain parts of the tongue and walls of the pharynx, served by branches of the

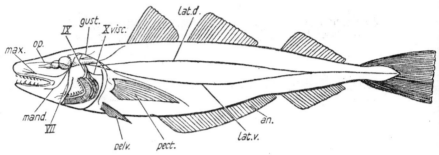

FIG. 140. Dissection of whiting to show the cranial nerves, and especially the nerves for the taste-buds.

an. anal fin; *gust.* gustatory branch of facial; *lat.d.* and *lat.v.* dorsal and ventral lateral line nerves of vagus; *mand.* and *max.* mandibular and maxillary divisions of trigeminal; *op.* ophthalmic; *pect.* pectoral fin; *pelv.* pelvic fin; *VII*, hyomandibular branch of facial; *IX*, glossopharyngeal; *X.visc.* visceral branch of vagus.

seventh, ninth, and tenth cranial nerves. In bony fishes, however, these organs are found over a considerable area of the surface of the body, the branches of the cranial nerves being correspondingly extended to supply them (Fig. 140). In some species these extensions of the cranial nerves reach to the tip of the tail, and it has been shown that the fish is able to turn and snap at a piece of food placed near the tail. This power is lost if the branches from the cranial nerves are cut. In mammals taste-buds serve to discriminate only four qualities (salt, sour, bitter, and sweet), most of our so-called 'tasting' being in reality the smelling of the food in the mouth. In fishes, also, the four taste qualities are discriminated by the taste-bud system, and it has been shown that the minnow (*Phoxinus*) continues to make such discriminations after the forebrain has been removed. Other chemical discriminations are made by the nose, however, and can only be performed with an intact forebrain. Thus *Phoxinus* tastes and smells the same classes of substances as man does.

16. Touch

Touch is, of course, well developed in fishes, and in many species
there are special sensory filaments,
which presumably serve this sense.
They are most usually developed
around the mouth, as in the catfish;
in other cases they are modifications
of the fins, for instance, the pectoral
fins of gurnards, which also contain
chemoreceptors (p. 204).

17. Autonomic nervous system

The autonomic nervous system of
bony fishes is organized on a plan
rather different from that both of
elasmobranchs and of land animals.
There is a chain of sympathetic
ganglia, extending from the level of
the trigeminal nerve backwards, a
ganglion being found in connexion
with each of the cranial dorsal roots
(Figs. 141 and 142). These ganglia
do not receive pre-ganglionic fibres
from the segments in which they lie,
but by fibres which run out in the
ventral roots of the trunk region and
thence forwards in the sympathetic
chain. This emergence of the pre-
ganglionic fibres for the head in the
trunk region very much recalls the
arrangement in land animals.

Each trunk sympathetic ganglion,
besides receiving a white ramus communicans of pre-ganglionic fibres
from its spinal nerve, also sends a
grey ramus back to that nerve, this
ramus carrying post-ganglionic fibres
to the skin. Some of these fibres have
been shown to control the melanophores, causing them to contract

FIG. 141. Diagram of ventral view of the
sympathetic system of the front part of the
body of *Uranoscopus*, showing the fibres
in the sympathetic and oculomotor that are
responsible for the light reflex.
(From Young.)

cil.brev. cil.long., short and long ciliary nerves;
cil.gn., ciliary ganglion; *dors.r.* dorsal root; *dil.*
dilatator muscle; *hypo.* hypoglossal; *n.splanch.*
splanchnic nerve; *opt.* optic nerve; *p.* pupil;
pal.VII, palatine branch of facial; *prof.* profundus; *r.b.* short root of ciliary ganglion; *r.comm.*
ramus communicans; *r.l.* long root of ciliary
ganglion; *sph.* sphincter muscle; *ventr.r.* ventral root; *III–X*, cranial nerves with their
sympathetic ganglia (*V.symp.* &c.); *VII hyo.*
hyomandibular branch of facial; *1–4 sp.symp.*
spinal sympathetic ganglia.

(p. 245). In elasmobranchs there are no grey rami communicantes and no sympathetic system in the head (p. 168); the differences between the two groups are therefore very striking.

FIG. 142. Diagram of the autonomic nervous system of *Uranoscopus* seen from the side.

bl. mesonephric bladder; *cil.gn.* ciliary ganglion; *dors.* dorsal root; *n.sph.* nerve to anal sphincter; *n.spl.* splanchnic nerve; *prof.* nervus ophthalmicus profundus; *rad. brev.* short root of ciliary ganglion; *r.comm.* ramus communicans (including both white and grey fibres); *stan.* 'corpuscle of Stannius' (adrenal cortical tissue); *ventr.* ventral root; *III*, oculomotor nerve; *V–X symp.* sympathetic ganglia associated with the cranial nerves. (From Young, *Quart. J. Micr. Sci.* 75.)

FIG. 143. Tracing of the contractions of a strip of the stomach muscle of the angler-fish, *Lophius*, attached to a lever. Time in minutes. At A, faradic stimulation of the vagus nerve. Drugs then added to the solution to make, at B acetyl choline 1/1,000,000; at C acetyl choline 1/100,000; at D adrenaline 1/100,000. (From Young, *Proc. Roy. Soc.* 120.)

Little is known about the parasympathetic system of bony fishes. The oculomotor nerve carries fibres to the iris, which work in the opposite direction to fibres from the sympathetic (p. 205). There is also a well-developed vagal system, but so far as is known no parasympathetic fibres in other cranial nerves and no sacral parasympathetic system. Electrical stimulation of the vagus nerve produces movements of the stomach but not of the intestine; the latter, however, shows movements when the splanchnic nerve is stimulated. Throughout the viscera acetyl choline causes initiation of rhythmic

FIG. 144. Tracing of contractions of the muscle of the urinary bladder of *Lophius*, attached to a lever. At A, D, and F faradic stimulation of vesicular nerve. Drugs added to make, at B acetyl choline 1/2,000,000; at C adrenaline 1/500,000; at E ergotoxine 1/50,000. Time, minutes. (From Young.)

FIG. 145. Tracing to show effect of atropine 1/50,000 added at A, on the contractions of the bladder of *Lophius* produced by faradic stimulation of the vesicular sympathetic nerve. Time, minutes. (From Young.)

contractions and these are inhibited by adrenaline (Figs. 143 and 144). This is equally true of the stomach, with motor-fibres from the vagus, intestine, with sympathetic motor-fibres, and of the muscles of the bladder, which contract on stimulation of the hinder sympathetic ganglia. The effect of these nerves to the bladder is prevented by atropine (Fig. 145) but not by ergotoxine (Fig. 144), though the latter is the drug which in mammals often inhibits sympathetic motor-fibres. In these fishes, therefore, it is not possible to divide up the autonomic nervous system into sympathetic and parasympathetic divisions by either anatomical, physiological, or pharmacological criteria. Presumably the two 'antagonistic' systems found in mammals are a late development, allowing for a delicate balancing of activities for the maintenance of homeostasis.

18. Behaviour patterns of fishes

The well-developed sense-organs and brain of the teleostean fishes constitute perhaps the most important of all factors in giving them their great success. Varied habits and quick actions enable the fish to make full use of the possibilities provided by the special features of their structure—the air-bladder, mouth, and so on. Unfortunately we are not provided with a great deal of detailed evidence about these potentialities of fishes. For instance, it is not possible to say clearly what use they make of their eyes; do these merely orientate the fish to movement in the visual field, or do they allow it to discriminate between shapes? The fisherman skilled in the use of 'flies' will assert the latter, but there are no critical experiments to prove it. Experiments by v. Frisch do, however, suggest the power of discriminating between colours.

There is no doubt that fishes possess very great powers of learning. Not only can they form conditioned reflexes, involving discrimination of tones, but also second-order conditioned reflexes in which after the animal has learnt to give a certain behaviour in response to a visual stimulus it is then taught to associate the latter with an olfactory stimulus (p. 201). There are very many other examples of such powers, but unfortunately we have as yet little information as to the way in which they are brought about by the brain. Nor have the naturalists provided us with very clear examples of the use of these powers by fishes in nature. There are many tales of carp coming to be fed at the ringing of a bell, and similar powers of association must play a part in the life of fishes in more natural situations. Bull has shown that fishes can be trained to discriminate between very small differences of temperature and salinity and no doubt it is by means of such powers that they normally find a suitable habitat.

The migrations of fishes have attracted much attention, but are still imperfectly understood. They vary from the downward migration of young animals to the sea and the reverse movement to breed to the astounding journeys of the eels, 3,000 miles westwards from Europe or eastwards from America to their breeding-place in the

FIG. 146. Migrations of the eels. The European species (*A. anguilla*) occurs along the coasts outlined with lines, the American species (*A. rostrata*) where there are dots. The curved lines show where larvae of the lengths indicated (in millimetres) are taken. (After Norman.)

FIG. 146a. The red belly of the stickleback releases attacking behaviour in other males and following by females. Of the above models only the two on the left acted as releasers. (From Tinbergen, *Wilson Bulletin*, 1948.)

Caribbean and the return of the elvers to the homes of their parents (Fig. 146). No one has yet discovered the factors that direct these movements, currents may play a part, but can hardly be the only influence.

Social behaviour is very marked in many species and shoals of some fishes may contain many thousands of individuals. The animals are presumably kept together in most cases by visual stimuli, though sounds play a part in some cases. Shoaling gives protection to small fishes, and in some cases the animals come together in this way to breed (herrings). There may also be some advantage for the finding of suitable feeding conditions, but on all these points we can do little more than speculate and hope for further information.

The social behaviour of many species includes the development of special 'releasers', shapes, colours, or postures displayed by one individual and eliciting specific reactions in another (Fig. 146a).

19. Sound production in fishes

A surprisingly large number of fishes can produce sounds audible to ourselves, and these noises are used by the fishes either for shoaling, to bring the sexes together, or to warn or startle enemies. Perhaps the loudest of the sounds is that produced by the drum-fish (*Pogonias*) of the Eastern Atlantic. The 'whistling' and other noises of the 'maigre' (*Sciaena*) are supposed to be the origin of the song of the Sirens, since they can easily be heard above the water. In both cases the sounds are made mostly if not wholly in the breeding-season. In other fishes, such as siluroids and *Diodon*, the noise is associated with the presence of spines and may be a warning.

The mechanism for sound production is very varied, involving either the vertebrae (some siluroids), operculum (*Cottus*, the bull-head), pectoral girdle (trigger-fishes), teeth (some mackerel and sun-fish), or air-bladder. The latter may be involved either by its use for 'breathing' sounds in physostomatous forms (p. 249) or as a resonator. Noise production is common in some families (Triglidae, Sciaenidae, Siluridae) but almost absent from others.

VIII

THE EVOLUTION OF BONY FISHES

1. Classification

Class Actinopterygii

Order 1. Palaeoniscoidei. Devonian–Recent. *Cheirolepis, *Palaeoniscus, *Amphicentrum, *Platysomus, *Dorypterus, *Tarrasius, Polypterus* (bichir)

Order 2. Chondrostei. Jurassic–Recent. *Chondrosteus, Acipenser* (sturgeon), *Polyodon* (paddle-fish)

Order 3. Holostei. Triassic–Recent. *Redfieldia, *Lepidotus, *Dapedius, *Microdon, *Amiopsis, Amia* (bowfin), *Lepidosteus* (gar-pike)

Order 4. Teleostei. Jurassic–Recent

Suborder 1. Isospondyli

*Leptolepis, *Portheus, Clupea* (herring), *Salmo* (trout)

Suborder 2. Ostariophysi

Cyprinus (carp), *Tinca* (tench), *Silurus* (catfish)

Suborder 3. Apodes

Anguilla (eel), *Conger* (conger eel)

Suborder 4. Mesichthyes

Esox (pike), *Belone, Exocoetus* (flying fish), *Gasterosteus* (stickleback), *Syngnathus* (pipe-fish), *Hippocampus* (seahorse)

Suborder 5. Acanthopterygii

Hoplopteryx, Zeus (john dory), *Perca* (perch), *Labrus* (wrasse), *Uranoscopus* (star gazer), *Blennius* (blenny), *Gadus* (whiting), *Pleuronectes* (plaice), *Solea* (sole), *Lophius* (angler-fish).

2. Order 1. Palaeoniscoidei

The actinopterygian stock has been distinct since Devonian times. The early representatives lacked many of the specializations which we find in the successful bony fishes to-day and showed features of similarity to the Crossopterygii. These Devonian Actinopterygii had not yet acquired the striking signs of full mastery of the water which are so characteristic of the group to-day. They resembled their ancestors the placoderms and their cousins the crossopterygians in being rather clumsy, heavily armoured creatures. From this early type many lines have been derived and can be followed with some completeness to their extinction or modern descendants.

The Devonian and Carboniferous forms are grouped together in the order Palaeoniscoidei, and animals of similar type survive to-day as *Polypterus*, the bichir of African rivers, which though showing some specializations remains in its general organization near the palaeoniscid level.

A typical Palaeozoic palaeoniscid such as *Cheirolepis* was a long-

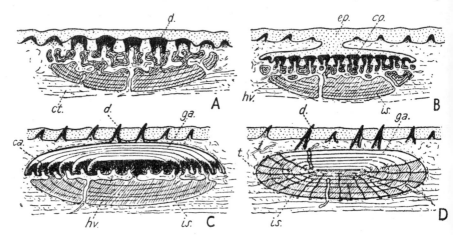

FIG. 147. Scales of some early fishes.

A, hypothetical condition with denticle-like substance (*d.*) attached to a basal bony plate lying in the connective tissue (*ct.*); B, 'cosmoid' scale of early crossopterygians, showing the cosmine layer (*co.*); vascular canals (*hv.*) and underlying 'isopedin' (*is.*); C, palaeoniscoid scale with layers of 'ganoin' (*ga.*); D, lepidosteoid scale of the gar-fish. (From Goodrich, *Vertebrata*, A. & C. Black, Ltd.)

bodied creature (Figs. 148 and 149) with a heterocercal tail, single dorsal fin, and pelvic fins placed far back on the body. The pectoral and pelvic fins had broad bases and the radials fanned out from a small muscular lobe present in all early actinopterygians but lost in later forms. The body was covered with thick rhomboidal scales, slightly overlapping, and having a structure known as palaeoniscoid (Fig. 147). The characteristic of this is that the scale is deeply embedded and grows by addition both to the bony or isopedin portion and of the shiny surface-layer, the ganoin, which thus becomes very thick. There is a middle layer of 'pulp' corresponding to the cosmine layer of the cosmoid scale of Crossopterygii (p. 256) and the two types have obvious similarities, though it is not clear how they are related. Each scale fits into the next by a characteristic peg and socket joint.

The skull was built on a distinctly different plan from that of

Crossopterygii, in that there is no joint such as was present in those fishes to allow the front part to flex on the hind. The jaw support is amphistylic, in the sense that the palatoquadrate is attached to the neurocranium by a basal process, but the otic process does not reach the skull and the hind end of the jaw is supported by the hyomandibula. There were even more dermal bones than are found in modern Actinopterygii, arranged so as to form a complete covering for the chondrocranium and jaws. These bones are derived from the original scaly covering of the head and the naming and comparing them with the bones of other forms is a matter of some difficulty. The plan varies considerably in different members of the group, and though some of the main bones resemble in appearance and shape those found in tetrapods, there are others for which no such homologues can be found, and sometimes there is considerable difficulty in recognizing even the main outlines of the pattern. The difficulty is that we have no rigid criterion by which to set about giving names to the skull bones. The use of the lateral lines for this purpose will be discussed later (p. 309). No system yet discovered is wholly satisfactory, and we must admit to almost complete ignorance of the factors which determine that bone shall be laid down in certain areas and that sutures shall separate these from each other. In this uncertain state of knowledge we must be cautious in comparing the patterns found in different skulls, but it is usual to consider that the bones of early Actinopterygii resemble those of Crossopterygii and of the early amphibians.

The roof of the skull usually shows a large pair of frontals, between the eyes, and parietals behind these. Between the frontals and the nostrils there are nasal bones and the front of the head usually also carries a number of rostral bones, not found in higher forms. Behind the parietals in the midline is a series of extrascapular bones.

The side of the skull of palaeoniscids is covered by numerous bones. There are lacrimals between the nasals and the orbit and usually a series of pre- and post-frontals, post-orbitals, and jugals around the eyes. The outer margin of the upper jaw is covered by premaxillae and maxillae, which are the main tooth-bearing bones. Behind the orbital series of bones the cheek is very variable. Sometimes there is a large bone identifiable as a squamosal, but often this region is occupied by a large pre-opercular, with a series of opercular bones behind it. The lower portion of the throat was covered by a series of gular plates. The spiracle in these early forms opened above the opercular bones. The pectoral girdle was attached to the back of the skull by a

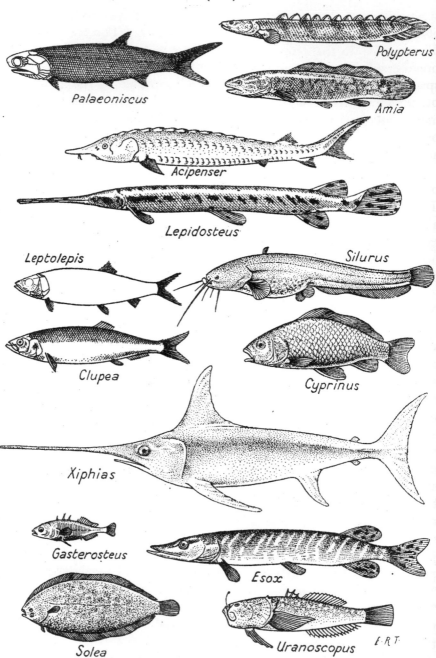

FIG. 148. Various actinopterygians.

supracleithrum, below which a cleithrum and clavicle made a series of dermal bones behind the gills, covering the cartilaginous girdle. The roof of the mouth contained a median parasphenoid, with paired prevomers in front of it, and a series of pterygoid bones occupying the space between it and the edge of the jaws, the palatine, ectopterygoid, pterygoid, and sometimes others. Finally the lower jaw, besides the main dentary carrying the teeth, shows many small bones such as the pre-articular and coronoid on the inner surface; splenial, angular, and surangular on the outside.

It will be clear that this skull of *Cheirolepis* may be closely compared with the skull of a crossopterygian or a modern teleostean. The general plan is related to that of the lateral line organs arranged along occipital, supratemporal, and infra-orbital lines. The numerous small bones are evidently similar in the different groups, though it is not easy to assign a suitable name to every one of the more numerous bones of the earlier forms.

These palaeoniscids from the Middle Devonian were rather rare freshwater fishes; they had sharp teeth and probably lived on invertebrates. We have no information about their internal anatomy, but it seems not unlikely that the air-bladder possessed a wide opening to the pharynx (as it still does in *Polypterus* descended from this stock) and that they breathed air, as did other Devonian fishes. However, they did not have the internal nostrils which are found in the crossopterygians.

During the Carboniferous and Permian the palaeoniscids became more numerous, mostly as small, sharp-toothed fishes. Several distinct lines became laterally flattened and acquired an outwardly symmetrical tail and blunt crushing teeth (Fig. 149). These characteristics probably indicate a habit of feeding in calm waters, perhaps mainly on corals, and they have appeared several times in the actinopterygian stock (p. 230). Palaeoniscids of this type were formerly placed together in a family Platysomidae, but it is now considered probable that the type arose independently several times; thus *Amphicentrum* is found in the Carboniferous, *Platysomus* and *Dorypterus* in the Permian. Similar forms arose again later among the holosteans and teleosteans and we have therefore evidence that this type of animal organization tends to evolve into deep-bodied creatures. *Dorypterus* further resembles modern teleosteans in a great reduction of its scales and in the forward movement of the pelvic fins.

Towards the end of the Triassic animals of typical palaeoniscid type became rare; they were replaced by their more active and speedy, mainly marine descendants, the Holostei (p. 223). Certain of the lines that branched off in the Palaeozoic have, however, survived to the present time, and in spite of subsequent specializations they give us some idea of the characteristics of these early Actinopterygii. Perhaps the most interesting of these survivals are *Polypterus*, the bichir, and the related *Calamoichthys*, both inhabiting rivers in Africa. Here the air-bladder opens to the pharynx by a median ventral aperture (Fig. 159). This is the arrangement found in lung-fishes (except *Ceratodus*) and in tetrapods, and it seems reasonable to suppose that it has survived in *Polypterus* from Palaeozoic times. However, it is not certain to what extent the air-bladder is still used as a lung, for *Polypterus* cannot survive out of the water.

This fish shows many other ancient characteristics. The covering of thick rhomboidal scales, hardly overlapping, gives the animal an archaic appearance; the structure of the scales is 'palaeoniscoid'. The presence of a spiracle, the arrangement of the skull bones, and many other features suggest in spite of its specializations that *Polypterus* is essentially a palaeoniscid surviving to the present day. In the intestine there is a spiral valve, which appears to have been present in the early Crossopterygii and Actinopterygii (as judged from fossilized 'coprolites') and occurs to-day not only in the Dipnoi but also in sturgeons and, though much reduced, in *Lepidosteus* and *Amia*. There is a single pyloric caecum in *Polypterus* (the caeca are well developed in sturgeons, *Lepidosteus* and *Amia*). The tail of *Polypterus* is no longer markedly heterocercal, but shows distinct signs of that condition. We can even find a parallel among Carboniferous palaeo-niscids for some of the special features of *Polypterus*. The long body and dorsal fin are found in the fossil *Tarrasius*, which may have been close to the ancestry of *Polypterus*, though it lacks the covering of scales. The pectoral fin in *Tarrasius*, as in *Polypterus*, has a peculiar lobed form which has been compared with the 'archipterygial' pattern (p. 174) and hence held to show that these animals are related to the Crossopterygii. The resemblance is, however, only superficial and the plan of the fin is essentially actinopterygian.

3. Order 2. Chondrostei

Another line of palaeoniscids that has left modern descendants is that of the sturgeons, whose characteristic is a reduction of bone in the skeleton. The Jurassic *Chondrosteus* was a marine fish of palaeoniscid form, but with this tendency already apparent. *Acipenser* and other modern sturgeons live both in the sea and in fresh water. They feed on invertebrates, which they collect from mud stirred up from the bottom by a long snout, flattened into a pear-shaped structure in *Polyodon*, the paddle fish of the Mississippi and Chinese rivers. The mouth of all these forms is small and the jaws weak and without teeth. In *Polyodon* there is a filtering arrangement in the pharynx, produced by the gill-rakers. The jaws of sturgeons hang free from the hyomandibular and symplectic, and can be swung downward and forward during feeding. The skull and skeleton is almost wholly cartilaginous and the dermal skeleton much reduced. The tail is covered with rhomboidal scales, but on the front of the body there are five lines of bony plates bearing spines, the skin in between carrying structures similar to denticles. There is an open spiracle. The internal anatomy of the sturgeons shows various features that, like the denticles, have been held to show affinity with the elasmobranchs; for instance, besides the spiral valve there is a conus arteriosus in the heart and a single pericardio-peritoneal canal. However, there can be no doubt of the actinopterygian descent of the sturgeons and in many features, for instance a thin roof to the cerebral hemispheres, they closely resemble the Teleostei.

4. Order 3. Holostei

During the later Permian period the palaeoniscids gave rise to fishes of a different type, the Holostei, which appear to have replaced their ancestors almost completely during the Trias. The typical holostean has a shorter, deeper body than a palaeoniscid and the tail is nearly but not quite externally symmetrical. The main body axis, however, is continued into the upper lobe, giving clear sign of the origin from a heterocercal arrangement. This 'abbreviated heterocercal' tail was presumably made possible by the changed swimming-habits resulting from the use of the air-bladder as a hydrostatic organ. If the fish floats passively there is no need for a heterocercal tail to direct the head downwards (p. 135). Similarly the head does not need to be flattened to produce an upward lift. The development of the air-bladder has thus made possible the lateral flattening and shortening of the body so characteristic of later Actinopterygii. The body of holosteans was at first covered with thick ganoid scales, but these become thinner in later types. There are various smaller distinctive holostean features, such as the loss of the clavicle.

We do not know whether fishes of this type arose from a single palaeoniscid stock; it is very likely that the change occurred several times, for throughout the Triassic and Jurassic there are several lines which have these holostean characteristics but evolve separately and only partly in the same direction. During the Cretaceous such types became fewer, being replaced by their teleostean descendants, but two holosteans survive to-day, *Lepidosteus* the gar-pike and *Amia* the bow-fin. These are freshwater fishes, living in the American Great Lakes, but the group is mainly a marine one, having taken to the sea in the Trias at a time when other groups were doing the same (palaeoniscids, coelacanths, elasmobranchs). The basic cause of this movement is not known, but perhaps there was an increase of planktonic and invertebrate life on which the fish depended.

The Triassic holosteans (Fig. 149) were recognizably similar to palaeoniscids and from these we may follow several lines of evolution. *Lepidosteus*, the gar-pike, shows a rather primitive structure and must have remained at approximately this Triassic stage. With its complete armour of thick scales (Fig. 148) it presents all the appearance of a primitive fish. On the other hand, it has developed certain special features, especially the long jaws, with which it catches other fishes, and the nearly symmetrical tail. Fossils similar to the modern gar-pike are found in the Eocene. Some of the later holosteans became very deep and short-bodied and developed a small mouth with flat crushing teeth or a beak. At the same time the scales became thin or lost altogether. Several stages in the transformation are known: for instance, *Lepidotus* (Trias to Cretaceous), *Dapedius* (Jurassic) show an increasingly round form and thinner scales and may well have been evolved from each other, though, of course, we cannot be certain of this. *Microdon* and other 'pycnodonts' became even more round-bodied and lost the scales altogether on the front part of the body. Probably several different lines of these subholosteans developed the habit of living among coral reefs and eating the polyps, like some palaeoniscids and the modern angel-fishes.

Another line of holostean evolution, developing from the original Triassic stock, retained the stream-lined body and from these both the modern teleosteans and the amioids were evolved (Fig. 149). *Caturus* (Trias to Cretaceous) was covered with thick scales, but in *Pachycormus* (Cretaceous) they are thinner and in *Amiopsis* (Jurassic) and *Amia* they became reduced to single bony cycloid scales, as in Teleostei. Meanwhile other changes took place, the tail fin becoming externally completely symmetrical and the maxilla and other cheek bones reduced.

5. Order 4. Teleostei

The groups so far considered have been nearly completely replaced by the Teleostei, fishes derived from a holostean stock, which have carried still farther the tendencies to shortening and symmetry of the tail, reduction of the scales, and various changes in the skull, such as reduction of the maxilla. The type apparently arose in the sea in late Triassic times, but remained rare until the Cretaceous, by which time several different lines of evolution had already begun. *Leptolepis* from the Jurassic and Cretaceous is generally considered to be close to the ancestry of all Teleostei and belongs to the sub-order Isospondyli, many of which are still alive. *Leptolepis* itself was a long-bodied fish with the pelvic fins placed far back, a skull with a full complement of bones, and a large maxilla. The scales still show traces of the ganoin layer.

From some fish like these leptolepids have been derived the 20,000 or more species of bony fish found to-day. It is natural that in any recently evolved group of animals classification will be difficult, because the separate twigs of the evolutionary bush will show little difference from each other. It is only when intermediate forms have become extinct that clear-cut major groups appear. It is therefore not easy to find useful subdivisions of Teleostei; we may, however, recognize five suborders (Figs. 148 and 149).

The first, Isospondyli, fish with soft rays, show primitive features in the large maxilla, the persistence of an open duct to the air-bladder, and the posterior position of the pelvic fins. Fishes of essentially similar type are known as far back as the Cretaceous (*Portheus*). Several familiar fishes are of this type, including the salmon and trout (*Salmo*) and herrings (*Clupea*). The suborder Ostariophysi is a large group of freshwater fishes, related to the Isospondyli. The anterior vertebrae are modified to form a chain of bones, the Weberian ossicles, joining the swim-bladder to the ear (p. 251). In this group belong the carp and goldfish (*Cyprinus*), roach (*Leuciscus*), and cat-fishes (*Silurus*). The eels (suborder Apodes) are rather isolated teleosts that diverged early from the main stock and retain many primitive features. The fourth suborder, the Mesichthyes, includes fishes such as the pike (*Esox*) and stickleback (*Gasterosteus*) of structure intermediate between that of the more primitive forms and the latest spiny-finned teleosts. The pipe-fishes (*Syngnathus*) and sea-horses (*Hippocampus*) are probably related to the sticklebacks. The flying-fish (*Exocoetus*) also belongs in this group.

The members of the suborder Acanthopterygii are the most highly developed fishes, characterized by the stiff spines at the front of the dorsal and anal fins. The maxilla is short, the duct of the air-bladder is closed, the body shortened, and the pelvic fins far forward. Fishes of this type already existed in the Cretaceous (*Hoplopteryx*) and the group includes a vast array of modern types. Here belong the perches (*Perca*), mullet (*Mugil*), wrasse (*Labrus*), john dories (*Zeus*), blennies (*Blennius*) as well as the gadid fishes such as the whiting (*Gadus*). Anglers (*Lophius*), gurnards (*Trigla*), and the flat fishes, the plaice (*Pleuronectes*) and sole (*Solea*) and others, are further members of this very large suborder.

6. Analysis of evolution of the Actinopterygii

Our knowledge of the history of the Actinopterygii is sufficiently complete for us to be able to state more definite conclusions about the process of evolution than has been possible from consideration of the more ancient and less perfectly known groups of fishes. First of all we may emphasize the persistence of change. No actinopterygian fish living in the Devonian is to be found to-day. *Polypterus* may be regarded as a living palaeoniscid, showing many features common in the Carboniferous, but it has undergone many changes since that time. Similarly the living sturgeons show the stage of organization present in the Jurassic Chondrostei, but they also have changed much. *Lepidosteus* is in general structure similar to a Triassic holostean such as *Lepidotus* and *Amia* to a Jurassic one such as *Caturus*, but both have their own more recent specializations. It is not until we come to the Tertiary history of fishes that types belonging to recognizable modern genera can be found.

The Actinopterygii have therefore been changing slowly, but continuously, throughout the period of their existence. Was this change dictated in some way by a change in their surroundings? Unfortunately we cannot answer this question very clearly. The sea is a relatively constant medium, though not as 'unchanging' as is sometimes supposed. In particular the relative extent of sea and freshwater changes frequently and perhaps because of such a change the early freshwater actinopterygians took to the sea. Probably the life in the sea is not constant over long periods. Almost certainly the available nitrogen, phosphorus, and other essential elements change in amount. We have reason to suspect that there was an increase in the extent and productivity of the sea during the Triassic period. It may be that such gradual changes in the life in the water, depending ultimately on climate or inorganic changes, have been responsible for the continual change of the fish population. However, it cannot be said that we can detect evidence of any such relationship; there is no clear proof that the changes in the fish populations follow changes in the environment. For the present we can only note the fact that change occurs, even in animals living in the relatively constant sea.

Very striking is the fact that as evolution proceeds not merely does each genus change but whole types disappear and are replaced by others. Thus the palaeoniscid type of organization had disappeared almost completely by the Trias and become replaced by the holostean. A few members retained the old organization and still survive to-day as *Polypterus* and the sturgeons. Similarly the Holostei, with their abbreviated heterocercal tails, hardly survived into the Tertiary, but were replaced by the Teleostei, only *Lepidosteus* and *Amia* remaining to show the earlier organization.

This replacement of one type by another appears much more remarkable when we reflect that by a 'type', say the palaeoniscid, we do not mean a homogeneous set of similar organisms all interbreeding. Quite the contrary; the palaeoniscids included many separate lines, each with its own peculiarities. When one 'type' therefore is thus replaced by another it must mean either that some one of these many stocks gives rise to a specially successful new population, which ousts the old ones or that *all* the members of the stock are changing their type together. It is not easy with a record such as that of the fish, which is far from continuous, to say which of these is true in any particular case, but we have sufficient evidence to be sure that either of them is possible.

There is no certain example in the Actinopterygii of a single new type replacing all the former ones, but the origin of the Teleostei may perhaps show a case of this sort. It is possible that the Teleostei is a mono-phyletic group, arising from a single type such as *Leptolepis and proving so successful that nearly all creatures of previous types soon disappeared.

The Actinopterygii provide also examples of the other, and perhaps even more interesting process, the parallel evolution of a number of different lines. There can be no doubt that from Palaeozoic times onwards several independent lines of fishes have shown similar changes. The tail has become shorter and more nearly symmetrical, the body has become flattened and deepened dorso-ventrally, while the pelvic fins have moved forward and the scaly armature has been reduced, all of these being signs of a more effective swimming and steering system (p. 223). As we come closer to modern times and the geological record becomes more complete we obtain more and more critical evidence that such changes have occurred in separate populations. Thus in the descendants of the holeosteans we can recognize at least three such lines, that leading to the spherical *Microdon, another leading through *Caturus to Amia, and a third through *Leptolepis to the Teleostei; probably there were many others. The important point is that although each line possessed peculiar specializations of its own, they all showed some shortening, development of symmetry of the tail, and thinning of the scales.

It is a considerable advance to be able to recognize such tendencies within a group. We begin to see the possibilities of a general statement on the matter. Instead of examining a heterogeneous mass of creatures called Actinopterygii we can recognize an initial palaeoniscid type and state that in subsequent ages this has become changed in certain specified ways and even at a specified rate. Imperfect though our knowledge still is, it enables us to approach towards the aim of our study, to 'have in mind' all the fishes of actinopterygian type.

This is to make the most of our knowledge: there remains a vast ignorance. We cannot certainly correlate this tendency of the fishes to change with any other natural phenomena. Put in another way, we do not know why these changes have occurred. The sea certainly did not stay the same, but it does not seem likely that its changes have been responsible for those in the fishes. It would be very valuable to be able to make a more certain pronouncement on this point, for the case is one of crucial importance. On land the conditions are constantly changing, and therefore we often find reason to suspect that environmental changes are producing changes in the animals. But can this be so in the water?

The evolutionary changes in the Actinopterygii certainly involve a definite difference in the whole life. By development of the air-bladder as a hydrostatic organ the animals have become able to remain at rest at any level of the water, and thus, by suitable modification of the shape of the body and fins, to dash about with remarkable agility in pursuit of prey or avoidance of enemies. This has enabled them to dispense with the heavy armour and thus further to increase their mobility. But what made it *necessary* to adopt these changes? Not surely any actual change in the sea itself. We must look then for some factor imposed on the situation by the fishes themselves or the neighbouring animals which constitute their biotic environment. Is it the pressure of competition that has been responsible for the change in fish form? It may well be that the presence of an excess of fishes

Fig. 149. Evolution of the Actinopterygii.

has led them continually to search for food more and more actively, and in new places, with the result that those types showing the greatest ability have survived. Given the initial genetic make-up of the palaeoniscids, further agility is most easily acquired by those fishes in which competition tended to produce shorter tails, thinner scales, and the other characteristics towards which the animals of this group tend.

The fact that the same set of changes can be produced independently from several different populations of approximately similar type (and presumably genetic composition) is strikingly shown by the specialized creatures evolved for life in the still waters of coral lagoons. Animals with rounded bodies and small mouths, sometimes with grinding teeth have appeared independently several times; in the Carboniferous, *Amphicentrum*; Permian, *Platysomus*, and *Dorypterus*; the Jurassic *Microdon* and *Dapedius*, and in some modern teleosteans. This is very valuable evidence of the way in which a common stimulus can work on genetical constitutions which are similar but not identical. In this case the stimulus is a particular set of environmental conditions; in other cases a similar effect may be produced by the stimulus of competition between animals, which was probably the 'cause', of the common changes that affected so many descendants of the palaeoniscids.

The case of these fishes therefore gives plausible ground for our belief that the driving 'forces' which have produced evolutionary change are the tendencies of living things to do three things: (1) to survive and maintain themselves, (2) to grow and reproduce, (3) to vary from their ancestors, all of these operating under the further stress of any slow change in the environment.

Finally we must consider whether this change in the fishes can in any way be considered to be an advance. Several times we have found ourselves implying that this is so, that the later teleosts are 'higher' than their Devonian ancestors. We shall be wise to suspect this judgement as a glorification of the present of which we are part. However, perhaps this danger is less marked when we are dealing with fishes not ancestral to ourselves, whose 'advance' does not therefore bring them nearer to man. The judgement can be put into quite specific terms: the later Actinopterygii are 'higher' than the earlier ones because they are more mobile, quicker, and can live free in the water with lesser expenditure of energy than their ancestors. Unfortunately we have no means of estimating the total amount or biomass of fish matter which is supported by the teleostean organization, but it seems possible that it is absolutely greater than that of any previous type, say the holostean or palaeoniscid. If this is true, the change in plan of structure has perhaps led to an increase not only in fish biomass but in the total biomass of all life in the sea.

The teleostean plan has certainly allowed for the development of a great range of specializations, fitting the animals to all sorts of situations in the sea and fresh water. We must therefore not forget this adaptability in judging the status of the group: it seems likely that modern teleosts are more varied than any of their ancestors. This power to enter a wide range of habitats not previously occupied is perhaps the clearest sign of all that a group has 'advanced', and we have already suggested that it is in this sense of suiting animals to new modes of life that there has been a progress in evolution. It is true that the sea and fresh water have been in existence relatively unchanged throughout the period that we are considering: in a sense the fishes have not found a 'new' environment. But they have found endless new ways of living in the water.

IX
THE ADAPTIVE RADIATION OF BONY FISHES

THE variety of Actinopterygii is so great that it would be impossible to try to give a complete idea of it and the best that we can do is to consider various functions in somewhat more detail and specify some of the ways in which the animals have become specially modified.

1. Swimming and locomotion

The teleosts have perfected in various ways the process of swimming by the propagation of waves of contraction along the body. The situation is different from that of elasmobranchs on account of the presence of the air-bladder, serving to maintain the fish steadily at any given level in the water. The stabilization of the animal during locomotion has therefore become a wholly different problem, and the fins are correspondingly changed. In the sharks the pectoral fins serve to correct a continual tendency to forward pitching and by adjustment of their position they are used to steer the animal upwards or downwards in the water.

With an air-bladder the fishes have become freed from the tendency to remain at the bottom, which was prevalent in the more primitive forms and is still so common in sharks that it has several times produced wholly bottom-living ray-like types. A fish with an air-bladder needs only very little fin movement to maintain it at a constant depth or to change its depth. As Harris puts it, 'the elaborate mechanism of pectoral "aerofoils" and a lifting heterocercal tail is no longer needed for the maintenance of a constant horizontal cruising plane. Concomitant with the loss of the heterocercal tail in evolution occurs a rapid and tremendous adaptive radiation of the pectoral fin in form and function.' A stage in this process seems to have been the use of the paired fins to produce oscillating movements during hovering, and this is still found in *Amia* and *Lepidosteus*, fishes that remain slow and clumsy.

Many of the lower teleosteans are relatively poor swimmers and some of them, like so many elasmobranchs, have become bottom-living. Thus in the catfishes there is a large anal fin, acting, like a heterocercal tail, to give lift and negative pitch. The pectoral fins are used to balance this tendency, very much as in sharks.

In the more specialized teleosteans, however, the pectorals are placed high up on the body and are used as brakes (Fig. 150). The plane of the fins' expansion is vertical and they thus produce a large drag force and a small lift force. This lift, of course, tends to make the fish rise in the water when stopping, and there is also a pitching

FIG. 150. Use of the paired fins for braking. A. Forces produced by the fins of *Lepomis* during deceleration. The pectoral and pelvic fin planes are represented by the heavy lines. P and V, the resultant forces on the pectoral and pelvic fin respectively. Dotted line and force P', condition during action of pectoral fins only, pelvic fins being held in 'neutral' position. G, position of centre of gravity. B. Sun-fish stopping by extending pectorals. Pelvic fins amputated, and although body remains horizontal, fish rises during the stop. C. Front view of sun-fish producing a rolling moment by the action of one pelvic fin. (From Harris, *J. exp. Biol.* 13.)

moment, depending on the position of the fin in relation to the centre of gravity, usually positive. That the fish does not rise in the water or pitch when it stops is apparently due to the anterior position of the pelvic fins, so characteristic of Actinopterygii, which has puzzled many morphologists. Experiments on the sun-fish (*Lepomis*) have shown that after amputation of the pelvic fins the fish rises in the water when stopping and raises its head (positive pitch). In fact the pelvic fins are able to produce a downward moment and they tilt the nose downwards. By alterations in their position they can be used to control the rising or diving movements and turning one of them outwards produces rolling (Fig. 150). It has been suggested that the pelvic fins function as keels to prevent rolling, but their amputation in *Lepomis* does not produce excessive rolling. Stability in the transverse plane is presumably assured by the dorsal and anal fins. The use of the fins for stopping was also developed in some Mesozoic

FIG. 151. Differences in form of fishes.

A, mackerel (*Scomber*); B, trunk-fish (*Ostracion*); C, sun-fish (*Mola*); D, globe-fish (*Chilomycterus*); E, sea-horse (*Hippocampus*); F, eel (*Anguilla*). (From Norman.)

fishes, for instance, in the Triassic coelacanth, *Laugia, which possessed high pectorals, and pelvic fins in the anterior position.

In the fishes with high pectoral fins, therefore, the pelvics are usually found far forward. In the flying fish (*Exocoetus*), however (Fig. 153), high pectoral fins are found with posterior pelvics. In this position the pelvics would tend to help rather than hinder any tendency by the pectorals to produce a rise; the condition is exactly that which would be expected in a flying fish.

With these increased opportunities for delicate control of movement without the devices of flattening of the front part of the body and a heterocercal tail, the bony fishes have also been able to make many other improvements in the efficiency of their swimming. The caudal fin has, of course, adopted its symmetrical shape and is used to increase the efficiency in turning. After its amputation a fish is not able to turn in its own length as normally.

With shortening of the body and its lateral flattening all sorts of new factors in stream-lining the body are developed, but the details are very difficult to understand. The nature of the turbulence produced by the movements of such a complicated structure is far from clear, but it seems probable that the shape of the higher fishes is such as to reduce the total skin-friction and to increase the efficiency of swimming. Other factors such as the flexibility, which has an important influence on the efficiency of the propulsive mechanism, have also been changed, again in ways not fully understood, by the special developments of the vertebral column and ribs.

Evidently the mastery that the Actinopterygii have acquired in the water has depended to a very large extent on the freedom given by the use of the air-bladder as a hydrostatic organ. This gives special interest to the question of how this use first began. If we are right in supposing that the bladder was first a respiratory diverticulum of the pharynx, can we suppose that its value as a hydrostatic organ depended on any exertion of effort of the fishes, or was this a case in which those born with the organ better developed found themselves with an advantage? It would seem that the latter orthodox Darwinian interpretation is the more likely; we can hardly imagine the fishes striving to make their bladders bigger. But it must be remembered that only those which were active swimmers, continually venturing into new waters, would be able to make full use of the new organ.

2. Various body forms and swimming habits in teleosts

Departures from the stream-lined body form typical of pelagic fishes have been very numerous; in nearly every case they are associated with a reduction in the efficiency of swimming as such and the development of some compensating protective mechanism (Fig. 151). Lateral flattening, which is already a feature of all teleostean organization, is carried to extremes in many types. Thus the angel-fish, *Pterophyllum*, often seen in aquaria, is provided with long filaments

FIG. 152. The angler-fish, *Lophius*. (From Norman.)

FIG. 153. Various fishes showing special conditions of the pectoral fins.

A, eagle-ray (*Myliobatis*); B, dog-fish (*Scyliorhinus*); C, tunny (*Thynnus*); D, thread fin (*Polynemus*); E, sun-fish (*Lepomis*); F, mud-skipper (*Periophthalmus*); G, scorpion fish (*Pterois*); H, cirrhitid fish (*Paracirrhites*); J, flying fish (*Exocoetus*); K, catfish (*Doras*); L, gurnard (*Trigla*). (From Norman.)

and a brilliant coloration, which, in its natural habitat (rivers of South America), give it a protective resemblance to plants, among which it slowly moves. The flat fishes (plaice, sole, halibut, &c.) have carried this flattening to extreme lengths. They feed on molluscs and other invertebrates on the sea bottom and lie always on one side. The upper side becomes darker and protectively coloured, the lower side white. In order to have the use of both eyes the whole head is twisted in a most remarkable manner during the post-larval period. These forms are mostly poor swimmers, but their coloration gives them a remarkable protective resemblance to the background (p. 243).

The john dory (*Zeus faber*) has made a different use of lateral flattening. The fish is so thin that its swimming is very slow, but being inconspicuous when seen from in front it can approach close to its prey, which it then catches by shooting out its jaws.

Flattening in the dorso-ventral plane is less common among teleosts than selachians. The flattened forms are mostly angler-fishes, of which there are several different sorts, *Lophius piscatorius*, the angler (Fig. 152), is common in British waters. It is much flattened, with a huge head and mouth and short tail. It 'angles' by means of a dorsal fin, modified to form a long filament with a lump at the end, which hangs over the mouth. Swimming, though vigorous, is slow, and protection (both for attack and defence) is obtained by sharp spines, protective coloration, and flaps of skin down the sides of the body which break up the outline. There is even a special fold of pigmented skin over the lower jaw, serving to cover the white inside of the mouth.

Other anglers are the star-gazers, *Uranoscopus* of the Mediterranean and *Astroscopus* from the Western Atlantic seaboard. Their lure is a red process attached to the floor of the mouth and they lie in wait buried in the sand, with the mouth opening upwards and only the eyes showing. The colour is protective, there are poison spines, and in *Astroscopus* there are electrical organs located in the most vulnerable spot, the eyeballs, and apparently formed from modified eye-muscles (p. 241).

Other fishes abandon the swift-moving habit for the protection afforded by the development of heavy armour, such as that of the trunk-fish (*Ostracion*) (Fig. 151) and the globe-fish (*Chilomycterus*). Special protective spines, such as that of the sword-fish (*Xiphias*) may be developed, without loss of the swift-moving habit; indeed these fish are among the fastest swimmers. There are many groups in which a very elongated body form like that of the eel has been developed. In *Anguilla* itself this is probably associated with the habit of moving over land, but this habit is not found in all long-bodied types. The Syngnathidae, sea-horses and pipe-fishes, no longer swim with the typical fish motion but by passing waves along the dorsal fins. The long and often grotesquely cut-up body form gives a strong protective resemblance to the weeds among which they live and on which they feed. The tail of the sea-horses has lost its caudal fin and is used as a prehensile organ, being wrapped around the stems of sea-weeds for attachment.

Deep-sea fishes often develop fantastic body forms, usually with greatly enlarged heads, but little is known of the way in which they swim or live.

Many different fishes are able to jump out of the water, presumably to escape enemies. Salmon and tarpon can jump to 8 or 9 ft. above the water: the devil-fish (*Manta*), though nearly 20 ft. long, also leaps to several feet. The flying fishes have special structures to assist in such jumps. In *Exocoetus* (Fig. 153) the enlarged pectoral fins serve for gliding for distances up to 400 metres, but in the flying gurnards (*Dactylopterus*) they are actually fluttered up and down, though the flight is feeble.

Several types of fish have the pectoral fin modified to allow 'walking'. The gurnards (*Trigla*) move in this way over the sea bottom (Fig. 153), and the mud-skipper (*Periophthalmus*) chases about catching crustacea and insects on land, using the pectoral fins as levers, provided with special anterior and posterior muscles.

Fishes that live in situations from which they are likely to be carried away develop suckers. Thus in the gobies, found between tide-marks, the pelvic fins form a sucker. The cling-fishes (*Lepadogaster*) are another group with the same habit. The remoras have developed a sucking-plate from the first dorsal fin and by means of this they attach themselves to sharks and other large fish. They are actively predaceous feeders and in order to catch their food leave the transporting host.

3. Structure of mouth and feeding-habits of bony fishes

Although perhaps the majority of fishes are carnivorous, there are species with all sorts of other methods of feeding. The more active predators have strong jaws and sharp teeth, such as those of the pike (*Esox*), cod (*Gadus*), and very many others. The teeth on the edge of the jaw serve to bite and catch the prey, those on the walls of the pharynx to prevent its escape if, as is often the case, it is swallowed whole. The teeth can often be first lowered to allow entrance of the prey and then raised to prevent its exit (e.g. in *Lophius*). In connexion with this habit the walls of the oesophagus and even stomach are often composed of striped muscle, capable of quick and powerful contraction.

Many carnivorous fishes are very fierce. For instance, the blue fish (*Pomatomus*) of the Atlantic move in shoals, cutting up every fish they meet, making a trail of blood in the sea. The barracuda (*Sphyraena*) of tropical waters may attack man. They are said to chase shoals of fish into shallow waters and to keep them there to serve for food as required. If this habit is accurately recorded it is a remarkable example of the exercise of foresight by a fish.

Other fishes feed on invertebrates and are then usually bottom-feeders. Thus the plaice (*Pleuronectes*) has developed chisel-like teeth on the jaws and flattened crushing teeth in the pharynx; it feeds largely on molluscs. The Labridae (wrasses) also have blunt teeth and eat molluscs and crabs. The sole (*Solea*) has a weaker dentition and eats mostly small crustacea and worms. Fish such as the herring (*Clupea*) that live on the minute organisms of the plankton have small teeth and weak mouths, but are provided with a filtering system of branched gill-rakers, making a gauze-like net, comparable to the filtering system found in basking sharks (p. 177), paddle-fish (p. 223), and whale-bone whales (p. 633).

Herbivorous fishes have crushing teeth similar to those of the mollusc-eaters; indeed, many forms with such dentition will take either form of food. Thus the parrot-fishes, including *Scarus* of the Mediterranean, have the teeth fused into rows, making sharp plates with which sea weeds are browsed. The Cyprinidae, including many of our commonest freshwater fishes (goldfish, carp, perch, and minnow), have no teeth on the edge of the jaw, hence the name 'leather-mouths'. There are, however, teeth on the pharyngeal floor, biting against a horny pad on the floor of the skull. These fishes are mainly vegetarians, but many take mouthfuls of mud and extract nourishment from the plants and invertebrates which it contains.

4. Protective mechanisms of bony fishes

In general teleosts depend for protection against their enemies on swift swimming, powerful jaws, good sense-organs, and brain. The majority of them have thus been able to abandon the heavy armour of their Palaeozoic ancestors. In very many cases, however, subsidiary protective mechanisms have been developed, and are especially prominent in those fishes which have given up the fast-swimming habit and taken either to moving slowly among weeds or to life on the bottom. These developments are a striking example of the way in which, following adoption of a particular mode of life, appropriate subsidiary modifications take place, presumably by selection of those varieties of structure that are suited to the actions of the animal.

These protective devices may be classified as follows:

1. Protective armature of the surface of the body.
2. Sharp spines and poison glands.
3. Electric organs.
4. Phosphorescent organs.
5. Coloration.

5. Scales and other surface armour

The typical cycloid teleostean scales have already been described. They form a covering of thin overlapping bony plates, providing some measure of protection, but not interfering with movement. The hinder edges of the scales are sometimes provided with rows of spines, and are then said to be ctenoid. In many fishes the scales bear upstanding spines and possess a pulp cavity, which recalls that of denticles. In the tropical globe-fishes (or puffers) and porcupine-fishes (*Diodon*) these spines are very long and sharp and the puffers are able to inflate themselves with air and cause the spines to project outwards, a very effective protective device. In a few cases the scales have become developed to form a bony armour even more complete than that of the Palaeozoic fishes. Thus in the trunk- or the coffer-fishes (*Ostracion*) the scales are enlarged and thickened into a rigid box, from which only the pectoral fins and tail emerge as movable structures, the former apparently assisting the respiration, the latter the swimming. These fishes live on the bottom of shallow coral pools and have a narrow beak with which they browse on the coral polyps.

6. Spines and poison glands

Sharp protective spines are often found in teleosts, especially on the operculum and dorsal fins. In some cases these spines are provided with modified dermal glands that inject poison into the wound. Thus the British weever (*Trachinus*) lives buried in the sand and has poison spines on the operculum and the dorsal fins. It is suggested that the dark colour of the fins serves as a warning. The related star-gazer, *Uranoscopus*, of the Mediterranean and tropical waters has powerful spines on the operculum, which inflict a most unpleasant wound if the animal is disturbed by hand or foot while lying in the sand angling for its prey (p. 237). *Lophius*, the angler, is also armed with dangerous spines. Several species of catfish have large spines, sometimes serrated. In the trigger-fishes (Balistidae and related families) of the tropics one or more of the fins is modified to make a spine, which can be raised upwards and locked in that position. These fishes have very brilliant coloration, but since some of them live in the highly coloured surroundings of coral reefs it cannot be considered certain that the colours serve as a warning.

7. Electric organs

The power to use electricity for defensive purposes (and perhaps also for stunning prey) has been developed independently in four distinct families of teleosts. The electric eel, *Gymnotus*, of the Amazon and nearby rivers is an elongated fish (not related to *Anguilla*) reaching a length of 8 ft. The whole of the muscles of the ventral region of the hind end of the body are transformed into a gelatinous mass, able to give a shock of several hundred volts. The fish lives in shallow marshes and can produce a most unpleasant effect upon man, being known locally as the 'Tremblador'.

The electric catfish (*Malapterurus*) of the Nile and other African rivers is called 'Raad' (Thunder) by the Arabs and can produce a powerful shock from the modified skin glands, which cover the whole body. The entire electric organ is innervated by a single nerve-fibre on each side, whose cell body lies at the front of the spinal cord.

The peculiar long-snouted Mormyridae, also from African rivers, have weak electric organs derived from muscles in the tail. In the American star-gazer, *Astroscopus*, an angler-fish related to the Mediterranean *Uranoscopus*, the eye-muscles are modified to produce an electric organ, innervated from the oculomotor nerve. The eyes are the only part of the fish that projects above the sand in which it lies.

8. Phosphorescent organs

These are included here as organs of defence since unless used to bring the sexes together it is probably their function to scare away attackers by exhibiting a sudden light, rather than, as is sometimes suggested, to illuminate the night of deep waters in order to catch their prey. Fishes of many different families live at great depths; the development of luminescent organs is therefore a further example of parallel evolution. The organs are apparently always formed by a modification of the mucus glands of the skin. They usually show as rows of shining beads of various colours on the sides and ventral surface of the fish. In only a few cases is there a single organ of complex structure, which might be compared with a searchlight. In *Pachystomias microdon* there are two suborbital organs of cup-like form on each side, with glandular tissue at the base and a mass of substance filling the cup and apparently functioning as a lens. There is also a layer of pigment and of reflecting spicules and the organ is innervated by the trigeminal nerve. In the deep-sea angler *Ceratias* the tip of the dorsal fin is luminous and is used as a lure.

9. Colours of fishes

The bony fishes show perhaps the most brilliant and varied coloration of any animals, rivalling even the Lepidoptera and Cephalopods in this respect. The enormous range of colour and pattern which they show provides an excellent example of the detailed adjustment of the structure and powers of animals to enable them to survive. A great difficulty is introduced into the study of animal coloration by the fact that we are usually ignorant of the capacity for visual discrimination possessed by the animals likely to act as predators. Moreover, it is very difficult for us to obtain this information. When we examine any two objects we are able to say not merely that they are different but that one is red and the other green. A person or animal that is colour-blind may also be able to detect a difference, but yet remain unaware of any distinction of colour; the objects appear to him only as differing in brightness. In order to decide whether animals are able to distinguish between light of two wave-lengths we must present them with objects of different colour but the same brightness.

We are therefore faced with the possibility that some of the colours that appear to us so brilliant are to other animals merely differences of tone, and animals to us conspicuous because coloured, when seen in monochrome, may be protected. Some of the colours of fishes may be only a means of producing a pattern of protective greys, as seen through the eyes of an attacker. However, there is no doubt that some fishes are able to discriminate between illuminated bodies which though of different wave-length reflect light of equal brightness. In the subsequent description of fish coloration we shall not be able to consider predators further, but shall describe the colours as they appear to the eye of a normal man.

The colour of fishes is produced by structures in the dermis, (*a*) the chromatophores and (*b*) reflecting cells or iridocytes (Fig. 154). The chromatophores are branched cells containing pigment, which may be either black (melanin) or red, orange or yellow (lipochrome pigments). The iridocytes contain crystals of guanin, making them opaque and able to reflect light so as to produce, where no chromatophores are present, either a white or a silvery appearance. This material is used in the manufacture of artificial pearls, the scales of the cyprinoid *Alburnus lucidus* (the bleak) being used for the purpose. The iridocytes may be either outside the scales, when they produce an iridescent appearance, or inside them, giving a layer, the argenteum,

Black chromatophore
Yellow chromatophore
Iridocyte

FIG. 154. Coloration elements in the skin of the upper side of a flounder (*Flesus*). (After Norman.)

that produces a dead white or silvery colour. By means of a combination of the chromatophores, and of these with the iridocytes to produce interference effects, a very wide range of colour is produced. Thus by mixing yellow and black either brown or green is produced. Blue is usually an interference colour.

The use of the colour by the fish may be classified, according to the scheme introduced by Poulton, as cryptic or concealing, sematic or warning patterns, and epigamic or sex coloration. Cryptic coloration may be achieved in various ways and may be subdivided into two main types: (1) assimilation with the background, (2) breaking up the outline of the fish. Assimilation is common, but is very often associated with some degree of disruption of outline. The absence of all pigmentation in pelagic fishes, for instance the Leptocephalus larvae of eels, is an example of assimilation. Fishes living among weeds, such as the sea-horses and pipe-fishes, or *Lophius* the angler, often resemble the weeds in colour, and in addition develop 'leaf-like' processes. The colour of many familiar fishes, such as the green of the tench, may be said to resemble that of the surroundings by

FIG. 155. Colour patterns of various tropical fishes.
A, Muraena (*Gymnothorax*); B, bat-fish (*Platax*); C, butterfly fish (*Holacanthus*); D, butterfly fish (*Chaetodon*); E, perch (*Grammistes*). (From Norman.)

assimilation. When we come to consider the much more numerous examples of patterns involving several colours the distinction between assimilation and disruption is more difficult to draw. Many free-swimming pelagic fishes have the upper side dark and striped with green or blue, whereas the under side is white, a pattern very well seen in the mackerel (*Scomber*). This gives them protection from above and below, the striping probably making the animal less con-spicuous in disturbed water than it would be if of uniform colour. The white under-side would also serve to lessen any shadows that might arise, an important factor for animals which live in shallow water; similar shading is used by land animals (p. 414).

Very various devices of spots and stripes are found on fishes that live against a variegated background (Fig. 155). The beautiful red and brown markings of a trout are a good example. Flat fishes, living on sandy or gravelly bottoms, adopt a spotted pattern, which gives them a high degree of protection, and we shall see later that they are able to change colour to suit the ground on which they rest. It seems probable that the very brilliant colours of many tropical fishes serve mainly to break up the outline, though no doubt the surroundings in which they live are also brilliant. Great variety of colours may be found on a single fish, especially in the trunk-fishes (*Ostracion*), one species of which is described as having a green body, yellow belly, and orange tail, while across the body are bands of brilliant blue, edged with chocolate-brown. Moreover, the female has another colour scheme and was for long considered as a different species!

Colour differences between the sexes are very frequent in fishes, the male being usually the brighter. Thus in the little millions fish, *Lebistes*, there are numerous 'races' of males with distinctive colours, but the females are all of a single drab coloration. The genetic factors that produce the various types of male are carried in the Y chromosome. Presumably the colour of the males acts as an aphrodisiac as a part of the procedure of mating, but the significance of the different races is not known.

Sematic or warning coloration involves the adoption of some striking pattern that does not conceal but *reveals* the animal. This type of colouring is found in animals that have some special defence or unpleasant taste (such as the sting of the wasp), and its use implies that animals likely to attack are able to remember the pattern and the unpleasant effects previously associated with it. It is not easy to be certain when colours are used in this way, but it is possible that the conspicuous spots on the electric *Torpedo ocellata* have this function. Among teleosts there is the black fin of the weevers (*Trachinus*), possibly a warning of their poison spines, and the spiny trigger-fishes and globe-fishes (p. 240) also have conspicuous colours.

10. Colour change in teleosts

In spite of the reputation of the chameleon the teleosts are the vertebrates that change their colour most quickly and completely. The melanophores are undoubtedly provided with nerve-fibres (Fig. 156), and these cause contraction of the pigment and hence a paling of the skin colour. The processes of the cells themselves are not withdrawn, the colour change is produced by a movement of pigment within them.

The nerve-fibres in question are post-ganglionic sympathetic fibres,

FIG. 156. Nerves of the melanophores of a perch. (From Ballowitz.)

FIG. 157. Diagrams showing, *left*, a cut in the tail of the fish *Fundulus* producing a band of dark melanophores; *right*, when the dark band has faded a second cut makes the melanophores again dark. (After Parker, *Quart. Rev. Biol.* 13.)

leaving the ganglia in the grey rami communicantes (Fig. 142) to all the cranial and spinal nerves. The pre-ganglionic fibres which operate them, however, emerge only in a few segments in the middle of the body (Fig. 211), so that severance of a few spinal roots will affect the colour of the whole body. When a nerve to any part of the skin is cut the chromatophores in that region at first expand, making a dark area (Fig. 157). After a few days, however, the skin involved gradually becomes lighter, the process, it is alleged, beginning at the edges and moving inwards. Parker, who has made a careful study of these phenomena, believes that they indicate the presence of melanophore-expanding nerve-fibres (said to be of 'parasympathetic' nature). Following the cut these fibres are supposed to be stimulated to repetitive discharge and hence to make the dark band. Later the band pales because the stimulating substances ('neurohumors') produced at the nerve-endings of the melanophore-contracting fibres in the neighbouring areas diffuse in gradually.

This hypothesis involves two physiological propositions which are so novel that they would require detailed evidence for acceptance. Firstly the act of cutting is presumed to set up a discharge of impulses lasting for several days, which is unlikely. Moreover, the discharge is presumed to be only in the melanophore-expanding fibres and not in those that produce contraction. Secondly, since electrical stimulation of nerves in teleosts always produces *paling* and never darkening, we must assume that this form of stimulation has the opposite effect to section and only stimulates the melanophore-contracting nerve-fibres. Since neither of these propositions is adequately demonstrated, we must reject the hypothesis and say that there is no sufficient evidence of melanophore-expanding nerve-fibres.

There is, however, another agent that causes expansion of melanophores in a wide variety of vertebrates, namely the posterior lobe of the pituitary (see p. 354), and there is evidence that this works also in teleosts. Hypophysectomized specimens of the Atlantic minnow *Fundulus* are nearly always lighter than normal individuals, especially when on a dark background. Injection of posterior pituitary extracts, or placing of isolated scales in the same, causes expansion of the chromatophores of any teleost. We may conclude that colour change is produced by the nerve-fibres tending to make the animals pale and secretion of the posterior pituitary to make them dark.

It is more difficult to decide how external influences are linked with this internal mechanism. Fishes mostly become pale in colour on a light background and vice versa, and the effect is produced predominantly through the eyes. There may also be a slight direct effect of light on the chromatophores. The change in colour begins rapidly, but its completion may take many days. Analysis of the rates of change in normal fishes and in those with anterior and posterior pituitary removal has led to the suggestion that the anterior lobe produces a substance tending to make the fish lighter in colour, at least in the eel. A similar hypothesis has been fully worked out by Hogben and his colleagues in amphibia (p. 286).

The value of the colour change in bringing the animals to the same tint as their surroundings is considerable. Fishes kept on a light background are very conspicuous for the first few minutes when transferred to a dark one. The fisherman acknowledges this by painting the inside of his minnow can white, to make the bait conspicuous. In the flat fishes, living on the sand, the protection assured by the colour change is of special importance. It has been suggested that it is possible for the fish to assume a pattern similar to that of the ground

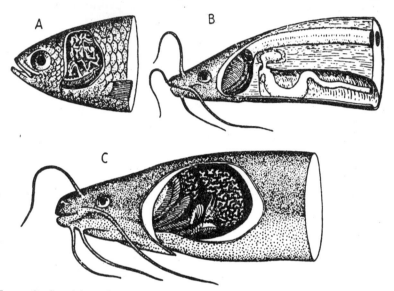

FIG. 158. Special respiratory apparatus, A, in climbing perch (*Anabas*); B, Indian catfish (*Saccobranchus*); C, African catfish (*Clarias*). (From Norman.)

on which it lies, but it is probable that the degree of expansion of the chromatophores is adjusted to suit the amount of light reflected from the ground; by increasing or decreasing the areas of dark skin effects approximately appropriate to various backgrounds are produced.

11. Respiration and the air-bladder

Many fishes are able to live outside the water. The excursions on to the land vary from the wriggling of the eel through damp grass to the life of the Indian climbing perch (*Anabas*) spent almost entirely on land. In the eel there is no special apparatus for breathing air (though oxygen may be taken in through the skin). The climbing perch is provided with special air chambers above the gills (Fig. 158) and even when in water it comes to the surface to gulp air and will 'drown' if prevented from doing so, even though it is placed in well-oxygenated water.

Many other fishes gulp air, either normally or when the water is foul, and there may be other special mechanisms for gaseous interchange. For instance in some loaches there is a special vascular air sac in the intestine, the waste gases being passed out at the anus. In

STURGEON AND
MANY TELEOSTS

LEPIDOSTEUS
AND AMIA

ERYTHRINUS

CERATODUS

POLYPTERUS AND
CALAMOICHTHYS

LEPIDOSIREN AND
PROTOPTERUS

REPTILES
BIRDS
MAMMALS

FIG. 159. Air-bladder of various fishes, seen from in front and from the left side. A, air- or swim-bladder; AD, air-duct; D, digestive tract. (From Dean, *Fishes, Living & Fossil*, The Macmillan Co., after Wilder.)

the Indian catfish *Saccobranchus* there are large air sacs growing a long way down the body from the gill chambers (Fig. 158).

There is considerable reason to suppose that the air-bladder, which has contributed so largely to the success of the later teleosts, arose as an accessory respiratory organ, used in the same way as those described above. In all the more primitive teleosts (Isospondyli) the air-bladder preserves in the adult its opening to the pharynx. Survivals of the still earlier Actinopterygii have the opening even better developed, though it varies in a peculiar way from group to group (Fig. 159). Thus in the sturgeons there is a wide opening into the dorsal side of the pharynx. In *Amia* and *Lepidosteus* the opening is also dorsal and the walls of the sac are much folded and used for respiration. In *Polypterus* the opening is ventral and the bladder has the form of a pair of lobes below the pharynx. This arrangement recalls that of the tetrapod lungs and is also found in the modern lung fishes and presumably in

Fig. 160. Diagrams illustrating the blood-supply of the air-bladder in A, *Polypterus*, B, *Ceratodus*, C, *Amia*, and D, a teleost. The blood-vessels are seen from behind, and cut short in transverse section.

a. dorsal aorta; *a.a.d.* anterior dorsal artery from the coeliac; *a.a.v.* ant. ventral artery; *a.b.* air-bladder; *a.v.d.* anterior dorsal vein to the cardinal; *ba⁶*, 4th aortic arch (6th of the series); *d.* ductus Cuvieri; *ev.* coeliac artery; *la.* left pulmonary artery; *oe.* oesophagus; *pr.* portal vein receiving posterior vein from air-bladder; *r.a.* right 'pulmonary' artery; *r.p.v.* right (branch of) 'pulmonary' vein; *rv.* right vein from air-bladder; *v.* left 'pulmonary' vein. (From Goodrich, *Vertebrata*, A. & C. Black, Ltd.)

their Devonian ancestors, from which we may suppose that the tetrapods arose (p. 259). This ventral position of the air-bladder was one of the features that for a long time led zoologists to suppose that *Polypterus* was a member of the crossopterygian line of fishes. It is probable, however, that the affinity is only that which persists between all primitive members of both Actinopterygii and Crossopterygii and is to be taken as an indication that the air-bladder was originally a widely open respiratory sac, or perhaps pair of sacs. Once the power to produce a pharyngeal diverticulum had been developed it is easy to imagine that the actual position of the opening might shift either dorsally, as in the later Actinopterygii, or ventrally, as in the tetrapods.

The blood-supply of the air-bladder should provide some indications both of its origin and function. In *Polypterus* and Dipnoi there are pulmonary arteries springing from the last (sixth) branchial arch and presumably containing venous blood (Fig. 160). Blood returns to the heart by pulmonary veins. Essentially the same arrangement is found in *Amia*, but in all other Actinopterygii oxygenated blood is supplied to the bladder from the dorsal aorta (or sometimes from the coeliac artery). Probably, then, the original function of the air-bladder was respiratory, and this may still be its function not only in *Amia* and *Lepidosteus* but also in some of the physostomatous Teleostei. However in the majority of teleosts its dorsal position, closed duct, and arterial blood-supply show that it has some other function and it has long been supposed that this is concerned in some way with flotation. The air-bladder is absent from bottom-living forms, such as flat fishes, *Lophius* and *Uranoscopus*, though it may be present in their pelagic larvae.

The bladder is provided with special glands by which it is filled and the gas they secrete is mostly oxygen; only in some physostomatous forms is the bladder filled by gulping air. In the more primitive forms gas is secreted all over the surface of the bladder, but later there develop special anterior oxygen-secreting and posterior oxygen-absorbing regions. The former, known as the red gland, has a special apparatus of blood-vessels, the rete mirabile, and the latter, or 'oval', developed from the closed end of the pneumatic duct, has sometimes a special flap by means of which it can be closed off. These glands are apparently under nervous control and it is presumed that the pressure in the bladder can be delicately adjusted.

There are various sacs and lobes developed on air-bladders, and many of these sacs reach forward to make contact with the ear. The highest development of such a system is the Weberian ossicles, found in cyprinoids and siluroids (Fig. 138). These consist of a series of modified parts of the anterior vertebrae, apparently serving to convey pressure movements from the air-bladder to the perilymph of the ear. It is significant that these fishes are among those with the greatest powers of discrimination of tones (see p. 208), but it has also been suggested that the apparatus serves to record changes in depth.

12. Special reproductive mechanisms in teleosts

The teleosts show great variation in breeding-habits, the eggs being sometimes left to develop entirely by themselves, in other cases looked after by one or both parents, while in a few species they develop viviparously within the mother. The method of association of the sexes is correspondingly varied and there are numerous devices for bringing the sexes together, such as colour differences, sound production, and probably the liberation of stimulating substances into the water. In some deep-sea fishes the male is very much smaller than the female, to which it remains permanently attached (Fig. 161). Breeding is often preceded by a migration of the fishes to suitable situations and the association into large shoals.

FIG. 161. Deep-sea fish *Photocorynus* with parasite male attached. (From Norman.)

The eggs may be classified as either *pelagic*, if they float, or *demersal*, if they sink to the bottom. In the former case they are generally provided with an oil globule and are exceedingly numerous. Thus a single female turbot has been calculated to contain nearly 10 million eggs, a cod 7 million, and a ling 28 million, whereas the herring, whose eggs sink to the bottom, probably does not lay more than 50,000 eggs. The large numbers laid by the pelagic species are presumably an insurance against failure of fertilization and especially against random elimination of the eggs and young. The greater the care devoted to the young by the parents the smaller the number of eggs produced (see, however, p. 269).

Demersal eggs, especially of freshwater animals, are usually laid with some special sticky covering, by means of which they are attached to each other and to the bottom or to stones, weeds, &c. Thus the eggs of many cyprinids (carp, &c.) are attached to weeds. The eggs of salmon and trout, however, though demersal, are not sticky. From depositing eggs on weeds it is only a short step to the building of a nest and guarding of the eggs by one or both parents. Thus the sand goby (*Gobius minutus*) lays its eggs in some protected spot, where they are guarded by the male, who aerates them by his movements. In many cases quite elaborate nests are built, a very

Fig. 162. Male and female bitterling (*Rhodeus*) with pond mussel in which eggs are about to be deposited. (From Norman.)

well-known example being that of the stickleback (*Gasterosteus*). In such cases the fishes are monogamous, forming pairs which remain together throughout the breeding-season. A still further development is the retention of the young within the body. In some catfishes they develop within the mouth of either parent. In the pipe-fishes the males are provided with special pouches for the young.

Although external fertilization is usual, various teleosts show internal fertilization and the young then develop within the ovary (*Zoarces, Gambusia, Lebistes*). The mechanisms by which mating and the nutrition of the embryos are assured in these cases show some interesting parallels with the conditions in mammals. Thus in

Lebistes the female adopts a special position of readiness for copulation, and this has been shown to depend partly on an internal factor in the female and partly on a substance secreted into the water by the male. The embryos in these cases are not attached to the wall of the ovary but develop free in the sac, feeding upon an 'embryotrophic' material, apparently produced by the discharged ovarian follicles, which become highly vascular and remain throughout the several months of 'pregnancy'.

Rhodeus amarus, the bitterling (Cyprinidae), shows somewhat similar conditions (Fig. 162). Association of the sexes at mating is here made necessary by the fact that the fish lays its eggs within the siphon of a swan mussel. For these purposes the cloaca of the female develops into a tubular ovipositor. This development takes place under the influence of a hormone produced by the ovary. Addition of progesterone and related substances to the water containing the fish causes growth of the ovipositor, but the effect is not a direct one and does not occur after hypophysectomy. It has therefore been concluded that the substance added to the water stimulates the pituitary and this in turn stimulates the ovary to form the substance 'oviductine' that causes growth of the ovipositor. The interest of this sequence of events (if confirmed) is that it shows a relationship between pituitary, gonad, and secondary sexual characters similar in a general way to that found in mammals.

The full growth of the ovipositor and preparation of the female for spawning is said to depend on the presence in the water not only of the male but also of the swan mussel. Water in which males have been kept stimulates growth of the ovipositor. When the female is ready to deposit the eggs she adopts a vertical position in the water and the spawning male, in full nuptial coloration, swims around her. An egg passes into the oviduct and erection of the ovipositor is produced by pressure of the urine, produced by contraction of the walls of the urinary bladder, the exit being blocked by the egg. The extended ovipositor is thus able to place the egg within the siphon of the mussel and the male then immediately thereafter sheds his sperms over the opening and they are presumably carried in by the current. The whole process shows the very elaborate interplay of internal devices and external stimuli necessary for the perfection of this remarkable method of caring for the young. Yet the various features are all special developments of systems found in other vertebrates.

X
LUNG-FISHES

1. Classification

Class Choanichthyes (= Crossopterygii)
    Order 1. *Osteolepidoti (= Rhipidistia). Devonian–Permian.
     Osteolepis, *Diplopterax*, *Eusthenopteron*
    Order 2. Coelacanthini (= Actinistia). Devonian–Recent.
     Coelacanthus, *Undina*, Latimeria
    Order 3. Dipnoi. Devonian–Recent.
     Dipterus, *Ceratodus*, Neoceratodus, Protopterus, Lepidosiren

2. Choanichthyes

Although the lung-fishes and their allies are here considered last of all the groups of fishes, because they lead on to the amphibia, it is important to realize that in many features they stand very close to the ancestral stock of gnathostomes. It is a mistake to consider them as 'higher' animals than, say, the elasmobranchs or actinopterygians. Only four genera belonging to this group are found at the present time, *Neoceratodus*, *Lepidosiren*, *Protopterus*, the lung-fishes of Australia, South America, and Africa respectively, and *Latimeria*, of which one specimen was recently discovered off the east coast of South Africa. These forms are relics of a group that can be traced back with relatively little change to the Devonian, and there is very little doubt that at about that period the first amphibia arose from some similar line. The characters of the modern lung-fishes are therefore of extraordinary interest, because they show an approach to the condition of the ancestors of all tetrapods.

The Choanicthyes fall into three distinct orders: the Osteolepids (Rhipidistia) of the Devonian and Carboniferous, the Coelacanthini (Actinistia) extending from the Carboniferous to the present day (*Latimeria*), and the Dipnoi from the Devonian to the present day. The osteolepid fishes show the most generalized structure, the other two lines representing specialized offshoots; the amphibia should really be included as a third such line of descent from the osteolepids.

3. Osteolepids

Osteolepis itself (Fig. 164), from the middle Devonian, was the earliest and most primitive member of the group. In appearance it shows an obvious similarity both to palaeoniscids and to early Dipnoi and it probably lay close to the line of descent from some placoderm ancestor to both of these groups and to the amphibia. The body was long and the tail heterocercal. A feature distinguishing all Crossopterygii from Actinopterygii was the presence of two dorsal fins. The paired fins have a characteristic scaly lobed form, from which the group derives its name, and the skeleton of the pectoral fin contained a basal element attached to the girdle and a branching arrangement at the tip (Fig. 180). This plan is distinctively different from that of the rayed fin of the Actinopterygii, but could also easily have led to the evolution of a tetrapod limb (p. 291).

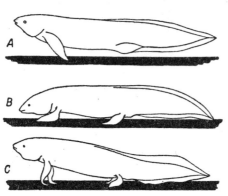

FIG. 163. *Neoceratodus*, showing the method of walking on the bottom. *A*, forwards; *B*, backwards; *C*, resting. (From Ihle, after Dean.)

The body was covered with thick rhomboidal scales, which do not overlap, and give an appearance very similar to that of the palaeoniscid scale. These scales have, however, a characteristic structure known as cosmoid. Each scale (Fig. 147) may be considered as composed of an upper layer of dentine (the cosmine), with a hard covering of shiny vitrodentine, possibly comparable with enamel. Below the cosmine is a 'vascular layer' consisting of pulp cavities in which lay odontoblasts whose processes made the dentine. This layer in turn rests on a bony layer of isopedin. The structure appears to have some relation to that of placoid scales and no doubt the morphogenetic processes that give rise to the isolated pulp cavities of placoid scales are similar to those which produce the cosmoid plates. It is usual to suggest that the latter are formed of 'fused denticles', but this is of course only a manner of speaking. Denticles do not fuse, but morphogenetic processes may occur in such a way as to produce flat plates of dentine. Indeed, it is possible that the evolution occurred in the other direction, that is to say that the placoid scale is a special case of the cosmoid. The condition in which a substance is formed nearly uniformly all over the surface of the body is a more general one than that in which such formation occurs only in isolated areas. Indeed, the discontinuous arrangement is a very remarkable condition, for which we have at present no explanation. The relationship of the cosmoid to the ganoid scale of early Actinopterygii is not quite clear, but the ganoid type seems to show a reduction of the pulp cavities and development of the shiny surface-layer. The early Dipnoi of the Devonian possessed cosmoid scales. In later osteolepids and Dipnoi there has

FIG. 164. Skull of *Osteolepis*.

d. dentary; *en.* external nostril; *esc.* extrascapulars; *gu.* gular; *j.* jugal; *la.* lachrymal; *l.gu.* lateral gular; *mgu.* median gular; *mx.* maxilla; *op.* opercular; *pa.* parietal; *pm.* premaxilla; *po.* postorbital; *pop.* preopercular; *ppa.* postparietal; *prf.* prefrontal; *qj.* quadratojugal; *sop.* subopercular; *sq.* squamosal; *sut.* supratemporal; *ta.* tabular. (After Säve-Söderbergh and Westoll, *Biol. Rev.* 1943.)

been a thinning of the scales, very similar to that which has occurred among the Actinopterygii, so that the later Dipnoi are covered with thin, overlapping, 'cycloid' scales.

The skull of osteolepids (Fig. 164) is well ossified; there is a series of bony plates arranged according to a pattern with a general similarity to that of palaeoniscids (p. 219) and which might well have been ancestral to that of amphibia. There is, however, a joint across the top of the skull between the parietal and post-parietal bones, and an unossified gap in the base of the skull. This suggests a movable joint at this level, a distinguishing feature which is usually held to show that the known osteolepids are off the direct line of descent of both Dipnoi and amphibia, but does not appear to be a character of very profound morphological significance. There was an open spiracle.

A most important feature, common to all choanichthyes, was that the attachment of the jaws was autostylic, that is to say, similar to the arrangement in amphibia and the earliest gnathostomes (aphetohyoids), but different from that of modern elasmobranchs and actinopterygians. The teeth of osteolepids were simple cones, not flattened plates such as are characteristic of Dipnoi, but the teeth on the palate show a somewhat broad folded surface and each tooth is replaced by another growing up near it, both of these being features found in the earliest amphibia. Sections of the teeth show a peculiar infolding of the enamel to make a labyrinthine structure, which is not found in other fishes but is characteristic of the teeth of the first amphibia (p. 337).

There was only one nostril on the surface of the head and there are gaps, which are considered to be internal nostrils, at the front end of the palate, bordered by the premaxillae, maxillae, palatines, and prevomers. It is supposed, therefore, that these fishes breathed air; they certainly also possessed gills, covered with an operculum.

Animals of this sort seem to have been abundant in Devonian waters and by the end of that period had diverged into several different lines. It is very interesting that the tendencies shown by these lines are very similar to those which we discovered in the evolution of the Actinopterygii. Some of the later osteolepids became shorter in body, the tails tended to become symmetrical (diphycercal) and the scales to become thinner and overlapping. *Diplopterax* and *Eusthenopteron* represent separate lines from the late Devonian, both showing these characters. Probably in all cases the development of these features depends on the use of the air-bladder as a hydrostatic organ and the associated changes in the method of swimming.

4. Coelacanths

The osteolepids became rare in the Carboniferous and disappeared after the early Permian, but a line descended directly from them remained common through the Mesozoic and apparently still survives to-day. These coelacanths (Fig. 210) show certain very characteristic features, which enabled the strange fish brought to the museum at East London, South Africa, to be recognized immediately as belonging to the group. They are rather deep-bodied animals, with a characteristic three-lobed diphycercal tail. The type first appeared in the late

Devonian and was obviously derived from osteolepid ancestry, having two dorsal fins, diphycercal tail, lobed fins, and a rhipidistian pattern of skull bones, including in most forms, a fronto-parietal joint. There was a calcified air-bladder. *Coelacanthus* and other Carboniferous forms lived in fresh water, but *Undina* and other Jurassic and Cretaceous types lived in the sea. The single living specimen of the group that has been discovered was fished in the sea off the east coast of South Africa. It was unfortunately skinned and the insides thrown away before any investigation of the soft parts was made. We therefore know little more of this amazing fish than of its fossil ancestors. It has been named *Latimeria*. There is no evidence that it breathes air, for there is probably only a single, external, nostril, a character which may necessitate a renaming of the whole class Choanicthyes.

5. Dipnoi

The Devonian Dipnoi were more like their osteolepid relatives than are the surviving modern forms. The early members of this group, such as *Dipterus* (Fig. 210), showed the typical elongated body, thick heavy scales, heterocercal tail, lobed fins, and well-ossified skull. The pattern of the bones was obscured by a seasonal deposit of cosmine, this being periodically absorbed to allow of growth.

The individual bones are found to be in general similar to those of osteolepids, but there are extra bones which are difficult to name. There was no premaxilla or maxilla, nor any teeth along the edge of the jaw; instead broad, ridged tooth-plates were developed on the palate and inside of the lower jaw, presumably as an adaptation for eating molluscs and other invertebrates. These crushing-plates are characteristic of the Dipnoi and preclude even the earliest of them from being the actual ancestors of the amphibia. By the end of the Devonian the Dipnoi were showing changes similar to those of the osteolepids and palaeoniscids. The body became shorter, the first dorsal fin disappeared, the tail became diphycercal, and the scales lost their shiny surface-layer and became thin. The teeth of *Ceratodus* appear in the Triassic and were known to geologists long before the related living animal was discovered. There has been very little change in this animal in more than 150 million years, though the recent members are placed in a distinct genus *Neoceratodus*.

The three surviving lung-fishes (Fig. 165) are all inhabitants of rivers and they all breathe air. *Neoceratodus* lives only in the Burnett and Mary rivers in Queensland, the pools of which become very low and stagnant in summer. *Lepidosiren* from the rivers of tropical

South America, and *Protopterus* from those of tropical Africa, can survive when the rivers dry up completely. They dig into the mud, leaving a small opening for breathing, and can remain in this state for at least six months. These three survivors all show similar deviations from the conditions found in *Dipterus, but *Neoceratodus* has diverged less than the other two. The tail fin is symmetrical (gephyrocercal) in all three, with no trace of separate dorsal fins. The paired fins are

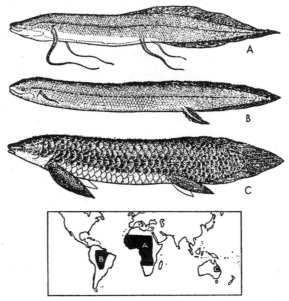

FIG. 165. The three living lung-fishes and their distribution. A, *Protopterus*; B, *Lepidosiren*; C, *Neoceratodus*. (From Norman.)

lobed in *Neoceratodus*, reduced to filaments in the other two. The scales are reduced to cycloid bony plates.

There are no vertebrae in the modern Dipnoi, the notochord remaining as an unconstricted rod. In the skull there is also a great reduction of ossification, the dorsal bones consisting of a few bony plates, forming a pattern not obviously comparable with that of other forms (Fig. 166). The jaw-suspension is autostylic, and the teeth are in the form of large grinding plates. The food consists of small invertebrates and decaying vegetable matter, which is eaten in large amounts. In the gut, the stomach and intestine are ciliated; there are no hepatic caeca, but a well-developed spiral valve is present.

The external nostrils lie just at the edge of the mouth and the internal nostrils open into its roof. The air-bladder is developed into a definitely lung-like structure (there is one in *Neoceratodus*, a pair in each of the others), divided into many climbers. *Neoceratodus* has been observed to come to the surface to breathe air and is said to be able to survive in foul water which kills other fishes, but it cannot live out of the water. The wall of the air-bladder of all forms contains muscle-fibres and the cavity is subdivided into a number of pouches

FIG. 166. Skull of *Neoceratodus*. Above, Lateral view; below, view of medial surface of right half.

a. angular; *bh.* basihyal; *br.* fifth branchial arch; *ch.* ceratohyal; *c.r.* 'cranial' rib; *d.* dentary; *eo.* 'exoccipital'; *hm.* hyomandibula; *h.n.* hyomandibular nerve; *hr.* hypohyal; *l.p.* lateral plate; *m.a.* median anterior, and *m.p.* median posterior plate; *n.a.* neural arch; *n.a.c.* cartilage of neural arch; *n.s.* notochordal sheath; *n.sp.* neural spine; *nt.* notochord; *o.* opercular, and *oc.* its cartilage; *pa.* parasphenoid; *pf.* post-frontal; *p.p.* pterygopalatine; *p.t.* palatine tooth; *pto.* pterotic (?), and *g.* its downward process covering the quadrate cartilage, *q.c.*; *s.* subopercular; *so.* suborbital; *s.t.* splenial tooth; *v.t.* vomerine tooth. (From Goodrich.)

or alveoli (Fig. 159). In *Protopterus* and *Lepidosiren* the edges of the slit-like glottis are controlled by muscles and there is an epiglottis. The lung is supplied with blood from the last branchial arch in *Neoceratodus* (Fig. 167), but in the other Dipnoi there is a more elaborate arrangement. The second and third gill-arches bear no lamellae and their afferent and efferent branchial vessels are directly continuous, so that blood flows from the ventral to the dorsal aorta and carotids. The pulmonary artery springs from the dorsal aorta. Blood returns in a special pulmonary vein to the left side of the sinus venosus.

The auricle is partly divided into two and a ridge partly divides the ventricle. The ventral aorta is shortened into a spirally twisted truncus arteriosus, provided with a system of valves such that the blood from the left side of the auricle is directed mostly into the first two branchial arches, that from the right side into the last two. In this way some separation of pulmonary and systemic circulations is achieved. Indeed, although there is every reason to believe that the mechanism has been in existence for nearly 300 million years, it shows us most clearly a possible intermediate stage between aquatic

FIG. 167. Branchial circulation of *Neoceratodus*.

I–V, five branchial slits; *abr.* anterior efferent vessel; *a.c.* anterior carotid; *af³⁻⁶*, four afferent vessels; *c.* conus; *cl.* coeliac artery; *d.* ductus Cuvieri; *eb²⁻⁴*, second and fourth epibranchial arteries; *h.a.* hyoid artery (from original second arch); *L.* air-bladder; *l.a.* lingual artery; *mes.* mesenteric artery; *p.a.* pulmonary artery; *pbr.* posterior efferent vessel; *p.c.* posterior carotid; *p.v.* pulmonary vein; *s.* position of closed spiracle; *v.a.* ventral artery; *v.c.* vena cava inferior. The gills are represented on the hyoid and next four branchial arches. (From Goodrich.)

and pulmonary respiration. It seems very likely that the earliest amphibia employed a similar system.

A further amphibian feature of the blood-vascular system is the presence of an inferior vena cava, a vessel collecting blood from the kidneys and reaching to the heart by passing round to the right of the gut in the mesentery. The more dorsal cardinal veins, joining the ductus Cuvieri, remain present, however, and there is a renal portal system.

The arrangement of the urinogenital system is similar to that of amphibia and is probably closer to that of the ancestral gnathostome than in any living elasmobranch or actinopterygian. In the male there are vasa efferentia by which sperms are passed through the excretory portion of the mesonephros, and in the female eggs are shed free into the coelom and carried out by a Müllerian duct, whose opening lies far forward. An interesting feature is that the Müllerian duct is very well developed in the male. This is one of several details (lack of ossification, unconstricted notochord) which raise the suspicion that the living Dipnoi have acquired their special characters by a process of paedomorphosis or partial neoteny, that is to say, becoming sexually mature in an early stage of morphogenesis.

The development, again, shows similarity to that of amphibia and dissimilarity from the other groups of fishes in that cleavage is total and gastrulation takes place to form a yolk plug. There is therefore no blastoderm or extra-embryonic yolk sac. However, the cells of the vegetative pole contribute little to the shape of the embryo and indeed may form a partially separate yolk sac. The larvae show distinct similarity to those of amphibia, especially the larvae of *Lepidosiren* and *Protopterus*, in which there is a sucker and external gills.

The nervous system shows the same affinities as the rest of the organization (Fig. 168). The forebrain is evaginated into a well-marked pair of cerebral hemispheres. The roof of these, though not very thick, is nervous and therefore is definitely of the inverted type, not everted as in Actinopterygii. The optic lobes are little developed, the mesencephalon being hardly wider than the diencephalon. The cerebellum is small. A peculiar feature is the development of the inner ear to form a special lobed saccus endolymphaticus, lying above the medulla oblongata. The significance of this is not known, but it is interesting that similar backward extensions of the ear are found in amphibia.

In very many features, then, the Dipnoi differ from modern fishes and resemble the amphibia. Their habits are also in a sense amphibious, but they are sluggish creatures, specialized for life in backwater, which they have occupied with little change during the

FIG. 168. Dorsal view of the brain of *Protopterus*.

1, spinal cord; 2, dorsal root of first spinal nerve; 3, diverticula of 4, the saccus endolymphaticus; 5, medulla oblongata; 6, fourth ventricle; 7, cerebellum; 8, mesencephalon (fused optic lobes); 9, stalk of pineal body; 10, thalamencephalon; 11, velum transversum; 12, pineal body; 13, lobus hippocampi; 14, choroid plexus; 15, cerebral hemisphere; 16, olfactory lobe. (After Burckhardt, from Goodrich.)

270 million years or more since the Devonian. Probably it was a backwater even then; although the relatively dry conditions of the Devonian

may have given some impetus to the development of air-breathing types, there is no reason to suppose that the earliest amphibia were numerous or important creatures. The early choanichthyes probably competed somewhat precariously with other fishes, as do the Dipnoi, and indeed many urodeles, to-day. It was only after tens of millions of years of evolution during the Carboniferous and Permian times that numerous land animals arose, in the form of the later amphibian and reptilian types (Fig. 210).

XI

FISHES AND MAN

MAN's influence, which has so altered the face of the land, also reaches
out into the water. During the last half-million years or so fishing
has grown continually, until at the present time in fresh and shallow
sea waters man has become the most important source of mortality
of fish. However, he still leaves vast regions of the sea, as of the
land, almost untouched. It may be that methods of catching the fish
that swim above deep waters will eventually produce changes there
too, providing a substantial extension of the food-supplies of man
and effecting great changes in the population of the sea.

Man has probably caught fish from his earliest times and he uses
many parts of their bodies. The skin, especially of elasmobranchs,
makes a useful leather and also a polishing material. The scales of
the bleak (*Alburnus*) yield a substance which when coated on to the
inside of glass beads makes artificial pearls. The lining of the air-
bladder, especially of sturgeons, makes isinglass, a shiny powder used
for various purposes as an adsorbent (i.e. in wine-making). Fish-glue
is obtained from the connective tissue of the skin and other parts.
Fish oils are used as food, and are also valuable in the manufacture
of soap and other things. Besides their direct use as human food fish
products may be fed to animals, and the liver makes excellent manure.

Fish therefore provide the raw material for very many human
activities, but it is, of course, principally for food that they are caught.
From a fish diet one can obtain not only abundant calorific value,
especially if the fish be fat, but also various proteins, often the fat-
soluble vitamins A and D, and usually considerable amounts of combined phosphorus and other elements. Fish are undoubtedly good
food, and what is perhaps even more important they are esteemed as
such; most people think that they taste good.

It is not possible to give an accurate estimate of the amount of fish
caught every year; 20,000,000 tons, of value £200 million, is certainly
not an overestimate for the catch of the whole world in each of the
years between the Great Wars. An appreciable fraction of the nutriment of the human race is derived from fish. The greatest single part
of the catch was that of Japan, valued at £30,500,000 (1922), next that
of Great Britain, £20,250,000 (1925), and the U.S.A., £19,000,000.

By far the greater part of all fishing is in the sea. In Great Britain

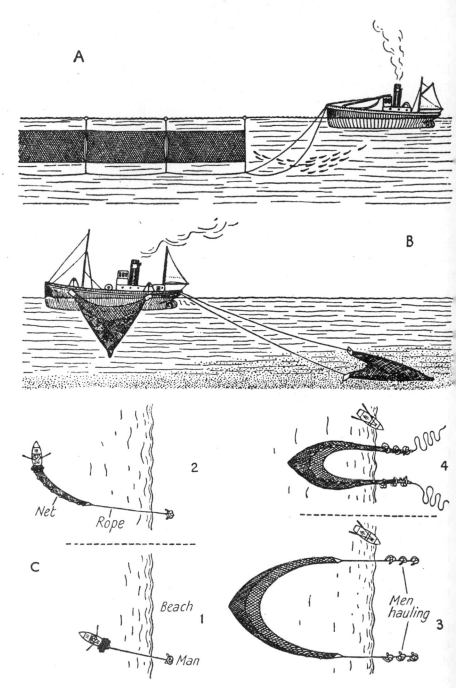

FIG. 169. Some methods of fishing. A, steam drifter; B, otter trawl; fishing and hauled; c, seining, four stages. (From Norman.)

the total catch in fresh water annually is reckoned at only 2,000 tons and the entire stock at 8,000 tons, whereas about 700,000 tons are landed every year from the sea. However, there are important fishing industries in the American Great Lakes and on the continent of Europe carp are raised on special fish farms, the water being manured to yield a good crop of the freshwater plants and invertebrates on which the carp feed.

Fishing in the sea is limited mainly by two considerations. First, the labour is only really profitable when the fish population is dense. Secondly, fish do not keep well unless they are treated in some special way and they are therefore best caught near to their market. For these reasons the big commercial fisheries are mostly in the relatively shallow waters of the continental shelf (down to 200 fathoms) and in the northern hemisphere. However, by packing the fish in ice, or cooling by other means, the vessels are now able to go longer distances than formerly.

For catching purposes fish may be divided into those which swim well away from the bottom, the *pelagic* forms, such as herring or mackerel, and the bottom-living or *demersal* fishes, such as the skates and rays, flat fishes, and angler-fishes. For the first the gear employed is usually *drift-net*. This is of narrow mesh and is shot and left overnight, floating vertically near the surface, often making a barrier two or three miles in length. The fish, such as herrings, swim into them, and become enmeshed, and are removed as the nets are hauled in (Fig. 169).

The success of such fishing with drift-nets depends on laying the nets in the path of large shoals of fish and it is therefore practised especially in regions where fish congregate seasonally. For instance, in the North Sea between East Anglia and Holland the herring congregate in the autumn; at certain times, for unknown reasons, all the fish in the area begin to move, making 'the swim', and they are then caught in great numbers. Other drift-net fisheries depend on intercepting the fish when rising to feed. Evidently these methods demand a close knowledge of the habits and migrations of the fish. The fishermen have learned enough to know when and where to expect the larger and nearer aggregations, but there is still very much to be done in tracing the migration and behaviour of pelagic fishes in more distant waters. It is not impossible that other pelagic fisheries could be developed which would be at least as advantageous as the herring fishery, and this provides millions of barrels of fish each year in Great Britain alone. Besides those eaten fresh, others are preserved as kippers by salting and smoking, or are heavily salted and smoked to make 'red herrings' for which there is a large export market.

Lining is a method that can be used for either pelagic or demersal fish. For instance, the cod fishery of Newfoundland uses lines with several thousand baited hooks. Inshore fishing may be accomplished by *seining*, a process of enclosure of the fish from the shore. There are also various forms of trap into which the fish swim and cannot escape. *Offshore seining*, completely surrounding the fish and some-times then also drawing the bottom of the net together, is also an effective method.

The greatest quantities of fish are caught, however, by the various forms of *trawling*. These depend essentially on dragging a bag along the bottom of the sea, and the different types adopt various means of keeping the bag open. The earlier way of doing this was by means of a rigid bar and these beam trawls sometimes used poles over 50 ft. long. More recently the method known as otter-trawling has replaced the beam trawl, the otter boards being flat wooden structures attached at each end, so as to sheer away when they are dragged through the water thus opening the net (Fig. 169). Various devices are used to stir up the fish from the bottom; in particular the otter boards are now usually separated from the net by long wires and a 'tickler' chain is attached in front of the mouth.

With such methods very large amounts of fish can be taken from the sea bottom. In 1860 sailing-ships landed 500 tons of fish at Grimsby; by 1901, 176,000 tons were landed from the steam trawlers; 50,000 tons of plaice alone are taken annually from the North Sea. There is evidence that the taking of such amounts of fish from rela-tively confined waters has a large influence on the population. For instance, it is estimated that 70 per cent. of the stock of plaice is caught each year in the North Sea. Clearly under these conditions man provides the main source of mortality for the fishes. It is less clear exactly how such mortality influences the total population of the fish in the area. There is reliable evidence that intensive fishing reduces the productivity of fishing effort in some cases, but there is also evidence that by reducing competition fishing may produce faster growth of the fish. The problem is worth some further discus-sion since, besides its economic importance, it gives us an insight into the life of the vast populations of the sea and a glimpse of the factors that control the numbers of each animal species.

It used to be held that one of the chief dangers of fishing was that it would destroy the breeding-stock, on the grounds that it is axiomatic that something is wrong if fish are destroyed before they have an opportunity to breed. We may detect something of anthropocentric sentimentality here, for reflection shows at once that it is impossible in any case for every fish that is hatched to survive and, further, that it may be possible to provide the total annual supply of fish from very few adults. The number of fish in the sea, indeed, bears no obvious relation to the number of eggs. A cod may shed as many as 8,000,000 eggs (usually fewer), which float at the sea surface and hatch into planktonic young. Yet herrings, which are much more numerous as adults, lay fewer eggs, not more than 100,000 each. Presumably the risks of life are less for the herring, but we cannot see clearly why; the herring's eggs are sticky and attached to gravel or sea-weeds, which may give them some protection; they are known to be eaten by other fishes, perhaps on a smaller scale than planktonic eggs. Both herring and cod fry are planktonic and feed on the nauplius and other larval stages of *Calanus* and other copepods. The cod, like other bottom-fishes, has to undergo the risks of metamorphosis, but this hardly seems sufficient to explain the much greater abundance of herring, especially since many fishes feed on the latter, including the cod themselves! As Graham puts it, 'no one really knows why the herring, which nearly everything eats, should be able to manage with a less rate of reproduction than the cod, which eats nearly everything'.

This brings us to face the difficult question of the pressure, force, or potential that ensures and controls the number of animals. Reproduction is only a part of the source of this pressure, the other element being the feeding and growth of the animals as a result of the skill and persistence with which they seek and consume their food. It is somewhat easier to study these questions in a marine than in a land community, the whole population being enclosed in one vast bath, the additions and subtractions to which can be known.

We must not forget, however, that conditions are very far from constant, even in the 'unchanging sea'. For instance, the extent to which fish-fry hatch and successfully overcome the hazards of the early stages of life varies most mysteriously from year to year. By study of the markings on the scales, bones, and otoliths it is possible to show the age composition of a fish population and it is found that the hatches of certain years predominate. Thus the herring hatched in the North Sea in 1904 dominated the population for years afterwards (Fig. 170). Subsequent good herring years occurred in 1913 and 1918. Similarly there were good cod years in 1904 and 1912.

(270)

FIG. 170. Age composition of Norwegian herring catches 1907-19, showing the preponderance of particular year-classes. (After Hjort.)

Haddock broods in the North Sea follow a rather regular rhythm with a period of about three years (Fig. 171). These cyclical changes in hatching do not appear to produce fluctuations in the total population of that species, though we have inadequate data on the point. It seems likely that there is a limit set to the total of fish of the species, irrespective of age-grouping (see p. 279).

In addition to such cyclical changes there are also larger ones, such as the increase of cod in the far north around Bear Island in recent

FIG. 171. Relative strengths of haddock broods in the North Sea, showing cyclical fluctuations. (After Raitt, from Russell, *The Overfishing Problem.*)

years, apparently due to a northerly extension of warm water, the reason for which is not known. Since so many changes are going on in the eternal sea is it to be wondered at that the animals in it are changing? We might be surprised rather at the slowness of their evolution.

All the fish-life in the sea depends ultimately on the diatoms, flagellates, and other green organisms of the plankton, reaching the fish usually after passage through one or more animals, especially copepods. Bottom-living fishes also depend on plankton, in this case after it has died and passed through a bottom-living invertebrate. Thus plaice feed on lamellibranchs and worms, soles on worms alone, haddock on star-fish and worms. The phytoplankton is, of course, built up by photosynthesis from carbon dioxide, water, nitrates, phosphates, and small quantities of other substances. The limiting factors in the plankton growth, granted adequate temperature and sunlight, appear to be nitrate, ammonia, and phosphate, the latter present only to the extent of less than one part in 20,000,000. During the spring and early summer nearly all the phosphate in the water may be taken up into the phytoplankton, which increases rapidly. The zooplankton (*Calanus*, &c.) increases somewhat later and by midsummer grazes down the phytoplankton to a considerable extent. It is at this midsummer period that the pelagic fishes feed most easily, and a little later it is the turn of the bottom-living invertebrates and fish, as some of the zooplankton dies and falls to the bottom. At the end of the season there may be a second increase in the phytoplankton, recovering due to break-down of the discontinuity layer (see below), and then with the onset of winter the plants die off and most of the phosphate is returned to the inorganic condition.

Thus to take the case of the cod, whose food chain is one of the longest: the activity of the plants turns carbon dioxide, nitrate, and phosphate into organic matter: the activity of the copepods makes this available to the herrings and the cod eat the herrings. There are, of course, many intermediate effects: *Sagitta* eat some of the copepods, fish-fry and large cod eat younger cod, and so on, but in general we shall not go wrong if we assume that the cycle depends on the activity of diatoms, calanoids, herrings, and codfish—all seeking, eating, growing, reproducing, and dying.

The pressure of these various activities produces a complicated set of interrelations that may without undue extravagance of fancy be called a macro-organism. The activities of all the members contribute to the balance that is set up, but often shortage of materials at certain key-points seems to determine the whole cycle. For instance, there can be little doubt that the amount of phosphate present may limit the growth of the total biomass in the sea and hence of each species in the food chain.

The phosphate in the sea is increased by drainage from the land and, further, in a restricted area such as the North Sea, by the upwelling of water from more open areas, in that case the Atlantic. Not all the phosphate in a given area of sea is available for organic growth, because there is usually a separation between upper and lower layers due to warming and lightening of the former. The phosphate in the water below this limiting discontinuity layer, usually lying 20–100 metres down, is thus usually not available, though it may be made available in certain areas by particular conditions which lead to up-currents and mixing of the layers. Generally speaking, however, the amount of life is limited by lack of phosphate and other growth-promoting substances present in small quantities, and it is conceivable that manuring the sea by the addition of phosphate and nitrate could lead to an increase in organic matter and a greater growth of fish. The possibility has been investigated in partly enclosed waters by Gross and his colleagues, who found that the salts are taken up so quickly that it may possibly be advantageous to undertake manuring even of more open waters. We do not know, however, what would be the effects of increased or unlimited phosphate and nitrate on the population of the sea.

It must be remembered that these salts represent only the necessary raw materials and that the formation of the living matter depends on the *activities* of the various animals in the food chains and we do not know how the activities would change under various circumstances. It is probable that addition of phosphate to open waters would lead to some increase of edible fish production, but it has not been demonstrated that this would be as efficient for food production as using the phosphate on land. There are those who hold the converse view that the continual escape of minerals into the sea as sewage constitutes a serious waste of one of our most essential raw materials.

With these facts in mind we can now make further inquiry into the effects on the population of the sea of removal by man of large quantities of organic matter in the shape of fish. There are sufficient data to give us hints of the changes which follow, and the hope that with sufficient further study we may eventually understand the Great Sea Beast sufficiently to be able, if we can sufficiently control ourselves, to regulate its growth to our advantage.

In a few cases it has been possible to follow the course of a fishery from its early beginnings, with few vessels and simple apparatus, through stages in which the fishing was progressively more intense. The statistics are seldom adequate to provide us with wholly satisfactory conclusions, but they suggest in several cases that (1) as fishing becomes more intense, the yield per unit of fishing power declines; that is to say, the industry becomes relatively less profitable. (2) In spite of this, the total yield may remain constant, or even somewhat increase, even though (3) the average size of the fish caught decreases.

For example, fishing for plaice in the Barents Sea, north of Norway, was begun in 1905, and the almost 'virgin' population in 1907 showed great preponderance of large mature fish (Fig. 172); whereas in the North Sea, which had already been fished for many years, the average size was much smaller and few of the plaice were mature. The fish taken in the Barents Sea were old and had grown slowly. Transplantation of fish of this stock to the North Sea, however, proved that they were able to grow as rapidly as the local fish. Some measure of the intensity of fishing is given by the number of days' absence of vessels fishing in a given area. No doubt the measure is inexact, particularly if the methods used are changed, but it provides the best estimate available. The landing of plaice taken from the Barents Sea per day's absence was 34·7 cwt. in 1906, 50·4 cwt. in 1909, and then fell to 46·3, 33·7, and 20·5 cwt. in the following years. The total yield showed some decline. The sequence of events is typical of what happens when a stock of mature fish is first exploited.

Graham described a good example of a similar situation in Lake Victoria-Nyanza, where he found two stocks of a carp-like fish *Tilapia*, one fished heavily and the other with primitive devices only. The less heavily fished stock contained five times as many fish as the other and they were much older. Yet by the intensive fishing the poorer stock was being made to yield a ten times greater weight than the richer stock. This desirable state of affairs for man in general is considered unsatisfactory by the fishermen, since the yield *per unit of effort* is much greater when the richer stock is fished.

Statistics of the main demersal fisheries of the North Sea suggest that changes have occurred similar to those indicated by these two examples. Figures collected by the International Council for the Exploration of the Sea show that the total landings of fish taken from the area have been rather constant. In 1906–14 they were around 400,000 metric tons annually, in 1914–18, 250,000 tons, 1919–22, 480,000 tons, and from then on until 1935 about 380,000 tons. The total yield is therefore fairly constant, but the fishing effort to provide this yield has changed. Data are available only for English vessels and they show a steady decline in landings per day's absence, from 17·6 cwt. in 1906 to 14·3 cwt. in 1913. After the war the figures rose to 30·6 cwt. in 1919 and then fell steadily to 14·0 in 1923 and fluctuated at about this figure till 1937. There has therefore been some fall in yield per unit of fishing effort, probably more than the figures indicate, because the efficiency of trawling methods has certainly increased with the adoption of special devices for stirring up the fish (p. 268). The greatly increased yields obtained after the partial fishing holiday during the 1914–18 war by themselves indicate that intense fishing could reduce the return which is to be obtained.

These figures for all landings in the North Sea are complicated by the inclusion of haddock, which fluctuate largely from year to year (p. 271). Consideration of the various fishes separately brings out the conclusion more clearly. The yield of haddock per day's absence

Fig. 172. Size distribution of plaice (♀). A, in Barents Sea, B, in North Sea in 1907. The vertical line *M* shows the average size at first maturity. (After Russell and Atkinson.)

averaged 5·8 cwt. between 1906 and 1913, rose to 15·8 cwt. in 1919, averaged 6·5 cwt. 1922–9, and 3·7 cwt. in 1930–7 (Fig. 173). The fish are divided into large, medium, and small categories, and the percentage of the last category was 50 before the war, 70 in 1922–9, and 85 in 1930–7; evidently the fish were becoming smaller throughout this period. Perhaps the most interesting fact of all is that the total haddock catch changed only slightly, from 121 million kilos (1910–13) to 138 million (1922–9) and 94 million (1930–6). Fishing

FIG. 173. Haddock landings per day's absence by English steam trawlers in North Sea. (After Raitt, from Russell, *The Overfishing Problem.*)

seems to have made the population consist of smaller fish, giving a smaller yield per unit of fishing effort, but, given sufficient effort, nearly the same weight of haddock can be removed from the sea. This suggests that though the population now consists of smaller fish the total biomass has not been reduced to the same extent as the yield per unit effort.

The figures available for plaice taken from the North Sea show much the same tendencies. The total landing in 1893–4 was probably about 48 million kilos and in 1931–5 the annual average was 51 million kilos. During the period between these dates the percentage of fish over 33 cm. long had dropped, however, from 58 to 21. In 1893 steam trawlers used the beam trawl, the intensity of fishing effort has certainly been increased since then with the introduction of modern gear—but the yield remains the same.

The fishing for cod in the North Sea shows very similar changes,

an average annual yield of 102 million kilos in 1910–13, falling to
75 million in 1922–9 and 67 million in 1930–7, with fall in landing per
day's absence from 4·2 cwt. 1906–13 to 3·4 cwt. 1922–9 and 3·6 cwt.
1930–7. Given the increased efficiency of more modern trawls these
figures certainly suggest a fall in yield per unit effort. At the same
time the percentage of 'small' fish showed an increase from 30 before
1929 to 43 in 1930–7.

Study of the fishing-grounds off Iceland shows similar declines in
the yield of haddock, plaice, and halibut, but in this area, as already
mentioned, the cod have increased in recent years, on account of the
northerly extension of warm water, which has more than compensated
for the increased intensity of fishing.

Over a long period fishermen have been afflicted by the consequences of the decline in yield per unit effort indicated by such
statistics. Already in the last century those giving evidence before
Royal Commissions expressed an uneasy feeling that the profitability
of their industry was declining. This situation has been met by
continual improvement in methods of fishing and the exploitation
of new grounds. The proportion of the total English catch that
is obtained from the nearer waters of the North Sea is now very
much less than formerly, although the catch is no greater. We have
already seen that steam trawling and better gear all mean increased
labour for the crews, at greater distances from port. With all the
improvements in technique and discovery of new grounds we
succeed in obtaining from the sea little more fish than at the end of
the last century; and there is no greater profit for those engaged in
the industry.

The situation is complicated by the discovery of new fishing-
grounds, which can hardly continue indefinitely. As far as any given
area is concerned it seems that as fishing increases in intensity the
yield per unit of effort falls: in order to keep the fishing profitable
still more intense fishing methods are then adopted, which make the
catch fall further still. It is by no means clear exactly what this means
in terms of the changes of the fish stocks. The usual conclusion is
that the stock falls during this process; all that is certain, however, is
that the proportion of young fish in the stock increases. The evidence
is sufficient to suggest strongly that fishing affects the stock in ways
which (a) reduce the productivity of fishing, (b) reduce the size of the
fish in the stock. This does not necessarily mean a decrease in the
total biomass of the stock, though it may be that such a decrease
does occur.

In any case the 'Great Law of Fishing', as Graham calls it, 'that fisheries that are unlimited become unprofitable' has been tested on at least three occasions. During the two recent Great Wars the intensity of fishing in the North Sea was reduced and thereafter both of the expected changes were seen: (*a*) fishing became more profitable, (*b*) there were found to be more old fishes in the stock. Perhaps more encouraging is a case where the intensity of fishing has been regulated not by war but by law. The halibut fishery of the Pacific coast of North America showed the typical history of increasing effort and decreasing yield. Fishermen went farther and farther afield in larger and more expensive boats, setting ever more and more lines, but yet brought home the same or a smaller amount of fish. Thus in 1907 there were 1,800,000 sets of lines used, in 1930, 6,400,000 sets, but instead of the 50 million pounds of fish caught in the first year there were only 23 million pounds in 1930! Then in 1932 a limitation of 23 million pounds was imposed on the total catch allowed. Thereafter the stocks rapidly increased and it was found possible to collect the standard catch in five months instead of nine, with very greatly increased profit.

Other attempts to regulate fisheries have been made; in particular by the mesh regulations designed to avoid taking small fishes. It is doubtful, however, whether we have yet sufficient knowledge to set a final mark at which regulation can aim. The idea of the earlier advocates of fishing regulations was to avoid taking fishes before they had reproduced. Possibly this aim is less sensible than it seems; it is not necessary for every fish to breed. The stock of spawning plaice in the North Sea must now be less than one-tenth of that present in 1870 and mature cod and haddock have been reduced almost as much. It may be that this is a dangerous reduction and some advocate hatching and release of the fish to improve the fisheries, but the value of such methods has still to be determined. The aim of regulation is nowadays not so much to save the stock from undue reduction or extinction but rather to *crop it in such a way as shall make fishing profitable*. Whatever we do it is unlikely that we shall destroy all the stocks of any species, but there is reason to think that the rate at which the stocks grow varies with the intensity of fishing. If this is so, it may be possible to find an optimum that suits both the fish and the fisherman.

Unfortunately the data about the rate of growth under various circumstances are still not adequate to allow us to find this optimum fishing-level. Graham gives the following figures for the weight increases at different ages for cod landed at Grimsby, showing the well-known fact that growth is faster in the younger animals:

Age (years)	2	4	6	20
Absolute annual increase (oz.) . .	13	41	71	2
Relative annual increase . . .	100	50	35	1

Probably there is a maximum total biomass of fish of any given sort that can be supported in any area, determined ultimately by the supply of inorganic salts. In the absence of fishing this biomass is carried in the form mainly of large fish, whose presence makes the growth of all fish in the population slow. The effect of fishing is to remove mainly these larger animals, with a resultant increased growth from all younger groups. Theoretically there is a certain intensity of fishing that would just crop off the weight increase produced in each year. Thus suppose all the cod in the above example were 20 years old; we could remove 1 per cent. of the total mass of cod and yet leave the biomass as it was at the beginning of the year. If, however, the population consisted wholly of cod of 6 years old, we could remove 35 per cent. of the mass each year, because our whole biomass would constitute a much faster growing organism. Theoretically the more severe our fishing and the more we limit the stock to small fishes the greater will be the crop that can be gathered from it, assuming always that sufficient adults survive to provide a breeding-stock. In practice, however, with intensive fishing the effort becomes less rather than more profitable, presumably because more effort is needed to catch a given weight in the form of small fish than large ones, and the small fish may be unsatisfactory as food.

It is therefore very difficult to determine the optimum age and still more so to fish in such a way as to hold the population in the optimum condition. However, the analysis of the situation suggests very interesting possibilities. The 'virgin' state of a population, with low total mortality, is not necessarily that which gives the greatest yield, considering only the quantitative criterion of biomass. There is evidence from several sources that fishes transplanted from such crowded virgin areas to waters more severely cropped by fishing can increase their growth rate. There is in fact an 'underfished' as well as an 'overfished' condition. Unfortunately the fisherman does not recognize the underfished grounds as such; on the contrary he finds on them a paradise of many large fishes, catching of which gives him a good return! Exploitation of such grounds then rapidly swings them from one extreme to the other. The population that at first consisted mainly of fish too old to grow at the maximum rate soon comes to consist of fish so young that it is unprofitable to catch them. No really satisfactory means for obtaining a result between these extremes has yet been discovered, but there is every reason to hope that with further study of growth, mortality, reproductive potential and utilization of food by fish the yield could be increased and the effort of getting it reduced, making fishing more profitable to the fisherman and providing the maximum amount of food. At present the economic conditions and psychology of the fishing populations interact with the factors limiting the stocks and the growth of the fish to produce a complicated system of interrelations that is unstable and unsatisfactory to all parties.

XII

TERRESTRIAL VERTEBRATES: AMPHIBIA

1. Classification

Class Amphibia

    *Subclass 1. *Stegocephalia. Devonian–Trias

      Order 1. *Labyrinthodontia. Devonian–Trias

        Suborder 1. *Ichthyostegalia. Upper Devonian

          *Ichthyostega, *Elpistostege

        Suborder 2. *Embolomeri. Carboniferous

          *Eogyrinus, *Loxomma

        Suborder 3. *Rhachitomi. Carboniferous–Triassic

          *Eryops. Lower Permian

          *Cacops. Lower Permian

        Suborder 4. *Stereospondyli. Triassic

          *Capitosaurus. Upper Triassic

          *Buettneria. Upper Triassic

      Order 2. *Phyllospondyli. Carboniferous–Lower Permian

        *Branchiosaurus. Lower Permian

      Order 3. *Lepospondyli. Carboniferous–Permian

        *Dolichosoma. Carboniferous

        *Diplocaulus. Permian

        *Microbrachis. Permian

      Order 4. *Adelospondyli. Carboniferous–Lower Permian

        *Lysorophus. Carboniferous

    Subclass 2. Urodela (= Caudata). Jurassic–Recent

      Molge, Salamandra, Amblystoma, Necturus.

    Subclass 3. Anura (= Salientia) Carboniferous–Recent

      *Miobatrachus

      *Protobatrachus

      Rana, Bufo, Hyla, Pipa

    Subclass 4. Apoda (= Gymnophiona = Caecilia). Recent

      Ichthyophis, Typhlonectes.

2. Amphibia

During the later part of the Devonian period a population of lung-fishes lived in the pools and there is every reason to suppose that some of these animals, first crawling from pool to pool and then spending more time on the land, gave rise to the terrestrial populations which we distinguish as amphibia. Many areas were drying up during later Devonian times (p. 19), giving a definite advantage to animals able to remain for some time out of the water. No doubt the early efforts at land life were very crude. The whole locomotory and skeletal system comes under a completely new set of forces when the support of the water is withdrawn and the effects of gravity become insistent. At the same time the skin must be changed to resist desiccation, the respiratory system adapted to use gaseous oxygen, the sense-organs to respond to strange configurations of stimuli. It is not surprising that these new conditions produced greater changes in vertebrate organization than had occurred in tens of millions of years previously. Nevertheless, so slow is the pace of evolution, the only known Devonian amphibia, and many of the Carboniferous ones too, still looked and presumably behaved very like fishes. Animals of this sort (e.g. *Eogyrinus*) floundered about on land for 30 million years or more before producing definitely terrestrial types such as the Permian *Eryops*.

Of all the features that arose at this time in connexion with the new life on land the presence of pentadactyl limbs is perhaps the most conspicuous. It is appropriate that this should be marked in zoological nomenclature: the amphibia are the first of the great group of land vertebrates, the Tetrapoda.

All existing amphibia have been very much modified since their Devonian ancestry, yet they retain many features that show how the transition from water to land was produced. These modern forms are by no means a precariously existing remnant but are quite numerous and successful in the ecological niches that they occupy; they form an important element in many food chains. There are some 2,000 species at present recognized, placed in 250 genera. However, contrasting this with the numerous species of teleosts, of birds, and of mammals we shall see that the amphibians, though well adapted for certain situations, do not succeed in maintaining themselves in many different types of habitat. Broadly speaking they are unable to survive for long except in the proximity of water. There are desert toads, such as *Chiroleptes* of Australia, but these survive by burrowing and by special abilities, such as the power to hold large amounts of water, associated with loss of the glomeruli of the kidneys.

Modern amphibia belong to three sharply separated subclasses. Urodela (newts and salamanders) retain the original long-bodied, partly fish-like form. The Anura (frogs and toads) have lost the tail and become specialized as jumpers. The Apoda are limbless, blind, burrowing animals found in the tropics. The urodeles and anurans are found as fossils back to the Cretaceous and Trias respectively, but we have only scanty information about their connexion with the earlier amphibians, which are grouped loosely together as the Stegocephalia. These are found in rocks about 275–160 million years old, that is to say from the late Devonian to the Trias (Fig. 210).

3. The Frogs

Perhaps the most successful of all amphibia are those belonging to the genus *Rana*, abundant in every part of the world except in the south of South America, on oceanic islands, and New Zealand. Ranid frogs are typical of the highly specialized subclass Anura, whose members usually inhabit damp places such as marshes or ditches, living for most of their life in the grass or undergrowth and feeding by catching flies and other insects with their tongue. They are preyed upon by birds, fishes, and especially snakes, and escape from these by their hind legs, used either for jumping or swimming. The young develop as tadpoles in the water, where they are vegetarian. The various species differ mostly in small points of colour, though there are also some which depart widely from the usual habits, e.g. *R. fossor* which burrows. *R. temporaria* is the species found in Great Britain, *R. esculenta* is a slightly larger form found on the continent of Europe and occasionally in east England, *R. pipiens* is the common small North American frog; *R. catesbiana* the giant bull-frog, whose body is up to 9 in. long, also lives in North America.

4. Skin of Amphibia

The earliest amphibia possessed the scales of their fish ancestors, but these were lost early in most lines, though retained in some Apoda; perhaps they were too heavy to be worth while for creatures contending for the first time with gravity, unaided by water. Amphibia differ from reptiles in that the skin is moist and used for respiration; on the other hand, the skin also shows a character typical of land animals in having heavily cornified outer layers. The epidermis therefore consists of several layers in the adult frog and is renewed at intervals by a process of moulting. The moult is under the control of the pituitary and thyroid glands and does not occur if either of these be removed, the keratinized cells merely accumulating in those circumstances as a thick skin. Local thickenings of the epidermis often occur in amphibia, for instance, to form the horny teeth by which the larva feeds. Such thickenings are also a conspicuous feature of the warty skin of the toads (*Bufo*), which mostly have a drier skin and are more fully terrestrial than are the frogs. The fact that the epidermis of amphibia can produce local thickenings is of interest in considering the origin of feathers and hairs. In larval amphibians the skin is ciliated.

The glands of the skin are more highly developed than in fishes, and are of two types, mucous and poison glands. Both of these consist of little sacs of gland-cells, derived from the epidermis. The mucus serves to keep the skin moist, this being essential if the skin is to respire; the secretion may perhaps also serve for temperature regulation. The problem of regulation of temperature is one which becomes important for all terrestrial animals, since air conducts heat much less well than water and therefore violent changes of temperature are met. Evaporation produces large influences on temperature and no doubt it was the adjustment of these effects which led to the development of temperature-regulating mechanisms in birds and mammals. Frogs in dry air are always found to be colder than their environment, the difference being sometimes as much as 5° C. It is probable that in some circumstances use is made of this cooling, since tree-frogs (*Hyla*) may be found fully exposed to tropical sunlight, which would be expected to raise their temperatures to a lethal level. On the other hand, the loss of water involved by evaporation in this way would presumably soon become serious.

The poison glands or granular glands are less developed in *Rana* than in *Bufo* ('the envenom'd toad') where they are collected into masses, the paratoid glands. The effect of the poison on man is to produce an irritation of the eyes and nose; only rarely does it affect the skin of the hands. When swallowed it produces nausea and has a digitalis-like action on the heart.

Some amphibia have characteristic smells, produced by secretions, and these are probably used to attract the sexes to each other. In some male newts (Plethodontidae) there are special collections of these gland-cells below the chin.

Another use of glandular secretions is to keep the eyes and nostrils free from obstruction. The demands of terrestrial life require the production of numerous such special devices and lead to that complexity which we recognize as an attribute of these 'higher' animals.

5. Colours of Amphibia

The use of colour is also highly developed in amphibia. The animals are generally greenish and the colour is produced by three layers of pigment cells, melanophores lying deepest, guanophores, full of granules, which by diffraction produce a blue-green colour, and yellow lipophores, overlying these and filtering out the blue.

FIG. 174. Stages of dispersal of pigment in the melanophores in the web of the frog *Xenopus*, as used by Hogben to assess the melanophore index. (After Hogben and Slome, *Proc. Roy. Soc. B.* 108.)

Change of colour is produced by expansion of the pigment in the melanophores under the action of the secretion of the pituitary gland (Fig. 174). Movements in the other chromatophores can also affect the colour, yellow being produced by disarrangement of the guanophores and so on. Other colours may contribute to the patterns which the animals present, blue (though rarely) by the absence of the lipophores, red by pigment in the lipophores.

Changes in the melanophores may be of two sorts, primary or direct and secondary or visual. The primary response depends on the direct effect of light on the skin, causing expansion of the melanophores. The secondary effect consists in contraction of the pigment if the animal is illuminated on a light-scattering surface (light background) but expansion (and hence darkening of the animal) when it is illuminated from above on a light-absorbing (dark) background. There are, therefore, distinct responses from different parts of the retina.

Illumination of the dorsal part produces contraction, of the ventral part expansion of the melanophores.

Hogben and his co-workers have shown that the control of the colour change of amphibians is mediated by variation in the secretion of the pituitary gland; there is no direct nervous control of the melanophores. There is still some doubt whether the pituitary produces its effects by means of one hormone or two. The most fully known influence is that of the posterior lobe, producing a B substance (Hogben), also known as intermedin, which makes the melanophores

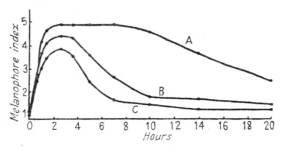

Fig. 175. Effect of an extract containing the B (melanophore-expanding) substance on three groups of *Xenopus*. All were of the same weight and received the same dose. A, whole pituitary removed; B, intact animals; C, posterior lobe only removed. (From Waring, after Hogben and Slome.)

expand. Extracts of the pituitary of mammals (or other vertebrates) produce this effect when injected into frogs and after removal of the pituitary a frog becomes pale in colour. There is also some evidence for the secretion by the anterior lobe of a W substance, which causes paling. After removal of the whole pituitary the melanophores are found to be not in the wholly contracted stage 1 of Hogben's melanophore index (Fig. 174) but in a state (stage 2 or 3) intermediate between this and full expansion (stage 5). If, however, the posterior lobe alone is removed the animal becomes completely pale (stage 1). This certainly suggests the secretion of a W substance by the pars anterior. There are also differences in the response to injection of B-containing extracts after total and partial removal of the pituitary (Fig. 175). The position is complicated by the fact that extracts of mammalian pineal or adrenal medulla will cause contraction of amphibian melanophores, though it is uncertain whether these effects have any physiological significance.

In amphibia there is no direct control of the pigment cells by nerve-fibres such as are present in bony fishes (p. 245). The colour change is therefore rather slow. After removal of the pituitary the melanophores still show slight changes correlated with change of incident illumination, indicating the small degree of direct response as independent effectors. Temperature and humidity also influence the colour in many amphibia.

The colour patterns adopted are usually cryptic or concealing in their effect, but the colour also has an important influence on the temperature and varies with it and with the humidity, as well as with the incident illumination. The uniform brilliant green of tree-frogs makes them very difficult to see among the leaves; on the other hand, *R. temporaria* and other species living among grass show a pattern of dark marks, which breaks up their outline. In other cases, however, the colour makes the animal very conspicuous, for instance, the black and yellow markings of *Salamandra maculosa*. This conspicuous colour is often associated with great development of the poisonous paratoid glands and is therefore presumably sematic or warning coloration, allowing recognition by possible attackers. This correlation is not always found, however; the toad *Ceratophrys americana* is dull coloured but poisonous, whereas *C. dorsata* has a bright pattern but is harmless.

Many frogs make a sudden exposure of brightly coloured patches on the thighs when they jump. This presumably serves to startle the attacker and such colours may be called dymantic or startling. A similar use of colour is made by the cuttle-fish (*Sepia*), which may suddenly produce two black spots when alarmed, and also by some Lepidoptera. It is interesting that the colour used in this way so often takes the form of black spots ('eye-spots'), which have an especially striking quality. In some

(a)   (b)

FIG. 176. Record of the movements of *Amblystoma* walking on a smoked drum, A, in rapid locomotion (with the body on the ground); B, in slow locomotion (raised up on the legs). (From Evans, *Anat. Rec.* 95.)

anurans these colours are irregular dark marks, but in *Mantipus ocellatus* they take the form of definite 'eye-spots'.

It must not be forgotten that the presence of pigment serves to protect the organs from the effects of light, which may cause contraction when it falls directly upon muscles. Dark colour may also assist in the absorption of heat, both in the adults and in the eggs.

6. Vertebral column of Amphibia

The general build of the body is essentially fish-like in stegocephalian and urodele amphibians. Such forms have two means of locomotion. When they are frightened and move fast they wriggle along with

FIG. 177. Drawings made from photographs of a newt (*Triturus*)
in slow locomotion. (After Evans, *Anat. Rec.* 95.)

the belly on the ground, the effective agent being serial contraction of the segmentally arranged myotomal musculature, by means of which the animal essentially 'swims on land', with the legs hardly touching the ground (Fig. 176). When moving deliberately, on the other hand, a newt raises up its body on the legs, which then propel it along as movable levers, the main part of the action being produced by drawing back the humerus or femur, the more distal muscles of the limbs serving to maintain the digits pressed against the ground (Fig. 177).

The carrying of the weight on four legs places an entirely new set of stresses on the vertebral column. Instead of being mainly a compression member as it is in fishes it comes to act as a girder, carrying the weight of the body and transmitting it to the legs. This new function produces a column whose parts are largely bony and articulated together, flexibility becoming less important than strength. The new types of strain involve new muscle attachments and the development of special processes and parts of the vertebrae (p. 339). These changes, however, have not proceeded very far in the amphibians;

FIG. 178. Reflexes associated with the transition from swimming to walking in toads. The shaded outlines show successive positions as the animal emerges on to solid ground. The first effective contact is by the left fore-limb whose retraction and extension elicits a crossed protraction reflex in the right fore-limb (L_1), a diagonal extensor response in the right hind-limb (L_2), and a placing response in the left hind-limb (L_3). The right fore-limb then touches the ground and produces corresponding responses R_{1-3}. The left fore-limb in response to stretch of its protractor muscles swings forward and this produces retraction of the left hind-limb (L_4) and protraction of the right hind-limb (L_5). Fixation of the right hind foot then produces a crossed flexor response (RH_1). (From Gray, *J. exp. Biol.* 23.)

the modern urodeles, especially, are still largely amphibious and their vertebrae often show a lack of ossification, parts of the notochord persist and provide the main compression member required for swimming.

In the anurans the entire skeletal and muscular system has become very specialized for the peculiar swimming and jumping methods of locomotion, by means of extensor thrusts of both hind limbs, acting together. Frogs, and especially toads, also walk on land, bringing into

FIG. 179. The skeleton of the frog, seen from the dorsal surface; the left suprascapular and scapular have been removed.

a. astragalus; *c.* calcaneum; *d.* suprascapular; *e.* exoccipital; *f.* femur; *fp.* frontoparietal; *g.* metacarpals; *h.* humerus; *i.* ilium; *k.* metatarsals; *l.* carpus; *m.* maxilla; *n.* nasal; *o.* pro-otic; *p.* pterygoid; *pm.* premaxilla; *q.* 'quadratojugal'; *r.* radio-ulna; *s.* squamosal; *se.* sphenethmoid; *s.v.* sacral vertebra; *t.* tibio-fibula; *u.* urostyle.

(After Marshall, *The Frog*, Macmillan.)

play a set of myotactic (proprioceptor) reflexes that depend on the contraction of the muscles against an external resistance (Fig. 178).

The actions of jumping and walking are possible because of very profound changes in the arrangement of the skeleton and muscles. The myotomal muscles no longer perform their primitive function of producing metachronal waves of contraction, and accordingly the vertebral column (Fig. 179) has lost its original flexibility. Instead, it is attached to the pelvic girdle and acts as a support by which the movement of the hind limbs is transmitted to all the rest of the body. Sinuous motion being no longer used, the number of vertebrae is very low (nine in the adult *Rana*), and behind them is an unsegmented rod of bone, the urostyle. Shortening of the body is a very characteristic feature of the change from aquatic to terrestrial life, and is seen in many lines of amphibian and reptilian evolution. It has proceeded farther in the frogs than in any other tetrapods.

The second to eighth vertebrae are concave in front, convex behind (procoelous), and have large transverse processes. They fit together by complex zygapophyses. The first vertebra has two concave facets for articulation with the two condyles of the skull; its centrum and transverse processes are much reduced. The ninth (sacral) vertebra has very large transverse processes, which articulate with the ilia of the pelvic girdle. There are free ribs in the primitive frogs *Ascaphus* and *Leiopelma*.

7. Evolution and plan of the limbs of Amphibia

The girdles of the paired limbs have become very much changed from their fish-like condition (Figs. 180 and 181). Their basic pattern is similar in the two limbs and has been retained throughout the whole tetrapod series. Whereas in fishes the girdles are rather small cartilages and bones, the pelvic girdle being restricted to the ventral region of the body, in amphibians they become much enlarged in connexion with the weight-bearing function of the limbs.

The details of the sequence of stages by which a tetrapod limb arose from a fish fin are still somewhat disputed. It is probable that the ancestral crossopterygian possessed a lobed fin, rather like that seen in *Eusthenopteron* (Fig. 180). As the fishes came on land the fin would be used as a lever, giving greater effect to the wave-like motions by which the creature 'swam on land'. The muscles of the limb, contracting in a serial manner, would tend to move it backwards and forwards relative to the body, thus assisting in locomotion. At first the limb perhaps carried only little weight, but as tetrapod evolution

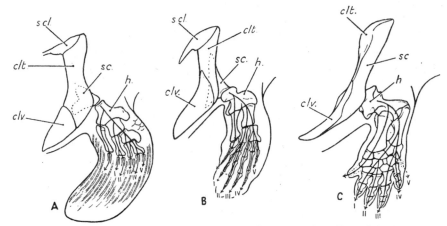

FIG. 180. Transformation of crossopterygian pectoral girdle and fin into pentadactyle limb. Oblique front view of left side.

A, *Eusthenopteron*; B, *Eogyrinus*; C, *Eryops*; *clt.* cleithrum; *clv.* clavicle; *h.* humerus; *sc.* scapula; *s.cl.* supracleithrum. (Modified from Gregory and Raven, *Ann. N.Y. Acad. Sci.* 42.)

FIG. 181. Transformation of crossopterygian pelvic fin into tetrapod limb.

A, *Eusthenopteron*; B, hypothetical; C, *Trematops*. *f.* femur; *fi.* fibula; *il.* ilium; *is.* ischium; *t.* tibia. (Modified from Gregory and Raven.)

proceeded the limbs became elongated and turned under the body, raising it off the ground. To work effectively in this way the limbs came to be held bent down at elbow and knee (Fig. 182) and a firm application to the ground was produced by bending outwards at wrist and ankle. Finally the limbs were brought in to the side of the body by rotation, such that the elbow points backward and the knee forward.

These are the changes that must have occurred at some time to

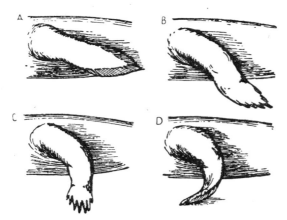

FIG. 182. Diagrams illustrating the probable changes in position during the evolution of a pelvic fin into a tetrapod limb. A as in *Ceratodus*; B, double flexure to give knee and ankle joints, leaving foot direct backwards; C and D, rotation of tarsus and digits turning foot forward. (From Gregory and Raven, after Romer and Byrne.)

produce the full tetrapod condition, but we cannot follow exactly the order in which they took place. Their effect is to convert a paddle-like fin, whose main movements were up and down, and were used for stabilization in the horizontal swimming plane, into an elongated jointed strut, on which the animal can balance, and which can be moved as a lever to produce locomotion.

The limbs and girdles and their muscles show a remarkable constancy of pattern throughout the tetrapods. The skeletal parts and the muscles are divided into a series of units, the bones and muscles, which show surprising similarity of arrangement in animals whose locomotion is as different as that of a newt, a frog, a horse, and a man. We do not yet fully understand either the hereditary or the mechanical factors that are responsible for this pattern of bones and muscles, nor how this particular arrangement of parts has been derived from that of a fish-like ancestor. The muscles of the fins of fishes are concerned mainly with lowering and raising (Fig. 192), and they run from a girdle in the body wall to the basal radials in the fin, and between the radials. After the animals came on land the muscles served not only to raise and lower the limbs but also to draw them forwards and backwards; indeed, many fishes already make such movements, including *Protopterus*. The muscles therefore become arranged around the shoulder and hip joints into groups serving as adjustable braces, by which the body is balanced on its legs and by whose contraction the latter are moved. Those muscles that draw the limb towards and away from the mid-ventral line can be called medial and lateral braces (adductors and abductors) and the muscles drawing the leg backwards

FIG. 183. Suggested protetrapod stage, between crossopterygian and labyrinthodont. (From Gregory and Raven.)

and forwards are posterior and anterior (retractor and protractor) braces. For the attachment of these muscles proximally the pectoral and pelvic girdles, small in fishes, become expanded into plates (Figs. 181 to 183), and these are divided into a number of characteristic pieces, though the mechanical reason for the division is not clear.

8. Shoulder girdle of Amphibia

The pectoral girdle of fishes was composed of several pieces (Fig. 180) and these appear also in the earliest stegocephalians (Fig. 184). The girdle has the form of a hoop of bone round the under side of the body. In *Eryops, for instance, there is a large scapulo-coracoid piece, with dermal bones along its anterior edge, cleithrum above, and clavicle and interclavicle below. In the mid-ventral line there was some ossification to make a sternum. This simple plate of bone presumably gave origin to sets of muscles such as we have already described, able to balance the animal, if precariously, on its legs. The weight was transmitted to the vertebral axis by modified somitic muscles attached to the girdle. Signs of the serial arrangement of these muscles are still seen in the segmented serratus muscles found in all tetrapods, including mammals.

In later amphibia the pectoral girdle became secondarily reduced in many urodela, and in anurans is specialized for the jumping habit.

In the more fully aquatic urodeles (Fig. 184) the girdle is almost wholly cartilaginous; only the scapular region is ossified, being presumably the only part that comes under compression force, by the action of the muscles proceeding from the dorsal (suprascapular) and ventral (coracoid) regions to the humerus. In frogs (Fig. 184) the fore-limbs serve mainly to take the weight during landing after a jump. The pectoral girdle shows the parts characteristic of other

FIG. 184. Pectoral girdles of lower tetrapods, regions mainly cartilaginous are stippled.

CL, clavicle; COR, coracoid; CTH, cleithrum; ECOR, epicoracoid; EP, episternum; GC, glenoid cavity; ICL, interclavicle; OM, omosternum; PCOR, precoracoid; S, sternum; SC, scapula; SCCOR, 'scapulocoracoid'; SSC, suprascapula; XI, xiphisternum. (After Evans, *J. Morph.* 74.)

tetrapods, a mainly cartilaginous suprascapula, bony scapula, clavicle and coracoid, with a glenoid cavity for articulation with the humerus where the three meet. In the midline there is a series of sternal cartilages and bones, serving for the attachment of the muscles of the abdomen and throat, by which the weight of the body is supported (p. 304).

9. Pelvic girdle of Amphibia

The pelvic girdle is very much larger in land animals than the small ventral cartilages found in fishes. It is formed of three main cartilage bones in all tetrapods (Fig. 185), but it is not clear how these originated, nor whether the division has mechanical significance. The dorsal ilium becomes attached to specially modified transverse processes of one or more sacral vertebrae. This ilium can be regarded mechanically as the ossification along a line of compression stress due to the weight-bearing.

The ventral portion of the girdle consists of an anterior pubis and posterior ischium, the three bones meeting at the acetabulum, where the femur articulates. The girdle thus provides a large plate, to which the muscles that brace the limb can be attached in such a way as to balance the body on the leg.

In urodeles the pelvic, like the pectoral, girdle becomes reduced

FIG. 185. Pelvic girdles of lower tetrapods. Regions mainly cartilaginous are stippled. *ac.* acetabulum; *il.* ilium; *is.* ischium; *of.* obturator foramen; *p.* pubis. (After Evans.)

and mainly cartilaginous. The pelvic girdle of anurans is very highly specialized and unlike that of any other vertebrate. The ilium is very long and directed forward to articulate with the single pair of sacral vertebrae. The base of the ilium is expanded to make the dorsal portion of a disk, of which the pubis is the anterior, the ischium the posterior part, with the acetabulum at the centre. The girdle is thus developed into a long lever for transferring force from the limb to the vertebral column during jumping.

10. The limbs of Amphibia

The pattern of bones and muscle in fore and hind limbs of tetrapods is surprisingly constant in spite of the various uses to which the limbs are put. Evidently similar morphogenetic processes are at work in both limbs. There are nearly always three main joints in each limb, at shoulder (hip), elbow (knee), and wrist (ankle). The hand and foot provide basically similar five-rayed levers, with several joints in the digits (Figs. 186 and 187).

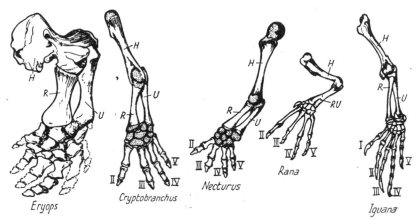

FIG. 186. Front legs of various lower tetrapods.

H. humerus; R. radius; U. ulna. (Modified from Evans, *J. Morph.* 74.)

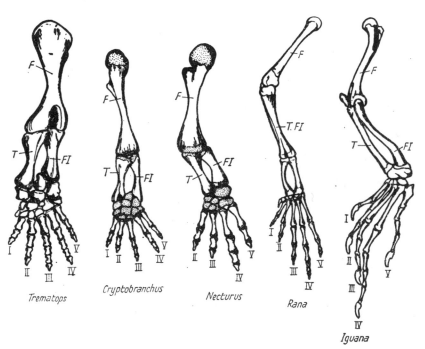

FIG. 187. Hind legs of various tetrapods.

F. femur; FI. fibula; T. tibia. (Modified from Evans.)

The bones of the·limbs can be plausibly derived from those of a crossopterygian fin, and indeed the condition in *Eusthenopteron* already distinctly suggests that of the limb of an early amphibian (Figs. 180 and 181). We know less about the origin of the hind than of the front leg, but the two are so similar that they may be treated together for elementary analysis. There is a basal humerus (femur), articulating distally with two bones in each case, a more anterior (pre-axial) radius (tibia) and a posterior (post-axial) ulna (fibula). These bones articulate at the wrist or ankle with a carpus or tarsus, consisting, in the fully developed condition, of three rows of little bones, namely 3 in the proximal row, about 3 centrals, and 5 distals. Each of the latter carries a digit, composed of numerous jointed phalanges. In naming these bones of the carpus and tarsus it is convenient to call the proximal carpals by their position radiale, intermedium, and ulnare and the tarsals tibiale, intermedium, and fibulare. The centrals and distal carpals may then be numbered beginning with 1 at the pre-axial border in each case. Unfortunately other less explicit systems of naming are in use, as shown in the following table.

Plan of the Tetrapod Carpus and Tarsus. (*The names used for the bones in man are shown in brackets.*)

CARPUS

	Pre-axial		Post-axial	
Proximal	radiale (scaphoid)	intermedium (lunate)	ulnare (triquetral)	
Central		centrale (tubercle of scaphoid)		
Distal	carpal 1 (trapezium)	2 (trapezoid)	3 (capitate)	4 and 5 (hamate)

TARSUS

	Pre-axial		Post-axial	
Proximal	tibiale (talus or astragalus)	intermedium (os trigonum)	fibulare (calcaneum)	
Central		centrale (navicular)		
Distal	tarsal 1 (medial cuneiform)	2 (intermediate cuneiform)	3 (lateral cuneiform)	4 and 5 (cuboid)

The plan of the carpals and tarsals can well be imagined to have been derived from that of a fin such as is seen in the fish *Eusthenopteron* (Fig. 180), which might be said to have humerus, radius, and ulna, carpals, and 7 or 8 digits. In the amphibian *Eryops* most of the digits radiate from the radius, in later forms mostly from the ulna. Moreover in the hand of *Eryops* there seem to have been six digits and it is usually stated that the first of these is a pre-pollex 'not comparable with the pollex of higher forms'. It is difficult to believe that such differences in number or position of parts are of serious importance in a repetitive system such as this, and there is no reason to doubt that the tetrapods have acquired their limbs by modification of developmental processes that produced fish fins.

The effect of this system is to provide a lever that can be held firmly against the ground while it is moved by the muscles running from the girdles to the humerus or femur. In addition the lever is itself extensible by means of its own muscles. Whatever may have been their origin in fishes these muscles in tetrapods work in such a way as to bend each segment up and down. The shoulder and thigh joints are usually such as to allow movement in several planes, both towards and away from the midline (adduction and abduction), and forwards and backwards (protraction and retraction). As we have seen, the animal balances at these joints by muscles arranged round them. Movements of rotation are also possible at these, and sometimes at other joints, the distal bone turning about its own axis on the proximal one. Such movements may be very important for the proper placing of the limbs in walking. Pronation is the rotation of the radius about the ulnar bone, so that the manus is directed caudally, supination being the opposite movement. The terms flexion and extension are convenient at certain joints (e.g. the elbow), but have no consistent meaning with reference to the main axes of the body.

The limbs of the earlier amphibians known to us were very ponderous affairs, with large bones and widely expanded hands and feet (Figs. 182 and 183). It is not certain exactly how they were used; probably they were held out sideways, giving a wide base on which the somewhat precarious balance was maintained, the body being often slumped on to the ground. In modern urodeles the limbs retain the full pattern of parts, but with imperfect ossification, as would be expected since they carry little weight.

In frogs, specialized for jumping, the radius and ulna are united and the carpals are reduced in number. There are only four true digits, the first digit (thumb or pollex) being reduced. There is, however, a small extra ossification, the pre-pollex, which becomes well developed as a copulatory organ in the male and may be compared with a similar digit found in some stegocephalians (p. 298). It is to be expected that in a system of repeated parts, such as a tetrapod limb, multiplications and reductions will be common. It can be imagined that they can be produced by changes in the rhythm of morphogenetic processes, and it is surprising that there is such constancy in number of digits.

FIG. 188. *R. temporaria* dissected from the back.

add. adductor; *anc.* anconeus ('triceps'); *c.* calcar; *c.sacr.* coccygeo-sacralis; *cocc.il.* coccygeo-iliacus; *cuc.* cucullaris; *delt.* deltoid; *dep.mand.* depressor mandibuli; *dors.sc.* dorsalis
scapulae; *ext.obl.* obliquus externus abdominis; *fasc. dors.* dorsal fascia; *fl.br.* flexor brevis;
gastr. gastrocnemius; *glut.* gluteus; *il.* ilium; *il.ext.* iliacus externus; *il.fib.* ilio-fibularis;
lat.dors. latissimus dorsi; *l.dors.* longissimus dorsi; *n.* nostril; *peron.* peroneus; *pir.* piri-
formis; *rhomb.* rhomboideus; *semi.m.* semimembranosus; *semi.t.* semitendinosus; *t.Ach.*
tendo Achillis; *t.f.lat.* tensor fasciae latae; *tib.ant.* tibialis anterior; *tr.* transversus abdominis; *tymp.* tympanum. (Partly after Gaupp.)

The hind legs of frogs are long, giving a good leverage in jumping. The tibia and fibula are united and the proximal row of tarsals is reduced to two, greatly elongated and known as the tibiale (astragalus or talus) and fibulare (calcaneum). The distal tarsals are reduced to a total of three, bearing five 'true' digits and an extra one, the calcar or prehallux.

11. The back and belly muscles of Amphibia

With the change in the method of locomotion the muscular system has become very greatly modi-
fied from that found in fishes. In urodeles, which still use the old method and hence may be said to swim on land, the dorsal musculature is well developed (Fig. 189*a*), but in anurans the dorsal portions of the myo-tomes, the epaxial muscula-ture, no longer have to produce the locomotory effect by lateral flexion. They remain in frogs only as muscles which bend the body dorsally, serving to brace up the vertebral column on the sacrum (Figs. 188 and 189). Short muscles run between the vertebrae, and dorsal to these is a continuous sheet of longitudinally arranged fibres, the longissimus dorsi muscle, running from head to sacral vertebra and urostyle. This

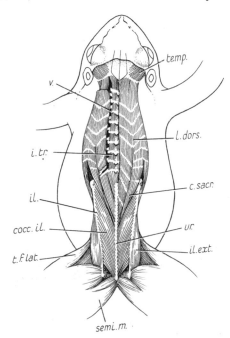

FIG. 189. Deeper dissection of muscles of back of frog.

i.tr. inter-transversarii; *ur.* urostyle; *v.* vertebra; other letters as Fig. 188. (Partly after Gaupp.)

muscle, though forming a continuous band, is crossed by a number of tendinous intersections, showing its segmental origin. At the hind end the coccygeo-sacralis and coccygeo-iliacus muscles brace the urostyle on the pelvic girdle.

The pectoral girdle is attached to the axial skeleton by a series of muscles. Rhomboid and levator scapulae muscles run from the suprascapula to the vertebrae and skull. The cucullaris muscle corre-sponds to the mammalian sternomastoid, running from the skull to the suprascapula; it is derived from lateral plate musculature and innervated by the vagus. The naming of these muscles of the scapula, and indeed all amphibian muscles, meets the difficulty that many of the bundles of fibres are similar in their general course to muscles found in mammals and yet differ sufficiently to raise serious doubts about the wisdom of using the mammalian names. The similarity of arrangement of the limb muscles is so striking throughout the tetrapods that there is probably no harm in keeping to the well-established

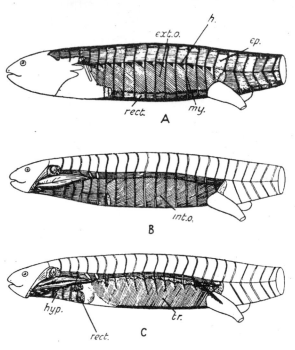

Fig. 189a. Muscles of larval *Amblystoma*. A, B, and C show successive layers. *ep*. epaxial muscles; *ext.o.* external oblique; *h.* horizontal septum; *hyp.* hypobranchial muscles; *int.o.* internal oblique; *my.* myocomma; *rect.* rectus abdominis; *tr.* transversus abdominis. (From Ihle, after Maurer.)

system of names, but we know so little of the hereditary or mechanical factors that control the arrangement of muscle-fibres into 'muscles' that no proper discussion of homologies is possible.

The hypaxial musculature, formed from the more ventral portions of the myotomes, is more developed than in fishes and differentiated into several parts, for the purpose of slinging the viscera, which of course need support in air in a way which is unnecessary in water.

These muscles are differentiated into layers whose fibres run in different directions. The plan found, with modifications, in all tetrapods is seen in amphibian larvae and includes four sets of fibres.

Fig. 190. *R. temporaria* dissected from the ventral surface.

add. aductor magnus; *add. long.* adductor longus; *anc.* anconeus; *br.r.* brachio-radialis; *cl.* clavicle; *co.* coracoid; *cr.* cruralis; *delt.* deltoid; *ep.* episternum; *ext.obl.* obliquus externus abdominis; *fl.c.rad.* flexor carpi radialis; *fl.c.uln.* flexor carpi ulnaris; *gastr.* gastrocnemius; *grac. maj.* and *min.* gracilis major and minor; *il.int.* iliacus internus; *o.h.* omohyoid; *o.m.* omosternum; *pect.* pectoralis; *r.s.* rectus sheath; *rect.* rectus abdominis; *sart.* sartorius; *st.h.* sterno-hyoid; *submax.* submaxillary; *sub.hy.* subhyoid; *t.Ach.* tendo Achillis; *t.f.lat.* tensor fasciae latae; *tars.a.* and *tars.p.* tarsalis anterior and posterior; *tib.ant.br.* and *long.* tibialis anterior brevis and longus; *tr.* transversus abdominis; *xi.* xiphisternum.

(Partly after Gaupp.)

The external obliques run backwards and ventrally; inside this layer is the internal oblique, running in the opposite direction, and within this again the transversus abdominis running approximately dorso-ventrally (Fig. 189a). The rectus abdominis consists of fibres in the midline running antero-posteriorly.

In the adult frog three of these sets of fibres can be recognized. In the mid-ventral region (Fig. 191) are the longitudinally arranged

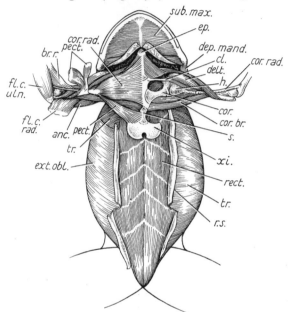

FIG. 191. Dissection of muscles of frog from ventral surface. *cor.rad.* coraco-radialis; *dep.mand.* depressor mandibuli; *h.* head of humerus; *s.* sternum; other letters as Fig. 190. (Partly after Gaupp.)

fibres of the rectus· abdominis, making a sling between the sternum and the pubis. These fibres are interrupted at intervals by transverse fibrous tendinous inscriptions, giving an appearance of segmentation. In the mid-ventral line is the linea alba, a tendon having no muscle-fibres. The sling formed by the rectus abdominis is supported laterally by thin sheets of muscle-fibres running up to the vertebral column, the obliquus externus and transversus abdominis (Fig. 191).

In the anterior region the hypaxial muscles have become restricted to the throat, where they form the hyoid musculature, which by raising and lowering the floor of the mouth is the main agent of breathing. The submaxillary muscle runs transversely between the rami of the jaw. Deep to this lie other muscles, including the sternohyoid, close to the midline, which is a forward continuation of the rectus abdominis.

12. The limb muscles of Amphibia

The muscles of the limbs were presumably derived from the radial muscles that moved the fins of fishes. These are formed from the myotomes and they are mainly arranged so as to raise and lower the fin (Fig. 192). In modern amphibia there is no evidence from

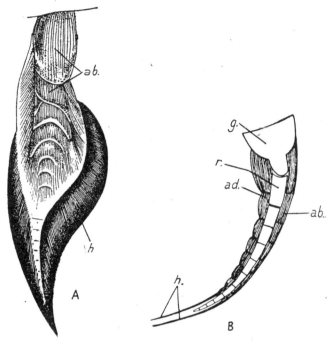

Fig. 192. A. Lateral surface of the fin of *Neoceratodus*, showing the abductor muscle-bundles. B. Section through the fin in the transverse plane, showing the arrangement of the muscle-bundles as abductors and adductors.

ab. abductor muscles; *ad.* adductor muscles; *g.* pectoral girdle; *h.* horny fin rays; *r.* radials. (From Ihle, after Braus.)

embryology of any relation between the limb musculature and the myotomes; the muscles form independently in the mesenchyme of the limb. However, the segmental origin of the limbs is shown by the fact that they are innervated by branches of the spinal nerves of several segments (2 for the fore-limb, 4 for the hind limb in the frog). Presumably the original arrangement was such as to move the limbs in association with the waves of contraction passing down the body. In modern urodeles the limb is brought forward and its joints flexed as the epaxial muscles at the level of its front end contract, and then passes back and extends as the wave of contraction moves past. This may have been the primitive movement, making the limb more useful as a lever during the early attempts to 'swim on land' (Fig. 182).

The muscles of the limbs of tetrapods are presumably derived from those that raise and lower the fins of fishes, modified, as we have seen, to brace the limbs and move them, allowing standing and walking. The muscles that run from the girdles to the humerus and femur are therefore able to draw the leg forward and backward, as well as to raise and lower it in the transverse plane. The actions of the various bundles are of course not confined to a single plane: all the muscles running from the back to the humerus can raise the upper limb, but the more anterior members also protract, the more posterior retract it. Similarly there is a ventral series whose anterior members work with the anterior dorsal muscles as protractors, although they antagonize the action of raising the whole limb. Moreover, many of the muscles have a rotating action on the humerus and femur. It is, however, possible to consider the muscles of the arm and leg in two great groups; first a more anterior and ventral ('ventro-lateral') set serving to draw the limb mainly forward and towards the midline (protraction and adduction) and to flex its more distal joints, second a more posterior, dorsal ('dorso-medial') mass serving mainly to draw the limb backwards and away from the body (retraction and abduction) and to extend its joints.

In the fore-limb the proximal members of the ventral group make a sheet of fibres running transversely to the main body axis and attached to the sternum and hypaxial muscles at one end and to the humerus at the other (Fig. 190). Within this sheet can be recognized the deltoideus, pectoralis, coracoradialis, and coracobrachialis muscles. In the limb itself this group is continued, there being, roughly speaking, a set of muscles in each segment that serves to flex it on the next. Thus the brachio-radialis flexes the elbow joint and in the forearm the flexor carpi radialis and flexor carpi ulnaris flex the wrist. The flexor digitorum longus muscle arises from the medial epicondyle of the humerus and is inserted by tendons to the carpus and terminal phalanges. Flexor digitorum brevis muscles arise from this tendon for insertion on the digits.

Of the dorsal muscle mass (Fig. 188) the latissimus dorsi and dorsalis scapulae are the most proximal, running from the middle of the back to the humerus and serving to abduct and draw back the whole limb. The triceps (anconeus) serves to extend the elbow; in the forearm are extensor carpi ulnaris and radialis and extensors for the fingers.

According to this plan protractor (flexor) muscles lie mainly anterior to retractors (extensors), corresponding to the ancient movement by which the limb was drawn first forward then back as a swimming wave passed down the body. It will be found that in all tetrapods flexor muscles are in general innervated by spinal roots anterior to those for the extensors. The locomotory movements of the limbs therefore still show the passage of an excitation wave backwards along the spinal cord, a relic of the swimming rhythm of fishes. However, the changes that have taken place in the relative positions of the parts of the limbs make it very difficult to follow out this simple pattern in detail. It must also continually be remembered that many muscles produce rotation as well as movement in the main planes of the body.

In the hind limb, muscles of the same two general types can be recognized, namely anterior muscles, which draw the limb forward and flex and adduct its joints, and posterior ones, which draw it back and extend and abduct. The specialization of the main muscle masses has gone much farther, however, so that more individual muscles are found, especially round the hip joint, each serving to move the limb in a special way.

In the thigh (Figs. 188 and 190) the muscles of the anterior group, lying on the ventral surface, are the pectineus and the adductors, running from the pelvic girdle to the femur and thus serving to move the whole limb inwards (adduction). The sartorius, biceps, semi-membranosus, and semitendinosus are two-joint muscles mainly producing flexion at the knee as well as at the hip.

The more posterior and dorsal group of muscles includes the gluteus and tensor fascia lata from girdle to femur, extending the thigh joint, and the very large cruralis (including the rectus femoris and triceps femoris) running from girdle and femur to tibia. This is the main extensor of the knee, being helped by gracilis and semi-membranosus. This extension is obviously an important part of the jumping movement of the frog.

In the shank the arrangement of the flexors and extensors into the anterior and posterior groups is much modified. The more conspicuous muscles are the tibialis anterior and peroneus running from the femur to the tarsus so as to flex the ankle joint. Long and short flexors move the toes, as in the fore-limb. At the back of the tibio-fibula the gastrocnemius (plantaris longus) runs from the femur to be attached by the tendo Achillis to the tarsus. Its main action is to extend the ankle in the movements of jumping and swimming. Tibialis posterior runs from the tibia to the tarsus. Within the foot there is an elaborate system of small muscles for bending and stretching the toes and abducting them away from each other, so as to expand the web for swimming.

The whole system is designed to produce the characteristic sudden simultaneous extension movement of all the joints of both hind limbs, by which the frog moves both in water and on land. The hind limbs can also be used for alternate walking movements, especially in toads (Fig. 178).

13. The skull of Stegocephalia

The skull of the Devonian and Carboniferous amphibia was essentially like that of the osteolepid fishes in the arrangement of the bones, but the proportions had been altered so that the pre-optic region was relatively large and the more posterior 'table' of the skull short (Fig. 193).

Fig. 193. Diagram of skull bones and other structures. A, an osteolepid; B, a stegocephalian.

Letters for this and Fig. 194: *ac.* auditory capsule; *ex.* extrascapular; *fr.* frontal; *hm.* hyomandibula; *it.* intertemporal; *j.* jugal; *na.* nasal; *mx.* maxilla; *p.* pineal; *pa.* parietal; *pi.* pituitary; *pm.* pre-maxilla; *po.* post-orbital; *pof.* post-frontal; *ppa.* post-parietal; *prf.* pre-frontal; *p.rost.* post-rostrals; *qj.* quadratojugal; *sq.* squamosal; *st.* stapes; *sut.* supratemporal; *t.* tabular. (After Westoll.)

The nasals and frontals, which were small in choan-ichthyes, were quite long in stegocephalians, whereas the parietals were shorter and the post-parietals absent altogether. The difference is so marked that for a long time people were deceived in identification of the bones and it was said that the pineal opening lay between the frontal bones in fishes but between the parietal bones in tetrapods. The bones identified as 'frontal' in the fish types were, of course, parietals, whereas the 'parietals' were the post-parietals, which have gone completely from most amphibians, though still present in the earliest Devonian forms (Fig. 194). This is a beautiful example of how study of changes of proportion can clear up morphological difficulties.

The opercular apparatus covering the gills was lost early in amphibian evolution; perhaps the reduction of the whole posterior part of the head was effected by a single morphogenetic change. In modern amphibia the skull is very much flattened and its ossification reduced, so that very large spaces are left; in the earlier forms, however, the skull was of the more usual domed shape and the roof and

jaws were covered by a complete set of dermal bones. Presumably the
loss of bone was another development producing that reduction of
weight which is so advantageous to a terrestrial animal.

Lateral line organs are present in aquatic amphibians and their
position is marked on the bones of the fossil skulls by rows of pits.
By using these lines as reference marks it is possible to compare the

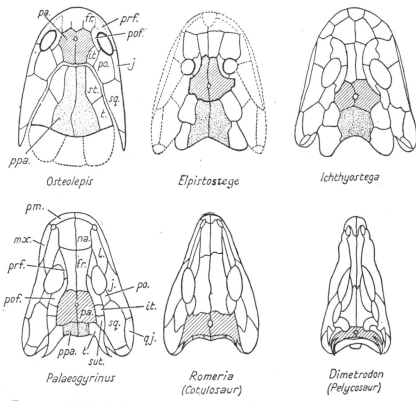

FIG. 194. Skulls of a, crossopterygian and various early tetrapods to show the
shortening of the posterior region. Lettering as Fig. 193. (After Westoll.)

pattern of the bones on osteolepid and early amphibian skulls and to
confirm in detail the remarkable similarity. The main new development found in the skull of early amphibians was correlated with the
modification of the Eustachian tube in connexion with the sense of
hearing, and the need for a sensitive resonator to pick up the air
vibrations. Already in the earliest amphibians the opercular coverings
of the gills were lost (there was a small pre-opercular bone in *Ichthyostega*) and the spiracular opening thus uncovered acquired a tympanic
membrane. The hyomandibular cartilage, no longer concerned (if it
ever had been) with supporting the jaw, was modified to form the

columella auris, serving to carry vibrations across to the inner ear. At first, however, there was no trace of the fenestra ovalis, the hole in the auditory capsule into which the columella fits in the frog. In modern urodeles the whole ear apparatus is much modified, there being no tympanum. Instead the columella is fused to the squamosal and the ear thus receives its vibrations from the ground.

Other small changes in the skull in passing from the fish to the amphibian stage include the increase in size of the lachrymal bone, which also came to have a hole to carry the tear duct, draining the orbit. A series of small bones surrounds the orbit in early amphibians, as in fishes; large squamosals and quadratojugals support the quadrate. At the back of the skull these stegocephalians possessed various of the small bones that are found in fishes but not in modern amphibians, the supratemporal and intertemporal, post-parietal (much smaller than in choanichthyes) and tabulars. In fact there are numerous small bones, arranged in a pattern clearly recalling that of the fish ancestor, but showing some reductions and less variation than in those very variable fish skulls. This simplification (which was later carried farther), together with some changes in the shape, are the chief transformations which have converted the fish skull into the amphibian skull.

The palate of the early amphibians also closely resembled that of choanichthyes, showing a complete plate made of vomer, palatines, pterygoids, and ecto-pterygoids. These bones, as well as the premaxillae and maxillae, often carried folded teeth (hence 'labyrinthodonts'), with a pit for a replacing tooth beside each one, an arrangement similar to that of their fish ancestors (p. 258). The internal nostril opened far forward, through the palate. The lower jaw was covered by a number of dermal bones (Fig. 207), but the actual jaw articulation was made between cartilage bones, the upper quadrate and the lower articular.

14. Skull of the Frog

The skull of the frog (Figs. 195 and 196) shows very great reduction and specialization from this early amphibian type. It may be considered as consisting of a series of cartilaginous boxes, in whose walls some ossifications occur, and which are partly covered by dermal bones. The cartilaginous boxes, well seen in a tadpole's skull, are the central neurocranium around the brain, and the olfactory and auditory capsules. Ossifications occur especially at the points of compression stress, namely, around the foramen magnum (the exoccipitals), where the auditory capsule joins the cranium (the pro-otic), and at the base of the nasal capsules (the mesethmoid). The paired occipital condyles are found only in modern amphibia, and are formed by the failure of the basioccipital to become ossified. Paired

FIG. 195. Ventral view of the skull of the frog.

col. columella auris; *ex.* exoccipital; *fp.* fronto-parietal; *m.* maxilla; *n.* nostril; *pa.* palatine; *par.* parasphenoid; *pm.* premaxilla; *pro.* pro-otic; *pt.* pterygoid; *q.* quadrate; *qj.* quadrato-jugal; *se.* sphenethmoid; *sq.* squamosal; *v.* vomer. (After Marshall, *The Frog*, Macmillan.)

FIG. 196. Side view of the skull of the frog.

ac. anterior cornu of hyoid; *art.* articular; *as.* angulosplenial; *d.* dentary; *m.m.* mento-Meckelian; *na.* nasal; *pc.* posterior cornu of hyoid; *II, IX,* and *X,* nerve foramina. Remaining letters as Fig. 195. (After Marshall.)

occipital condyles have also arisen, independently, in the mammal-like reptiles.

The cartilaginous palato-pterygo-quadrate bar of the frog is attached by its own basal and otic processes to the skull (autostylic), leaving the hyomandibula free to form the columella. There is, however, some doubt about the homology of the latter, since it does not actually develop from the hyoid arch during ontogeny (nor does the Eustachian tube develop from the spiracular gill-slit).

The dermal bones covering the roof of the skull are the nasals and frontoparietals, while on the floor is the large dagger bone, the parasphenoid, and a small tooth-bearing vomer. The remains of the cartilaginous palato-pterygo-quadrate bar can be recognized as a rod, covered in front by premaxillae and maxillae, and dividing behind into an otic process fixing it to the skull and a cartilaginous quadrate region holding the lower jaw. This region is covered by the pterygoid ventrally, the quadrato-jugal laterally, and the squamosal dorsally. The palatines are membrane bones forming the anterior wall of the orbit. The upper jaw is thus supported by struts formed from the nasals and palatines in front and the squamosal and pterygoid behind, an arrangement which gives a large mouth for eating insects, combined with the advantages of strength, mobility of the lower jaw, and lightness in weight.

The lower jaw consists of Meckel's cartilage, covered on its outer surface by a dentary and on its inner by an angulo-splenial bone. The anterior tips of the cartilages ossify as the mento-Meckelian bones.

The visceral arches are well formed in the tadpole but are considerably modified in the structure of the adult frog. In the tadpole the skeleton of the hyoid arch consists of a large pair of ceratohyals which are attached to a basal hypohyal. As a result of subsequent metamorphosis the ceratohyals form the long anterior cornu of the hyoid, attached to the prootic bone. The body of the hyoid is a plate which lies in the floor of the mouth and which is formed from the hypohyal and from the hypobranchial plate situated at the base of the remaining arches. The posterior cornua support the floor of the mouth and it is presumed that the whole apparatus assists in the process of respiration. The sixth and seventh of the series of branchial arches give rise respectively to the arytenoid and cricoid cartilages of the larynx.

The lateral plate muscles of the branchial arches are well developed only as the muscles of the jaws. Certain muscles of the scapula (the cucullaris (p. 301) and interscapularis) are innervated from the vagus and recall the sternomastoid and other muscles innervated by the spinal accessory nerve in mammals.

The muscles of the hyoid arch, innervated by the facial nerves, remain mainly as the depressor mandibuli (Fig. 197) running from the back to the angle of the jaw and serving to lower the floor of the mouth. The jaw-closing muscles, m.m. adductor mandibuli, belong to the mandibular segment and are innervated by the trigeminus.

They run from the hind end of the jaw to the surface of the skull and squamosal.

The skull and jaws of the frog thus constitute a protection for the brain and special sense-organs, a feeding apparatus, and a means of respiration. The very heavy protection afforded by the dermal bones of fishes and early amphibians has been largely dispensed with, probably for lightness. The front part of the skull, concerned with the nose, eyes, and brain, has become increased in size and the hind part, originally concerned with the gills and pharynx, greatly reduced. These changes, carried to extremes in frogs, have been in progress throughout the evolution

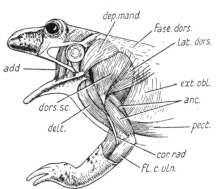

FIG. 197. Muscles of head and neck of frog dissected from the side.

add. adductor mandibuli. Other letters as in Figs. 188 and 191. (Partly after Gaupp.)

of amphibia. It is not difficult to imagine that they have been the result of rather simple genetic changes, affecting the relative growth of various parts of the skull. We are still far from the knowledge necessary to say exactly what developmental changes have occurred, but we know enough to imagine how selection through millions of years has changed the quantities of certain substances so as to produce gradually less bony and shorter heads, such as enabled their possessors to maintain sufficient mobility to hold a place in a world peopled by the reptiles and other still more active descendants of the early amphibians.

15. Respiration in Amphibia

The new problems presented by life on land have led to the production of very varied means of respiration among amphibia. In a terrestrial habitat oxygen is available in plenty; the difficulty is evidently to arrange for a regular interchange of air in contact with adequately moistened surfaces. The interchange is provided for in most cases by modifications of the apparatus used in fishes, but pumping air presents new problems and it seems that these are not easily solved, since in many amphibians the skin is used as an accessory respiratory mechanism. The retention of moisture becomes more difficult as the ventilation becomes efficient; probably for this reason air is often only transferred to the lungs after it has remained for some time in the mouth. We see again that the new way of life, in a medium remote from water, makes it necessary to possess more complicated methods of self-maintenance.

16. Respiration in the Frog

The lungs of the frog are paired sacs, opening to a short laryngeal chamber, which communicates with the pharynx by a median aperture, the glottis. The glottis and laryngeal chamber are supported by the arytenoid and cricoid cartilages. The arytenoids guard the opening of the glottis and are moved by special muscles. During breathing the mouth is kept tightly closed, the lips being so arranged as to make an air-tight junction. Air is sucked in through the nostrils by lowering the floor of the mouth by means of the hypoglossal musculature, and can then either be breathed out again or forced into the lungs by raising the floor. The external nares are closed by a special pad on the anterior angle of the lower jaw, supported by the mento-Meckelian bones. This pad is thrust upwards and pushes the premaxillaries apart, so altering the position of the nasal cartilage that the nostrils are closed. This is a special mechanism, found only among anurans. In urodeles the nostrils are closed by valves provided with smooth muscles. Such valves are present in the frog but are said to be functionless.

The movements of the floor of the pharynx are not continuously of the same amplitude. After a period of relatively slight movements the nostrils are kept closed while the throat is lowered. Air is thus drawn from the lungs and then again returned to them once or twice before the nostrils are reopened. The whole procedure presumably ensures the maximum gaseous interchange for the minimum water-loss.

This method of taking in air is clearly derived from the movements of the floor of the mouth of fishes, by which water is passed over the gills. In amphibian larvae water is pumped in this way and there is direct continuity between the mechanism of larva and adult. The basic rhythmic mechanism, centred on the nerve-cells of the medulla oblongata, is no doubt the same throughout, but the anurans have improved upon it by the addition of special features, requiring intricate co-ordination of the muscles of the larynx and the apparatus for closing the nostrils.

The skin is very vascular over the outer surface of the body, and especially in the buccal cavity. It plays a large part in respiration, actually serving to remove more carbon dioxide than do the lungs. There is, however, little power to vary the amount of exchange through the skin, which is therefore constant throughout the year. There is considerable regulation of the exchange in the lungs. The rate of breathing depends, as in mammals, on the effect of the carbon dioxide tension of the blood on a respiratory centre in the medulla. There is also a vasomotor control of the blood-supply to the lungs and, through the vagus nerve, of the state of contraction of the latter. By such means the rate of respiratory exchange is greatly increased during the breeding season, and made to vary with the activity of the animal.

17. Respiratory adaptations in various Amphibians

The skin and the lungs show many variations according to the habitat of the species, special devices being adopted to enable the animals to live in particular environments. The lungs vary from the very well vascularized sacs with a highly folded surface found in the frogs, and especially in the drier-skinned toads, to very small simple sacs in some stream-living amphibia. The lung will serve of course to lift the animal in the water; for this reason it is reduced in the frog *Ascaphus*, which lives in mountain streams in the eastern U.S.A. In newts this hydrostatic function of the lungs is predominant and the inner surface is often very simple. The lung is entirely lost in some salamanders, the stream-living types, such as the European alpine *S. atra*, showing greater reduction than those that live in ponds. Probably in all mountain animals the coldness of the water reduces activity and lowers the need for respiratory exchange to a level at which it can be fully met by the skin. The skin shows increased vascularity in these forms with reduced lungs, capillaries reaching nearly to the outermost layers of the epidermis.

Gills are present in amphibian larvae, and also in certain adult urodeles that may be considered as larvae that have failed to undergo metamorphosis (p. 345). The gills are extensions of the branchial arches, and carry branched villi, richly supplied with blood. Where the main trunk is long the gill projects and is 'external', whereas in other cases, as in the later frog tadpole, the filaments are directly attached to the arches and are called 'internal'. There are no profound differences between the two types.

18. Vocal apparatus

Sound is produced by the male frog as a call to attract the female. Both sexes have vocal organs, but those of the female are much the smaller. The noise is produced by the vibration of the elastic edges of a pair of folds of epithelium of the laryngeal chamber, the vocal cords. Air is passed backwards and forwards between the lungs and a large pair of sacs (or a single median sac), the vocal pouches, formed below the mouth. These also serve as resonators, and are developed only in the male.

FIG. 198. Diagrams illustrating development and fate of aortic arches in *Amphibia*, left-side view completed. Vessels carrying most arterial blood white, most venous blood black, and mixed blood stippled.

a^{1-6}, Primary arterial arches; *ca.* conus arteriosus; *cb.* carotid gland; *cc.* common carotid; *da.* median dorsal aorta; *db.* ductus Botalli; *dc.* left ductus Cuvieri; *ec.* external carotid; *eg.* blood-supply to external gill; *ic.* internal carotid; *la.* left auricle; *lda.* lateral dorsal aorta (*d.* obliterated part, ductus caroticus); *lg.* lung; *oph.* ophthalmic; *or.* orbital; *pa.* pulmonary artery; *pca.* pulmo-cutaneous arch; *pv.* pulmonary vein; *s.* closed spiracular slit; *sa.* systemic arch; *sv.* sinus venosus; *tra.* truncus arteriosus (ventral aorta); *v.* ventricle; *vci.* vena cava inferior. (From Goodrich.)

19. Circulatory system of Amphibia

The venous and arterial systems are partly separated in Amphibia, as in lung-fishes. The auricles are completely divided by an inter-auricular septum, venous blood returning to the right, arterial to the left auricle. There is only a single ventricle, but this is provided with spongy projections of its wall, which may prevent the mixing of the blood. The ventral aorta (conus arteriosus), springs from the right side of the ventricle and may thus receive first the venous blood. The conus arteriosus has transverse and longitudinal valves.

FIG. 199. Diagram to show the chief arteries and their anastomoses in the frog. (After Gaupp.)

The ventral aorta is very short and the arches much modified in the adult (Fig. 198). Of the original six that can be recognized the first two disappear, the third on each side gives rise to the carotid artery, the fourth remains complete and forms the systemic arch. The fifth remains also in some urodeles, but disappears in anurans. The sixth arch becomes the pulmonary artery and loses its connexion with the dorsal aorta: special 'cutaneous arteries' carry de-oxygenated blood from this arch to the skin (Fig. 199). These pulmonary arches probably offer a lesser resistance than do the systemic and carotid ones, the pressure in the latter being increased by a special network, the 'carotid gland'. The first blood leaving as the ventricle contracts therefore flows to the lungs. In anurans this separation may be further assisted by an arrangement such that the pulmonary arteries

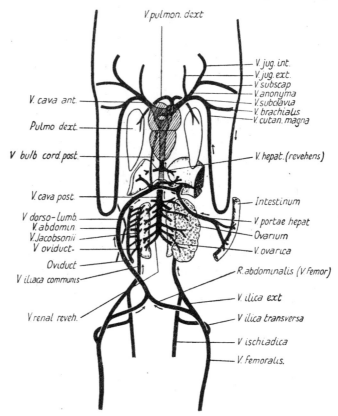

FIG. 200. Diagram to show the chief veins of the frog. (After Gaupp.) The r. abdominalis is often called the pelvic and the v. iliaca communis the renal portal vein.

join at their base and open to the dorsal part of the truncus arteriosus (cavum pulmocutaneum), which is partly separated from the more ventral cavum aorticum, leading to the carotid and aortic arches. The classical view of this system is that as the pressure rises the truncus contracts and the spiral valve moves in such a way as to force all the blood that leaves the ventricle during the later part of its contraction into the ventral portion and hence to the systemic and carotid arches. In this way a separation of blood from the right and left auricles would be achieved. The view that the heart allows such a separation has, however, been challenged on the basis of experiments made by injection of X-ray opaque material, allowing the course of the circulation to be watched. It is stated that by this method it can be shown that blood returning to either auricle reaches all parts of the ventricle and that no separation occurs. Since the blood from the skin returns to the right auricle (Fig. 200) it is not clear that a separation of the streams would be advantageous.

The venous system (Fig. 200) is based on the same plan as that of Dipnoi. The posterior cardinal veins are replaced early in life by a vena cava inferior. Most of the blood from the hind limbs passes through the renal portal system, but there is an alternative path through pelvic veins and a median anterior abdominal vein, which breaks into capillaries in the liver.

The blood-pressure is regulated by the extrinsic nerves of the heart, fibres from the vagus tending to slow and from the sympathetic nervus accelerans tending to speed the beat. The latter nerve is a new development, there being no sympathetic innervation of the heart in fishes (the condition in Dipnoi is unknown). The diameter of the arteries throughout the body is also under control from sympathetic vasoconstrictor and perhaps also vasodilator nerves. The arterioles in the web of the foot can be seen to constrict when the medulla oblongata is stimulated. Substances extracted from the posterior lobe of the pituitary and from the adrenal medulla also serve to cause constriction of the arteries and perhaps also of the capillaries.

There is therefore a complex mechanism for ensuring that the pressure of the blood is maintained and the flow directed into the part of the body that requires it for the time being.

20. Lymphatic system of Amphibia

The transfer of substances between the cells and the blood-stream is effected in any vertebrate by a transudation through the walls of the capillaries into the tissue fluids. Under the pressure of the heart-beat, water and solutes leave the capillaries, passing through their walls, while proteins remain behind. The blood passing into the venous ends of the capillaries therefore has a very high colloid osmotic pressure and this serves to suck back fluid from the tissues. In this way a circulation from the capillaries into the spaces around the cells is produced. Clearly, however, it is essential for this mechanism that the pressure of the ventricular heart-beat shall exceed the colloid osmotic pressure of the blood. This it does by about three times in the frog.

The lymphatic system consists of a set of spaces which, in the frog at least, communicate with the tissue spaces around the capillaries. Injection of gum into the lymphatic system, by increasing the colloid osmotic pressure in the tissue spaces, prevents the back suck of fluid into the venules and hence leads to swelling of the part injected. The lymph spaces in the tissues join to form larger channels and great sinuses, such as that below the loose skin of the back of the frog. The lymph is kept circulating by the action of lymph hearts. In the frog there are anterior and posterior pairs of these, opening into veins. The more posterior pair lies on either side of the coccyx and can be seen if the skin is removed. The lymphatic vessels also assist in the process of repair. If, after injury, red cells come to lie in the tissues the lymphatics send out sprouts for as far as $\frac{1}{10}$ mm. to pick them up and return them to the blood-stream.

21. The blood of Amphibia

The red corpuscles of amphibia are much larger than those of mammals, reaching in the urodele *Amphiuma* the immense size of 70 μ; they nearly always exceed 20 μ. The red cells are formed mainly in the kidney, and are destroyed, after a life of about 100 days, by the spleen and liver. The bone-marrow is a source of red cell formation in *Rana temporaria* but not, except during the breeding-season, in *R. pipiens*. A remarkable process of breaking up of the red cells occurs after they have entered the blood-stream, giving a number of enucleated fragments, and this, when the part remaining with the nucleus is small, produces a result like the extrusion of the nucleus during the development of the red cell of mammals. In *Rana* only small portions of the cytoplasm are broken off in this way, but in *Batrachoseps* a large proportion of enucleated corpuscles is produced.

The haemoglobin of the frog has a lower affinity for oxygen than that of mammals, even when both are considered at the same temperature, and in this respect is notably less efficient. Moreover, although the power of the blood to combine with carbon dioxide is great, there is a less delicate regulation of the reaction of the blood than in mammals.

The white cells of amphibia are of three types, lymphocytes, with a large nucleus and small cytoplasm, monocytes, which are larger phagocytic macrophages, and polymorpho-nuclear granulocytes. These last may be neutro-, eosino-, or basiphil and are migratory and phagocytic. The white cell picture with which we are familiar in mammals was evidently established a very long time ago.

There is a globular spleen near the head of the pancreas.

The blood of frogs also contains numerous small platelets (thrombo-cytes), which probably break down when in contact with foreign surfaces to produce the thrombin that combines with the fibrinogen of the blood-plasma to produce clotting.

22. Urinogenital system of Amphibia

The excretory organs of adult amphibia are always the tubules of the mesonephros. In *Rana*, where there is a general shortening of the body, these extend over only a small number of segments and the kidneys are compact. In urodeles and the primitive frog *Ascaphus* the kidneys are elongated and show some evidence of their segmental nature. The mesonephros consists essentially of a series of tubules leading from the nephric funnels to the Wolffian duct. In the frog the funnels do not open into the tubules, however, but into the veins; moreover, they form independently of the rest of the tubule. In the adult there are some 2,000 glomeruli, from each of which a short ciliated tube leads to the proximal convoluted tubule. There follows a second short ciliated region, corresponding in position to the Henle's loop of mammals, and leading to a distal convoluted tubule, which joins the Wolffian duct.

The blood-supply of the kidney differs from that of mammals in that blood arrives from two distinct sources; the branches of the renal artery run mainly to the glomeruli, those of the renal portal vein to the tubules. This corresponds to the functions now well established for those two parts, namely that the glomerulus filters off water and crystalloids, some of which are then reabsorbed by the tubule. Many details of this process are not clear, however, for instance how the urea concentration in the urine is raised many times above that of the blood.

The frog, having a moist skin, is presumably in constant danger of osmotic flooding with water when it is submerged, and of desiccation when on land. The flooding is prevented by the efficient functioning of the glomeruli; they allow the frog to excrete as much as one-third of its weight of water per day (man 1/50th). The mechanisms for resistance to desiccation are less perfect. There is no long water reabsorbing segment, the part of the tubule corresponding to Henle's loop being short. There is, however, a large cloacal (allantoic) bladder (to be distinguished from the mesodermal bladder of fishes) from which water can be reabsorbed. Moreover, certain desert amphibia, such as *Chiroleptes* already mentioned, conserve water by losing the glomeruli altogether.

The Müllerian duct, by which eggs are carried to the exterior, develops separately from the Wolffian system in the frog, but arises from the latter during development in urodeles. In this, as in many other features, the frog shows a greater degree of specialization of its developmental processes. The ovaries are mere folds of the peritoneum, having no solid stroma such as is found in mammals. There are, however, follicle cells around each egg; these presumably produce the ovarian hormones. Sections of an ovary show eggs in various stages of development, but not all those which begin complete their maturation; many degenerating, atretic eggs are found. Ripening of the eggs proceeds under the influence of a hormone produced by the anterior lobe of the pituitary. This in turn is controlled by external environmental factors to ensure breeding in the spring. Suitable injections of mammalian anterior pituitary extracts will ensure ripening of the ovaries and ovulation at any time of year. The 'prolans' excreted in the urine of pregnant women have a similar effect, and the production of ovulation in *Xenopus* is used as a test for the diagnosis of human pregnancy.

Having left the ovary the eggs find their way to the mouths of the oviducts mainly by ciliary action of the latter. The walls of the oviduct are glandular and secrete the albumen; they are dilated at the lower end to form uterine sacs, in which the eggs are stored until laid.

The testes discharge directly through the mesonephros by special ducts, the vasa efferentia, formed by outgrowths from the mesonephros into the gonad. This is presumably a secondary development from the original vertebrate condition in which the sperms were carried away by the nephrostomes. The fact that the sperms pass through the kidney emphasizes that the amphibia have diverged at a very early stage of the evolution of the vertebrate stock, and remain still in many respects at a lower level of evolution than the modern fishes, all of which have acquired separate urinary and genital ducts.

In some frogs (*R. temporaria*) there is a special diverticulum, the vesicula seminalis, leading by several small channels to the lower end of the Wolffian duct. It contains spermatozoa during the breeding season and its appearance suggests a secretory activity.

Most of the amphibia have failed to effect the complete transfer to land life: they return each year to the water to breed. Special modifications of the reproductive system for land life are therefore not found. Secondary sexual differences are very marked in many species. In frogs the males precede the females to the water and then attract the latter by their vocal apparatus. The male clings to the back of the female by means of a 'nuptial pad', developed as an extra digit, pre-pollex, on the hand (p. 299). Injection of male hormones or implantation of testis will cause this organ to develop in young female frogs.

In newts fertilization is ensured by an elaborate courtship. Sperms are made into spermatophores by special pelvic and cloacal glands and there are also abdominal glands, which produce a secretion attractive to the female. After a courtship ceremony the spermatophores are picked up by the cloaca of the female and stored in a spermathecal chamber.

23. Digestive system

Nearly all adult amphibia feed on invertebrates, mainly insects, partly also worms, slugs and snails, spiders and millipedes. In the larval stages anurans are usually and urodeles often herbivorous, but they may be cannibalistic, feeding on the tadpoles of the same or other species—an interesting form of provision for the next generation by excess productivity of the mother. There are only minor modifications of particular species in relation to their diet; amphibia in this respect are generalized creatures; as regards their food they occupy a generalized or 'easy' habitat. The fact that they are not particular in choice of diet has no doubt been part of the secret of their success.

The tongue is the characteristic organ for catching the food and is one of the special features required for terrestrial life, being reduced in aquatic amphibia. In *Rana* it is attached to the floor of the mouth anteriorly and flicked outwards by its muscles. To keep it moist and sticky a special inter-maxillary gland is found. From the shape of the premaxillae it can be deduced that this gland was present in labyrinthodonts. Other mucous glands are found in the mouth, but there are no salivary glands comparable to those of mammals; no digestion takes place in the mouth.

Another feature made necessary by terrestrial life is the presence of cilia to keep the fluids moving over the oral surfaces. These cilia are absent in aquatic amphibia.

The teeth on the premaxillae, maxillae, and vomers are used only to prevent the escape of the prey; few amphibia bite. Biting teeth are present, however, in the adult *Ceratophrys ornata*, whose larvae also have powerful jaws and are cannibalistic. The South American tree-frog *Amphignathodon* has teeth in the lower as well as the upper jaw and presumably has re-developed them, a remarkable case of the reversal of evolution. Teeth are also present on the lower jaw of most urodeles.

The oesophagus is not very sharply marked off from either mouth or stomach and the latter is a simple tube. Its lining epithelium of mucus-secreting cells is folded and simple tubular glands open at the base of the folds. These glands, unlike those of mammals, are composed of only a single type of cell, which secretes both the acid and the pepsin found in the stomach.

The intestine is sharply marked off from the stomach by a pyloric sphincter. It is relatively short and dilates into a large intestine, there

Fig. 201. Transverse section of the spinal cord of a frog, showing cells in the grey matter with their axons and dendrites spreading into the 'white' matter.

ax. axon of ventral horn cell, leaving cord in ventral root; *d.* dendrite of ventral horn cell; *dhc.* small cells of dorsal horn; *dr.* dorsal root entry; *m.* cell body of ventral horn cell; *neur.* neuropil at periphery of spinal cord; *vhc.* small cell of ventral horn. (After Gaupp.)

being a valve interposed in the frogs, though not in all amphibia. The liver and pancreas have the structure common to all vertebrates and produce juices of the usual type.

The intestine of the herbivorous tadpole is more coiled than that of the adult frog. It is said that this is in part a result of the food supplied, there being a shortening if meat is given.

The actual type of food taken depends on what is available, most species of amphibia are not particular feeders. However, they can learn with only one or two trials to avoid distasteful insects. Frogs and toads devour large numbers of insects. If the common species available are pests the amphibian's part in controlling their number works to the advantage of man.

24. Nervous system of Amphibia

The organization of the nervous system of amphibia might be said to be essentially similar to that of fishes. In both groups there are highly developed special centres in the brain, each centre related to a

special sense-organ. In neither group is there a dominant part, integrating the activity of the whole, as the cerebral cortex in mammals.

The plan of the spinal cord is like that of fishes, but well-marked

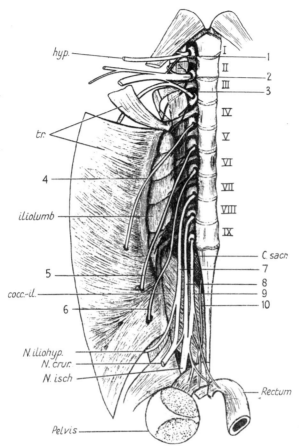

FIG. 202. Ventral branches of the spinal nerves (1–10) of the frog. The short
branches are shown black, the long branches light. Pelvis bisected and turned
aside. Sympathetic chain removed.

I–IX, bodies of the vertebrae; *hyp.* hypoglossal nerve; *iliolumb.* iliolumbar muscles;
N.crur. crural nerve; *N.iliohyp.* iliohypogastric nerve; *N.isch.* sciatic nerve. Other labels
as Fig. 188. (After Gaupp.)

dorsal and ventral horns are present. However, the nerve-cell bodies
are still mostly in their primitive position, close to the central canal.
The large motor-cells of the cord have dendrites that spread widely
in the white matter, where their synaptic connexions are made in a
complicated 'neuropil' (Fig. 201). This is a much more simple
arrangement than is found within the grey matter of the mammalian cord.

The arrangement of the spinal nerves is much modified by the development of the limbs. Ten spinal nerves are found and since an embryonic first one is missing they are sometimes numbered 2–11.

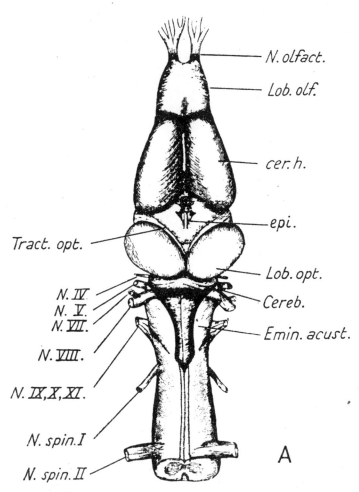

N. olfact.

Lob. olf.

cer. h.

epi.

Tract. opt.

Lob. opt.

N. IV
N. V.
N. VII.

Cereb.

Emin. acust.

N. VIII.

N. IX, X, XI.

N. spin. I

N. spin. II

A

Fig. 203a. The brain of *Rana*. (After Gaupp.)

cer.h. cerebral hemisphere; *cereb.* cerebellum; *emin.acust.* acustic eminence; *epi.* epiphysis; *hypothal.* hypothalamus; *hypophys.* pituitary gland; *lam.term.* lamina terminalis; *lob.olf.* olfactory lobe; *n.olfact.* olfactory nerve; *N. III–XI,* cranial nerves; *N.spin. I and II,* spinal nerves; *Tract.opt.* optic tract.

Two spinal segments contribute to the brachial and four to the sciatic plexuses in the frog. From these plexuses fibres are distributed to the muscles and skin of the limbs (Fig. 202).

The brain (Fig. 203) resembles that of Dipnoi very strikingly. The prosencephalon is based on an inverted plan (p. 200); the large

FIG. 203*b*, *c*. Two further views of the brain of *Rana*. (After Gaupp.)

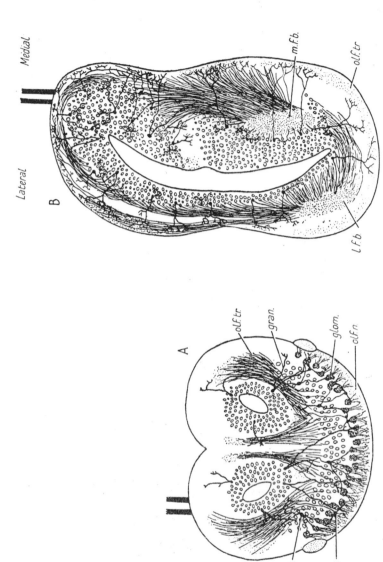

FIG. 204. Diagrams of the structure and probable cell connexions in, A, the olfactory bulb, and B, the cerebral hemisphere of the frog.

glom. glomerulus in which fibres of olfactory nerve make contact with dendrites of mitral cells; *gran.* granule cell (cell without any axon); *l.f.b.* lateral forebrain bundle; *m.f.b.* medial forebrain bundle; *mit.* mitral cell; *olf.tr.* olfactory tracts; *olf.n.* fibres of olfactory nerve; *p.c.* periglomerular cell. The electrodes are shown as they would be placed for recording the potentials recorded in Fig. 205. (From Gerard and Young.)

evaginated cerebral hemispheres therefore have a thick nervous roof as well as floor. In the frog there is only a short unpaired region of the forebrain (diencephalon) but this is longer in urodeles. The walls of each hemisphere may be divided into a dorsal pallium, medial ventral septum, and latero-ventral striatum (Fig. 204). The cell bodies lie around the ventricle in all parts of the hemisphere and there are several layers of them. The cells are pyramidal in shape and the connexions are made in the outer 'white' matter.

Nearly all parts of the hemisphere are reached by olfactory tract fibres, the axons of the mitral cells of the olfactory bulb (Fig. 204).

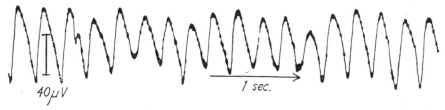

FIG. 205.   Rhythmical changes of potential between electrodes placed on the surface of the olfactory bulb of the frog as in Fig. 204. (After Gerard and Young.)

In the frog there are regions at the hind end of the hemispheres that receive forwardly directed fibres, some probably connected with tactile and others certainly with optic impulses. There is therefore some opportunity for the hemispheres to act as correlating centres, but we have little information as to the functions performed in them. Their backward projections are made by means of two large tracts, the lateral and medial forebrain bundles, but these reach only to the thalamus, hypothalamus, and midbrain, not back to the cord. Electrical stimulation of the forebrain does not produce movements of the animal; presumably such a crude method, though it may excite a few neurons, cannot imitate the more subtle patterns in which they are normally active.

Removal of the cerebral hemispheres is said to have very little influence on the normal feeding and other reactions of the frog. After this operation the animals are said to be more sluggish, to show less 'spontaneity', and to learn less well. If the latter is true it shows a considerable advance in the functioning of the hemispheres over the stage reached in fishes, whose learning can certainly take place in other parts of the brain, and is apparently little affected by removal of the forebrain (p. 203).

Some indication of the function of the cerebral hemispheres is given by the fact that by placing electrodes connected with a suitable amplifier upon them, rhythmical changes of potential can be recorded (Fig. 205). These are most marked in the olfactory bulb and probably propagate backwards along the hemisphere. The rhythms continue even in a brain that has been completely removed from the head. They are therefore a sign of some intrinsic activity of the brain, rather than of response to peripheral stimulation.

The diencephalon is interesting chiefly for the considerable number of optic tract fibres that end in its walls; other sensory projections also reach here. In anurans, but not in urodeles, there is a partial division into separate thalamic sensory nuclei, such as are found in mammals, for touch, sight, and other receptor modalities.

The pineal organ is slightly eye-like in a few amphibia; in most it is a simple sac.

The pituitary body is well developed and the usual partes, anterior, intermedia, nervosa, and tuberalis can be recognized, though they are not in the same relative position as in mammals.

The midbrain is very well developed and shows many similarities to that of fishes. The cells which it contains do not all lie round the ventricle, many have moved out to make an elaborate system of cortical layers. Electrical stimulation of various parts of the optic tectum produces movements of the limb and other muscles; there can be no doubt that this region plays a dominant part in behaviour. Most of the fibres of the optic tract end here, and there are also other pathways from the olfactory, auditory, medullary (gustatory?), and spinal regions. Efferent fibres leaving the tectum pass to the midbrain base, medulla, and perhaps back into the cord. This region therefore has wider connexions than any other part of the nervous system and thus nearly reaches the status of a dominant integrating organ.

The cerebellum of amphibia, on the other hand, is very small; perhaps because these are mostly animals that do not have to adjust themselves freely in space during locomotion, they move mainly in a single plane.

25. Skin receptors

Lateral line organs are present in the skin of all aquatic amphibian larvae and in some aquatic adults, such as those of the anuran family Pipidae. They are of simple form, consisting of groups of cells in an open pit. In newts they are present in the larvae, which are aquatic, but are covered by epidermal layers during the first post-larval stage during which the newt lives on land. In the final aquatic adult stage the organs reappear.

The skin, of course, also contains tactile organs, and in addition is often sensitive to chemical stimuli. This chemical sense is mediated by fibres running in the spinal nerves, not by special elements such as the taste-buds found spread out over the body in fishes. The skin is also sensitive to heat and cold, and there is some evidence that these senses are served by fibres different from those which mediate touch, pain, or the chemical senses. Histologically, however, there is little sign of the development of the special sensory corpuscles that are so conspicuous in the skin of birds and mammals. All the nerve-endings are of the type known as 'free nerve-endings', except for a few touch corpuscles on special regions such as the feet. In this the amphibia again resembles the fishes and show less differentiation than do the higher animals.

The taste-buds on the tongue and palate are probably able to respond to the presence of only two of the four types of substance that are discriminated by mammals. Applications to the tongue of the frog and recording nerve-impulses in its nerves show that there are chemoreceptors present able to respond to salt and sour substances, but that no reaction is given to substances which in mammals are classed as sweet or bitter.

The olfactory organ functions both on land and in the water, special mucus glands being present to keep it moist when in air. A continual circulation of water or air is maintained over the olfactory epithelium by cilia or the movements of respiration. The internal nostril may have originally developed from the double nostril of fishes, in order to make a circulation around the olfactory receptors possible. Jacobson's organ is a special diverticulum of the olfactory chamber, serving to test the 'smell' of food in the mouth.

The Apoda, being blind, have a special development of the sense of smell, including a hollow tentacle or olfactory tube.

26. The eyes of Amphibia

Provided that certain requirements are met the air gives more scope for the use of photoreceptors than does the water. Light is transported with less disturbance through the air and image formation is facilitated by the refraction of the air-corneal surface. The amphibia have exploited these advantages and sight has become the dominant sense of most of the forms. For clear vision it is essential that the surface of the eye be protected, kept free of particles, and kept moist, and for these purposes the eyelids and lachrymal glands are present. The upper lid is fixed, but the lower is very mobile and folded to make a transparent structure, the nictitating membrane, able to move rapidly across the surface of the eye.

The eyeball is almost spherical, with a rounded cornea. The lens is farther from the cornea than in fishes and is flattened, more so in Anura than in urodeles. These modifications allow focusing of a more distant image. There is an iris, with a rapidly moving aperture,

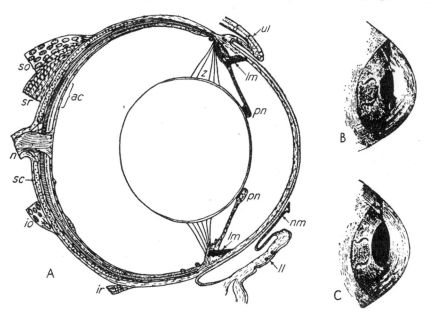

Fig. 206. The amphibian eye and its accommodation.

A, anuran eye in vertical section. *ac.* area centralis; *io.* inferior oblique; *ir.* inferior rectus; *ll.* lower lid; *lm.* lens muscles (protractors); *n.* optic nerve; *nm.* nictitating membrane; *pn.* pupillary nodules; *sc.* scleral cartilage; *so.* superior oblique; *sr.* superior rectus; *ul.* upper lid; *z.* zonule. B, anterior segment of *Bufo* in relaxation. C, in accommodation; note forward movement of lens. (From Walls, after Franz and Beer.)

operated by powerful circular (sphincter) and radial (dilatator) muscles. Although these muscles are partly actuated by a nervous mechanism they are also directly sensitive to light, and the pupil of the isolated eye of the frog shows wide excursions with change of illumination.

Accommodation is effected by protractor lentis muscles, attached to the fibres by which the lens is supported (Fig. 206). These muscles move the lens forward, whereas the muscles of the lens of teleostean fishes move it backwards. Other fibres, the musculus tensor choroidea, run radially and around the lens. They may help the protractors, and are probably the ancestor of the ciliary muscles of higher forms.

In amphibia living in the water the eye is based much more on the fish plan and the lens is rounder. There are then no lids and no lachrymal glands and the eye is enabled to make an image, in spite of the absence of the air-corneal interface, by means of a thickening of the inside of the cornea.

Rods and cones are present in the retina, the former containing visual purple, which may be red or greenish. The two sets of receptor are apparently found throughout the retina in urodeles, but in *Rana* there is a macular region in which the cones are in excess and this is still further developed in *Bufo*. The method of use of the eyes is little understood, though it is clear that the sense is an important one, especially for the forms which catch insects. It is not certain whether the animal responds only to movement in its visual field or whether it is able to make discrimination between shapes. Frogs are said to be able to learn to respond to light of certain wave-lengths.

The skin is probably sensitive to light in all amphibians: frogs react to light even after removal of the eyes and cerebral hemispheres. This skin sense is especially developed in certain cave-living urodeles, *Proteus*, in which the eyes are not developed. A similar degeneration also occurs in Apoda.

27. Ear

The inner ear of amphibia is divided into a utricle, from which the semicircular canals arise, and a saccule, from which there is a diverticulum, the lagena, part of whose sensory surface is covered with a tectorial membrane somewhat similar to that of mammals. There is, however, no coiled cochlea.

The sense of hearing is certainly well developed, especially in Anura, which can respond to vibrations from 50 to 10,000 a second. The hearing is used especially in the breeding-season, when the croaking serves to attract both sexes to the water. The prey may also be located by sound. Urodeles have been shown to give no response to the ringing of a bell suspended from the ceiling, which, however, produces reactions in *Rana* and *Bufo*. Urodeles, lacking a tympanum, probably receive vibrations mainly through the ground.

A peculiar feature of many Anura is an immense backward development of the inner ear, forming a sac extending on either side of the spinal cord as far back as the sacrum. Portions of this sac emerge between the vertebrae, showing as whitish masses on account of the granules of chalk which they contain. The significance of this development is quite unknown.

28. Behaviour of Amphibia

The habits of amphibia, like their special structures, enable them to deal with the various emergencies that threaten the continuation of life on land. Frogs and toads have a strong sense of place and they show distinct 'homing' reactions. They are able to learn to find their way out of mazes and to remember the way for periods of at least 30 days.

Complex migrations are made by many species; nearly all migrate to the water in spring. In this migration the males usually precede the females, then attract the latter by their calling. The sensory basis for the orientation towards the water is not known, but has been held to be a direct sense of smell for water. This is particularly clear in the case of urodeles, in which sound plays no part in the migration. The power to find water is obviously of first importance for any animal living on land, and further study of the sensory mechanism involved would be interesting.

The search for food and the avoidance of enemies are not in principle more difficult on land than in the water, but they nevertheless probably demand new mechanisms. For example, the greater range of visibility can be a disadvantage, especially when it is exploited by one's successful and predatory descendants. A hawk or owl makes fuller use of its opportunities in this respect than does the frog, who can only remain safe from them by behaviour that keeps it concealed. Similarly there are dangers in certain situations, for instance, of desiccation, which are additional to those met with by an animal in the water.

In the emergence of the first land vertebrates we thus see a conspicuous example of the invasion by living things of a medium far different from themselves. This produces a situation that calls forth all the powers of the race to produce new types of individual, and necessitates that the individuals make full use of their capacities. New patterns of structure and behaviour are developed as the various possible situations emerge. The types of organization that at first manage to survive gradually give place to others, still more complex or 'higher'. Some traces of the organization of the early venturers can still be seen in the amphibia, which to-day exploit the damper situations on the earth.

XIII

EVOLUTION AND ADAPTIVE RADIATION OF AMPHIBIA

1. The earliest Amphibia

There are such close resemblances between the skulls of the earliest

FIG. 207. Skull of *Ichthyostega*. (From Westoll, after Säve-Söderbergh.)

d. dentary; *en.* external nostril; *ept.* ectopterygoid; *fr.* frontal; *in.* internal nostril; *ina.* internasal; *j.* jugal; *la.* lachrimal; *mx.* maxilla; *na.* nasal; *pa.* parietal; *pal.* palatine; *pm.* premaxilla; *pn.* postnarial; *po.* postorbital; *pof.* postfrontal; *pop.* preopercular; *ppa.* postparietal; *prf.* prefrontal; *ps.* parasphenoid; *pt.* pterygoid; *q.* quadrate; *qj.* quadratojugal; *san.* sur-angular; *sq.* squamosal; *sut.* supratemporal; *t.* tabular; *v.* vomer.

amphibians and those of the Devonian crossopterygian fishes that there can be no doubt of the relationship (Fig. 194). At present there is, however, no detailed fossil evidence of the stages of transition from the one type to the other. The fossils which appear to be closest to the possible tetrapod ancestor are the osteolepids of the Lower and Middle Devonian periods, about 300 million years ago. These were definitely fishes, though they may have breathed air. *Elpistostege* is a single Upper Devonian skull intermediate between such fishes and the earliest undoubted tetrapods, *Ichthyostega* and similar forms, found recently in freshwater beds of Greenland. These are dated as

FIG. 208. Various urodele amphibians, not all to same scale (mostly from life).

very late Devonian or early Carboniferous, that is to say about 280 million years ago. They are the oldest members yet found of the great group of Stegocephalia, which, throughout the succeeding 100 million years of the Carboniferous and Permian periods, flourished and developed many different lines, one giving rise to the reptiles and others to the modern amphibia. The term Stegocephalia is convenient to cover the whole group of palaeozoic amphibia, all undoubtedly of common descent. At least seven types can be recognized, but attempts to group these have not been altogether successful; the nomenclature remains confused. The Labyrinthodontia were the central stock and were in the main terrestrial forms, giving off at intervals lines that returned to the water. The characteristic labyrinthodont feature is a folded pattern of the teeth, usually found associated with division of the vertebrae into a number of parts (see below).

The earliest Stegocephalia were definitely tetrapods and already showed sharp changes from the fish type. *Ichthyostega* is known chiefly from the skull (Fig. 207), which shows all the characteristic amphibian features, but retained traces of fish ancestry in its shape, with a short, wide snout and long posterior region (table), and presence of a preopercular bone. The nostril lies on the very edge of the upper lip, apparently partly divided by a flange of the maxilla into internal and external openings.

2. Terrestrial Palaeozoic Amphibia. Embolomeri and Rhachitomi

We possess more complete information about the slightly later forms, the Embolomeri, such as *Eogyrinus*, from the Lower Carboniferous (Fig. 210). These were long-bodied animals, rather newt-like, and their small limbs cannot have made very effective progress on land. They probably lived mostly in the water, eating fish. The pectoral girdle was still joined to the skull by a process of the tabular bone, as in fishes. The pelvic girdle does not form a full articulation with the sacral vertebrae but was apparently attached only by ligaments. The skull shows the full series of bones that we have already discussed; there is therefore no reason to suppose that these animals represent a secondarily 'degenerate' branch, which had returned to the water. They were probably very close to the ancestors of all tetrapods. They were numerous in the Carboniferous swamps, but disappeared early in the Permian. So close were these Embolomeri to the ancestry of the reptiles that many workers classify them near

FIG. 208a. Various anuran amphibians, not all to one scale.

(*Ascaphus*, *Nectophrynoides*, and *Polypedates* after Noble, *Breviceps* after Thompson, *Nototrema* after *B.M. Guide*, others from life.)

the Permian *Seymouria*, which we shall consider as a cotylosaurian reptile (p. 366).

Also descended from embolomerous forms were the other suborders that make up the order Labyrinthodontia, the Rhachitomi and Stereospondyli, the technical distinctions between which depend on study of their vertebrae (Fig. 209). In the earliest Embolomeri, such as *Eogyrinus*, the centrum was double, formed of an anterior

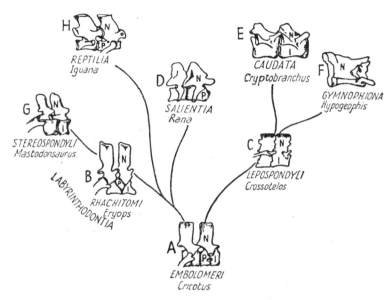

FIG. 209. Evolution of the vertebrae of Amphibia.
N. neurocentrum, I. intercentrum; P. pleurocentrum. (From Evans.)

intercentrum and posterior pleurocentrum, lying one in front and the other behind the point at which the myoseptum joined the notochord. This presumably means that the main method of locomotion was still a sinuous fish-like movement, with large myocommas attached to the vertebrae, as in fishes. In crossopterygii the intercentrum is large, the pleurocentrum consists of paired small cartilages.

In the terrestrial stocks of amphibia, and in the reptiles, the intercentrum has become reduced. Its place is taken by a great development of the pleurocentrum, which is the element lying opposite to the myotome itself. This change is presumably a reflection of the fact that when the animals become fully terrestrial the muscles directly attached to the vertebra must support the weight of the body. The part of the vertebra opposite the myotome therefore becomes developed. The change occurred markedly in the line leading to the

FIG. 210. Chart of evolution of amphibia.

reptiles and also proceeded some distance in the Rhachitomi, a terrestrial stock probably following the Embolomeri.

Many amphibian stocks, however, have tended to return to the water and show return to the fish-like condition of the vertebrae, reduction of the pleurocentrum and development of the intercentrum. This reversal of the previous direction of evolution is presumably necessary to make the column a flexible compression strut suitable for movement through the water by means of contraction of myotomes (p. 128). Unfortunately our knowledge of the sequence of fossil amphibia is so incomplete that it cannot be regarded as certain that this reversal of evolutionary direction actually occurred. Romer claims that the series may have been wrongly interpreted and that the original amphibian condition was more 'rhachitomous' than 'embolomerous'. If this is true there is no need to postulate a reversal of trend of evolution. All we can say is that embolomerous forms are certainly much more numerous than rhachitomous ones in the early Carboniferous deposits, whereas later the proportions were reversed.

Other amphibian stocks achieved a similar result by other means; for instance, in the mixed group of aquatic forms known as Lepospondyli the basidorsal and basiventral elements are united, so that each vertebra consists of a single piece, often very thin, surrounding a continuous notochord, which serves its original function as a compression strut.

Throughout the Carboniferous, Permian, and Triassic, there were very abundant amphibia of partly terrestrial habit, the Rhachitomi, in which both vertebral centra were present, the pleurocentrum being the larger. *Eryops* (Fig. 210) was a typical form living in the Permian, about 200 million years ago. The animals were 5 feet or more in length, rather like crocodiles, relatively shorter in body and tail than *Eogyrinus* and with stronger limbs. Nevertheless they probably lived partly in the water and may have been fish-eaters. The skull was long and narrow in the front and short in the 'table' behind the eyes, continuing the previous tendency. A characteristic feature of later labyrinthodonts now began to appear, namely, a dorso-ventral flattening of the skull. The pectoral girdle was no longer attached to the skull, but there was a joint between the pelvic girdle and the sacrum. Some Permian Rhachitomi became still more completely terrestrial than *Eryops*, for instance *Cacops* had very large limbs and protective plates along its back.

3. Aquatic Amphibia of the later Palaeozoic

Other lines of amphibia, however, show an accentuation of the tendency to return to the water. In the vertebrae the anterior intercentrum became large, while the pleurocentrum disappears. At the same time the skull became very flattened and the limbs weak. Several stages are known leading from the Rhachitomi to these fully aquatic forms of the Trias, which are placed in the suborder Stereospondyli. *Capitosaurus* and *Buettneria* are typical of the group, which remained numerous until near the end of the Triassic period, about 150 million years ago. Probably this change from rhachitomous to stereospondylous condition occurred on several independent lines of descent. Thus amphibia, after becoming semi-terrestrial in the Carboniferous and then probably giving rise to the early reptiles, later returned to the water.

We also have record of various other secondarily aquatic amphibians whose affinities are less certain. They have in common a reduction of ossification in general and in particular in the centra, which seem not to be formed from separate cartilaginous elements as in Labyrinthodonts but as thin continuous sheets of bone. Some of these animals classed as Phyllospondyli or 'Branchiosaurs' were almost certainly larval Rhachitomi; the external gills can be recognized and stages found connecting them with known adults of that group. It is necessary, however, to retain the order for the present.

Other early aquatic Amphibia are less easy to classify and are grouped for convenience as an order Lepospondyli, all having vertebrae composed of a single piece, and a continuous notochord. They show, however, at least three distinct lines, probably separate offshoots from the main labyrinthodont stock. *Dolichosoma* and other forms from the Carboniferous were very like snakes and had lost the limbs. *Diplocaulus* from the Permian possessed remarkable horned skulls. These creatures with broad flat heads and upward-looking eyes and small limbs were presumably bottom-dwellers and the development parallels that of the Stereospondyli. A third aberrant group placed here, the Microsaurs, such as *Microbrachis*, were animals with long bodies and small limbs, presumably aquatic, but showing many similarities to the reptiles in the skull.

The order Adelospondyli has been created for a further collection of presumably secondarily aquatic Amphibia such as *Lysorophus*, in which the neural arch and centrum are not fused but articulate by means of a jagged suture. The skull shows reduction and variation of the bones, and for this and other reasons it has been suggested that the urodeles may have arisen from an adelospondylous line.

The relationship of the modern amphibia to these palaeozoic stegocephalians remains uncertain. The earliest undoubted anuran is *Protobatrachus* of the Triassic, possessing ribs and a tail, but with elongated ilia and an anuran type of skull. *Miobatrachus* of the Carboniferous is a form in which the posterior portion of the skull is shortened and the temporal bones lost. In other respects the skull is like that of a rhachitome and suggests that the frogs diverged from the Labyrinthodonts at this very early stage.

The urodeles can be traced back only to the Jurassic. It is often suggested that both they and the Apoda have arisen from aquatic Lepospondyli, such as the microsaurs, but there is no real evidence of this.

4. Tendencies in the evolution of fossil Amphibia

The changes in the form of amphibia can be followed from the beginning of the Carboniferous to the end of the Triassic period, and, indeed, in the form of their reptilian descendants far beyond. There are signs, however, of very many distinct lines (as we should expect), and it is not possible to trace details of the history or fate of particular populations. Two distinct tendencies appear over this period: (1) to become fully terrestrial, (2) to return to the water. The terrestrial forms became very gradually shorter in body and stronger in leg. The skull remained fairly high and domed and the otic notch became deeper, as a more effective tympanum developed. In the vertebrae the anterior intercentrum became reduced as muscles developed attached to the pleurocentrum.

Return to the water led to animals of two distinct types, (a) a snake-like or (b) flattened, but in both there was a reduction of limbs and a secondary lengthening of the body, with return to the sinuous movements of fish-like locomotion. In the bottom-living forms, such as some Stereospondyli and *Diplocaulus* among Lepospondyli, the skull became flattened, with the eyes looking upwards, the otic notch being shallow. The snake-like *Dolichosoma* retained the more normal skull shape but became immensely elongated and lost the limbs altogether.

These observed tendencies can be understood to result from the situation that developed as the vertebrates first colonized the land. The earlier amphibia, such as *Eogyrinus*, were partly aquatic, by force, one might say, of inexperience. Throughout the Carboniferous various lines of them became more fully equipped for terrestrial life, moving faster, seeing and hearing better, and so on. The competition and predatory attacks of these more successful lines then drove others back into the water and so the process continued, until later the earlier reptilian lines, themselves driven back to the water by their own descendants, removed most of the amphibians from the waters as well as from the land, leaving only some few remaining populations, from which the modern orders have evolved.

It certainly does not seem necessary to postulate any special directive force to explain all this. We could wish, of course, for much more information, but it seems reasonable to imagine that these changes were produced by the action of the animals with each other and with the environment, supposing all the time that the animals continually strive to feed, grow, and reproduce others rather, but not quite, like themselves.

It must be stated, however, that Watson, who has contributed more than anyone to knowledge of amphibian evolution, believes that it is possible to recognize a number of non-adaptive trends, which are independent of environmental influences. Changes suggested by Watson and others as non-adaptive include flattening of the skull, doubling of the occipital condyles, reduction of the number of roofing bones and loss of ossification in the neurocranium, the changes in the vertebrae already mentioned, and many other features. It is not entirely clear how the 'non-adaptive' nature of these features is established. Palaeontology necessarily deals with small points of structure, whose significance for the animal may be difficult to determine, but it does not follow because we are not able to discern the significance of a part that it therefore has none. It is not at all easy in biology to hold the balance between credulous acceptance of a function for every character and a sceptical attitude that insists on regarding the organic world as a jumble of unrelated substances. The only safe rule is to search continually for signs of regular recurrence of similarities of structure and action, and then to make hypotheses about function, which can be tested by experiment and forecasting.

5. Newts and Salamanders. Subclass Urodela

The urodeles, also called Caudata or tailed amphibia, show less deviation from the general form and habitats of the amphibia as a whole than do the specialized anurans (Fig. 208). The adult and larval urodeles differ little from each other, and characters suitable for aquatic life are frequently found in the adult. Indeed, all stages of suitability for land occur, from the terrestrial salamanders, such as *Salamandra maculosa*, the European salamander, which is viviparous, to the fully aquatic forms, for instance *Necturus*, the mud-puppy of North America. In many of the aquatic animals there is a tendency to retain in the adult characters usually found in larvae. This process of paedomorphosis has developed to various extents, and independently in several groups. Thus the giant salamander *Megalobatrachus*, $5\frac{1}{2}$ feet in length, in China and Japan, has no eyelids, but loses its gills in the adult. In *Cryptobranchus*, the hell bender of the United States, the spiracle remains open and is used for the outlet of water during respiration.

Amphiuma, also from the southern U.S.A., is a very elongate form, with absurdly small legs, no eyelids, and four branchial arches. In the still more modified forms, such as *Necturus*, external gills are present and the lung is so reduced that the animals can live walking along the bottom. *Proteus* from European caves is a blind urodele with external gills and no pigment. *Siren* shows almost entirely larval characteristics and has no hind limbs.

The more typical terrestrial newts are of several sorts. In North America the common genus *Ambystoma* (usually written *Amblystoma*) has eleven species, many adapted to special habits, including *A. mexicanum*, in which some races become mature without metamorphosis, because of lack of iodine in the water, whereas others, the axolotls of Mexico, are genetically neotenous.

The common British newt *Triturus vulgaris* is a typical example of the more definitely terrestrial urodeles, though it is not able to live in very dry situations. However, the limbs support much of the weight of the body, and their soles are applied to the ground and turned forwards. The tail shows various degrees of reduction to a circular organ, but in the breeding-season, when both sexes return to the water, it develops a large fin, especially in the male. The common newts of America form a distinct family, including *Plethodon* and many specialized forms, such as the blind *Typhlomolge*, inhabiting the waters of caves.

6. Frogs and Toads. Subclass Anura

Among the frogs and toads are very many suited for special modes of life and it must again be emphasized that this is far from being a static and precariously surviving group. We have already mentioned the frog *Ascaphus*, which lives in mountain streams in the north-west of the United States and has reduced lungs, showing a combination of specialized and primitive features. Internal fertilization is assured by a penis-like extension of the cloaca. In this genus and the New Zealand *Leiopelma* (Fig. 208*a*) there are several primitive features, including tail muscles, absent in all other anurans.

In *Alytes*, the midwife toad of Europe, the male carries the eggs wrapped round the legs. *Pipa* is a related and still more specialized aquatic frog from South America; it has no tongue, and, curiously enough, has developed an elaborate arrangement by which the young are carried in pits on the back. *Xenopus* of Africa is related to *Pipa*, but without the habit of carrying its young (Fig. 208*a*).

The bufonid toads are among the most successful of all amphibian groups and are more fully adapted than most for a terrestrial life, but return nearly always to the water to breed. *Bufo* itself is found in almost all possible parts except in Australia and Madagascar; related genera, many of them with special features, are found all over the world. Curiously enough only one genus, *Nectophrynoides* from East Africa, is viviparous, the young being in that case provided with a long vascular tail, by means of which they maintain contact with the wall of the 'uterus', even though embedded in a mass of embryos.

Hyla and other tree-frogs, very widely distributed, are similar to the bufonids but have pads on the toes by which they climb, and many other adaptations to arboreal life. *Gastrotheca* (= *Nototrema*), the marsupial frog, is a genus in which the young develop in a sac on the back of the female, this sac being in one species protected by special calcareous plates. *Rana* and its allies, the true frogs, are also cosmopolitan. A number of frogs related to *Rana* have taken to a tree-living habit, developing pads on the tocs. *Polypedates* is a widespread genus and there are several others, each independently derived from ranids. This is therefore a striking illustration of parallel evolution—the hylid tree-frogs having arisen from bufonids and probably several sorts of polypedatids from ranids.

The burrowing habit has also been evolved several times by anurans, usually with formation of a narrow front to the head, as in *Breviceps* (Fig. 208*a*).

7. Subclass Apoda (=Gymnophiona = Coecilia)

These (such as *Ichthyophis*) are burrowing, limbless creatures living like earthworms, in the tropics. They show several interesting primitive features, including the retention of small scales in the skin. They are specialized, however, in having a very short tail and some features suited to their terrestrial life, such as copulatory organs. The animals are blind, the place of the eyes being taken by special sensory tentacles. The eggs are large and yolky and cleavage is meroblastic; they are laid on land and the embryos develop around the yolk sac, but often have long, plumed gills. Vivipary is found only in the aquatic form *Typhlonectes*!

8. Adaptive radiation and parallel evolution in modern Amphibia

Even this superficial study of the 250 genera and about 2,000 species of modern amphibians shows that the features we have already recognized in fish evolution are found also in evolution on land. It is difficult in a short time to gain an impression of the very great variety that is characteristic of any group of animals when closely studied. Besides the main types that can be distinguished, countless lesser variations will be found, and one gains the impression that the characteristics of the populations are still to-day in process of continual and perhaps rapid change. Anyone trying to discover the relationships of the various derivatives of ranids or bufonids must be impressed by the presence of series of parallel lines of development, so that it is impossible to disentangle the relationships. Evolution viewed at close quarters by the student of abundant modern animals looks very different from the simple picture seen by the lucky collector of a few rare fossils, who can arrange his types in genealogical trees and is apt to forget that they represent only an infinitesimally small sample of abundant and varied populations.

We can perhaps find certain tendencies in the modern amphibian populations similar to those of the fossils. Many return to the water, especially among the urodeles. Others become more fully terrestrial, either by climbing trees or by burrowing in the earth. Both of these habits have been independently adopted many times by recently evolved lines and, no doubt, still more often in the past by creatures that have died out, leaving no trace.

9. Can Amphibia be said to be higher animals than fishes?

It is not easy to decide whether there is a clear sense in which amphibians can be said to have advanced over their fish ancestors. They have moved from the water into environments that are in a sense less suitable for life. In order to maintain a watery system, such as a frog or toad, outside the water, various special structures and methods of behaviour have been evolved. The presence of such additional systems can be said to add complexity to the organization.

It is difficult to make a count of the number of 'parts' involved in the organization of any animal. Amphibia possess many special devices, for instance, for respiration without loss of moisture, for control of water intake and water loss, for return to water to breed, and so on. Even without making a proper quantitative computation it seems reasonable to say that these add up to make an organization more complicated than that of a fish. The integration of the action of so many parts requires an elaborate nervous system, and there is evidently some connexion between the increased size and importance of the nervous system and the development of this more complicated organization that enables life to continue in a different environment.

Considering the matter in this way it is hardly sensible to ask the question 'Are the amphibians more efficient than the fishes?', the work they do in maintaining life is so different that a comparison of 'efficiency' is fallacious. One method of assessing living efficiency might be to judge each animal organization by the extent to which it maintains its constancy—by its power of homeostasis. Data about the fluctuations of the internal environment are so scanty among lower vertebrates that we cannot proceed very far on these lines. It is probable that the blood of fishes shows greater fluctuations, for instance in osmotic pressure, than does that of amphibians, such fluctuations being perhaps even an advantage in allowing life in waters of differing salinity. In fact, to say that the whole mechanism of homeostasis becomes more complicated in land animals is only to say over again that they are 'higher' because they have more special work to do to maintain themselves in a difficult environment. Almost every part of the body shows signs of this greater complexity; the central nervous system becomes larger, the autonomic nervous system develops more elaborate control of the viscera. The endocrine glands become more numerous and differentiated, the muscular system shows more distinct parts, enabling the animal to act in new ways.

However difficult such comparisons may be it is hardly possible to deny them some validity. Amphibian organization differs from that of fishes and may be said to be 'higher' in the sense that it is more elaborate and allows life in conditions which the fish organization cannot tolerate.

XIV

LIFE ON LAND. THE REPTILES

1. Classification

Class. Reptilia

  Subclass 1. Anapsida

    Order 1. *Cotylosauria. Carboniferous–Trias
        *Seymouria, *Captorhinus, *Diadectes*

    Order 2. Chelonia. Permian–Recent
        *Eunotosaurus, *Triassochelys, Chelys, Emys, Chelone, Testudo*

  Subclass 2. *Parapsida

    Order 1. *Protorosauria. Permian–Trias
        *Araeoscelis, *Tanystropheus*

    Order 2. *Plesiosauria. Trias–Cretaceous
        *Nothosaurus, *Pliosaurus, *Plesiosaurus, *Placodus*

    Order 3. *Ichthyosauria. Trias–Cretaceous
        *Mixosaurus, *Ichthyosaurus*

  Subclass 3. Diapsida

  Superorder 1. Lepidosauria

    Order 1. *Eosuchia. Permian–Eocene
        *Youngina, *Prolacerta*

    Order 2. Rhynchocephalia. Trias–Recent
        *Homoeosaurus, Sphenodon (= Hatteria), *Rhynchosaurus*

    Order 3. Squamata. Jurassic–Recent

      Suborder 1. Lacertilia. Jurassic–Recent

        Infraorder 1. Platynota. Jurassic–Recent
          *Varanus, *Dolichosaurus, *Aigialosaurus, *Tylosaurus*

        Infraorder 2. Iguania. Cretaceous–Recent
          Iguana, Anolis, Phrynosoma, Draço, Lyriocephalus, Agama

        Infraorder 3. Scincomorpha. Eocene–Recent
          Lacerta, Scinca, Gecko, Anguis, Amphisbaena, Chameleo

      Suborder 2. Ophidia. Cretaceous–Recent
        Palaeophis, Python, Tropidonotus, Naja, Vipera

1. Classification (*cont.*)

 Superorder 2. Archosauria
  Order 1. *Pseudosuchia (= Thecodontia). Trias
   *Euparkeria, *Saltoposuchus*
  Order 2. *Phytosauria. Trias
   *Phytosaurus, *Mystriosuchus*
  Order 3. Crocodilia. Trias–Recent
   Protosuchus, Crocodilus, Alligator, Caiman, Gavialis
  Order 4. *Saurischia. Trias–Cretaceous
   Suborder 1. *Theropoda
    *Compsognathus, *Ornitholestes, *Allosaurus, *Tyranno-saurus, *Struthiomimus*
   Suborder 2. *Sauropoda
    *Brontosaurus, *Diplodocus, *Yaleosaurus, *Plateo-saurus, *Brachiosaurus*
  Order 5. *Ornithischia. Trias–Cretaceous
   Suborder 1. *Ornithopoda
    *Camptosaurus, *Iguanodon, *Hadrosaurus*
   Suborder 2. *Stegosauria
    Stegosaurus
   Suborder 3. *Ankylosauria
    *Ankylosaurus, *Nodosaurus*
   Suborder 4. *Ceratopsia
    Triceratops
  Order 6. *Pterosauria. Jurassic–Cretaceous
   *Rhamphorhynchus, *Pteranodon*
 Subclass 4. *Synapsida. Carboniferous–Permian
  Order 1. *Pelycosauria (= Theromorpha)
   *Varanosaurus, *Edaphosaurus, *Dimetrodon*
  Order 2. *Therapsida. Permian–Jurassic
   *Scymnognathus, *Cynognathus, *Bauria, *Droma-therium*
  Order 3. *Mesosauria (= Proganosauria). Permian
   Mesosaurus

2. Reptilia

In the early part of the Carboniferous period, say 275 million years ago, the vertebrate organization produced a population of amphibian creatures and from this has been derived not only various modern groups classed as amphibia but also the more fully terrestrial populations that do not need to breed in water—the Amniota. Since that time many divergent lines have evolved from this stock, including the birds and the mammals, and it is evident, therefore, that it is likely to be difficult to specify what is meant by a reptile, as distinct from an earlier amphibian or a later bird or mammal. The term does not define a single vertical line of development or branch of the evolutionary tree, but is rather a horizontal division, marking a band on the evolutionary bush, specifying a level of organization beyond that of an amphibian but before that of either bird or mammal. Attempts have been made to divide the reptiles vertically into sauropsidan (bird-like) and theropsidan (mammal-like) lines, but such a division obscures the fact that their bush-like evolutionary radiation has produced not two but many types.

The existing reptiles belong to four out of the dozen or more main lines that have existed. The only successful modern forms are placed in the order Squamata, the lizards and snakes, which are of relatively recent appearance in their present state. Secondly, the crocodiles are an older offshoot from the same stock, from which also the modern birds were derived. Thirdly, the tuatara lizard, *Sphenodon*, of New Zealand is a relic surviving with little change from the Triassic beginnings of this group. Finally, the tortoises and turtles (Chelonia) have retained the organization of still earlier times, presumably by the special protection of their shells; though they are much modified in some ways, they show us several characteristics of the earliest Permian reptiles.

These four modern types are all that remain of the reptiles that flourished throughout the Mesozoic, culminating in the giant dinosaurs of the Jurassic and Cretaceous. At the end of the Cretaceous period very many reptilian lines became extinct, leaving only the four relic groups which we have mentioned. Evidently a very profound change affected the population of the world, including the sea, between the end of the Cretaceous and the Eocene. This change will be discussed further in Chapter 21, but we must briefly discuss here the possible relation of the decline of the reptile populations to the rise of their descendants, the birds and mammals. It can hardly have been only the 'more efficient' organization of the warm-blooded types which gave them their opportunity, for there were forms in the Trias so similar to mammals in their skeletons that we may reasonably (though not certainly) suppose them to have been warm-blooded: there were birds with feathers in the Jurassic, and it is probable that they already had warm blood. However, as a working hypothesis, we may suppose that the climate, which had been suitable for reptiles in the Mesozoic, became less so in the early Tertiary, the most obvious suggestion is that colder conditions developed all over the earth's surface. The modern reptiles survive only in the temperate and tropical zones, indeed they flourish only in the latter. However, it must be remembered that climatic fluctuations are rhythmical (p. 15); it is dangerous to make generalizations about conditions over such long periods as the Cretaceous.

3. The lizard

The organization we call reptilian is suitable for life on land in warm conditions. No doubt the limitation is imposed largely by the fact that no reptile has the power of maintaining a constant temperature above that of its surroundings (see p. 354). This cold-bloodedness determines the behaviour. The lizards, for instance, such as *Lacerta vivipara*, when warmed up by the sun are active creatures, exploring the walls and banks in search of the insects, worms, and snails on which they feed; but they are sluggish in damp or cold weather and spend the winter hibernating in holes in the ground. The distribution of the genus *Lacerta* is evidently controlled largely by the temperature. Lizards occur all over Eurasia and Africa (except Madagascar), including the whole of Britain and the south of Ireland, but with a sharp northern limit. There are numerous species in the genus. *L. vivipara* is found throughout the British Isles, including Scotland and Ireland, being the only reptile that avoids St. Patrick's ban. *L. agilis*, the sand lizard, occurs in the southern counties of England (especially Dorset, Hampshire, and Surrey) and resembles *L. vivipara*, except that in the latter the eggs hatch immediately after laying, whereas the sand lizard buries them in sand for incubation. *L. viridis*, the green lizard, is a form reaching 17 inches in length and is found in central and southern Europe and Asia, including the Channel Islands, but not on the English mainland. *L. muralis*, the wall lizard, is the common form in southern Europe; it also reaches the Channel Islands.

In spite of many minor differences the habits of these various species, and, indeed, of many other members of the order, are much alike. *L. vivipara* lives usually in a hole in a wall or bank and returns to this home when startled. Its chief mode of defence is by flight, but if necessary it will threaten with open mouth and will bite fiercely. The tail is readily cast off when the lizard is seized, by the sudden contraction of the muscles acting to stiffen the tail; any force then breaks one of the vertebrae, which have a weak point across the middle of the centrum. The tail remains writhing for some time and presumably distracts the pursuer.

4. Skin and colour of reptiles

The skin is characteristically reptilian in that it is dry; unlike the skin of amphibia and mammals it contains few or no glands. The Malphigian layer of the epidermis produces the horny outer covering of a reptile, this being shed in flakes. Underneath the skin many reptiles develop bony plates in the dermis, but in lizards such scales

FIG. 211. Diagram of the nervous control of the melanophores in the chameleon (above) and minnow (below).

c, spinal cord; F, pathway of pigmentomotor fibres (the synapse in the sympathetic ganglia is omitted); M, melanophore; N, spinal nerve; P, pigmentomotor centre; s, sympathetic.
(From Sand, minnow after v. Frisch.)

are found only on the head, forming an extra covering of plates outside the bones of the skull and more numerous than the latter. The arrangement of these head plates varies greatly in different reptiles and is used as a character for the determination of species, a curious contrast to the constancy of pattern of the skull bones. Since these skull bones are themselves derived from scales (p. 189), we have in the osteoderms an interesting case of a morphogenetic process reappearing in its original form after it has first been modified during evolution. This is very close to a reversal, or at least a repetition, of evolution, contrary to the tenets of the so-called Law of the Irreversibility of Evolution.

Like many reptiles the lizards have strong and elaborate patterns of coloration. *L. vivipara* is reddish-brown, with dark and light spots on the back; on the under side the male is orange-red with black spots, the female yellow. The colour changes from time to time in lizards as, proverbially, in the chameleons, and the ecological significance of the various patterns adopted is sometimes clear. It may be that in some cases the coloration is used for concealment, but it also serves to give the animals a measure of temperature regulation. Lizards placed in the sun above about 40° C. become pale in colour and this retards their increase in temperature. If replaced in the shade they quickly darken and remain for hours at temperatures above their surroundings.

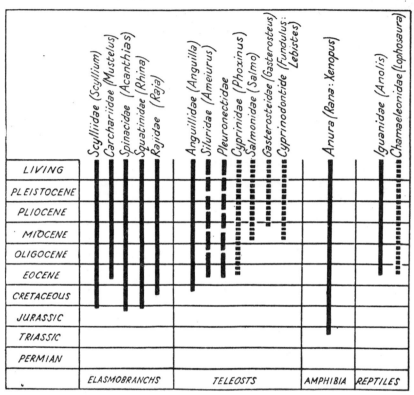

Fig. 212. Correlation of the geological ages of vertebrate groups with the methods of co-ordination of responses of the melanophores. The groups whose organization has remained fixed for the longer times mostly show purely humoral control; nervous control is found in those that have changed more recently. Continuous black shows humoral, long black dots mixed, and short dots mainly nervous control. (From Waring.)

The critical temperature for the colour change lies between 35 and 43° C. and was found to be higher in the American desert horned toad (*Phrynosoma blainvilli*) than in a relative (*P. platyrhinos*) that lives in cool valleys. There is a lizard (*Uta*) of the Californian deserts that is active in the winter and during the cool of morning and evening, and this genus becomes light coloured at a much lower temperature (25° C.) than the horned toads.

The physiological mechanism of colour control varies in different reptiles. In lizards (*Anolis*) there are probably no nerves to the melanophores; secretion of the posterior pituitary causes expansion and of the adrenal medulla contraction of the pigment. In chameleons, however, the situation is complicated by the presence of sympathetic nerve-fibres, whose action causes contraction of the melanophores (Fig. 211).

Nerve-fibres for the melanophores are found in rather isolated groups of vertebrates, namely, some fishes and some reptiles. Fig. 212 suggests that it may be the later members of these groups that have evolved the nervous control, but further data are required.

5. Posture, locomotion, and skeleton

The elongated body and small laterally projecting legs of the lizards recall those of a urodele, and the method of locomotion is in general similar in the two groups. Indeed, the limbs of the lizards are the more primitive in that five digits remain in both hand and foot. With the similarity of movement goes a general similarity in plan of the skeleton: there are, however, certain most significant features, characteristic of the reptiles. The head is carried off the ground, on a well-developed neck. The two first cervical vertebrae are modified to form atlas and axis. The atlas is a ring of bone without centrum, but with a facet in front for the single occipital condyle and one behind for the odontoid process, a peg attached to the front of the axis but derived in development from the centrum of the atlas segment.

In the vertebral column the interventrals (pleurocentra) have become well developed, while the basiventrals (intercentra) are reduced to little nodules of cartilage (p. 339). The vertebrae articulate with each other by a system of interlocking processes much more elaborate than that found in fish-like vertebrates and presumably serving to allow the column to carry weight. Each centrum is concave in front, covering the convex hind end of the vertebra next to it, a condition known as procoelous. In aquatic vertebrates the centra articulate by flat surfaces and this condition is retained in the amphi-coelous vertebrae of many primitive reptiles. Besides this articulation of the centra the vertebrae are also united by the zygopophyses, facets on the neural arches, so arranged that the upwardly facing surfaces of the anterior zygopophyses slide over the down-facing surfaces of the posterior zygopophyses, an arrangement found throughout the amniotes.

Ribs are well developed in the middle or trunk region; each articulates with the body of the vertebra by a single capitular facet.

The vertebrae may be divided into four sets. The eight cervical vertebrae have short ribs, not reaching the sternum. Sternal ribs occur in the twenty-two thoraco-lumbar segments (Fig. 213). The ribs of the two sacral vertebrae are short and broad and articulate with the ilia. The numerous caudal vertebrae show reduction of all parts, especially towards the tip of the tail. The chevron bones are ossicles attached to the caudal centra and representing the reduced intercentra.

The girdles and limbs (Figs. 184–7 and 213) show the same general

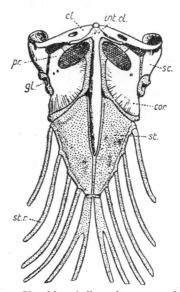

FIG. 213. Shoulder girdle and sternum of a lizard.
cl. clavicle; *cor.* coracoid; *gl.* glenoid; *int.cl.* interclavicle; *pr.* precoracoid process; *sc.* scapula; *st.r.* sternal rib; *st.* sternum. (From Reynolds, after Parker.)

structural and functional features as those of amphibia. The limbs form the main locomotor system, the metachronal contraction of the myotomes playing a lesser part than in urodele amphibians. The humerus and femur are normally held in such a position that their outer ends lie higher than the inner, that is to say, in a position of abduction. The radio-ulna and tibio-fibula proceed downwards towards the ground (at right-angles to the proximal bones) and the hand and foot are turned outwards at right-angles to rest on the ground. The main muscles thus draw the humerus and femur backwards and forwards as well as downwards, and the ventral regions of the girdles are large and flattened to receive these muscles; in mammals, with a different system of progression, the more dorsal parts of the girdles have become developed.

In the pectoral girdle (Figs. 184, 213) the large ventral coracoid element may be divided into an anterior procoracoid, posterior coracoid, and medial (cartilaginous) epicoracoid. There is a median

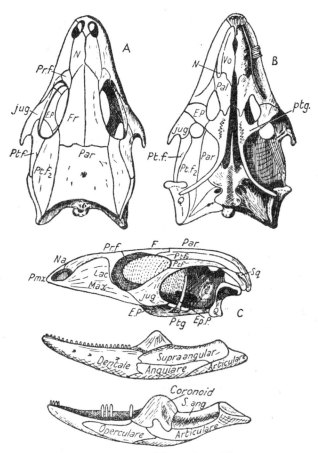

FIG. 214. Skull and lower jaw of *Lacerta*.

A, dorsal view; B, ventral view; C, from left side; D, right half of lower jaw from inner side, showing the pleurodont arrangement of the teeth. *E.P.* ectopterygoid; *Ep.P.* epipterygoid; *F, Fr.* frontal; *jug.* jugal; *Lac.* lachrymal; *Max.* maxillary; *N, Na.* nasal; *N,* in B, inner narial opening; *Pal.* palatine; *Par.* parietal; *Pmx.* premaxillary; *Pr.f.* prefrontal; *Pt.f.* post-orbital; *Pt.f₂.* post-frontal; *Ptg.* pterygoid; *Q.* quadrate; *S.ang.* supra-angular; *Sq.* squamosal; *Vo.* vomer. (After Gadow.)

dermal interclavicle. In the pelvic girdle (Fig. 185) the characteristic dorsal ilium, anterior pubis, and posterior ischium are found, the last two meeting their fellows in midline symphysis.

The characteristic modifications of the reptilian skull are discussed on p. 371. The general plan is very similar to that of primitive amphibians, but with a development of holes (fossae) in the temporal region to provide space for the bulging temporal muscles.

The jaws are more powerful than those of amphibia and are used freely for grasping the prey. The teeth set along their edges are replaced from below when worn away. In *Lacerta* all the teeth are alike; in some other reptiles there are suggestions of the differentiation found in mammals. The skull (Fig. 214) is stoutly built and well ossified, the dermal bones being more complete and the chondrocranium less obvious than in modern amphibia. The naming of some of the smaller bones is a matter of controversy; there are, of course, no

FIG. 215. Diagram of the skull of *Lacerta* to show temporal fossa.

a. articular; *an.* angular; *bo.* basioccipital; *bs.* basisphenoid; *c.* coronoid; *d.* dentary; *da.* dermal articular; *do.* dermal supraoccipital; *ept.* ectopterygoid; *eo.* exoccipital; *fr.* frontal; *j.* jugal; *l.* lachrymal; *mx.* maxilla; *n.* nostril; *na.* nasal; *o.* orbit; *op.* opisthotic; *pa.* parietal; *pal.* palatine; *pv.* prevomer; *pm.* premaxilla; *po.* post-orbital; *pof.* post-frontal; *pr.* prootic; *pra.* prearticular; *prf.* prefrontal; *ps.* presphenoid; *pt.* pterygoid; *q.* quadrate; *qj.* quadratojugal; *sa.* surangular; *sf.* upper temporal fossa (this is shown diagrammatically, as it occurs in many lizards; in *Lacerta* it is largely covered by an extension of the post-frontal—see Fig. 214); *so.* supraoccipital; *sp.* splenial; *sq.* squamosal; *st.* supratemporal; *v.* vomer. (From Goodrich.)

lateral lines to use as reference marks. The roof is covered by a complete series, including nasals, prefrontals, frontals, supra-orbitals, parietals, and supratemporals. The side of the skull is less complete, composed of tooth-bearing premaxillae and maxillae, postorbitals, two bones in the position of squamosals, and a quadrate. In many squamata these bones are so arranged as to leave an upper temporal fossa between the parietal above the postorbital and squamosals below (Fig. 215), but in *Lacerta* this fossa is covered over. The postorbital and squamosal make the upper margin of a large space, presumed to be comparable to the lower temporal fossa found in some other reptiles (see p. 371). In lizards and snakes this space has no complete lower margin, the jugal being a short bone in front, not united with the quadrate by a quadratojugal. The effect of this plan is to leave the quadrate free to make a movable articulation with the otic capsule, allowing great freedom of movement of the jaws. The lower jaw consists of six bones, the articular forming the joint with the quadrate and the dentary carrying the teeth.

The margins of the palate are formed by flanges of the premaxillae and maxillae, and the internal nostrils lie far forward between maxillae, vomers, and palatines. More posteriorly the floor of the skull is made up mainly by two pterygoid bones and a parasphenoid, and farther back still by a basisphenoid. Occipital bones surround the foramen magnum and make the single occipital condyle. A large part of the lateral wall of the skull is thus left incomplete, the epipterygoid bone standing out conspicuously in this space. This bone is the ossified pila pro-otica or portion of the wall of the chondrocranium uniting the parachordals with the orbital cartilages.

The whole plan of the skull thus shows us a reduced chondrocranium, covered, especially above and below, by a series of dermal bones, so arranged as to leave large fossae laterally for the bellies of the muscles of mastication, and allowing also a freely movable quadrate.

The post-mandibular visceral arches play no part in the jaw support, but are incorporated into the ear and hyoid apparatus. There is a rod-like columella auris, carrying vibrations from the tympanum stretched across the side of the back of the head to the fenestra ovalis and inner ear. This rod is presumably derived from the hyoid arch, but there is some doubt as to its relationship to the hyoid apparatus, which in the adult consists of a basal plate and three pairs of ascending horns, the first attached to the otic capsule. Presumably these cartilages represent the remains of the hyoid and branchial arches.

6. Feeding and digestion

Food is seized either with the teeth or tongue, the latter being in reptiles frequently very elongated and well supplied with sense-organs. There are no true salivary glands, but the mucous labial glands of the mouth may be well developed and in the gila monster (*Heloderma*) and some snakes they are modified to form poison glands. Digestion proper begins in the stomach. The alimentary canal is built on the typical vertebrate plan, with a tubular stomach, rather short small intestine (lizards being carnivorous), and wider large intestine, leading to a short caecum.

There is a very well-marked cloacal chamber in all reptiles and this is subdivided into a coprodaeum for the faeces and urodaeum for the products of the kidneys and genital organs, these two chambers opening into a final common proctodaeum, closed by a cloacal sphincter. This division of the cloaca is associated with the necessity for the retention of water, the cloacal chambers serving for water reabsorption from both the faeces and urinary excreta (p. 361).

7. Respiration, circulation, and excretion

The method of respiration is no longer as in amphibia a simple modification of that of fishes, but involves expansion of the lungs by

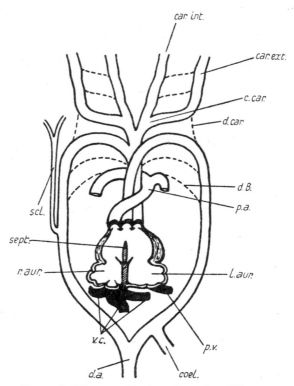

FIG. 216. Diagram of heart and arteries of *Lacerta*.

car.ext. external carotid; *car.int.* internal carotid; *coel.* coeliac artery; *d.a.* dorsal aorta; *d.car.* ductus caroticus; *d.B.* ductus Botalli (arteriosus); *for.* foramen of Panizza; *l.aur.* left auricle; *p.a.* pulmonary artery; *p.v.* pulmonary vein; *r.aur.* right auricle; *scl.* subclavian artery; *sept.* interventricular septum; *v.c.* caval veins. (From Ihle, after Goodrich.)

a backward movement of the ribs, produced by the muscles attached to the latter. There is, however, no separation of the thorax from the abdomen by means of a diaphragm. The glottis is a slit at the back of the mouth and leads into a larynx with supporting cricoid and arytenoid cartilages. The lizard is able to produce small sounds, but the voice-box is less developed than in either amphibia or birds.

The lungs are sacs whose walls are folded into ridges, separating a number of chambers or bronchioles. The hinder part of the lungs is nearly smooth and in other reptiles and birds becomes developed into characteristic air sacs. The tendency is for the more anterior portions of the lungs to become the effective vascular and respiratory region, allowing the air-stream to be drawn across it at both inspiration and expiration.

The circulation (Fig. 216) still shows an incomplete separation of venous and arterial blood; there are two auricles, but only one ventricle, this being partly divided by a septum into right and left sides. However, the cavity of the ventricle is so arranged that during its contraction the two halves become separated. The conus arteriosus is completely divided by two spiral septa, so that there are one pulmonary and two aortic channels opening from the ventricle. The single pulmonary opening lies opposite the right side of the ventricle and receives venous blood. The left systemic arch opens opposite to the incomplete ventricular septum and receives mixed blood, whereas the right systemic arch opens from the left side of the ventricle and carries almost pure arterial blood. The carotid arteries of both sides arise from the right systemic arch.

The venous system is based on the same plan as that of the frog, with pelvic veins receiving blood from the tail and hind legs and returning it to the heart through either an anterior abdominal vein or renal portals and the inferior vena cava.

In the urinogenital system is seen another feature characteristic of amniotes, the development of a posterior region, the metanephros, concerned solely with excretion, leaving the mesonephric (Wolffian) duct to function as the vas deferens in the male. There is an endodermal (allantoic) bladder. The waste nitrogen is largely excreted as uric acid and this allows the reabsorption of much of the water in the urodaeum, the organic matter precipitating as a chalky white mass of urates. The advantage of this form of excretion is that it avoids the high concentrations of toxic substances that would be reached if the end-product was the more soluble urea. The final excretory product varies with the manner of life of the species. Thus among Chelonia the more aquatic forms (*Emys*) produce considerable amounts of ammonia and urea, relatively little uric acid, whereas the latter is the main excretory product of the fully terrestrial types, such as the Grecian tortoise (*Testudo graeca*), which can live under almost desert conditions.

8. Reproduction of reptiles

Some of the most serious difficulties in the colonization of the land are concerned with reproduction and these problems have been largely solved in the reptiles, allowing the animals to reproduce without returning, as amphibia must do, to the water. For the eggs to develop on land they must be given the physical support which they previously obtained from the water and they must be protected against desiccation. These requirements are met by inclusion in a shell, and this necessitates the provision of nourishment adequate for a long development, and of special means of gaseous exchange and

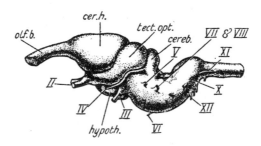

Fig. 217. Three views of the brain of a lizard.
cereb. cerebellum; *cer.h.* cerebral hemispheres; *hypoph.* hypophysis; *hypoth.* hypothalamus; *olf.b.* olfactory bulb; *tect.opt.* tectum opticum; *II–XII*, cranial nerves. (After Frederikse.)

removal of waste products. Before the egg can be surrounded by the necessary membranes it must be fertilized high up in the oviduct, and this determines the development of the organs and behaviour patterns of copulation. In the lizard the wall of the proctodaeum forms tubular folds which can be turned inside out, apparently by vascular erection, to make a pair of penes. The vasa deferentia open into the urodaeum and the sperms are carried by grooves to the penes. It is said that only one penis is inserted at a time.

The eggs are very yolky and the cleavage only partial. The most remarkable features of the development are the production of the embryonic membranes. The amnion is a series of folds which cover the embryo, making a sac in which development can proceed in the absence of the pond that was necessary for the earlier vertebrates. The allantois probably began as an enlarged bladder for the reception of the waste products during the life within the shell; coming close to the surface it became the vehicle for transport of oxygen to the

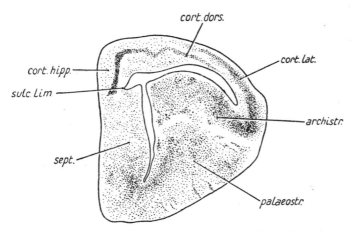

FIG. 218. Transverse section through forebrain of *Lacerta*.

Archistr. archistriatum (upper part of corpus striatum); *cort.dors.* dorsal cortex; *cort.hipp.* medial (hippocampal) cortex; *cort.lat.* lateral (pyriform) cortex; *palaeostr.* palaeostriatum (basal part of corpus striatum); *sept.* septum; *sulc.lim.* sulcus limitans. (After de Lange and Kappers.)

embryo. The shell itself is secreted by the walls of the oviduct and is often impregnated with lime to give the support necessary to avoid the action of gravity on so soft a system. In *Lacerta vivipara* the eggs are retained within the oviduct to the very end of development and the young lizard ruptures the soft shell as soon as the egg is laid. In order to allow hatching from the egg all reptiles develop a special 'egg tooth' on the top of the front of the head. This is a special epidermal structure known as a caruncle in the reptiles with a hard shell, *Sphenodon*, chelonia, crocodilia and also in birds; but in Squamata, where the shell is membranous, the 'egg tooth' is a modified true tooth, having a point or cutting edge. It may be that the ovo-viviparous habit has enabled *L. vivipara* to extend farther north than the majority of the members of the genus, where the eggs develop in the soil. *Anguis*, the slow-worm, which is also ovo-viviparous, also has an extended range northwards.

9. Nervous system and behaviour of reptiles

All the modifications of structure that fit the reptiles for life on land would be useless without the development of appropriate behaviour. This in turn depends on suitable structure and function of the nervous system. The brain accordingly shows some interesting developments. The cerebral hemispheres are relatively larger in

Fig. 219. Diagram to show the mechanism of accommodation in the eye of reptiles.

ap. annular pad of lens; *bm.* Brucke's muscle; *bp.* base plate of ciliary body; *c.* cornea; *ch.* chorioid; *cp.* ciliary process; *i.* iris; *lb.* lens body; *ot.* ora terminalis; *pl.* pectinate ligament; *s.s.* sclera; *sc.* scleral cartilage; *scs.* sclerocorneal sulcus; *so.* scleral ossicle; *sr.* sensory retina; *tbm.* tendon of Brucke's muscle (continuous with inner layers of corneal substantia propria); *tl.* tenacular ligament; *z.* zonule. (From Walls, *The Vertebrate Eye.*)

reptiles than in amphibia (Fig. 217). The increased bulk lies mainly in the ventral portions, the roof of the hemispheres being little developed and without the elaborate cortical arrangement found in mammals (Fig. 218). There are more tracts from the thalamus to the forebrain than in amphibia, and there is evidently a beginning of that transfer of all nervous functions to the forebrain which is so characteristic of mammals. The outward sign of this is the relatively large size of the cerebral hemispheres compared to the optic lobes. The walls of the thalamus are thick and many of the optic tract fibres end there, as well as others in the midbrain.

The behaviour of lizards, like that of other reptiles, remains of a relatively simple type. The eyes are probably the main exteroceptive sense-organs and are provided with lids, including a third eyelid or nictitating membrane. The lachrymal glands and Harderian glands provide secretions that keep the surface of the cornea moist. The front of the eye is supported by a ring of bony sclerotic plates and accommodation is produced by striated ciliary muscles, so arranged that they cause the ciliary process to squeeze the lens, making its anterior surface more rounded (Fig. 219). Lizards, like many other reptiles, are diurnal and possess a high proportion of cones in the retina. The vitreous contains a vascular protrusion of the optic nerve head, the conus papillaris or pecten, whose function is probably to provide nourishment for the retina.

The tympanum lies at the back of the jaws, sunk a little below the surface. The range of response to sound waves is not known in lizards, but the ears of tortoises are very sensitive to sound over a narrow range of about 110 cycles per second; apparently there is some resonating mechanism, perhaps the columella auris, that vibrates at this frequency. Jacobson's organ (vomeronasal organ) is more highly developed in the Squamata than in any other vertebrates. In many lizards there is a ciliated choanal groove that carries odorous particles to its lumen. In forms where these grooves are small or absent it is usually possible for particles to be inserted directly by the tongue tips; there is evidence, however, that there may also be some other filling mechanism by which particles are sucked in. The lachrymal duct, carrying away the secretions of the large glands of the orbit, especially the Harderian gland, opens close to the duct of Jacobson's organ and it is possible that the secretion enters the latter and has some special function there. Lizards and snakes have acute chemical senses. After removal of the tips of the tongue a snake is no longer able to follow a food trail. The response of striking by snakes is elicited by scent particles reaching Jacobson's organ.

XV

EVOLUTION OF THE REPTILES

1. The earliest reptile populations, *Anapsida*

The organization of a reptile, such as a lizard, is well suited in many ways to maintain life on land. There are features which show a considerable advance in this respect over the amphibia. Especially noticeable are the dryness of the skin, the method of reproduction, and the devices for economizing the use of water. The immense radiation of the reptiles into every sort of land habitat during the Mesozoic period shows the efficiency of these mechanisms. They were probably present, at least in imperfect form, in the earliest Carboniferous and Permian offshoots from the ancestral Stegocephali (p. 337).

We have sufficient knowledge to be able to trace the early stages of reptilian evolution with considerable certainty. The most amphibian-like forms are placed in the order Cotylosauria, the 'stem-reptiles', known mainly from the Permian, though certainly existing already in the Carboniferous. *Seymouria*, found in the Lower Permian of Texas, perhaps 220 million years ago (Figs. 220 and 221), is the classic example of these animals. It was a lizard-like creature, about 2 feet long, living on insects and perhaps some larger animals. Its characteristics are so exactly intermediate between those of amphibians and reptiles that it is not possible to place it definitely with either group and many zoologists class it with the amphibia. This intermediacy is shown in almost every structure of the body and is often a subtle matter of the shape or size of the parts. Although a list of anatomical features is apt to give an unreal picture of any living organization it is the only method available to us in the absence of any more ingenious calculus, and we may therefore give first some of the striking reptilian characters of *Seymouria*. (1) The general shape of the skull was reptilian, with a pointed 'nose', dorsal nostrils, and laterally directed eyes. (2) The anterior cervical vertebrae were modified to form axis and atlas. (3) The basiventrals were reduced to ventral wedges, the intercentra, though these are much larger than in later reptiles. (4) The pectoral girdle possessed a long interclavicle and a ventral coracoid. (5) The pelvic girdle was attached to the vertebral column by two sacral vertebrae. (6) The ilium was expanded dorsally for attachment of the large muscles used in walking. (7) There were five

Fig. 220. Skeleton of *Seymouria*. Actual length 20 in.
(From Williston, *Osteology of the Reptiles*, Harvard University Press.)

Fig. 221. Skull and pectoral girdle of *Seymouria* (after Williston).

c. coracoid; *cl.* clavicle; *icl.* interclavicle; *j.* jugal; *l.* lachrimal; *m.*
maxilla; *po.* post-orbital; *qj.* quadratojugal; *sc.* scapula; *sq.* squamosal.

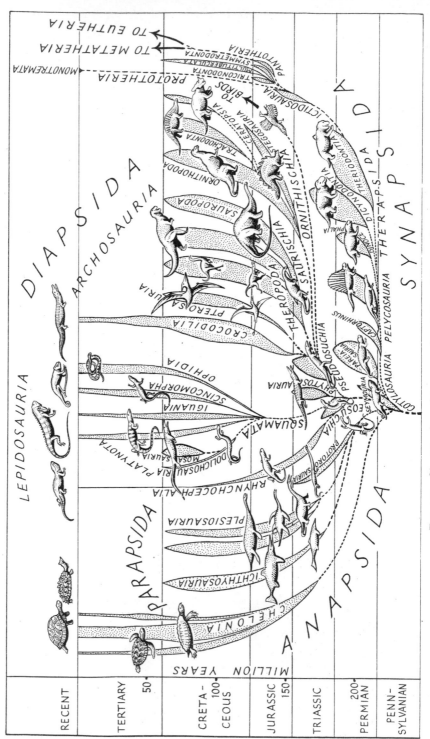

FIG. 222. Chart to show the course of evolution of the reptiles.

digits in hand and foot, and numerous phalanges. In the tarsus the tibiale has been lost, leaving two proximal bones. The general shape of the skeleton thus suggests that *Seymouria* was reptilian in its carriage and probably to some extent in its habits.

On the other hand, there are many characteristics that would lead one to classify this fossil as an amphibian. (1) In the skull the ossification is very complete, both dorsally and on the palate: there are no fossae in the temporal region. The pattern of the bones is very like that of early amphibia, for instance, an intertemporal bone is present. (2) The tympanum was stretched across an 'otic notch', bounded by the supratemporal bone above and the squamosal below; in later reptiles the tympanum lay behind the jaw. (3) The neck was very short, the pectoral girdle lying close behind the skull. (4) There was very little differentiation between the vertebrae, all those of the cervical region bore ribs. (5) The ribs were double-headed, the knob for attachment to the 'intercentrum' being still present. (6) The teeth still showed the labyrinthine structure and distribution in pairs (on the palate as well as the edge of the jaw) which was present not only in the Stegocephali but in the more remote crossopterygian ancestors. (7) Most cotylosaurs, though not *Seymouria*, still possessed a cleithrum. (8) Perhaps the most significant point of all is that some specimens show signs of the presence of lateral line canals. This may perhaps indicate that *Seymouria* passed through an aquatic larval stage and the case for classifying it as an amphibian thus becomes very strong.

There is no doubt that these animals were very close to the earliest amphibia and therefore not far removed from the fish ancestors from which the whole group of tetrapods had arisen 50 million years earlier, at the end of the Devonian period. Yet *Seymouria* and its allies show distinct tendencies towards adaptation for land life, and from them there soon arose a great number of different types, which came to dominate not only the land but also the sea and air throughout the subsequent Mesozoic period.

The cotylosaurs must have existed as separate populations throughout the later part of the Carboniferous, but our fossils of that period are from swamps and we have little evidence of the reptiles before Lower Permian times, presumably because they lived on drier ground. From the Red Beds of Texas we have, besides *Seymouria*, others such as *Limnoscelis*, *Captorhinus*, and *Labidosaurus*, all with the rather high narrow skulls and pointed nose characteristic of reptiles rather than amphibia, but differing from the latter, and from *Seymouria*, in the absence of the otic notch. This and other features suggest that these animals were close to that part of the early reptile population which later developed into the mammals (see p. 513).

Other rather later cotylosaurs were larger forms, such as *Diadectes* (Fig. 223) and *Bradysaurus* and other 'pareiasaurs' from the Permian and Triassic of Europe and America. These were up to 10 feet long and probably carried the body well off the ground, the limbs being

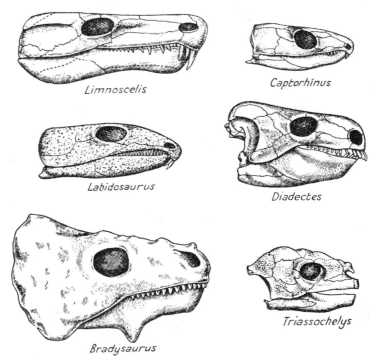

FIG. 223. Skulls of various early reptiles. After Romer and various authors.

held underneath the body and showing some reduction of digits. This, together with the large size of the animals and their large folded teeth, suggest that they may have been the first of the many types of large herbivore to appear on the land. In some of them the skull developed grotesque protective protuberances, a feature recalling similar later developments in reptiles (Ceratopsia, p. 403) and mammals (Amblypods, p. 676). A characteristic structural feature was the presence of an otic notch low down on the side of the skull. This distinguishes the pareiasaurs from the more mammal-like forms and suggests affinity with some of the other reptilian descendants of the early cotylosaurs. These cotylosaurs multiplied and became very diversified throughout the 30 million years of the Permian period, by which time the main reptilian types had appeared. The individual orders were nearly all established during the subsequent 30 million years of the Trias and most of the orders reached their maximum development in the Jurassic and Cretaceous.

2. Classification of reptiles

Since our knowledge of these populations depends mainly on fossil remains it is convenient to classify the reptiles by means of the

FIG. 224. Diagrams of reptilian skulls to show arrangement of the temporal openings. Anapsida, no opening. Synapsida, a lower opening, with post-orbital and squamosal meeting above it. Parapsida, an upper opening with post-orbital and squamosal meeting below it. Diapsida, two openings, separated by a bar.

j. jugal; *pa.* parietal; *po.* post-orbital; *sq.* squamosal. (From Romer, *Vertebrate Paleontology*, Chicago University Press.)

skull into four great groups (Fig. 224). Types in which, as in *Seymouria*, there were no fossae in the temporal region are placed in the subclass *Anapsida*, because they show no arches or 'apses' of bone in this region. Typical forms of this sort occur in the Carboniferous, Permian, and early Trias, and the Chelonia (tortoises and turtles) probably represent relatively little-modified descendants from the stock. In one line of cotylosaurs (such as *Captorhinus*) the tympanum moved to the back of the jaw, the stapes forming a long rod running from the auditory capsule to articulate with the quadrate. This line, which was already established in the Carboniferous, led to the mammal-like reptiles, known as *Synapsida*. When the disappearance of the otic notch left the whole side of the skull as a compact support for the jaw a temporal fossa developed between the postorbital and squamosal bones, presumably to accommodate the belly of the jaw-muscles. In this way a single arch was formed, and early workers supposed this arch to be the result of a fusion of the two arches found in many other reptiles, hence the mammal-like forms were called 'synapsid' or 'fused-arch' reptiles. The name is unfortunate because it is now considered that the temporal fossa in question, though corresponding roughly to the lower fossa of the two-arched forms, has arisen independently. We shall take up consideration of this line of animals again as we approach the mammals (p. 513).

The *Diapsida* are another, most successful, line leading from the cotylosaurs, and characterized by the presence of two temporal fossae (Fig. 224). The diapsids include many of the most conspicuous Mesozoic reptilian types. The tuatara and the crocodiles have survived from early offshoots of this line and the lizards and snakes (Squamata) represent a late development of the same stock, the lower temporal fossa having lost its lower margin. The birds are also undoubtedly derived from Mesozoic diapsid ancestors.

Finally, in the fourth type of reptile to be recognized (*Parapsida*) there is one temporal fossa, lying not between the postorbital and squamosal, as in *Synapsida*, but higher up the skull, so that the postorbital and squamosal meet below it. No existing reptiles possess this arrangement, but it was found in certain terrestrial Permian types, the Protorosauria, and in the aquatic Plesiosauria and their allies of the Triassic and Jurassic. The Ichthyosauria is another group of aquatic animals that possess an upper temporal fossa, but in this case it is bounded behind by the supratemporal bone, which is absent in plesiosaurs. However, the general similarity of the skulls is sufficient to allow us to class all these forms provisionally together as *Parapsida*, admitting that the relationship is only a distant one. The Mesosauria, on the other hand, aquatic reptiles from the later Carboniferous and early Permian times, possessed a lower temporal fossa resembling that of the mammal-like reptiles, and they are therefore of uncertain affinities, since they show no other likeness to *Synapsida*. For the sake of a complete classification, however, we can place them as synapsids, thus including all reptiles in the four subclasses.

3. Order 1. Chelonia

Shut away in their boxes the tortoises and turtles have retained some of the features of the earliest anapsid reptiles. Even to-day they are a not unsuccessful and quite varied and widespread group, with more than 100 species. These include terrestrial animals, such as *Testudo graeca*, the Grecian tortoise of south Europe, which is herbivorous; the freshwater tortoises, such as *Chrysemys* and other American terrapins, and *Emys* the European water-tortoise, all of which are carnivorous. The marine Chelonia, usually known as turtles, are often very large. *Sphargis*, the leathery turtle, which has no shell, is over 6 feet long and weighs half a ton. *Chelone mydas*, the green or edible turtle, is over 3 feet long.

The characteristic of chelonian organization is the shortening and broadening of the body, together with the development of bony plates, forming a box into which the head and limbs can be withdrawn. The total number of segments is only about 8 in the neck,

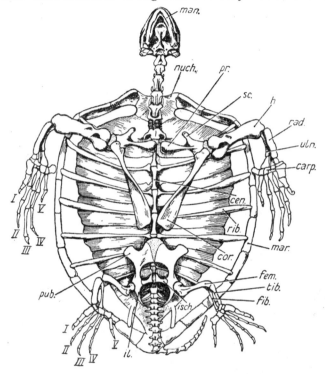

FIG. 225. Skeleton of turtle (*Chelone*).

carp. carpus (note hook-shaped 5th metacarpal); *cen.* centrum of vertebra; *cor.* coracoid; *fem.* femur; *fib.* fibula; *h.* humerus; *il.* ilium; *isch.* ischium; *mar.* marginal plate; *nuch.* nucal plate; *pr.* 'proscapular' process; *pub.* pubis; *rad.* radius; *rib,* rib, partly fused with costal shell-plate; *sc.* scapula (foreshortened); *tib.* tibia; *uln.* ulna. (After Shipley and McBride and Reynolds.)

10 in the trunk, and a series of reduced caudals; the body is therefore morphologically shorter than in any other vertebrate except the frog. Probably this shortening and broadening is the result of some quite simple change in morphogenesis. The shell is usually considered to include a dorsal carapace and ventral plastron. Each of these is made up of inner plates of bone, covered by separate outer plates of horny material, comparable to the scales of other reptiles. The carapace includes five rows of bony plates, namely, median neurals, and paired costals and marginals (Fig. 225). These plates are ossifications in the

dermis, attached to the vertebrae and ribs, but not actually formed from the latter. The plastron is developed from the expanded dermal bones of the pectoral girdle, together with dermal ossifications comparable to the abdominal ribs found in crocodiles and other reptiles. The whole is covered in most chelonians by rows of special smooth epidermal plates forming the 'tortoise shell' (Fig. 226). A new and larger layer is added to each of these plates each year, the old one remaining above it, thus making a number of 'growth rings' from

FIG. 226. Diagram of the arrangement of the shell of the tortoise (*Testudo*). The horny shields are shown only on the left.

cap. capitulum of rib; *cost.pl*. costal plate; *cost.s*. costal shield; *marg.pl*. marginal plate; *marg.s*. marginal shield; *neur.pl*. neural plate; *neur.s*. neural shield; *plast*. plastron; *sp.c*. spinal cord. (After Gadow.)

which the age of the tortoise can be calculated, though the outer members often become rubbed off.

In order to support this box the limb girdles have become much modified and lie inside the encircling ribs. The pectoral girdle has three prongs, a scapula that meets the carapace dorsally, and a backward coracoid and special 'precoracoid', the two last attached to the plastron. The ilia are attached to two sacral vertebrae and the ischia and pubis are broad. The limbs are stout, but otherwise typically reptilian, with five digits in each. In the marine turtles they are transformed into paddles.

The interpretation of the skull is still somewhat doubtful, but it seems not unlikely that the turtle, *Chelone*, shows the simplest case, namely, the original anapsid condition (Fig. 227). Here the roofing is complete, the dermal bones being widely separated from the braincase, forming a tunnel for the muscles supporting the head and producing retraction of the neck. The tympanum is stretched across a sort of otic notch, bounded by the squamosal, quadratojugal, and quadrate, the columella auris articulating with the latter. In other groups of chelonia, however, the dermal roofing has been reduced or 'emarginated', presumably to give still better attachment for the neck

Chelone

Trionyx

FIG. 227. Skulls of *Chelone* and *Trionyx*. Lettering as Fig. 215, p. 358. (After Goodrich from Parker and Haswell, and Zittel.)

muscles (Fig. 227). It has been argued that the condition in *Chelone* is secondary, but there is no evidence of true temporal fossae in any chelonian, and since the early form **Triassochelys* also had a fully roofed skull there seems no reason for denying that we have here essentially an anapsid condition.

A peculiarity of chelonia is the entire absence of teeth, alike in the

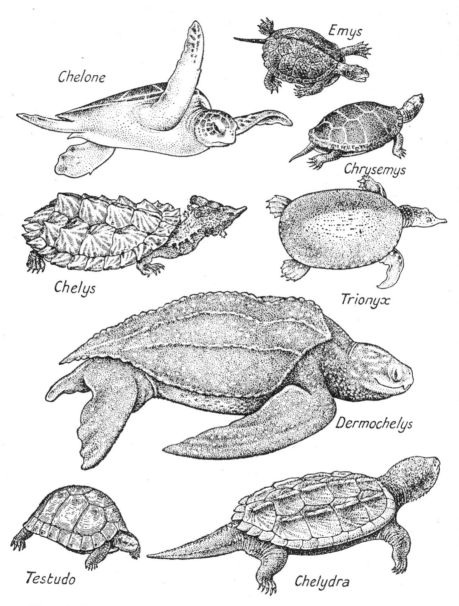

FIG. 228. Various chelonians, not all to same scale. (*Emys* and *Chelys* after Gadow, *Dermochelys* after Deraniyagela.)

herbivorous and carnivorous forms. The edges of the jaws form sharp ridges, covered with a formidable horny beak.

The similarity of the soft parts of chelonia to those of other surviving reptiles (which are all diapsids) suggests that the general organization of the group has changed little since the Permian. The heart possesses an undivided ventricle and there are two equal aortic arches (Fig. 243). Respiration is modified on account of the rigidity of the body wall, the lungs being spongy structures attached to the dorsal surface of the shell, sometimes enclosed in a separate pleural cavity (*Testudo*), and filled by the protrusion of the head, movements of the girdles and limbs, and the pumping action of the well-developed hyoid apparatus. This latter arrangement is presumably a survival from that of early tetrapods, and further emphasizes that the chelonia is an ancient group. Some aquatic forms (*Emys*) also respire by taking water into special vascular anal sacs, diverticuli of the urodaeum. The metabolism of tortoises is slow and they can remain for long periods without breathing. In temperate climates all species hibernate regularly.

The kidney is metanephric and the nitrogenous excreta are mainly uric acid, there being a typical subdivision of the cloaca and reabsorption of water to form a solid whitish excretory product (see p. 361). There is a single copulatory organ and hard-shelled whitish eggs are produced. The terrestrial nature of the group as a whole is emphasized by the fact that the aquatic turtles all come ashore to breed. Thus the marine *Chelone* breeds in the West Indies, in the Straits of Malacca, and on the coast of West Africa; they are caught as they come ashore and made into turtle soup. On the Amazon chelonian eggs are (or at least were) so plentiful that large numbers were collected for their fats. The eggs are usually carefully placed in holes made by boring with the tail and scooping with the feet (*Emys*). The traces of the nest are then covered, often with considerable success. Nevertheless Bates reckoned that at least 48 million eggs were taken annually on the upper Amazon. The chief enemies of the young are vultures and alligators and these were presumably the ultimate losers when collection by man began, though the numbers of turtles have also decreased as a result of the human depredations.

The proverbial slowness of the tortoise is a necessary corollary of its heavy armour, but the nervous organization and behaviour is more complex than is sometimes supposed. The brain shows well-developed cerebral hemispheres, with not only the basal regions but also the pallium quite large. This was therefore probably true also of the earliest reptiles, as it is of amphibia. In the mammals, also derived from cotylosaur ancestors, there has been still further development of the dorsal regions of the hemispheres to form the cerebral cortex, whereas in the remaining reptile groups, and in the birds, the ventral portion has become large, the dorsal thin. The eyes are probably the chief receptors of chelonians, but the nose is also well developed and the animals are very sensitive to vibration. The tympanum is often covered with ordinary skin and hearing is probably not acute (p. 365). The voice is also small.

The various species show many special habits, some of them complicated and ingenious, especially among the aquatic forms (Fig. 228). For instance, the snapping turtles (*Chelydra*) and alligator turtles (*Macroclemmys*) of North America and *Emys* in Europe show considerable care and skill in stalking and capturing not only fish but also young ducks and other birds. Similarly the smaller forms such as *Chrysemys picta*, the painted terrapin, with bright yellow, black, and red colours, feed not only on insect larvae, but also on flies, which they catch near the water surface. Many observers have shown that the common Grecian tortoise has a marked sense of locality, returning to a favourite spot even after hibernation.

Our knowledge of the geological history of the chelonia extends back to the Trias. *Triassochelys* (Fig. 223) was an early turtle, with a shell like that of modern forms, but still possessing teeth on the palate. The skull was anapsid and the pectoral girdle contained inter-clavicles, clavicles, and perhaps cleithra; these dermal bones were already somewhat enlarged and incorporated in the plastron. The head, tail, and limbs could not be withdrawn into the shell and were protected by spines. In the later evolution of the chelonia retraction of the head became possible by one of two methods. In the suborder Pleurodira, 'side-neck turtles', the neck is folded sideways. The group is known from the Cretaceous and survives to-day in tropical Africa (*Chelys*), South America, and Australia. The more successful group is the suborder Cryptodira, in which the neck is curved in a dorso-ventral plane. This type is also known from the Cretaceous and includes most of the modern types. The aquatic chelonians show various modifications and it is probable that several lines have independently returned to the water. As a result of this habit the bony shell is often reduced, presumably in the interests of lightness and because of absence of enemies. This had occurred already in *Archelon* of the Cretaceous, which is very similar to the modern *Chelone*. *Dermochelys*, the leathery turtle, has only small bony scales embedded in the skin and *Trionyx* is a freshwater turtle with neither bony or horny scales. All of these forms are best considered as aberrant cryptodirans.

We can trace the history of the Chelonia back rather satisfactorily to the Triassic, but unfortunately there is little to show how they evolved to that stage from some Carboniferous cotylosaurian ancestor. *Eunotosaurus* from the Permian of South Africa had a small number of vertebrae, with very broad, expanded ribs. This perhaps suggests some affinity with Chelonia, though in the latter the ribs themselves are not expanded. There is therefore little to tell us how, when, or why one of the early reptilian populations shortened its bodies and covered them with armour for protection against the hazards of the land they had recently invaded.

4. Subclass *Parapsida

The animals placed in this group all possessed an upper temporal fossa, but it must be admitted that they had little else in common. Collecting them together in this way is more of a convenience than an indication of close phylogenetic affinity. The ichthyosaurs and plesiosaurs that make up the greater part of the group were numerous animals in the Mesozoic. No member of the subclass is known to have survived beyond the end of the Cretaceous, although it has often been suggested that tales of sea-serpents indicate the continued survival of plesiosaurs; since the discovery of the coelacanth fish *Latimeria* zoologists have become cautious about rejecting such possibilities!

5. Order *Protorosauria

The earliest parapsids were small terrestrial lizard-like creatures, such as *Araeoscelis* from the Lower Permian (Fig. 229). The skull was like that of anapsids in shape but possessed a small upper temporal fossa, between the parietal, postorbital, squamosal, and supratemporal bones. The vertebrae were of the primitive amphicoelous type, and the limbs were probably held out sideways from the body. A few other terrestrial parapsids are known, including the remarkable Triassic *Tanystropheus* with a long neck and short body (Fig. 222). These animals seem never to have been an important element of the land fauna, but they probably gave rise to the plesiosaurs and possibly also to the ichthyosaurs. The theory that diapsida were derived from protorosaurs by 'emargination' of the lower temporal region is now held to be unlikely (p. 385).

6. Order *Plesiosauria

This was a very successful line of marine reptiles, extending from the Trias to the end of the Cretaceous. The earlier forms, such as *Lariosaurus* (Fig. 229) from marine Triassic deposits, were small (3 feet long) and recognizably similar to the protorosaurs, with a long neck, and limbs partly converted into paddles. The upper temporal fossa was enlarged, the nostrils lay rather far back, and a false palate was produced from medial extensions of the pterygoids.

All of these features were further developed in the plesiosaurs of the Jurassic and Cretaceous, such as *Muraenosaurus* (Fig. 229). In some the neck became very long, presumably for catching fish; 76 cervical vertebrae have been recorded. In others the neck was shorter and the skull longer. The limbs were developed into huge paddles, the ventral portions of the girdles being large for the attachment of muscle masses inserted on the flattened humerus and femur. The dorsal portion of the girdles, so well developed in terrestrial reptiles, was here small: the ilium hardly articulates with the sacral verte-brae. The hands and feet were enlarged by increase in number of joints (hyperphalangy), but there was no increase of digits (hyper-dactyly) such as is seen in ichthyosaurs. The skull was as in notho-saurs, but with the nostril still farther displaced on to the upper surface.

These forms were numerous in Jurassic and Cretaceous seas and some of them reached 50 feet in length. They were obviously fish-eaters, but little is known of their habits. There is no evidence that they were viviparous; perhaps, as their limbs were moderately well developed, they laid eggs on the seashores. *Placodus* and related forms were Triassic plesiosaurs specialized for mollusc-eating by the presence of large grinding teeth on the jaws and palate.

7. Order *Ichthyosauria

These animals, found mainly in the Triassic and Jurassic seas, were even more modified for aquatic life than the plesiosaurs (Fig. 229). They occupied a position comparable to that of the dolphins and whales during the Tertiary period. The body possessed a stream-lined fish shape and swimming was by undulatory movements. The vertebrae were amphicoelous disks and there were large dorsal and caudal fins, the vertebral column apparently being continued into the lower lobe of the latter. The paired fins were small and presumably used as stabilizing and steering agents. The pelvic girdle did not articulate with the backbone. In the limbs the number of digits was often greater or less than the usual five, and there was often hyperphalangy. Evidently this type of skeleton gives better support for a

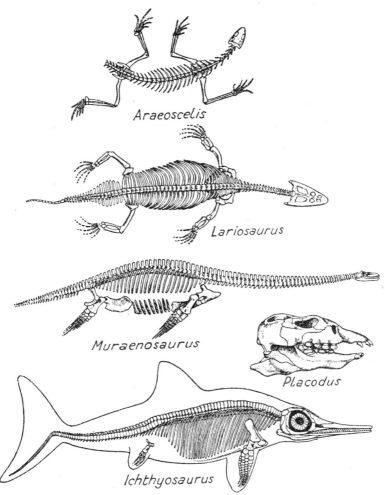

FIG. 229. Various parapsids. (Partly after Romer.)

fish-like paddle than does the pentadactyl tetrapod type and it is interesting to find it evolved again in vertebrate stocks that return to the water. This seems to be a case of reversal of evolution.

The head was much modified for aquatic life, with a very long snout, armed with sharp teeth and nostrils set far back. The eyes were large and surrounded by a ring of sclerotic bony plates. The upper temporal fossa was bounded by post-frontal and supra-temporal bones, and is therefore often held not to be strictly comparable with that of other Parapsida.

The stapes was very thick, as are the ear ossicles of whales.

The Triassic ichthyosaurs were already greatly modified and we have no trace of the origin of the group. There is nothing against the view that these animals developed from some amphibious protorosaur

FIG. 230. Diagrams of skulls of A, eosuchian, B, pseudosuchian, showing the plan of the diapsid skull.

Lettering as Fig. 215. *lf.* lower temporal fossa; *pl.* pre-orbital fossa; *sf.* upper temporal fossa. (From Goodrich.)

stock in the Permian, becoming adapted to aquatic life by reduction of the limbs rather than by the enlargement that occurred in plesiosaurs. Certainly the ichthyosaurs were very fully aquatic and seem to have been viviparous, since the skeletons of small specimens have been found within larger ones. Like the plesiosaurs they developed a special mollusc-eating type, *Omphalosaurus*, in the Triassic.

8. Subclass Diapsida

Order *Eosuchia

Most of the animals popularly considered as characteristic of the period of reptilian dominance have a two-arched or diapsid skull. This group contains all the surviving reptiles except the Chelonia, and it also gave rise to the birds. The group made a relatively late appearance, in the form of certain creatures from the late Permian and early Trias, grouped together as the order *Eosuchia. The best known of these, *Youngina* (Figs. 230 and 231) was a lizard-like creature, found in the Upper Permian of South Africa, and having many cotylosaur features, for instance, teeth on the palate and no opening between the bones of the snout (antorbital vacuity). The two fossae at the back of the skull immediately show the affinity with other diapsids. Little is known of the post-cranial skeleton. The fifth metatarsal does not show the hooked shape, which is found in

Fig. 231. Skull of *Youngina*. Lettering as Fig. 215. (After Romer, *Vertebrate Paleontology*, Chicago University Press.)

other diapsids and also in chelonia. It is difficult, however, to ascribe very great weight to this single point, as against the general features of the skull, which indicate that *Youngina* could have given rise to the later two-arched reptiles and, by loss of the lower margin of the lower temporal fossa, also to the lizards and snakes. *Prolacerta*, from the Lower Trias, shows how this may have come about; it is so like *Youngina* that is classed as an eosuchian, but the lower temporal fossa is open below.

The Squamata are now almost universally considered to be diapsids, that is to say, related to the great dinosaurs and birds. However, the Squamata and the dinosaur-bird lines have been separate since the Triassic and are often given separate names, superorder Lepidosauria for the Squamata and their allies and superorder Archosauria for the dinosaurs, crocodiles, and ancestors of the birds.

9. Lepidosauria

Order Rhynchocephalia

Sphenodon (= *Hatteria*), the tuatara lizard of New Zealand, is the oldest surviving lepidosaurian reptile; it still remains in essentially the eosuchian condition. Very similar Mesozoic fossils (e.g. *Homoeosaurus* from the Jurassic) show the continuity of the type (Fig. 222). Among the many primitive features that this race has preserved unchanged for 200 million years are the two complete temporal fossae (Fig. 232),

FIG. 232. Skull of *Sphenodon*. Lettering as Fig. 215. (After Romer, *Vertebrate Paleontology*, Chicago University Press.)

the well-developed pineal eye (the pineal foramen is marked in the early diapsid fossil skulls), the complete palate, which is very similar to that of *Youngina*, and amphicoelous vertebrae with intercentra. *Sphenodon*, alone of surviving reptiles, has no copulatory organ. Specialized characters are the teeth, fixed to the edge of the jaws, and the horny beak on the upper jaw, from which the group derives its name.

The tuatara was once widespread throughout New Zealand but became much reduced and in danger of extinction. Recently rigid conservation measures seem to have allowed it to recover in numbers on some small northern islands. The animals are up to 2 feet long and are carnivorous. They live in burrows usually shared with a petrel.

The rhynchosaurs were a Triassic offshoot of this order, in which the beak and jaws became specialized for crushing, presumably, the shells of molluscs. *Sphenodon* evidently shows us a type which has departed relatively little from the condition of diapsids in the late Permian. Yet its appearance, habits, and soft parts are very like those of lizards, and provide us with evidence that these animals remain in essentials rather close to the original amniote populations.

10. Order Squamata

The lizards and snakes are the most recent offshoot of the reptiles, the former appearing in the Jurassic and the latter in the Cretaceous. Their origin is not quite certain, but it is very probable that they came from a diapsid stock, probably one close to the Rhynchocephalia. The skull possesses a clear upper temporal fossa and a lower space, resembling a second temporal fossa, but with no lower margin. The quadratojugal is absent and the squamosal is very small, leaving the quadrate freely movable, a condition made especial use of in the snakes to give a wide gape for swallowing the prey. It is not difficult to suppose that this condition arose by the loss of the thin lower bar of a typical diapsid. In favour of this view is the general similarity of lizards to the tuatara, extending to details such as the structure of the palate, and the considerable development of the pineal eye. However, it might also be argued that these are characteristics of all primitive reptiles. An alternative view of the ancestry of the Squamata is that they arose from an early parapsid form, such as *Araeoscelis*, by 'emargination' of the lower side of the temporal region of the skull. The discovery of the eosuchian *Prolacerta* (p. 383), almost exactly intermediate between *Youngina* and modern lizards, goes far to settle this controversy in favour of the diapsid ancestry of the group.

11. Suborder Lacertilia

The lizards have shown considerable adaptive radiation (Fig. 233) and include terrestrial, arboreal, burrowing, aquatic, and aerial forms; the majority are carnivorous, but there are some herbivores. The central group, from which all the various lizards and snakes have been derived, is the infraorder Platynota, represented to-day by the monitor-lizards, *Varanus*, large carnivorous, often semi-aquatic creatures, widely distributed in the Old World. Similar animals were found in the Cretaceous and the group must have arisen in the Jurassic from some such eosuchian as *Prolacerta*. Throughout the history of the Squamata, as indeed of reptiles in general, there is seen a persistent tendency for the animals to return to the water, often with reduction of the limbs. Three lines of platynotan lizards became aquatic during the Cretaceous period. The dolichosaurs and aigialosaurs were small semi-aquatic lizards, with reduced limbs and a long tail. The mosasaurs, such as *Tylosaurus* of the later Cretaceous, were very fully aquatic, with the limbs changed to paddles and showing some hyper-phalangy. Some of them were 20 feet long.

The infraorder Iguania is the next oldest group of Lacertilia, including iguanas and agamas and dating back to the Cretaceous. The agamas include both terrestrial and arboreal forms, one of them, *Draco*, with various species in Indo-Malaya, has a large lateral web, supported by elongated ribs, but not attached to the limbs. This web can be spread out and serves for gliding, but is not moved in true flight. *Lyriocephalus* from Ceylon is an agama with a remarkable convergent similarity to the chameleons.

The iguanas all occur in the New World, except for two genera in Madagascar and Fiji. *Anolis* is a very common North American arboreal lizard. *Iguana*, from South and Central America, is a South American form reaching 6 feet in length. *Phrynosoma*, the horned toad, with spikes on the head and back, is found in the Western American deserts and has the habit of burrowing in the sand. This is the only iguanid in which the eggs develop within the mother.

The remaining lizards may all be placed in one large infraorder Scincomorpha, including various aberrant types as well as the main lizard stock. Here belong, besides *Lacerta*, also the skinks and various other lizard types, some modified for burrowing. The group is known from the Eocene. The geckos are mainly nocturnal and arboreal insectivorous lizards of warm climates, with ridges on the toes to give them power to climb an almost smooth surface. They also have sharp retractile claws. The eyelids are reduced, but the nictitating membrane permanently covers the eye with a clear, lens-like skin. The inner ears are greatly expanded to form sacs in the neck, filled with otoliths. The affinities of these strange creatures are uncertain. *Ptychozoon* is a gecko that has developed webs on the limbs and along the body, for assistance in gliding leaps. *Scincus* and other skinks are forms that live on sandy ground and may burrow. Various members of the group have independently lost either fore- or hind-limbs, or both. The Anguidae, such as *Anguis fragilis*, the slow-worm, are lizards in which the limbs have been entirely lost. They live mainly on slugs, eating also earthworms and snails, and are vivi-parous, producing twelve or more young whose colour, instead of the green-brown of the adult, is white along the back with longitudinal lines of black and a black underside. Other groups, e.g. the amphis-baenas, have lost the limbs and live a worm-like existence, completely underground. These burrowing forms probably include several inde-pendent lines derived either from the Anguidae or from the skinks.

FIG. 233. Various Squamata (*Draco* after B.M. Guide).

The chameleons are highly modified arboreal lizards from Africa, especially Madagascar, and India. The tail is prehensile and the digits are arranged in groups of two or three so as to be opposable and

FIG. 234. Chameleon catching a fly, showing its changes in colour.

A, cream with yellow patches, the usual night colour. B, grey-green with darker patches. C, dark brown patches and yellow spots. D, reaction produced by pinching tail, inflation and darkening of all spots. (After Gadow.)

allow the grasping of branches. They live on insects, which are caught by means of the very long tongue (Fig. 234), everted by filling with blood and the use of the hyoid muscles, the tip being provided with a sticky club. Their movements are remarkably slow and deliberate, but they show considerable care and pertinacity in reaching a position from which to seize the prey.

12. Suborder Ophidia

The snakes arose from a population of lizards, perhaps from one of those that had adopted a burrowing habit. Snakes closely resemble lizards in many features and the differences suggest that structures which were lost while the animals lived underground have been reacquired in a new form. This is especially conspicuous in the case of the eyes, which differ widely from those of lizards (Fig. 237). Thus there are no scleral ossicles; the eye is nearly round, and focusing is by the pressure of the iris on the lens. The visual cells are a peculiar

FIG. 235. Diagram of skull in ophidians. Lettering as Fig. 215. (From Goodrich.)

type of cone, suggesting independent derivation from rods. The yellow droplets that serve to protect lacertilian retinae from excessive light are absent, and instead some colubrine snakes, which are very fully diurnal, protect their pure cone retina by a yellow-tinted lens.

The sense of hearing was probably also lost while the snakes lived underground and has remained very poorly developed. Even loud sounds fail to set up nerve-impulses in the 'auditory' nerve of the grass-snake; hence 'deaf as an adder'.

Throughout ophidian organization many such features attributable to underground life can be found. Thus the limbs have disappeared; the remains of the pelvic girdle found in some boas and pythons constitute the only remaining traces of them. Locomotion is produced by lateral undulations of the body, made more effective by the development of special articulations on the neural arches of the numerous vertebrae, and by scales on the ventral surface, moved by the very long ribs. The eyes have no lids but are permanently covered by the third eyelid, a special naso-lachrymal duct serving to carry away the tears. The columella auris articulates with the quadrate and there is no tympanum or Eustachian tube.

The tongue is slender, protrusible, and sensory. The whole structure of the jaws and skull is greatly modified, especially in those forms, such as the vipers, that kill their prey by means of poison fangs, instead of the more primitive crushing by coils used by the boas and pythons. The squamosal bone is horizontal and loosely attached to the skull; the quadrate is attached to the squamosal. The premaxilla is always reduced and sharp backwardly curved teeth are carried on the maxillae and palate (Fig. 236). In the most highly modified snakes

Fig. 236. Skull of rattle-snake (*Crotalus*) with jaws partly and fully opened. Lettering as Fig. 215; *sph-pt.* the spheno-pterygoid muscle, which pulls the pterygoid forward, causing it to push the ectopterygoid, which rotates the maxilla and erects the fang; *di.* the digastric muscle that assists in opening the jaw; *temp.ant.* the anterior temporal which shuts the mouth. The diagrams at the right show the actions of the levers that erect the fang; *g* is the groove characteristic of crotaline snakes. (Modified after Gadow.)

(the vipers) the maxilla is also very short and hollow and it carries a single large fang. A special spheno-pterygoid muscle pulls the ptery-goid forward and this rotates the maxilla (Figs. 236 and 238). Closure of the jaws thus pushes the tooth home and poison is injected along a groove in the tooth. The paralysed prey is then swallowed whole. The jaw articulation is very loose and there is a joint in the brain-case to allow wide opening of the mouth. The two halves of the lower jaw are joined only by an elastic ligament, allowing them to come apart.

This remarkable apparatus enables the snake to swallow animals larger than the diameter of its own head. Since the process is a slow

Lizard

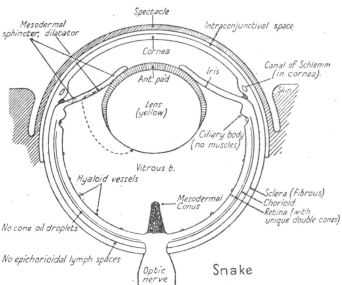

Snake

FIG. 237. Diagrams of eyes of lizard and snake, to show the marked contrasts resulting from presumed loss during underground life and later acquisition by the snakes of features paralleling those present in their ancestors. The dotted arrows show the direction of application of force during accommodation. (From Walls, *The Vertebrate Eye*.)

one breathing must be continued and there is a special device by which the tracheal opening is pushed forward between the two halves of the lower jaw. The brain is protected during the operation by special ventral flanges of the parietals and frontals. This series of modifications constitutes one of the most highly specialized mechanisms found in any vertebrate. Its great effectiveness is seen in the large number of species and individuals in the group. Many other special features are found, for instance the vipers are viviparous. The lungs are

FIG. 238. Head of crotaline snake (*Lachesis*) after removal of skin.
d. duct of poison gland, bending where it enters tooth; *dig.* digastric muscle; *g.* sensory groove; *n.* nostril; *pg.* poison gland; *ta.* and *tp.* anterior and posterior portions of temporalis muscle; *tr.* trachea. (From Gadow.)

unequally developed in all snakes, the left being reduced to a small thin-walled sac with no alveoli.

With these general features the snakes have invaded many special environments. Some, such as the Typhlopidae, are burrowing forms, widely distributed in the tropics; the eyes are covered over and the diet is of insects. The boas and pythons are primitive, non-poisonous forms with many teeth, they live mainly in trees. The earliest snakes such as *Palaeophis* of the late Cretaceous were similar. The colubrine snakes include more than 1,000 species, all non-poisonous. They first appeared in the Oligocene. *Tropidonotus* is a genus occurring almost all over the world, *T. natrix* being the common grass snake found throughout Europe and much of Asia, but not in Scotland or Ireland. These snakes not only have no poison but also do not bite. They hiss and strike, however, in an alarming way, and have large cloacal glands, which produce an unpleasant smelling substance. *Dasypeltis* is an egg-eating snake; it swallows the eggs whole and crushes them with specially developed processes of the neck vertebrae.

The elapine snakes, first appearing in the Miocene, are a large group of highly poisonous forms, including the cobra (*Naja tri-pudians*), in which there is great development of the power seen in many snakes to dilate and expand the neck, showing the characteristic markings, presumably to warn or terrify. It may be suspected that the evolution of such peculiarities, assuming considerable learning powers in possible attackers, was correlated with the development of the birds and mammals. The Hydrophinae or sea snakes are related forms; they live wholly in the sea and are viviparous.

The viperines are the most modified of all snakes and include the

FIG. 239. Drawings of three frilled lizards (*Chlamydosaurus*) and a *Grammatophora* (at right) to show the bipedal habit. (Drawings made by Heilmann from photographs of the lizards running at full speed, taken by Saville Kent.)

true vipers of the Old World and the rattlesnakes of the New. *Vipera berus*, the European viper or adder, has a bite which is serious, but not usually fatal, for man. The rattle of the rattlesnake is composed of the cast of skin, carried at the tip of the tail, and is vibrated to make a considerable noise, as a warning, it is suggested, to the large mammals of the plains, which might tread on the snake.

13. Superorder Archosauria

We have seen that about 130 million years ago the diapsid stock produced the only successful modern reptile group, the Squamata (Fig. 222). Much earlier an even more successful type had developed from the eosuchian populations, having as its outstanding feature the habit of walking on the hind legs. Creatures of this type were the dominant land animals of the later Mesozoic, and they include the dinosaurs and pterosaurs. Crocodiles are the only living descendants of the group that have remained at the reptilian level. They have of course abandoned the bipedal habit and survive as a specialized amphibious remnant. The birds, which are also undoubtedly

descendants of this archosaurian group, give us in some ways a
better idea of the characteristic structure than do the crocodiles.

All the lines of archosaurs are characterized by certain common

Saltoposuchus

Mystriosuchus

Crocodilus

Compsognathus

FIG. 240. The skeletons of various archosaurian diapsids.
(Modified after various authors.)

tendencies, mostly associated with bipedalism, possible also in lizards
(Fig. 239); features barely indicated in the earlier forms become
developed in the later. In all archosaurs the hind legs were much
longer than the front and the acetabulum formed a cup, open below,
so that the legs were held vertically below the body. At the same time
the ischium and pubis became elongated, presumably to allow for the

attachment of muscles producing a fore-and-aft movement (see p. 356). In later forms the ilium became fused with several sacral vertebrae. The femur has a lateral head and the tibia becomes long and strong and fused with the proximal tarsals; the distal tarsals fuse with the metatarsals and the digits are reduced, usually to three long ones turned forward while the first is turned back. The skull is typically diapsid, but tends to have certain modifications, such as the development of antorbital vacuities behind the nostrils and other spaces in the palate, presumably serving to give lightness without loss of strength.

14. Order *Pseudosuchia

The earliest archosaurs were the Triassic pseudosuchians, creatures evidently not far removed from the Permian eusochians. These animals (*Saltoposuchus*) can be visualized as lizards that ran on their hind legs (Fig. 240). They were small, and carnivorous, having sharp teeth set in sockets along the edges of the jaws (hence 'thecodont'). The skeleton showed all the archosaur characters in a most interesting incipient form. Thus the bones of the pelvis were still plate-like, but arranged in the characteristic triradiate manner. The front legs were already much shorter than the hind. The skull was considerably narrower in proportion to its width than in *Youngina*, giving a suggestion of the beak-like form characteristic of all archosaurs and birds. Antorbital vacuities were present and there was no pineal foramen.

15. Order *Phytosauria

Even in the Triassic at least one line, the phytosaurs, abandoned the bipedal habit, becoming amphibious. These creatures were not actually ancestral to the crocodiles, but show remarkable parallelism to them in the elongated jaws and general build (Fig. 240). However, the nostrils were set far back. There can be no doubt that the phytosaurs were derived from pseudosuchians and the two groups are often placed together in an order Thecodontia.

16. Order Crocodilia

In the crocodiles the nostrils are at the tip of the snout and the air is carried back in a long tube, the maxillae, palatines, and pterygoids forming a bony secondary palate, as in mammals. There is a flap on the hind end of the tongue, which, with a fold of the palate, enables the mouth to be closed off from the respiratory passage and hence kept open under water. The crocodiles use all four limbs in walking, but the front are shorter than the hind. Jurassic types are known which, though undoubted crocodiles, show still greater dissimilarity in length of the legs, and there can be no doubt that the early members of the group were bipedal. The pelvis of the crocodiles shows signs of the

FIG. 241. Diagram of the skull of Crocodilia.
Lettering as Fig. 215, p. 358. (From Goodrich.)

FIG. 242. Anterior cervical vertebrae of *Crocodilus*.

c. capitulum; *hp*. hypocentrum; *na*$^{1-4}$, neural arches; *pa*. pro-atlas; *pl*. 1–4, pleurocentra; *prz*. prezygopophysis; *ptz*. postzygopophysis; *r*. rib; *t*. tuberculum; *tp*. transverse process. The first neural arch and the pro-atlas of the left side have been removed to show the first pleuro-centrum (*pl*^{1}) which is the odontoid process. (From Goodrich.)

typical triradiate structure, but there are only two sacral vertebrae, which may be a primitive feature retained, or perhaps the result of secondary reduction. Rapid locomotion is produced by lateral movements of the body in the water, another case of reversion to the fish type. This reversion has produced considerable modification of the vertebrae, with development of cartilaginous rings ('intercentra'), which in the tail region are continuous with the chevron bones, the remains as we have seen (p. 355) of the original basiventrals. This tendency for the vertebral column to contain more elements in fish-like types is of great interest; the redevelopment of the extra elements in connexion with the old chevron bones suggests a direct reversal of evolution. That there is truly a redevelopment of the genetic mechanism of the old type of vertebra is shown dramatically by the fact that the axis and atlas both have well-marked basiventrals (Fig. 242). If the 'intercentra' of the trunk were new structures, developed to give flexibility, it is not likely that the genetic mechanism for producing

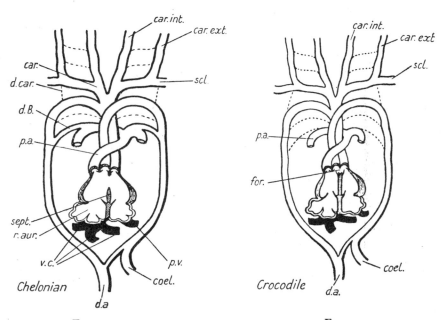

FIG. 243.   FIG. 244.

Diagram of heart and arterial arches of a chelonian and of a crocodile. Lettering as Fig. 216, p. 360. (From Ihle, after Goodrich.)

them would similarly affect the highly modified axis-atlas. The vertebrae are mostly concave in front (procoelous) and considerable traces of the notochord persist.

Other primitive archosaurian features of crocodiles are the well-developed osteoscutes in the skin, and the ossifications in the abdominal body wall known as abdominal ribs.

The soft parts of the crocodiles are of special interest as they are, except the birds, the only living creatures closely related to the great group of dinosaurs. The heart (Fig. 244) shows a complete division of the ventricle, but there are still two aortic arches. The truncus arteriosus is divided in a spiral manner to its base, so that the aortae cross and the right arch opens from the thick-walled left ventricle, while the left opens with the pulmonary arteries from the weaker right ventricle. The left arch would therefore contain venous blood, but an aperture, the foramen of Panizza, connects the two arches near the base and presumably the higher pressure in the left ventricle ensures that the left arch receives at least some oxygenated blood, but it may be that when the crocodile dives the pressure in the right ventricle is increased and that blood flows through the foramen from right to left.

The lungs are very well developed, having a system of tubes ending in sacs. A transverse partition separates off a thoracic from the main abdominal cavity. This 'diaphragm' is not itself muscular, but is continued into a diaphragmatic muscle attached to the abdominal sternal plates. This muscle, innervated by abdominal spinal nerves, presumably assists in respiration. It is a development for this purpose quite distinct from the mammalian diaphragm. It is not impossible that the dinosaurs possessed further developments of this arrangement of the heart and lungs, and that they owed some of their success to this mechanism.

The modern crocodiles represent only the survivors of a once much more abundant group. *Crocodilus* is the most widespread genus, occurring in Central America, Africa and Asia, Malay and East Indies, and North Australia. *Alligator*, with one of the lower teeth penetrating into a hole in the maxilla, is found in Central and South America, with one species in China. *Caiman* of Central and South America is related to *Alligator*. These 'short-nosed crocodiles' eat a variety of meat, whereas the 'long-nosed crocodiles' are fish-eaters. They are represented to-day only by *Gavialis*, the ghavial of India, and *Tomistoma* from the East Indies; formerly, however, there were many crocodiles of this type. The crocodiles seem to have changed little since they first appeared in the late Triassic, perhaps 160 million years ago. *Protosuchus* of that time had a pelvis like that of crocodiles but was otherwise very like a pseudosuchian. There were numerous types of crocodile in the Jurassic and Cretaceous, living both in fresh water and in the sea. In these forms the palate was supported only by the palatine bones; the addition of flanges of the pterygoids took place only in the Eocene crocodiles, which were numerous in many parts of the world, including northern continental regions to-day too cold for such animals. In spite of their specializations for aquatic life the crocodiles show us many features which were present in the earliest archosaurs and they therefore give some idea of the characteristics of the ancestors of the pterodactyls, dinosaurs, and birds.

17. The 'Terrible Lizards', Dinosaurs

In the ten million or so years at the end of the Triassic some of the descendants of the pseudosuchians became very successful and numerous and individually very large. The large size was not a characteristic only of one line but of two quite distinct ones, each with several subdivisions. The term dinosaur is applied to all of them, but the two main lines have little in common beyond the characters common to all archosaurs. The desire to explain this extraordinary exuberance of reptiles has attracted very much attention to these giants.

18. Order *Saurischia

These include forms with a triradiate pelvis, very like that of the pseudosuchians. The earlier types, like their ancestors, were bipedal carnivores of no great size, such as *Compsognathus from the Jurassic of Europe and *Ornitholestes from that of North America (Fig. 240). The front legs were short, with 4 or 3 digits, provided with claws; the pectoral girdle was reduced to scapula and small coracoid, with no trace of clavicles. Early on some members of this line, the theropods, developed into large carnivores, such as *Allosaurus (Fig. 245), over 30 feet long (Jurassic, North America). These animals apparently swallowed their food whole and to help with this the quadrate was not firmly connected with the skull and there was a joint between the frontals and parietals. Similar modifications are found in snakes and birds, and the character provides another example of the parallel evolution that is so marked a feature of the archosaurs. In other respects the skull was very similar to that of the pseudosuchians.

At the end of the Cretaceous this theropod line produced the largest carnivores that have appeared on the earth, such as *Tyrannosaurus rex, nearly 50 feet long and 20 feet high, from North America. All the previously mentioned tendencies were here accentuated, producing creatures with bipedal habit, very powerful head and jaws, and much-reduced fore-limbs. They presumably preyed upon the large herbivorous dinosaurs of the Cretaceous and became extinct with their prey, either from a common inability to meet the rigours of the climate or in competition with the mammals and birds. Throughout most of the Jurassic and Cretaceous the theropods were the dominant carnivores of the world, taking the place occupied earlier by the synapsid reptiles (p. 516) and later again by descendants of the synapsids, the carnivorous mammals.

In the Cretaceous the organization of this saurischian line also produced some exceedingly bird-like forms, *Struthiomimus and

Allosaurus

Struthiomimus

Tyrannosaurus

Brontosaurus

FIG. 245. The skeletons of various saurischian dinosaurs.
(Modified after various authors.)

Ornithomimus, walking on three toes and having three also in the hand, one opposable and used for grasping. The skull became very lightly built and the teeth disappeared, being replaced by a horny beak, possibly in connexion with an egg-eating habit (Fig. 245).

All of these carnivorous, bipedal saurischians may be grouped together as the suborder Theropoda. Another line of organization, starting from the bipedal carnivorous Triassic theropods, adopted a herbivorous diet and reverted to the quadrupedal habit. This line, known as the suborder Sauropoda, culminated in the immense Jurassic forms, *Brontosaurus and *Diplodocus, the largest of all terrestrial vertebrates. Several stages of the transition from bipedal to quadrupedal habit can be traced. *Yaleosaurus from the Trias was a bipedal creature 6 feet long but with rather long front and short hind legs. *Plateosaurus, also of the Trias, was 20 feet long, but still bipedal. Soon the animals became clumsy and the front limbs less disproportionate to the hind and more used for walking, though the disparity always remained. The neck became immensely elongated and the head very small, with a lightly built skull. The nostrils lay on the top of the head and in *Diplodocus actually formed a single opening. This seems to indicate that the animals were aquatic or amphibious, as would in any case be suspected from the very large size, making it unlikely that the legs could bear the full weight. *Diplodocus and *Brachiosaurus were over 80 feet long and the weight must have been nearly 50 tons. However, the structure of the vertebral column shows that much weight was carried on the legs, for the vertebrae are strong, though hollowed in places. Footprints of the animals have been found. One or more of the digits bore claws. The skull became relatively short and broad, and among the many puzzling features of these giant animals is the weakness of the jaws and small size of the teeth, mostly crowded towards the front of the mouth. These teeth would have served well enough for cropping, but there are no teeth on the hind part of the jaws and no provision for grinding the food. Animals of large size can only have been supported by this feeble apparatus if some very nutritious food was readily available. This perhaps agrees with the very small size of the brain, which was several times smaller than the lumbar enlargement of the cord. However, it must be remembered that beyond a certain limit the efficiency of working of a nervous centre does not depend on its size.

19. Order *Ornithischia

The second main group of dinosaurs appeared later than the sauropods and possessed a peculiar 4-radiate pelvis, with the pubis directed backwards and an extra pre-pubic bone pointing forwards. The teeth were restricted to the hind part of the jaws, the front bearing a beak. At the front end of the lower jaw there was an extra bone (predentary).

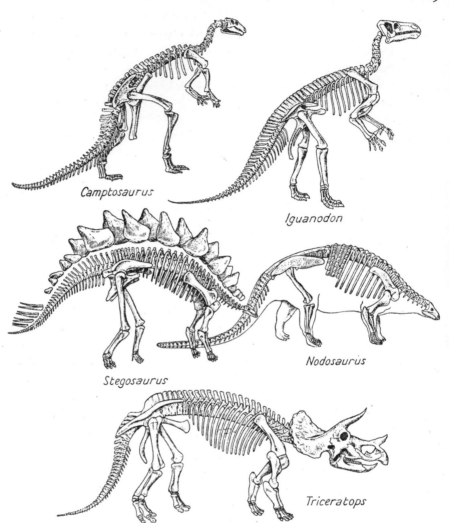

FIG. 246. The skeletons of various ornithischian dinosaurs.
(Modified after various authors.)

These were herbivorous forms and they appeared in the Jurassic and
achieved their maximum in the Cretaceous, by which time the sauropods had become less common. The earliest of the ornithischians
were bipedal animals, included in a suborder Ornithopoda, from the
Jurassic and Cretaceous. These animals, such as *Iguanodon*, were
built on the same general lines as the pseudosuchians, from which
they were presumably derived. The skull was heavily built and
adapted for a herbivorous diet, with a horny beak and powerful

muscles attached to a coronoid process of the lower jaw. The bipedalism was less marked than in saurischians and the fore-limbs less reduced. Several separate lines then reverted to a quadrupedal habit. The trachodonts (*Hadrosaurus*) were a very successful group of amphibious forms in the Cretaceous, with webbed feet. The teeth were suited for grinding, parallel rows being present, making as many as 2,000 teeth in one animal. In several types of hadrosaur the top of the head was prolonged in various ways, making a structure which perhaps allowed the nostrils to remain above water while the animal was feeding below. These animals reached 30 feet in length and may have supplanted the sauropods as marsh-living forms, possibly when the soft foods gave place to harder plants.

Other lines of ornithischia became more fully terrestrial and quadrupedal and were mostly heavily armoured. Thus the stegosaurs of the Jurassic carried immense spines on the back and the tail bore sharp spikes. The hind legs were much longer than the front, a relic of bipedal ancestry. The feet carried hoof-like structures. The skull was very small and the brain much smaller than the lumbar swelling of the cord. The teeth were in a single row and small. The ankylosaurs of the Cretaceous were covered all over with bony plates, somewhat in the manner of the mammalian glyptodonts (Fig. 246).

Finally, the ceratopsians, such as *Triceratops* of the late Cretaceous, developed enormous heads, with huge horns and a large bony frill, formed by extension of the parietals and squamosals to cover the neck. These later Cretaceous forms appear to have lived on dry land and to have walked on all fours, although the bipedal ancestry is shown in the shortness of the front legs. There are several indications that the climate at the close of the Cretaceous was becoming drier and the organization of the giant reptiles became modified accordingly. They survived successfully for a while, but were ultimately replaced by the mammals, perhaps as a result of still further change in the climate (see p. 545).

20. Order *Pterosauria

The Triassic archosaurian reptiles gave rise to two independent stocks which took to the air, the pterodactyls and the birds. Both of these appear first in the Jurassic as animals already well equipped for flight, although obviously basically of archosaurian structure. We cannot therefore say anything about the steps by which their flight was evolved and can only speculate about the influences that drove them to take to the air. The early archosaurs were bipedal animals, and the fore-limbs were therefore free and available for use as wings. There has been much speculation about the intermediate stages by which flight was produced. Other reptiles, such as *Draco*, the flying lizard (p. 386), develop a membrane between the limbs and the body to assist them in making soaring jumps. The flight of pterodactyls and birds may have originated thus or, as suggested by Nopsca, by the flapping of the fore-limbs during rapid running on the ground, the animals then becoming airborne for longer and longer periods.

The stages of the evolution of flight may have been different in the two cases, for whereas the birds are obviously bipedal animals and the similarity to such reptiles as *Struthiomimus* and *Ornithomimus* is obvious, the pterodactyls probably could not walk on their hind legs and may have used the wing more for soaring than for flapping flight. In spite of great differences there are very interesting parallelisms in the structure of the fully evolved fliers of the two groups, for instance the limb bones became light, the skull bones fused, and the jaws toothless. This parallelism in lines known to be distinct, although of remote common origin, is similar to that which we have noticed before in aquatic animals, and it can be interpreted as showing that populations with similar genotypes will respond to similar environmental stimuli in the same way (p. 732).

The pterodactyls are most commonly found in the Jurassic strata, less often in the Cretaceous. Nearly all specimens have been found in marine deposits and they seem to have been fish-eaters, but of course this does not prove that none lived on land, where the chance of fossilization would have been much less. The characteristic features that have produced the pterodactyl structure from a thecodont ancestry may be described as a lengthening of the head and neck, shortening of the body and ultimately of the tail, lengthening of the arms and especially of the fourth digit, shortening of the legs, and development of the ventral parts of the limb girdles. These are the changes that can be recognized in the bony parts available for study; no doubt there were many others in the soft parts also paralleling the evolution of birds, for instance the animals may have been warm-blooded. However, there is no evidence that they possessed feathers; the wing was a membrane (patagium).

Rhamphorhynchus of the Jurassic is still recognizably of archosaurian structure, especially in the skull, which has two fossae and large forward-sloping teeth (Fig. 247). The fore-limb was elongated, but the carpus still short, with an extra 'pteroid' bone in front, presumably to support the wing. The first three digits were short and hooked, the fourth long, and the fifth absent. The hind limb was slender, with five hooked digits. There was a long tail, ending in an expanded 'fin'. Both girdles had well-developed ventral regions and there was a large 'sternum'. The scapula articulated directly with the vertebral column.

FIG. 247. The skeleton of a pterodactyl.

A, extra wrist bone; *C*, coracoid; *D*, elongated digit; *F*, femur; *H*, humerus; *MC*, metacarpal; *P*, pelvis; *RU*, radio-ulna; *SC*, scapula; *ST*, sternum; *T*, tail; *TF*, tibio-fibula; *W*, wing. (From Thompson, *The Biology of Birds*, Sidgwick & Jackson, Ltd.)

*_Pteranodon_, of the late Jurassic and Cretaceous, showed further modifications. The trunk became shortened to ten or fewer segments, the fore-limb further lengthened, the carpus being long and the fourth digit much longer than the other three. The hind limb remained small and the tail became very short. The very large and elongated head gradually lost its teeth, presumably acquiring a horny beak. In the latest forms the skull was drawn out backwards into an extraordinary process. Some of the earlier of these forms were only a few inches long, but *_Pteranodon_ of the late Cretaceous had a wing-span of 25 feet.

Zoologists have not yet succeeded in reconstructing the life of these animals. They must have either flown or swum, for they could not have walked. It is presumed that they lived in the air and not in the water, but the membrane which stretched between both legs and the body, and perhaps also included the head, must have been easily torn, unless it was very thick and heavy. The feathers of birds can be ruffled without breaking and the loss of a few does no great harm: the bat's wing can be torn, but at least it is supported by many digits, whereas that of the pterodactyl was a huge continuous membrane. Again it is difficult to see how the animals can have perched; if they hung, as the claws suggest, was it with the front or with the hind legs? And how can they have staged a take-off, which in birds is greatly helped by the jump of the hind legs? It is possible that they always came to rest hanging from cliffs, which they could leave by soaring. Even the flight itself presents many difficulties; although there is a sternum and a strong humerus, neither suggest the presence of muscles sufficiently strong to carry a creature as large as *Pteranodon*. We cannot solve any of these mysteries, but one clue is that the pterodactyls were mostly, if not all, marine. The largest flying birds alive to-day are the albatrosses, which use their great weight to gain height with the increasing velocity of the wind a few feet above the sea (p. 437). It is possible that the pterodactyls used a similar method of soaring.

If they were so fully marine it is curious that, like their terrestrial cousins, they all died out at the end of the Cretaceous. Indeed even the plesiosaurs, ichthyosaurs, and mosasaurs shared this fate. The factors that favoured the birds and mammals at this time must have been more than merely the onset of warm and dry conditions on land.

21. Conclusions from study of evolution of the reptiles

Many of the conclusions that appeared from study of vertebrate evolution in the water also apply to the forms which have come on land. The fossil record leaves no doubt that almost all the populations have changed very markedly. No form of reptile alive to-day is closely similar to any found in the Permian or Triassic periods. *Sphenodon* has shown relatively less change than most other forms and it is significant that it is found in an isolated island region.

The data are not sufficient to show the rate of evolutionary change. We cannot be sure whether it has been constant or even continuous, but particular types are found only from a very limited range of strata and there is little evidence that any terrestrial form remains unchanged for more than a few million years, at most. Each type is successful for a while and then the niche which it fills becomes occupied by another type, either descended from the first or, more usually, from some related stock. Thus the earliest large land herbivores were probably the pareiasaurs; these were later replaced by other reptilian types including sauropods (in so far as these were terrestrial) and various types of ornithischia, perhaps by the hadrosaurs in the more watery habitats and the stegosaurs, ankylosaurs, and ceratopsia on drier ground. Finally, all these gave place to the earliest mammalian herbivores, which were in turn replaced by others (p. 730).

Throughout early tetrapod evolution there is a tendency to return to the water, perhaps under some pressure of competition from descendants on land. This is marked among reptiles, where besides the chelonians and ichthyosaurs and plesiosaurs there are the phytosaurs and crocodiles, and among Squamata the mosasaurs and tylosaurs, not to mention the later aquatic lizards and snakes.

The large size of many reptiles has been one of their most striking features, but it is of course not true to say that there is a strong tendency for size to increase in all reptile groups. While many have become enormous, others, such as the lizards, have produced probably as great a biomass spread over huge numbers of small individuals. It is not certain what advantage is gained by a reptile from large size, since it is not warm-blooded. Up to a point size is a protection, but it involves the dangers of those who place all the eggs in one basket; incidentally, the actual eggs of these large animals must have provided formidable physical problems for their support.

Parallel evolution of several lines descended from a single stock is as common among reptiles as other groups of vertebrates. Thus the bipedal habit, with hind legs longer than the front, has been adopted independently by a number of diapsids; again, elongated jaws are found among fish-eaters, whether ichthyosaurs, plesiosaurs, phytosaurs, crocodiles, or mosasaurs.

Although it is difficult to see in all this any persistent tendency except to change, yet the very fact that each type is so rapidly replaced suggests that descendants in some way more efficient are continually appearing. In the case of the reptiles the more interesting of these are the birds and mammals, and we shall therefore leave the problem of serial replacement among amniotes for later discussion. Meanwhile we may note once again that the reptiles surviving to-day, although not of large size or obviously better suited for life than their mesozoic ancestors, yet exist in considerable numbers alongside and even in competition with the birds and the mammals.

XVI

LIFE IN THE AIR: THE BIRDS

1. Features of bird life

The quality we define as 'life' is perhaps more fully represented in birds than in other vertebrates, or indeed in any animals whatsoever. It is very difficult to find units by which accurate comparisons can be made of such matters, but only a very unimaginative and dull-sensed person would be unable to find any meaning in the statement that the life of a bird is more intense than that of, say, a reptile or a fish. Following out our definition of the life of a species as the total of the activities by which that particular type of organization is preserved, we shall find that the birds have many and very varied activities, by means of which a great deal of matter is collected into the bird type of organization. Moreover, this is achieved under conditions very remote from those in which life first arose; the birds get a living in the air, the most difficult medium of all.

Flight is of course the characteristic that gives us most fully the feeling that the birds are active animals; it impresses us as a technical marvel and as a means by which the animals obtain a most enviable and valuable freedom, enabling them to avoid their enemies and to seek new habitats. Almost equally important items in the active life of birds are the high and constant temperature and very large brain. These features have been acquired quite independently by birds and mammals, and have led to profound changes in behaviour. A homoiothermic animal does not need to change its activity with the changes in environmental temperature; it can be continuously active, and, perhaps even more important, it can acquire that continuity of life which makes possible the utilization of the fruits of past experience. Probably only with a high and constant temperature can full use be made of the possibilities of delicate balance of activities within large masses of nervous tissue. In homoiothermic birds and mammals we find larger brains and more elaborate social and family habits than in any other animals.

2. Bird numbers and variety

Flight necessitates a large surface-volume ratio, therefore birds do not become so large as some mammals; nevertheless, an immense biomass is produced by their very large numbers. Any attempt to enumerate the bird population is largely guess-work, but the density of breeding birds in different habitats in Britain has been estimated, and varies from 200 per 10 acres in woodland to 20 on agricultural land and 10 or less on moorland. Calculating from such figures Fisher estimates that there may be 100 million land birds in Great Britain and 100,000 million birds in the world altogether, including sea birds. This is perhaps a low estimate; it would represent a total biomass of the same order as that of the 2,000 million human beings. With all their activity, therefore, the birds organize less matter into themselves than do the mammals.

One of the most striking features of bird life is that with a basic organization that remains fairly constant they combine a variety of special features, fitting them for a great number of different habits. Besides differences in behaviour, in body form, and in powers of flight there are found others in the shape of the bill, and hence of food habits, and in the details of many other parts, such as the feet, that make fascinating studies in adaptation to environment.

3. The skin and feathers

The skin of birds differs from that of mammals in being thin, loose, and dry; there are no sweat glands, indeed the only cutaneous gland present is the uropygial gland or preen gland at the base of the tail. The bird cleans its feathers with its beak, obtaining oil from this gland, which is especially well developed in aquatic birds.

The keratin-producing powers of the skin are of course mostly devoted to producing feathers, but scales like those of reptiles are present on the legs and feet and sometimes elsewhere. The bill (p. 443) and claws (p. 425) are also specialized scale-like structures and are sometimes moulted.

Nerve-endings are present throughout the skin, and the cere at the base of the bill is perhaps an organ of touch. The bill may itself have special endings, such as the corpuscles of Grandry found in the ducks.

The feathers of modern birds provide a covering whose uses vary from heat insulation and flight to protective coloration and sexual display. It is likely that in evolutionary history the function of heat regulation came first. The two main functions of heat conservation and flight are indeed to-day performed by feathers of different types (Fig. 248). The down-feathers or plumules, which form the covering of the nestling and may be present also in the adult, are simpler than the contour feathers or pennae, the elaborate flattened flight feathers.

FIG. 248. Various types of feather.

A, filoplumes; B, nestling down feather; C, primary wing feather of pigeon; D, permanent down feather; E, feather with free barbs; F, emu's feather with long aftershaft; G, contour feather of pheasant with aftershaft. (Partly after Thompson, *The Biology of Birds*, Sidgwick & Jackson, Ltd.)

Filoplumes are a third type, being very fine, hair-like feathers. Usually several generations of feathers are produced; first the nestling feathers (neossoptiles), then one or more generations of juvenile feathers, which may be of various types, prefiloplumes, preplumules, and pre-pennae; finally, the adult feathers (teleoptiles).

Each feather, of whatever type, is formed from a dermal papilla or

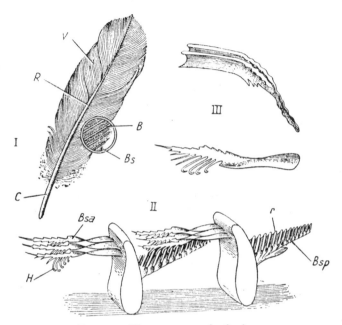

FIG. 249. The structure of a feather.

I. Whole feather showing calamus (quill), *C*; rhachis (shaft), *R*; and vane, *V*. On the right side a small area is shown as it appears under a lens; *B*, barb; *Bs*, barbule. II. A section cut at right angles to two barbs in the plane of the barbules of the anterior series (*Bsa*). Note how the hamuli, *H*, of the anterior barbs interlock with ridges (*r*) on the posterior barbules (*Bsp*). III. Shows one anterior and two posterior barbules isolated. (After Pycraft, *A History of Birds*, Methuen & Co., Ltd.)

follicle, over whose surface keratin is produced. In down feathers the surface of the papilla is ridged all round and the result is to produce a number of fine threads or barbs of keratin, covering the body with a coat of fluff, which acts as a heat insulator by preventing air circulation.

Feathers, like other epidermal structures, are moulted, either at a certain stage in the life-cycle or seasonally, a new generation being produced from the old papillae. Most birds moult in the autumn, some also again in the spring. The down feathers of the nestling are partly replaced by contour feathers; the follicle, instead of producing equal barbs, now forms two large ones at one side, which together become the central axis (rhachis), carrying a series of further barbs that spread at right angles to it to form the vane (vexillum). Each feather (Fig. 249) thus consists of a central rhachis, forming the hollow calamus or quill below and carrying the barbs, which make the vane. The calamus opens at the base by the inferior umbilicus, the entrance of the mesodermal papilla, and at the beginning of the vane there is a second hole, the superior umbilicus. At this point there is often a loose tuft of barbs or an extra shaft, the aftershaft, perhaps in some way representing the down feather.

The barbs or rami that make up the vane are held together by rows of barbules (radii) running nearly at right angles to the barbs and carrying hooks (hamuli) by which the barbules of one radius become fixed to grooves in those of the next (Fig. 249). Anyone who has played with a feather knows that these connexions can be broken down so that the barbs become separate, but can be joined again by 'preening' the whole feather.

The feathers are provided with muscles at the base and the control of their position is important for the regulation of heat loss, for flight, and in many other activities, for instance sexual display. Like the hairs of mammals the feathers are also used as organs for the sensation of touch, nerve-fibres being wound round the base of the papilla. In owls and other night-birds special vibrissae, analogous to those of mammals, are present. Various specialized feathers are used for eyelashes, ornament, and other purposes, and in some birds patches of special feathers without rhachis break up to make a 'powder down' of greasy nature.

The feathers are not spread uniformly over the body but localized to certain tracts, the pterylae, separated by bare areas, apteria. Among the contour feathers it is usual to recognize the remiges of the wing and rectrices of the 'tail'. The former are divided into primaries on the hand, secondaries on the forearm, and tertiaries on the humerus and elbow (Fig. 255). Each large feather, whether in wing or tail, is usually covered above and below by several rows of upper and under coverts. In many birds there is a peculiar gap in the secondary feathers of the wing, the fifth covert feather being absent (diastataxis); the condition in which this feather is present is called eutaxis. The feathers have a remarkably flexible structure, so that they adopt different shapes with different positions of the wing. The shape of the quill and barbs varies between feathers and parts of a feather, for instance the barbs at the tip of the primary feathers provide a stream-lined cross-section, like that of certain aeroplane propellers. The small covert feathers at the front of the wing stand up vertically, but have a right-angle bend, thus providing the wing camber.

The rectrices vary greatly, being almost absent in birds that live near to the ground, such as the wrens, but very large in fast-moving birds that change direction quickly (swallows). In these latter the outer rectrices are enlarged for steering purposes. The rectrices may be put to special uses, as in the wood-peckers, where they make a rigid brace, or in the peacocks, whose display feathers are the tail coverts.

4. Colours of birds

Birds possess colour patterns more vivid than those of any other vertebrates, using them not only for concealment but also as the chief means of recognition and sexual stimulation and hence as the basis of their social life. Like other animals that live far from the ground and move fast (primates) the birds have a poor sense of smell, in some cases none at all, but they have very good vision, and in many species the turn-ing of discriminating eyes by one sex upon the other has led to the development of a very gorgeous covering. The feathers alter the ap-pearance of the bird so completely that it is not fantastic to compare their effect with that of clothing in man.

FIG. 250. Deposition of pigment in feather germ. Transverse section through a develop-ing arm feather.

c.b. cell body of pigment cell; *p.* process of pig-ment cell; *r.* cells forming a radius; *sh.* sheath of feather germ. (After Strong, from Stresemann.)

As in other animal groups the colours are produced partly by pig-ments and partly by reflection and diffraction effects (structural coloration). The most common pigments are melanins, ranging from black through brown to yellow, and laid down in the feathers by special cells in the papilla. The processes of these amoeboid chromato-phores convey pigment to the epidermal cells (Fig. 250). Lipochrome pigments (soluble in alcohol) are also found, such as the yellow zooxanthin of the duck's bill and feet and the red zooerythrin of the flamingo. White is usually given by reflection. In blue colours incident light is reflected from a turbid porous layer overlying a deposit of melanin pigment. In iridescent feathers interference of light in thin surface films gives colours like those of soap bubbles. The more specialized iridescent feathers produce Newton's rings, with colours of the second and even third orders. The turacos or plantain-eaters of Africa contain two very peculiar pigments, a copper-containing red porphyrin turacin, which is water soluble and dissolves out in the rain, and the green, iron-containing turacoverdin.

The actual colour patterns vary with the habits of the bird. Concealing (cryptic) coloration is very common; even the brighter colours may serve this purpose, by breaking up the outline of the bird when at rest or in motion. Water birds are often dark above and white below and this form of obliterative shading is found also in many large land birds. The feathers often show mottled or speckled patterns rather than a homogeneous colour. Finches and other birds living in the sunlit upper branches show bright yellow, yellow-green, and blue colours, either singly or combined. Birds living in thickets, such as the thrush and blackbird, are usually duller brown or black. An example of disruptive coloration easy to observe is the white patch on the throat of a thrush. If the nest is approached while the bird is sitting the head is held rigidly still with the beak upwards; the white mark on the neck breaks the outline and instead of an obvious bird's head there appear only the meaningless shapes of the sides of the jaws.

Some colour patterns seem to make the bird conspicuous and may be a warning of a distasteful quality. The black and white pattern shown by the magpie may be an example of such sematic coloration; certainly this bird is seldom preyed upon, no doubt partly because of its large size. The conspicuous black of rooks and starlings may be connected with their social life, making it desirable that the birds should easily follow each other, the group being protected by the combined senses of its many members and the quick response of all to escape movements by any one.

The protective functions of the colour very often give place in one or both sexes to garments used for display, either as an attraction for the pairing up of the birds, or an actual excitant to copulation, or, in some cases, as means of keeping the birds together during the period of rearing of the young. Display colours are very varied; commonly they occur in one sex only and often they have a striking character and are presented, by characteristic movements, with a suddenness that startles the partner into acceptance (p. 459).

5. The skeleton of the bird. Sacral and sternal girders

The arrangement of the whole locomotor apparatus is based on the plan of the bipedal archosaurian reptiles, modified and simplified for the purposes of flight and balancing and walking on two legs. The bones are very light and often of tubular form, but sometimes with internal strutting well suited to the stresses they must bear (Fig. 251). Many of the bones contain extensions of the air-sacs; even the wing and leg bones are pneumatized in this way in very good fliers, such as some birds of prey and the albatross. Fusion of bones has proceeded

Fig. 251. Metacarpal bone from the wing of a vulture, sectioned to show the arrangement of the struts similar to that known to the engineer as a Warren's truss, such as is often used in aeroplane wings. (After Prochnow and D'Arcy Thompson.)

so far that the skeleton consists of a few hollow girders and large plates of special shape (p. 417). This result is achieved by limiting the joints at which movement occurs and simplifying the muscular system. The bones do not grow in length by means of epiphyses, as they do in mammals.

The skeleton of the backbone and limb girdles is so modified as to allow the weight of the body to be carried in two quite distinct ways, on the wings or on the legs. For this purpose there are two plate-like girders, the sternum and the synsacrum, curved in opposite directions. The muscles around the shoulder and hip joints balance the weight on these girders and produce propulsion. The main thrusts come from the pectoralis major in flying and from the leg retractors in walking. Perhaps no other animals are suited so perfectly for locomotion by two distinct means, and of course many birds can swim as well as fly and walk.

The whole axis of a bird is morphologically very much shorter than that of any other vertebrate except a frog (Fig. 252): only the neck remains a long and mobile structure. The number of cervical vertebrae varies and is greater in the birds with longer necks; there are fourteen in the pigeon, if we include two that bear ribs not articulating with the sternum. The cervical centra have saddle-shaped surfaces, the concavity running from side to side on the front and up and down behind, allowing very great mobility in all directions.

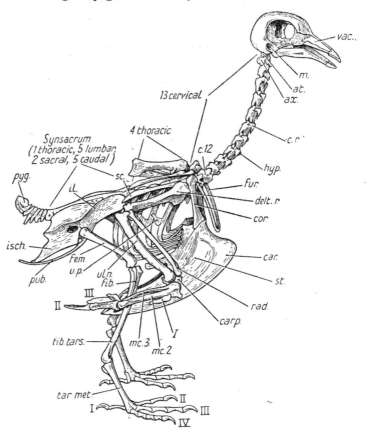

FIG. 252. Skeleton of the pigeon (*Columba*).

at. atlas; *ax.* axis; *C12*, 12th cervical vertebra; *car.* keel of sternum; *carp.* carpus; *cor.* coracoid; *c.r.* cervical rib; *delt.r.* deltoid ridge of humerus; *fem.* femur; *fib.* fibula; *fur.* fúrcula; *hyp.* hypapophysis; *il.* ilium; *isch.* ischium; *m.* auditory meatus; *mc. 2* and *3*, metacarpals; *pub.* pubis; *pyg.* pygostyle; *rad.* radius; *sc.* scapula; *st.* body of sternum; *tar.met.* tarso-metatarsus; *tib.tar.* tibio-tarsus; *uln.* ulna; *up.* uncinate process; *vac.* vacuity in side of skull.

There are four or five thoracic vertebrae, all except the last united into a single mass. The ribs are large, double-headed, and jointed to the vertebrae. They bear uncinate processes on their vertebral portions, hook-like projections overlapping the rib next behind and thus strengthening the whole thoracic cage. There is a well-marked joint between the vertebral and sternal portions of the ribs. The latter are bony, not cartilaginous as in mammals, and are jointed to the sternum, which is a very large keeled structure in all flying birds, serving to

carry the weight of the body to the wings by the attachment of the
main wing muscles (Fig. 253). The pectoralis major, which depresses
the wing in flight, is attached to the edge of the sternum and the great
depth of the keel serves to increase the length and mechanical advantage of the fibres of the muscle and also, by its shape, to strengthen
the sternum. When the bird is in the air the sternum is carrying a
large part of the weight.

The last thoracic (rib-bearing) vertebra is united with about five
that can be regarded as lumbars, two sacrals and five caudals to make

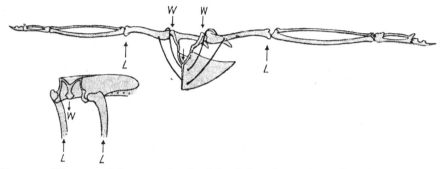

FIG. 253. Diagrams of the pectoral and pelvic girdles of an eagle, to show the methods of
support in flying and walking. In each case the weight is carried on an arch, the strength
of which is obtained by the peculiar kinked shape of the thin sheets of bone.

a synsacrum, which is also fused with the ilium. This produces a very
thin plate-like structure, whose ridged shape gives it sufficient strength
to carry the bird's weight. Finally, there is a short bony tail of about
six free caudal vertebrae, carrying four that are fused together to
form the upturned pygostyle, supporting the tail feathers.

The joints of the vertebral column are therefore reduced so as to
allow movement only in the cervical region, between the thorax and
synsacrum and in the tail. The axial muscles have been correspondingly reduced. Those of the neck are large and the hinder cervical
and the thoracic vertebrae have special ventral hypapophyses for
attachment of the flexor muscles of the neck. The other back muscles,
except those of the tail, are reduced and the whole back forms a single
rigid strut, carrying the weight of the breast and viscera through the
ribs and the abdominal muscles either to the pelvic girdle or to the
sternum. In flying this weight is suspended on the wings and there
is therefore a compression stress throughout the ribs, no doubt
accounting for the ossification of their ventral parts; in many flightless
birds the sternal portions of the ribs are reduced and cartilaginous,
like those of a mammal. The weight of the bird resting on its wings

(Fig. 253) is thus carried by the pectoralis major as a tension member, through the plate-like sternum; the ribs, and especially the coracoid, acting as compression members. The last-named bone lies nearly in the plane of the pectoralis major and is very strongly built.

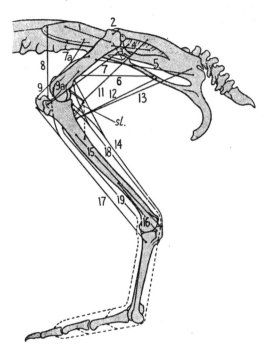

FIG. 254. Diagram of muscles of the hind leg of a bird. Tendons shown dotted.

1, Mm. ilio-trochanterici; 2, M. ilio-femoralis; 3, M. obturator; 4, M. ischio-femoralis; 5, M. caud-ilio-femoralis; 6, M. pub-ischio-femoralis; 7, M. ilio-tibialis posterior; 7a, M. sartorius (ilio-tibialis internus); 8, M. ilio-tibialis anterior; 9, M. femoro-tibialis medius; 9a, M. femoro-tibialis externus; 11, M. ilio-fibularis; 12, M. ischio-flexorius; 13, M. caud-ilio-flexorius; 14, M. gastrocnemius; 15, M. peroneus superficialis; 16, M. peroneus profundus; 17, M. tibialis anterior; 18, Mm. flexores digitorum; 19, Mm. extensores digitorum. sl. sling for M. ilio-fibularis. (After Stolpe.)

6. The sacral girder and legs

In standing, perching, and walking the weight is balanced on the legs. To achieve this posture the type of girder found in the vertebral column of other terrestrial vertebrates has been abandoned, and with it the system of braces (back muscles) holding up the weight of the forepart of the body. Instead the whole axis is so shortened that the centre of gravity lies far back and low. The ribs and abdominal muscles transfer the weight to the greatly elongated ilia, which are fused to the vertebrae, making a long girder of approximately parabolic form. Though this is composed of bone of almost paper thinness,

FIG. 255. Dissection of pigeon from back.

c-h. coraco-humeral; *caud-il-fem.* caud-ilio-femoralis; *delt.* deltoid; *e.c.r.* extensor carpi radialis; *ex.dig.* extensor digitorum; *ex.poll.* extensor pollicis; *fl.dig.* flexor digitorum; *fl.met.uln.* flexor metacarpi ulnaris; *fl.poll.long.* flexor pollicis longus; *gastr.* gastrocnemius; *il-caud.* ilio-caudalis; *il.fib.* ilio-fibularis (cut); *il.tr.* ilio-trochantericus; *int.* interosseus; *isc.f.* ischio-femoralis; *lat.d.* latissimus dorsi; *lat.lig.* lateral ligament of knee; *m.* external auditory meatus; *n.* sciatic nerve; *nos.* nostril; *per.* peroneus; *pub-isc-fem.* pub-ischio-femoralis, *rh.* rhomboid; *sart.* sartorius; *sc.* scapula; *s.c.h.* scapulo-humeral (cut); *serr.* serratus anterior; *sl.* sling for tendon of ilio-fibularis; *t.* tongue; *tend.* tendon of pectoralis minor; *tens.acc.* tensor accessorius; *tens.long.* tensor longus; *tri.* triceps; *ur.gl.* uropygial gland; *vin.* vinculum elasticum.

it is strengthened by longitudinal ridges (Fig. 253). Its strength, like that of the sternum, lies not in its arched shape in the transverse plane, but in the distribution of weight by virtue of its longitudinal

FIG. 256. Leg of pigeon dissected from lateral side.

amb. ambiens tendon; *dist.fl.* flexors of distal phalanges; *fib.* fibula; *gastr.* gastrocnemius; *il-fib.* ilio-fibularis; *il-tib.* ilio-tibialis; *isch-fl.* ischio-flexorius; *lig.* lateral ligament of knee; *peron.brev.* peroneus brevis; *peron.long.* peroneus longus; *pr.fl.* flexors of proximal phalanges; *sart.* sartorius; *sc.n.* sciatic nerve; *sl.* sling for tendon of ilio-fibularis; *t.t.* tibio-tarsus; *t.mt.* tarso-metatarsus.

curve and peculiar kinked shape. The whole pelvic girdle is modified to allow this arrangement. The ischium and pubis are directed backwards and do not meet in a symphysis, which would prevent the underslinging of the viscera.

The legs are used for balance and walking in ways that show interesting similarities and differences from those of man. The femur is turned under the body and articulates with the acetabulum in such a

FIG. 257. Pigeon dissected from ventral surface.

amb. ambiens; *bas.* bastard wing; *br-rad.* brachio-radialis; *b.* biceps; *b.t.* biceps tendon; *caud-il-flex.* caud-ilio-flexorius; *cl.* clavicle; *c.br.* coraco-brachialis; *cor.* coracoid; *d.II.* 2nd digit; *e.c.r.* extensor carpi radialis; *ex.* extensor; *ext.obl.* external oblique; *fl.carp.uln.* flexor carpi ulnaris; *gastr.* gastrocnemius; *oes.* oesophagus; *il-tib.* ilio-tibialis; *int.obl.* internal oblique; *lig.* lateral ligament of knee; *nic.* nictitating membrane; *pect.* pectoralis major; *p.m.* pectoralis minor (supracoracoideus); *per.long.* peroneus longus; *pr.long.* pronator lungus; *pub-isc-fem.* pub-ischio-femoralis; *sart.* sartorius; *tens.acc.* tensor accessorius; *tib.ant.* tibialis anterior; *trac.* trachea; *tri.* triceps; *uln.* ulnar.

way that movement is almost restricted to the antero-posterior direction. The bird balances on its hips only in the sagittal plane; there are no movements of abduction and adduction such as are found in man. Abduction of the leg, or the falling medially of the bird's body when standing on one leg, is prevented by the fact that besides the ball and socket articulation of the femoral head there is also a second joint surface between the trochanter and an anti-trochanter of the ilium. The ligaments across the top of this joint are very strong and they limit abduction movements, while movements of adduction are restricted by a very well-developed ligamentum teres attached to the femoral head.

In life the femur is held nearly horizontal, bringing the legs well forward. The bird replaces the movements of abduction and adduction, which we make at the hip during walking (to prevent falling over while only one leg is on the ground), by movements of rotation at the knee. The muscles around the hip-joint form a system of braces allowing balancing and locomotion much as in man, but they are well developed only anteriorly and posteriorly; the lateral and medial (abductor and adductor) elements are weak (Figs. 254–7). The anterior group (protractors) includes a sartorius (ilio-tibialis internus) running from the ilium to the tibia, an ilio-femoral, and a large anterior ilio-tibial inserted through a patella to a ridge on the front of the tibia. Associated with this muscle, which crosses both hip and knee joints, there are also, as in man, femoro-tibial muscles, making up with the longer muscles, the extensor system of the knee.

The lateral side of the hip joint is supported by rather small abductor braces, the ilio-trochanteric muscles, corresponding to our glutei, and acting mainly as medial rotators, opposed by obturator and ischio-femoral muscles, which work as lateral rotators. The main locomotor muscles are the posterior braces or retractors, lying behind the hip joint and including muscles known as the posterior ilio-tibial, ilio-fibular, caud-ilioflexorius, pub-ischio-femoral, ischio-femoral, and caud-ischio-femoral. Some of these also act with the obturator muscle as lateral rotators, and those placed more medially function as adductors or medial braces, so far as such are required.

The femur articulates with both tibia and fibula at the knee. The fibula is not fused with the tibia, but the two are joined by a ligament. The joints of the foot are greatly simplified by the union of the proximal tarsals with the tibia to make a tibio-tarsus, articulating at an intertarsal joint with the remaining bones of the foot, fused to make a single tarso-metatarsus. There are usually four digits articulating with the tarso-metatarsus; three directed forwards and one backwards. In standing, the weight is usually balanced in tripod fashion on three of the four points provided by the front and back portions of the feet.

The knee joint has some remarkable similarities to that of man. It is stabilized by lateral, medial, and cruciate ligaments and contains a pair of lunate cartilages or 'menisci'. The joint allows movements of flexion and extension and the femur as it extends on the tibia in walking rotates laterally because of the arrangement of the joint surfaces. The bird thus balances in the medio-lateral plane by rotation at the knee, somewhat as we do by abduction–adduction at the

FIG. 258. Drawings from photographs of a goose, A, standing; B, stepping. The centre of gravity S is brought over the foot on the ground by lateral rotation of the femur on the tibia. Note the position of the tail in B. (After Heinroth, from Stolpe.)

hip (Fig. 258). When it makes a step forward the weight is brought by this rotation at the knee over the leg that remains on the ground.

The intertarsal joint allows mainly movements of flexion and extension. It is largely supported by ligaments and has a very strong capsule and lateral and cruciate ligaments rather like those of the knee; there is even a meniscus on the lateral side. The back of the tibia is occupied by the gastrocnemius and the flexor muscles of the toes and at the front there is a tibialis anterior acting across the intertarsal joint, and also extensors of the toes. The calf muscles are mainly concerned with producing flexion of the toes in the act of perching and they form an elaborate system of tendons attached to the phalanges. These tendons often act as a single unit, and there is an arrangement by which the flexion is passively maintained by the weight of the body, even during sleep. Many of the muscles are specially arranged to allow support of the joint whether in the flexed or extended position. The iliofibular muscle passes through a conspicuous sling for this purpose (Figs. 254 and 256). The flexor muscles of the toes are inserted largely above the knee and thus tend to tighten as the bird sinks. In this they may be assisted by the ambiens, a muscle found in reptiles and some birds, which takes origin from the ilium. The

FIG. 259. Various types of feet in birds.

1, shag (swimming); 2, crow (perching, lifting); 3, ptarmigan (stockinged by feathers); 4, jungle fowl (walking, scraping); 5, coot (lobate, swimming); 6, jacana (suited for walking on floating plants); 7, sea-eagle (raptorial). (From Thompson, *Biology of Birds*, Sidgwick & Jackson, Ltd.)

muscle belly lies on the medial side of the thigh, and its tendon runs beneath the patella on to the lateral surface of the lower leg, where it is attached to the upper end of the muscles that flex the toes. This arrangement provides a single string crossing hip, knee, and ankle and allowing the weight of the body to flex the toes as the joints bend.

The second mechanism for maintaining the bird on its perch is a locking device that holds the toes flexed. The under surface of the flexor tendon is ridged at the metatarso-phalangeal joint, where the weight of the body presses it against a branch. The upper side of the tendon sheath is also ribbed and as the bird settles on its perch the two sets of ridges interlock.

The feet show a wide variety of adaptations for special habitats (Fig. 259). In the cursorial and walking birds there are often long digits in front and behind to give a long base for balance, but the number may be reduced —to two in the ostrich. Many different groups of birds have acquired webbed feet for the purpose of swimming. In birds exposed to cold the digits may be enclosed in a coat of feathers. Birds of prey develop long raptorial talons. Throughout the great group of perching birds one digit is directed backwards, allowing firm grasp of a branch.

7. Skeleton of the wings

The apparatus of flight depends on a very great development of some parts of the fore-limb and reduction of others. The wing feathers are carried along the post-axial border of the humerus, ulna, and specialized hand, and the shape of the wing depends on the position in which the feathers are held by their muscles, as well as on membranes, the pre- and post-patagia, developed where the limb joins the body. The active movements of flight are produced mainly by the pectoral muscles; the joints and muscles of the wing itself serve to spread the wing and to adjust its shape during each beat. The humerus is short and broad, with a large head and an expanded surface for attachment of the pectoral muscles. Radius and ulna are both large, especially the latter. There are two free proximal carpals and the remaining wrist bones form two rod-like carpo-metacarpals. Only one digit, the second, is well developed, it has two broad phalanges; the third and the first digits consist of single rods, the latter, standing somewhat apart at the front of the base of the hand, is capable of independent movement; it carries the bastard wing (alula or ala spuria).

The glenoid cavity is formed at the union of a thin blade-like scapula and a stout coracoid. The former serves to brace the wing away from the ribs. The coracoid holds the wing away from the sternum, with which it makes a joint, and is assisted in this by the furcula, probably consisting of the combined clavicles and interclavicles, loosely attached to the sternum.

8. Wing muscles

Depression of the wing is produced mainly by a single mass of muscle, the huge pectoralis major, making up as much as one-fifth of the whole weight of the body. It runs from the sternum and furcula to the under side of the humerus, to which it is attached, at some distance from the joint, by a complicated tendon of insertion. The fibres of this muscle are very red in strongly flying birds, white in the flightless fowl. Elevation of the wing is produced by a muscle also attached to the sternum, lying deep to the pectoralis major and often called the pectoralis minor, but more properly supracoracoideus. Its tendon passes through the foramen triosseum, between the furcula, scapula, and coracoid, to be inserted on the upper side of the humerus. It is assisted by latissimus dorsi and deltoid muscles.

The chief muscles of the shoulder are thus a massive set serving to raise and lower the wing. There is little development of the other muscles such as are present in more normal vertebrates for the purpose of balance and drawing the limb backwards and forwards for standing and locomotion. Such a system of braces all round the joint is unnecessary; the bird balances on its wings mainly by the action of the pectoralis major as the chief brace, between the sternum and the humerus, with the coracoid as a compression member between. Stresses must of course arise in other directions besides those tending to produce a vertical fall and these are met by the muscles that produce rotation of the humerus and various other movements of the wing, especially a pronation, depressing the leading edge. The muscles used in other tetrapods to sling the weight of the body to the pectoral girdle and fore-limb are little developed. The scapula is held to the vertebral column by small rhomboid muscles and there is a short series of slips attached to the ribs, the serratus anterior.

Other muscles running from the body to the humerus produce rotation of the humerus at the glenoid and adjustments of the patagia, movements which are very important in flight. From the outer surface of the scapula arises a scapulo-humeral muscle, inserted in such a way as to produce adduction and lateral rotation of the humerus, raising the hinder edge of the wing. The coraco-humeral muscle is a compact bundle attached near to the last and producing the opposite effect of abduction and medial rotation, lowering the hinder aspect of the wing.

The deltoid muscle is divided into several parts and besides its main abductor action on the wing also has slips inserted into the skin of the anterior patagium, muscles known as the long and short tensors of that membrane. There is also a tensor accessorius, running from the surface of the biceps to the skin of the leading edge of the wing.

The muscles within the arm itself serve to extend and fold the whole wing and to alter the positions of the parts, especially by pronation and supination during flight. Large triceps and smaller biceps muscles act at the elbow. In the forearm there is a large extensor carpi radialis and an extensor carpi ulnaris, serving to keep the wing extended at the wrist. Flexor carpi ulnaris folds the wing. There are also two large pronators, brevis and longus (brachioradialis), rotating the radius medially and lifting the back of the wing. A system of digital flexors and extensors, inserted into the distal phalanx of the main digit, keeps the wing tip spread out or folds it. The position of individual feathers is controlled by an elaborate system of tendons and muscles along the back of the hand. The first digit is moved independently by abductor and adductor pollicis muscles, controlling the position of the bastard wing, which helps to give extra speed at the take-off (p. 431).

9. Principles of bird flight

A plane surface moved through the air in a direction inclined at an angle to this plane is known as an aerofoil. The forces generated can be resolved into a lift force acting upwards and a drag force tending to stop the motion. On this fact depends the power of supporting weight in the air possessed by birds and human heavier-than-air machines. Both lift and drag forces are proportional to the square of the speed, and the requirement for sustained flight in still air is that the object shall have sufficient speed to generate a lift force equal to its weight. When an aerofoil falls below this critical speed it stalls; that is to say, drops suddenly, being no longer supported.

The flow of air over the upper surface of the wing reduces the pressure there and provides the main portion of the lift (Fig. 260–1). By tilting the wing (increasing the 'angle of attack') the pressure on the underside can be increased, but the air flow now tends not to follow the upper surface but to become turbulent, especially at the hind edge, destroying the lift (Fig. 260–1). The smooth flow of air over the wing tends to be especially disturbed at its hinder ('trailing') edge and by eddies round the end ('tip vortex'). The proportion of length to breadth (aspect ratio) in the wing suitable for a particular type of flight depends on the need to provide an undisturbed area between these edges.

The shape of the aerofoil is of critical importance in determining its aerodynamic capacities. For birds, as for aeroplanes, there are differing shapes, suitable for various types of flight. To understand them we must classify the means by which birds attain the necessary forward velocity. First and most obvious is flapping flight. Though the details of this are varied and not fully understood, it can be regarded as a screw-like motion of the wings, providing forward and upward components (p. 434). The primary feathers provide the greater part of the forward component, acting as propellers, while the lift comes mainly from the secondaries of the forearm.

In still air the only alternative to flapping flight is to glide downwards, which obviously cannot continue indefinitely. Yet some birds, such as the gulls, and especially the albatrosses and the buzzards, condors, and other birds of prey, can be seen to soar for many minutes, gaining height without flapping the wings. Lord Rayleigh showed how they can do this by making use of the fact that the air is seldom still. Theoretically the bird can use three types of air movement: (1) ascending currents, usually thermal; (2) variations in the wind velocity at any one level (gusts); (3) differences in wind velocity at different levels. The first method is that used by human sail-planes and is certainly adopted by many soaring land birds. The gustiness of the wind is probably turned to advantage by gulls, rooks, and many birds, and the decrease in wind velocity near the sea surface is used by marine soaring birds, notably the albatross.

10. Wing shape

A wing of the shape that allows an albatross or swift to make its superb manœuvres would stall immediately at the speed of flight adopted by a crow. In discussing wing shape the chief factors to be considered are (1) the wing area, (2) the aspect ratio (wing length/breadth), (3) the wing outline and taper, (4) the presence of holes or slots, (5) the camber or curvature of the wing.

11. Wing area and loading

A small wing area is necessary for fast flight, since the drag $\propto$ area $\times$ speed^2, at least for high speeds. For this reason fast aeroplanes and birds have small wings, but in the case of the bird the fact that the wing provides the forward momentum as well as the lift greatly complicates matters. For flapping flight the wings must be moved relatively fast and for this small size is an advantage. On the other hand, a large wing area allows slow flight (lift $\propto$ area $\times$ speed^2) and is

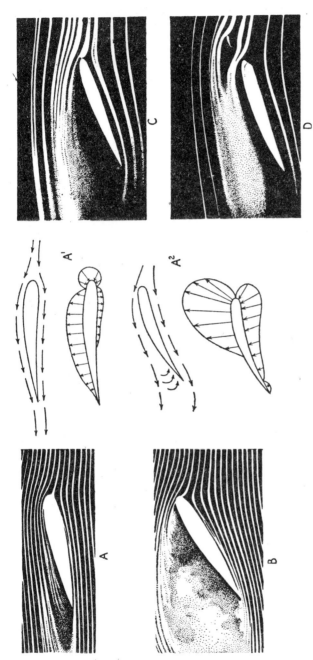

FIG. 260–1. Effect of an air stream flowing past a wing under various conditions in a wind tunnel. The white lines are jets of smoke. In A they are close together below the wing and farther apart above it. These increased and reduced pressures produce the lift and the arrows in A¹ and A² show the actual pressures registered by gauges, with different angles of attack. In B and C the angle of attack is so large that the stream does not follow the upper surface, turbulence develops, the stream produces drag instead of lift, and the wing stalls. D shows how this is prevented by slotting. (After Storer from official photographs of the National Advisory Committee for Aeronautics and from Jones.)

found in hawks, vultures, storks, and other birds that fly slowly to hunt, especially if they soar on thermal currents, for which a large lift is necessary (p. 437).

The loading of the wing varies considerably. Since the weight increases with the cube but the wing area only with the square of the linear dimensions, it follows that large birds must have relatively larger wings than small. However, the larger birds usually have a heavier loading of the wing, for instance, 10 kg./m.^{2} in the duck (*Anas*), 20 in the swan (*Cygnus*); 1 in the goldcrest (*Regulus*), 3 in the crow (*Corvus*). A considerable 'safety margin' remains in most birds, for instance, pigeons were found to be able to fly until as much as 45 per cent. of the wing surface was removed; hawks and owls have an especially high safety margin and they can carry prey almost as heavy as themselves.

12. Aspect ratio

Although a small wing area reduces drag, many fast-flying birds have a large wing-span. The aerodynamic advantages of this allow a low rate of descent when gliding, reducing the expenditure of energy necessary to sustain flight. High aspect ratio is therefore found in birds which fly fast by flapping flight (swifts and swallows) and especially in those, such as the albatross, that glide fast in order to obtain sufficient kinetic energy to convert into altitude. However these wings with very high aspect ratio stall at relatively high speeds and the birds that soar slowly on thermal up-currents over the land mostly have a low aspect ratio. Some figures for aspect ratios are:

Albatross (*Diomedea*) .	.	25	Vulture (*Neophron*)	.	6
Gull (*Larus*) .	.	11	Rook (*Corvus*) .	.	6
Swift (*Apus*) .	.	11	Sparrow (*Passer*)	.	5
Shearwater (*Puffinus*) .	.	10			

13. Wing-tips, slots, and camber

A pointed wing tends to stall first at its tip and is therefore only suitable for fast fliers. Such birds therefore show great development of the hand feathers, producing a long narrow wing, whereas birds built for slower flight and manœuvre have a shorter broader wing with long arm feathers (Fig. 260-1).

The condition of the air around the wing is of first importance for the maintenance of lift; if there is not a smooth stream over the upper and under surfaces the air becomes turbulent, and the aerofoil stalls (Fig. 260-1). This tends to happen either if the speed falls too low or if the angle of the wing relative to the line of motion increases above about 20°. Turbulence is mitigated, however, by the provision of openings, known as slots, which let through part of the air and provide the necessary smooth stream. The spaces that occur between the feathers, especially towards the wing tip, almost certainly function as slots. Probably the arrangement provides a series of such apertures,

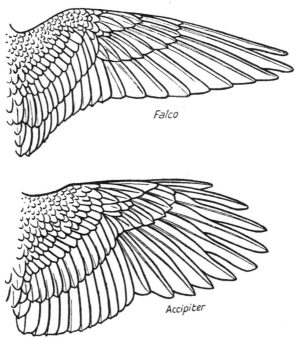

FIG. 262. Wings built for speed (falcon, *Falco*) and for manœuvring (hawk, *Accipiter*). The former is long and narrow, with relatively large hand feathers. The latter is short and broad, the arm feathers being long and the primaries arranged to make slots. (After Fuertes.)

giving a very efficient high-lift device. Such slots are conspicuous in slow fliers (rooks) and especially in those that soar on thermal up-currents (vultures). The feathers of such birds are often individually tapered (Fig. 262). Slots are also found in the wings of large birds which are fast fliers (pheasants), the wing being liable to stall in certain phases of the down strokes.

It is possible that the bastard wing acts as a slotting device; indeed, consideration of it has played a large part in development of the theory of turbulence and slotting. However, it may be that the effect produced by the bastard wing at take-off is rather to produce forward momentum.

The shape of the wing has a very important influence on the

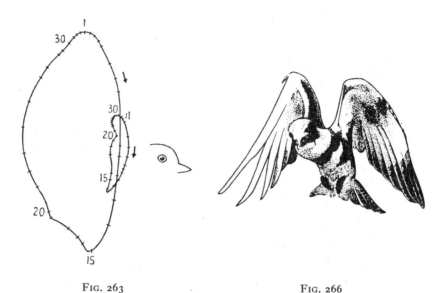

FIG. 263   FIG. 266

FIG. 263. Pathway of the wing tip and wrist joint relative to the body during free flapping flight of a gull. Equal time-intervals are shown. Note the great speed of the upward beat and that the forearm is raised before the wing tip. (After Demoll.)

FIG. 266. Bill-fisher leaving its hole in a bank, showing wings half-way through the upstroke. The upper arm has reached its highest point and the forearm is just starting upwards; its primary feathers have opened on the right wing, reducing resistance. (Drawn from photograph by Aymar, *Bird Flight*, published by John Lane, The Bodley Head, Ltd.)

FIG. 264. Pigeon (*Columba*) with wings at bottom of stroke during rising. From a photograph taken at very short exposure. Note forward position of wings but upward and backward curled primary feathers. (After Aymar.)

Fig. 265. Drawings from four photographs from film of a take-off by an eagle (*Aquila*). A. The legs are jumping and the upper arms nearly vertical before the wrist joint is extended. B. Wing fully extended with bastard wing spread out, some pronation. C. Marked pronation as the upper arm reaches its lowest point. D. The upper arm is proceeding upwards, although the hand has not yet reached its lowest point. (Drawn from photographs by Knight, from Streseman.)

air stream. In most birds there is a stiff leading edge and a thinner trailing edge. Nearly all wings are cambered, that is to say, they taper from the leading to the trailing edge, especially in the region of the forearm (Fig. 260–1). This arrangement directs the air stream over the upper surface of the wing in such a way as to provide an extra lift by creating a 'suction zone' of reduced pressure. However, high camber, like low aspect ratio, reduces the speed of the bird.

14. Flapping flight

Flapping flight involves a complex, screw-like motion of the wing, usually downwards and forwards then upwards and backwards, more rapid upwards than downwards (Fig. 263). When rising, or in hovering, the wings move almost straight forwards and backwards. While moving down the wing is held rigid, producing the upward and forward effects, the force being given, of course, by the pectoralis major.

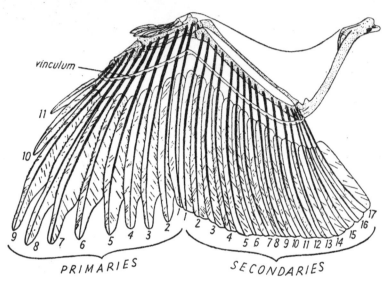

FIG. 267. Diagram of wing to show arrangement of the flight feathers. (From Pycraft, *A History of Birds*, Methuen & Co., Ltd.)

This muscle weighs as much as one-fifth of the body weight in flappers, such as the lapwing, as little as one-ninth in soarers, such as the gull. Whereas the feathers of the arm mainly provide the lift it is those of the hand that produce the forward movement, there being a pronation during each downward stroke, the anterior margin being lower than the posterior, so that although the whole wing moves forwards the feathers of the hand are directed backwards (Fig. 264). The anterior patagia and the bastard wing also play a special part in providing forward movement, being so placed as to increase the forward component of the pressure of the air on the wing. The bastard wing is spread out for this purpose during the take-off and before landing (Fig. 265).

During flight the tip of the wing describes an elliptical path in relation to the body of the bird (Fig. 263). Before the tip has reached its lowest point the inner portion of the wing begins to rise, so that at one stage the wing is bent downwards at a right angle at the wrist (Fig. 266). As the upward stroke proceeds, the wing ceases to be pronated and other adjustments are made, such that the resistance to the upstroke is reduced. The feathers are held by an elaborate system of tendons and in some birds they are allowed to twist only when the wing is being raised and the barbs of the feathers themselves are so arranged that they open like the vanes of a blind when under pressure from above, but close when the pressure is from below (Fig. 267). In other birds, especially those that fly fast with a slow wing beat, such as gulls and swans, the wing is probably rigid on the up as well as on the down strokes, and is twisted so as to produce forward and upward components on the up stroke.

The whole upward movement is usually faster than the downward one. Before the wing tip has reached its highest point the upper arm is already beginning to descend and in this way the line of flight is maintained almost straight and does not follow a wavy path as it would do if the parts of the wing vibrated together. In small birds the wing works more nearly as a whole and the flight differs in several respects from that of larger birds.

FIG. 268. Spotted fly-catcher hovering. The wings are passing backwards and there are spaces between the feathers. (Drawn from a photograph by E. Hosking, with permission.)

The whirring flight of some small birds, especially of humming birds, enables them to remain almost in one place in the air, or even to move backwards. The wings beat backwards and forwards (Fig. 268), often as fast as 200 times a second, and the 'pectoralis minor' is almost as large as the major.

15. Soaring flight

Many birds economize the energy needed for flapping flight by making skilful use of the possibilities presented by movement of the air. All birds glide for short distances, some small birds with wings folded, others with wings outstretched. Sustained gliding and soaring upwards without flapping the wings is found only in large birds, probably because considerable weight is necessary to provide kinetic energy sufficient to ensure continuous flight and efficient use of wind variations. As has been suggested, there are two distinct types of soaring birds: (1) land birds using thermal up-currents, (2) marine birds using variations in wind above sea-level.

FIG. 269. Flight of an eagle (*Aquila*).

A–B, flapping flight; B–C, soaring at constant height; C–D,
soaring in ascending spirals; D–E, gliding. (After Ahlborn.)

FIG. 270. Soaring flight of kite (*Milvus*).

Losing height downwind and gaining it upwind. Time-marks one second.
(After Hankin.)

FIG. 271. Wings of vulture (*Gyps*).

A, soaring upwind, gaining height; B, upwind on level; C, downwind, losing height;
D–F, gliding flight. (After Ahlborn.)

16. Soaring on up-currents

Up-currents of air arise in the neighbourhood of large objects on the ground (cliffs or even a ship) and particularly from variations in the rate of heating of the earth's surface in the sun, over rocks, vegetation, mountain shadows, &c. Birds using such currents usually

Fig. 272. Wings of the albatross (*Diomedea*), used for soaring flight. Wing very narrow, with long upper arm region. (Drawn from photograph by Aymar.)

proceed upwards in a series of small circles, a behaviour seen in buzzards and other hawks and especially characteristic of vultures, which may ascend in this way above 1,000 feet (Figs. 269–71). The characteristic features of such thermal soarers are large wing area, low aspect ratio, and wings broad at the tip and usually provided with well-marked slots.

17. Use of vertical wind variations

The decreasing effect of surface friction causes the wind to blow faster at greater heights and this phenomenon is used by some birds at sea, where conditions are presumably more uniform than over the land. The albatross (*Diomedea*) (Fig. 272) is the classic example of this type of bird, proceeding in a regular series of movements, without flapping the wings, downwind losing height and gaining speed and then upwind gaining height and passing into a faster-moving layer. Each downwind tack is longer than the upwind one. During the upwind tack the wings are spread forwards, downwind backwards.

FIG. 273. Heron (*Ardea*) leaving its perch. The legs have been used to make a jump and the wings are fully spread. (Drawn from photograph by Aymar.)

The albatross remains all the time within 50 feet of the sea surface, the variations in wind velocity being marked only at low levels. The albatross shows the characteristics suitable for this type of flight, namely, large size (it is the largest of all flying birds), great wing span (11 feet), high aspect ratio (25), and pointed wing tips, without slots.

Other sea birds, such as the gulls, though not so highly specialized, can take advantage of variations in horizontal wind velocity, including gusts at any one level. The bird moves upwards as it meets an accelerating gust and turns when the wind decelerates. Gulls also use up-currents at cliff faces and, no doubt, air movements of all sorts are widely used, especially by large birds. However, it is evident that the wing equipment only allows the bird a limited range of choice and probably even the slightly different wing shapes of related species depend on the differing conditions they are called upon to meet. A vulture could no more zoom backwards and forwards over the waves

FIG. 274. Pigeons (*Columba*), photographed during take-off, with exposures of 1/825 second. A, front, and B, rear view, with wings together. C, nearly, and D, quite at bottom of downstroke; note pronation and forward movement of wing. E and F, wings during the upstroke; in F the primary feathers have opened; note that the wing moves backwards and that the motion is faster than on the downstroke. (From photographs by Aymar.)

than an albatross could circle slowly on a gentle thermal up-current. A pigeon cannot equal a gull at steady gliding and soaring, but the pigeon can rise more steeply or descend more rapidly without stalling.

18. Speed of flight

Estimation of the speed of flight involves distinguishing between air and ground speeds. The speed relative to the ground may be very high; there are records of birds covering more than 100 land miles in an hour, with the help of the wind. Racing pigeons can average 40 miles an hour or more for considerable periods. Air speeds of

30–50 m.p.h. can certainly be reached by many birds: swifts are said to reach 100 m.p.h. in still air. The distinction of air and ground speeds is not, however, very significant from the bird's viewpoint; it is the essence of bird flight that the animals are sufficiently at home in the air to use all possible help from their environment.

19. Take-off and landing

At the take-off the bird has to acquire sufficient forward momentum

to provide lift, and yet must leave the air sufficiently undisturbed for subsequent beats to be effective. In many birds, especially the smaller, the jump provided by the legs is adequate for the take-off (Fig. 273). Large birds must run or swim rapidly to obtain sufficient speed. Eagles are said to be unable to rise without a very long run, and many large birds nest on a cliff or tree, which gives them an up-current for the take-off. Swifts usually come to rest high up and can only rise off the ground with difficulty. The albatross is unable to take off from the sea surface in a dead calm.

The first beats are usually very large, beginning with the wings above the back and held at such an angle as to produce a large forward component. The wings may be heard actually clapping together in pigeons (Fig. 274). During very rapid ascent, as in the larks, the body is nearly vertical and the wing changes its angle at the shoulder very sharply between the downward and recovery strokes. The

FIG. 275. Jackdaw about to land. The wings are fully extended on the downbeat, and the tail is fanned out and bent downwards. (From photograph by Aymar.)

bastard wing is held in such a position that the beat provides extra forward momentum.

Landing is also a very delicate operation, especially since it often involves coming to rest suddenly on a branch (Fig. 275). This is achieved by lowering and fanning out the tail, which thus acts as a flap, providing both lift and braking. The legs are then lowered; often one further wing stroke is given to bring the bird forward to drop onto the perch. The adjustment of braking in such a way as to prevent stalling involves a very special system of co-ordination (Fig. 276).

Other methods of landing are possible, for instance, rooks may make a roll and sideslip to the ground.

20. The skull in birds

The arrangement of the parts of the bird's skull is similar to that of archosaurian reptiles (Fig. 241). Individual bones can be recognized in the young, but they mostly become united in the adult to form a continuous thin-walled structure that encloses the brain and sense-organs and supports the beak (Fig. 277). Most birds are microsmatic; the nasal passages are simple and the turbinals reduced. There is no false palate, the internal nostril opening into the mouth relatively far forward. The large size of the brain and reduction of its olfactory portions are responsible for the rounded form of the top of the head, and there are very large orbits at the sides. The base of the skull is formed by a basioccipital behind, carrying a single occipital condyle. There is a large basisphenoid, covered ventrally by a pair of basitemporals, probably representing the parasphenoid, the front part of which makes a 'basisphenoid rostrum', as in archosaurs.

Fig. 276. Hawk striking at a dummy owl. Note long legs and the method of braking. The wings are broad and rounded, giving a large safety factor. (From photograph by Aymar.)

The jaws are characteristically slender and elongated; in the more advanced birds they have a very special form of support. The upper part of the front of the skull is composed of the enlarged premaxillae, the nostrils lying very far back and the nasal bones being small. The palatines are long and fused far forward with the maxilla, while they articulate movably behind with the pterygoids and base of the skull. The pterygoid is a slender rod, itself movably articulated with the skull and with the quadrate, which is a triangular bone with clearly separate otic and basal articular

FIG. 277. Skull of young gosling (*Anser*).

A. angular; *Ar*. articular; *As*. alisphenoid; *Bo*. basioccipital; *Bsh*. basisphenoid; *D*. dentary; *E*. ethmoid; *Eo*. exoccipital; *F*. frontal; *Ip*. interparietal; *J*. jugal; *L*. lachrymal; *Mx*. maxillary; *N*. nasal; *O*. supra-occipital; *Op*. opisthotic; *P*. parietal; *Pa*. palatine; *Pm*. premaxillary; *Po*. postorbital; *Pt*. pterygoid; *Q*. quadrate; *Qj*. quadratojugal; *R*. rostrum of basisphenoid; *S*. squamosal; *Sa*. sur-angular; *V*. vomer. (From Heilmann, **The Origin of Birds**, H. F. & C. Witherby, Ltd.)

processes. The upper jaw is thus a long thin bar composed of maxillae, quadratojugal, and jugal, and is capable of considerable movement at its hind end. The lower jaw, also elongated, consists of the articular bone and four membrane bones. This type of palatal arrangement

FIG. 278. Various bird beaks.

1, Merganser; 2, Flamingo; 3, Shoveller; 4, Scissor-bill (adult); 5, Scissor-bill (young); 6, *Anastomus*; 7, Hornbill; 8, Humming bird; 9, Avocet; 10, Parrot; 11, Parrot; 12, Spoonbill; 13, Crossbill; 14, Nightjar; 15, Eagle; 16, *Balaeniceps*. (From Pycraft, *A History of Birds*, Methuen & Co., Ltd.)

is known as neognathous, but in some birds, presumed to be the more primitive, the palatines are shorter and the pterygoids more reptilian in form and not movable. Such a palaeognathous palate is found in the flightless ratites, for instance the ostrich (p. 491).

21. The jaws, beak, and feeding mechanisms

The bird's skull shows no separate temporal fossae and it is not certain by what modifications the present state has been reached from that of a presumed diapsid ancestor. There is a complete lower temporal bar, composed of jugal and quadratojugal bones, but no sign of a postorbital bar. Presumably the two fossae have become filled out. Unfortunately the temporal region is badly damaged in the Jurassic fossil bird *Archaeopteryx* and it must be admitted that we can only guess at the stages of the transformation of this part of the skull. There are moderately large temporal and pterygoid muscles, but the jaws are not usually very powerful, though, of course, formidable in carnivores. Having completely lost the teeth, the birds must rely largely on internal processes to break up the food. The beak is, however, characteristically modified according to the food habits (Fig. 278). There is very great variety in the feeding, as in so much of the life of birds, and though many species keep strictly to one diet others are able to adapt themselves to the food available. The ingenuity and persistence with which birds seek and collect food must be a main factor in their success.

Many birds with a moderately long bill, such as the song-thrush (*Turdus*), can eat either flesh (snails, earthworms, or caterpillars) or fruit. Incidentally we may notice the ingenious behaviour by which the snail's shell is cracked open to obtain the food, by beating it against a stone; a very indirect approach to the desired end. Birds that mainly eat seeds, such as the finches, usually have short, thick, strong bills. Very large strong bills are present in the hornbills and toucans, they push through dense foliage to obtain the fruit, which may have a hard case. The beak of the parrots is operated by an amazing arrangement; the premaxilla is moved on the skull, pushed up by the upper jaw when the latter is pulled forward by the digastric muscle.

The carnivorous birds, such as most eagles and owls, have very short and sharp beaks, whereas fish-eating, as in other vertebrates, results in very long jaws. Another widely found arrangement is the flattened bill of some ducks, similar to those of some sturgeons and of the platypus, which also sift out food from water or mud. The very long, thin beak of the curlew selects food from mud in a different way, presumably in this case mostly worms and other soft-bodied invertebrates. Some flamingos feed wholly on blue-green algae, collected by a filter system on the jaws, using a current of water produced by the sucking mouth and piston-like tongue. Some insectivorous birds have long beaks for finding their prey under bark. The woodpeckers have a strong beak like a pick-axe for excavating in wood, and most elaborate special modifications for the purpose of licking up insects; there is an enormously long protusible tongue and special hyoid. The woodpecker finch (*Camarhynchus pallidus*) on the Galapagos Islands probes

insects from the bark by means of a cactus spine, a remarkable case of
the use of a tool by a bird (Fig. 279). Among the most specialized
feeders are the humming-birds, eating nectar, the beak being long or
short according to the type of flower visited, and the tongue provided
with a special tubular tip.

Thus the beaks of birds show every degree of specialization from the
moderate jaws of the rook, able to eat almost any food, to the peculiar
arrangements of the woodpecker or humming-birds. The tongue is a

FIG. 279. The Galapagos woodpecker finch (*Camarhynchus pallidus*) using
its stick. (From Lack, drawn by R. Green from photograph by R. Leacock.)

rather horny structure and the sense of taste is probably poor in most
birds. Food tainted with repellent substances (asafoetida or aloe) may
be readily swallowed.

22. Digestive system of birds

Once the food is in the mouth it is manipulated by the long, thin
tongue, moistened with saliva, which usually consists of mucus but is
said to contain diastatic enzyme in the seed-eating finches (*Fringillidae*). Food swallowed down the oesophagus may be stored in a
large receptacle, the crop, found especially in grain-eating birds; its
lining is of oesophageal structure (Fig. 280). The true stomach is
divided into two parts, a glandular proventriculus and a very muscular
gizzard. The structure of the anterior chambers of the gut varies
greatly with the diet. In grain-eating birds, such as the pigeon, the
crop is large and the seeds are first macerated by storage there. They
are then mixed with peptic enzymes in the proventriculus and ground
up in the muscular gizzard, which in pigeons has a horny lining and

also contains numerous small stones. In insectivores and carnivores the crop is usually smaller or absent, but is very large in some fish-eating birds. In carnivores the gizzard has the character of a more normal stomach. It was stated by John Hunter that herring gulls, normally living on fish, readily take to eating grain, and that after a year or so of this diet the gizzard becomes muscular and has horny walls.

FIG. 280. Dissection of pigeon.

b.d. bile-ducts; *cl.* cloaca; *coec.* coeca; *cr.* crop; *giz.* gizzard; *int.* intestine; *k.* kidney; *l.* liver; *oes.* oesophagus; *p.* pancreas; *p.d.* pancreatic ducts; *pr.* proventriculus; *sp.* spleen; *test.* testis. (After Schimkewitsch and Streseman.)

The peptic juice has very powerful digestive powers and many carnivorous and fish-eating birds dissolve even the bones of their prey, though in owls these are regurgitated with fur or feathers, making characteristic pellets. The crop of pigeons is also remarkable for the milk which it produces to nourish the young. There are special glands for this purpose and they become active in the breeding-season under the influence of a pituitary hormone, which is similar if not identical to the galactogenic hormone of the mammalian pituitary, an amazing and unexplained correspondence!

The duodenum and coiled intestine are of characteristic vertebrate type, relatively rather short, though somewhat larger in grain-eating birds. The bile and pancreatic ducts usually open into the distal limb of the duodenum; in pigeons the left bile-duct enters close to the pylorus (Fig. 280). There is a peculiar pair of coeca at the junction of rectum and intestine. The food enters these coeca, but it is not clear what function they perform, possibly it is related to the absorption of water. The arrangements of the cloaca are certainly concerned with this end (Fig. 281). The rectum opens into a coprodaeum and this in turn receives a urodaeum, which is the terminal portion of the urinary and genital ducts. A final chamber, the proctodaeum, opens at the anus. The urinary products are made solid by subtraction of water in the urodaeum and the walls of the other chambers serve a similar purpose. The bursa Fabricii is a blind sac with much lymphoid tissue, opening into the proctodaeum; its function is probably to protect

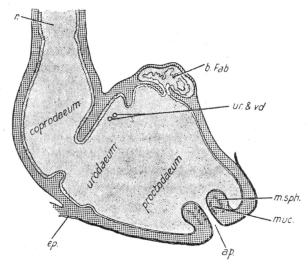

FIG. 281. Diagrammatic section through cloaca of pigeon.
ap. external aperture; *b.Fab.* bursa Fabricii; *ep.* epidermis; *m.sph.* sphincter muscle; *muc.* mucus glands; *r.* rectum; *ur.* and *vd.* papillae for ureter and vas deferens (or oviduct). (After Clara, from Streseman.)

locally against infection and to produce lymphocytes for the blood-stream, hence it has been called a 'cloacal thymus'.

The large surface area, high temperature, and great activity of birds necessitate a very high food intake, especially in the smaller types. This is made possible by very rapid passage of food through the gut. Thus a shrike (*Lanius*) is said to digest a mouse in 3 hours, and hens take only 12–24 hours over the most resistant grain. The amount of food taken per day may reach nearly 30 per cent. of the body weight (6 gm.) in the very small goldcrest (*Regulus*) but is about 12 per cent. in a starling (*Sturnus*) weighing 75 gm.

23. Circulatory system

Very many of the features characteristic of birds depend on an efficient circulation, allowing of a high rate of metabolism, and hence a high and constant temperature. It is significant that the birds and mammals are the only vertebrates that have achieved complete separation of the respiratory and systemic circulations, making possible a high arteriolar pressure, which allows materials to reach the tissues rapidly. The fact that this condition has been arrived at twice, independently and by rather different arrangements, is a challenging demonstration that there must be some common elements in the situations controlling the direction of evolution.

The heart shows its sauropsidan characteristics very clearly in that the ventral aorta is split to its base into an aortic trunk, arising from the left ventricle and curling round the pulmonary trunk to form a single right aortic arch. The heart has lost the sinus venosus, as in mammals no such extra chamber is necessary to step up the venous return pressure. The ventricles are very large, especially the left. The right auricle and ventricle are separated by a flap-like valve, the left side having valves with chordae tendinae, somewhat as in mammals. There are enormous innominate arteries to supply the pectoral muscles. In the venous system there are renal portal veins.

The size of the heart and rate of heart-beat vary with the size and activity of the bird, larger birds having in general relatively smaller and less rapid hearts. In a turkey the rate of beat may be less than 100 per minute, in a hen about 300, and in a sparrow nearly 500.

The red corpuscles of birds differ from those of mammals in being oval and nucleated. They carry a very large amount of a haemoglobin that gives up its oxygen suddenly at a relatively high oxygen tension. The red corpuscles are smaller in actively flying birds than in the larger flightless ratites. There is a very high basal metabolic rate and a temperature considerably higher than that of mammals, usually about 42° C., reaching nearly 45° C. in some cases. The means by which this is kept constant in the absence of sweat glands are not known certainly. Presumably there is a considerable heat loss from the surface of the air-sacs and lungs, though this is perhaps not easily regulated. In ducks there is a system of direct arterio-venous connexions in the feet, perhaps serving to prevent venous stagnation. The anastomotic regions have powerful muscles, whose contraction closes them and forces the blood through the capillary system. There must be a whole system of nervous pathways for the control of upward and downward temperature regulation, evolved independently of that found in mammals.

24. Respiration

Special arrangements are present to provide the very large supply of oxygen necessary for the active metabolism and these are based on the plan found in some reptiles. Beyond the respiratory portion of the lung there are membranous air-sacs, which are filled at inspiration and then sweep the used air out of the lungs at expiration, thus avoiding the 'dead space' of unrespired air, which is considerable in mammals. The lung surfaces are therefore continually in contact with a high tension of oxygen.

The larynx of birds is a small structure guarding the entrance to the

FIG. 282. Diagram of lungs and air-sacs of pigeon, seen from ventral side on left, dorsal on right. On the left side only the ventral surface of the lungs and the expiratory bronchi and air-sacs are shown (dotted). On the right are the inspiratory bronchi and air-sacs (in black).

B. main bronchus; *C*. cervical ventrobronchus; *M*. mesobronchus; *V*. vestibule; *s.abd.* abdominal air-sac; *s.cerv.* cervical air-sac; *s.clav.* clavicular air-sac with diverticulum (*ax.*) in axilla; *s.thor.ant.* and *post.* thoracic air-sacs. (After Brandes and Ihle.)

trachea. The latter is often long and coiled, perhaps to warm the air. The tracheal rings are bony and complete. The voice is produced in the syrinx, a slight enlargement at the *lower* end of the trachea, containing a pair of semilunar membranes with muscles that alter the pitch of the sound. The apparatus is simple in many birds, but the muscles are very complicated in the singing birds and are especially large in the males. The voice is used for communication in various ways, including, in social birds such as rooks, the giving of warning and the frightening away of intruders. The more elaborate song of male birds is used in courtship both as a sexual stimulant and as a threat to other birds invading the chosen territory (p. 480).

The lungs are rather small spongy organs, with little elasticity. The air passes backwards in a large main bronchus running through the lungs and giving off branches to the lung substance, but continuing beyond to the inspiratory air-sacs (Figs. 282 and 283). These are very thin walled chambers, divided into two sets, the posterior inspiratory and anterior expiratory. The posterior, inspiratory, air-sacs are the abdominal and posterior thoracic and they are filled by the air rushing into them through the main bronchus. The anterior or expiratory air-sacs include an anterior thoracic, median interclavicular and cervical, these often communicating with spaces in the bones. At expiration the air passes from the more posterior sacs through the lungs by special recurrent bronchi into the anterior sacs. From these the air may be expelled to the exterior, return to the lungs being prevented by closure of sphincters. In some conditions, however, especially in diving birds, the air may be passed backwards and forwards through the lungs several times, until all its oxygen has been used. The branches of the bronchi in the lungs do not end blindly in alveoli, but make an elaborate system of lung capillaries. Air sweeps through the larger channels at inspiration and expiration, but probably reaches the finer capillaries by diffusion.

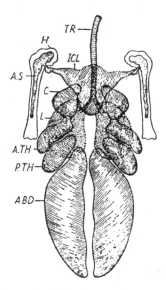

FIG. 283. The air-sacs of a bird. L. right lung; C. cervical air-sac; ICL. interclavicular; A.S. outgrowth into humerus (H.); A.TH. anterior thoracic air-sac; P.TH. posterior thoracic; ABD. abdominal air-sac; TR. trachea. (From Thompson, *Biology of Birds*, Sidgwick & Jackson, Ltd.)

The mechanism by which the ventilation is produced is complicated and depends largely on the movements produced during locomotion. The upper surface of the lung adheres to the ribs, its lower surface is covered by a special membrane derived from the peritoneum and known as the pulmonary aponeurosis (Fig. 284). This is connected with the ribs by costopulmonary muscles. The floor of the thoracic air-sacs, which lie below the lungs, is also covered by a fibrous membrane, the oblique septum, but the walls of the remaining air-sacs are very thin. Quiet respiratory movements are produced by the intercostal (inspiratory) and abdominal (expiratory) muscles, acting upon the thoracic and abdominal cavities so as to enlarge and contract the thorax, drawing air in and out of the air-sacs, through the lungs. During flight the movements of the pectoral muscles provide the ventilation, the sternum moving towards and away from the vertebral column.

25. Excretory system

The kidneys are, of course, metanephric and are relatively large,

FIG. 284. Diagram of transverse section through the thorax of a bird.

ec. Excurrent passage from lung to air-sac through pulmonary aponeurosis; *h.* heart; *lls.* left liver-sac; *lg.* lung; *m.* muscle; *ms.* mesentery below oesophagus; *obl.* oblique septum; *p.* pericardial coelom; *pa.* pulmonary aponeurosis; *plc.* reduced pleural coelom; *r.* dorsal rib; *rc.* recurrent bronchus from sac to lung; *rl.* right lobe of liver; *rpr.* right pulmonary recess; *st.* sternum; *thas.* posterior thoracic air-sac; *vr.* sternal rib. (From Goodrich.)

elongated, and lobulated. They are provided with venous blood by the renal portal veins and arterial blood from the renal arteries. The arrangement is essentially as in amphibia and reptiles, the renal arteries supplying the glomeruli and the portal veins, which break up into inter-lobular branches, sending blood to the renal tubules, whence it is collected into a central intra-lobular vein. It is not certain, however, exactly how the system operates, and it is possible that much of the blood-flow is directly from the renal portal to the renal veins, making little contact with the tubule walls.

The excretory system is highly specialized for water-saving. For this purpose the end product of nitrogenous metabolism is the relatively insoluble uric acid, synthesized in the liver, probably from ammonium lactate. After excretion by the kidney the urine is concentrated in the cloacal chambers and the uric acid precipitates as whitish granules. More soluble excretory end substances, such as urea, would reach toxic concentrations. The urinary tubules effect a considerable concentration of the urine by means of long loops of

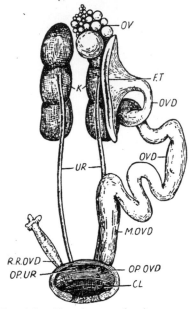

FIG. 285. Female reproductive organs of a hen.

OV. ovary; K. kidneys; F.T. funnel; OVD. oviduct; M.OVD. muscular part of oviduct; OP.OVD. opening of oviduct; UR. ureters; OP.UR. opening of right ureter; R.R.OVD. rudimentary right oviduct; CL. cloaca (From Thompson, *Biology of Birds*, Sidgwick & Jackson, Ltd.)

Henle. The viscous fluid that enters the urodaeum then passes up into the coprodaeum, where further water is abstracted, and the mixed faeces and urinary products are then excreted as the characteristic semi-solid white guano. The water-conservation system is certainly very effective, and some desert-living birds are said to be able to survive for many weeks without water. In this respect the birds have freed themselves from the original aquatic environment to a remarkable degree.

26. Reproductive system

The testis consists of coiled tubules of the usual type, joining to form a long epididymis and vas deferens, opening into the urodaeum by an erectile papilla that is the only copulatory organ of most birds. During copulation the proctodaea of male and female are everted and pressed together, so that the sperm is ejaculated direct into the female urodaeum and finds its way up the oviduct. A definite penis (and also clitoris) is formed in ratites, anseriformes, and a few other birds. The condition of the testis and its ducts varies greatly with the time of year, the weight of the gland being as much as 1,000 times greater in the breeding-season than it is in the non-breeding, when it contains only spermatogonia.

The provision of material sufficient for the development of a warm-blooded creature is, of course, made possible in birds by the extremely yolky eggs, so large that they allow room for development of only one ovary, nearly always the left (Fig. 285). The right ovary remains present as a rudiment and if the left is destroyed by operation or disease the right is able to differentiate, but then forms not an ovary but a testis. Complete sex reversal can thus occur and the transformed bird may acquire cock plumage and tread and fertilize hens (Fig. 286). Sex reversal very rarely, if ever, takes place in the opposite direction, and as in other cases of the same sort we must suppose that there is in birds some switch over in the balance of male and female determining

FIG. 286. Secondary sexual characters of the fowl (*Gallus*).
Left cocks, *right* hens.

A, normal; B, castrated; C, cock with implanted ovary and hen with implanted testis. (After Zawadowsky.)

processes, taking place relatively early in the case of normal definitive males but later on in life also in 'females', so that all birds become potentially 'male' at the end of their life.

Of the large number of oocytes only very few ripen to make the enormous follicles. After each follicle has burst it very quickly regresses; there is no 'corpus luteum'.

The egg is taken up by the ciliated and muscular funnel of the left oviduct, and passes down a tube with circular and longitudinal muscles and a very glandular, ciliated mucosa. The albumen of the egg is produced by long tubular glands, opening to the lumen. The oviduct has various parts, the upper secreting mainly albumen, the lower producing the shell, and the lowest part mucus, to assist the act of laying. The background colour of the egg is produced during shell-formation in the upper part of the tube; spots of red-brown ooporphyrin are added lower down.

27. The brain of birds

The brain is larger relative to the body in birds than in any other

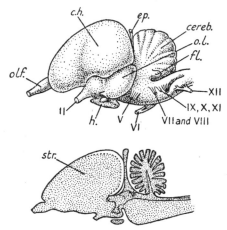

FIG. 287. Brain of a duck (*Anser*).
c.h. cerebral hemisphere; *cereb.* cerebellum; *ep.* epiphysis; *fl.* flocculus; *h.* hypophysis; *o.l.* optic lobe; *olf.* olfactory lobe; *str.* striatum; II–XII, cranial nerves. (After Butschli and Ihle.)

vertebrates except mammals (Fig. 287), and there is no doubt that one result of the high temperature has been to allow opportunity for a very elaborate nervous organization and complicated behaviour. Unfortunately we have little information about the way in which the large masses of tissue of the brain function; they are certainly very different from anything found in mammals. There are considerable differences in the development of the parts in various birds, for instance, the forebrain is especially large in the rooks and crows (*Corvus*) and in the parrots, the behaviour of whom also shows signs of outstanding 'intelligence'.

In the spinal cord the most characteristic feature is the relatively small size of the dorsal funiculi, and their nuclei in the medulla are also small. Evidently the sense of touch is less developed over the body than it is in mammals, perhaps less than in reptiles. No doubt movement of the feathers provides impulses leading to evasive action, but it is not surprising that the loose covering does not allow elaborate organization of the sense of touch. The finer senses of birds are restricted to the eyes, ears, and bill. On the other hand, there are very large spino-cerebellar tracts, presumably proprioceptive and concerned with the delicate adjustments necessary for flight. The spinal cord is controlled by large efferent tracts from the brain, including cerebello-spinal, vestibulo-spinal, and tecto-spinal pathways. There is no direct tract from the forebrain to the spinal cord, but the influence of the very large corpora striata is probably exercised through fibres running to the red nucleus and tegmentum of the midbrain, from which others pass to the cord.

The cerebellum is also large (Fig. 287), a state of affairs perhaps connected with the precise control of movement in all planes of space during flight. Besides large spino-cerebellar and vestibulo-cerebellar pathways there are also tecto-cerebellar and a strio-cerebellar tracts, the latter perhaps conducting in both directions. The effect of the cerebellum on other parts of the brain is exercised through cerebellar nuclei, the cells of which give the origin to the cerebello-spinal tract.

The optic tracts are completely crossed and end mainly in the midbrain, as in lower vertebrates; there are very large optic lobes, with many layers of cells. However, a considerable portion of the optic tracts passes to the thalamus, and the midbrain and thalamus are both very highly developed and have intimate and reciprocal connexions with the striata of the cerebral hemispheres. The optic lobes also receive ascending fibres from the trigeminal nuclei and from the spinal cord. Their efferent pathways run to the oculomotor nuclei, to the underlying tegmentum, and to the medulla and spinal cord. Evidently they play a very large part in correlating visual with other afferent impulses. The thalamus is large and its dorsal part well differentiated into nuclei. It receives, besides optic fibres, also projections from tactile, pain, temperature, and perhaps auditory sources. There are large thalamo-striatal tracts, probably conducting in both directions. The ventral thalamus receives impulses from the striatum and sends them to the tegmentum, this being the main efferent pathway of the forebrain. The hypothalamus is rather small, probably because of the reduction in the olfactory system.

The cerebral hemispheres are very much larger than any other part of the brain and show an exaggeration of the condition found in the lizards (Fig. 288). The ventro-lateral portions are enormously developed, whereas the medial ventral walls are thin and the pallium is quite small, thin, and not folded. The olfactory regions of the brain are small, including the hippocampus.

The corpus striatum is a huge solid mass of tissue, receiving projections forward from the thalamus and sending them back through the latter, to the midbrain roof and floor, to the cerebellum, and thence to the medulla and spinal cord. This very characteristic striatum can be divided into various regions. The part representing the 'original' or lower striatum is called the 'palaeostriatum'; other parts, lying above this, are known as the mesostriatum and hyperstriatum.

28. Functioning of the brain in birds

Some light is thrown on these questions by experiments in which

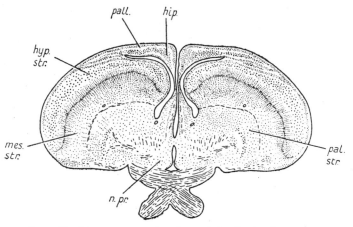

FIG. 288. Transverse section through forebrain of sparrow.

hip. hippocampus; *hyp.str.* hyperstriatum; *mes.str.* mesostriatum; *n.pr.* preoptic nucleus; *pal.str.* palaeostriatum; *pall.* pallium. (Partly after Kappers, Huber, and Crosby.)

parts of the forebrain are removed from pigeons. Loss of one complete hemisphere is not followed by any gross motor defect or asymmetry of movement. This suggests that the corpora striata do not control individual muscle movements, which agrees with the fact that there is no direct pathway from the forebrain to the spinal cord, corresponding to the pyramidal tract of the mammals. Electrical stimulation does not produce movements; the striata are 'silent areas' to stimulation, at least when simple changes of potential are made to occur at localized points.

Complete removal of both hemispheres does not reduce a pigeon to a helpless state. The animal can still maintain its temperature and its balance and can feed itself if the food is placed near to it. However, a bird so treated is far from normal. It may show a lack of activity, remaining inert for long periods, and then become aimlessly restless for a while. Evidently the normal balance of excitation and inhibition has been upset. Deficiencies in vision can be detected in birds with various portions of the cerebral hemispheres removed, and the mating and nesting behaviour are also affected. Even small removals of the cortex and top of the striatum are said to prevent incubation (though not copulation) and with deeper lesions the whole process of rearing the young becomes impossible.

These observations on the functions of the brain of pigeons may not be applicable to birds in general. The forebrain is larger in many other birds than in the pigeon, and there is some evidence that in the parrots movements and even 'phonation' can be elicited by electrical stimulation of the corpora striata, which are especially large. Removal of a particular area is said to lead to disturbances of 'speech'.

It seems, therefore, that the large masses of nerve-cells in the striata are concerned in some way with the elaboration of the more complex acts of behaviour. This is a very vague statement, but is the best that we can give at present. It may be that further investigation of the reciprocal actions of striatum and thalamus will show whether the essentials of their action consist in some reverberating or scanning systems and whether these actions are at all similar to those in the forebrain of mammals. The fact that the striatum consists of solid masses of tissue suggests that the arrangement does not depend, as does the mammalian cerebral cortex, on the projection of patterns of excitation onto an extended surface where it can be scanned for the selection of details.

Birds are usually said to show more stereotyped patterns of instinctive behaviour than primitive mammals. Once they have embarked on a line of action, even a complex one like nest-building, they are supposed to pursue it in a given manner, without ability to adapt themselves to unusual happenings. Watching the exploratory behaviour of a robin or a tit it is difficult to feel that the existence of this difference is adequately proved, but whatever distinction exists is presumably a reflection of the difference between the functions of large masses and spread-out sheets of nervous tissue.

Certainly there are many signs that a suitable initial stimulus sets off in the bird a whole train of behaviour, coming as it were from within. A bird will continue to attack the empty space recently occupied by a stuffed specimen (a 'rival') after the latter has been taken away. On the other hand, inappropriate stimuli may sometimes set off a reaction, as if the 'keys' to these cerebral 'locks' were not very elaborate or specific. A robin held in the hand may burst into song, cock ostriches frightened by an aeroplane fall to the ground in their characteristic sexual display. In some cases such reactions seem to provide a sort of substitute means of release of 'nervous energy'. Thus, birds frightened or disturbed may proceed to the actions of bathing, preening, feeding, or drinking, performed in a ritual and cursory manner for a long time. Such substitute actions show that the organization of the bird's nervous system, like that of a mammal,

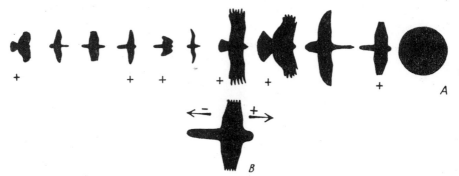

FIG. 289. A. Models used by Lorenz and Tinbergen. Small birds reacted with escape movements to the models marked +. B. The model induced escape reactions when towed to the right ('hawk') but not when towed to left ('goose').
(From Tinbergen.)

provides for some strange deviations, whose study may reveal much about the method of working of the brain.

A number of experimental studies have thrown light on the way in which a bird reacts only to certain elements in its environment. Thus the reaction of escape was given by small birds to certain shapes towed above them (Fig. 289). Much of the elaborate social life of birds depends on particular 'sign stimuli' displayed by one bird (the 'actor') and serving as 'releasers' setting off particular actions or trains of action in another bird (the 'reactor'). Many of the elaborate forms of display evolved by birds (p. 476) are releasers of this sort (Fig. 290), and structures and actions on the part of the young release the appropriate behaviour of the parent. The red breast of the robin (*Erithacus*) is the agent that releases attacks by other birds (Fig. 291). Similar phenomena are known in fishes and other vertebrates (p. 216), and it remains to be shown whether they can be attributed to any single or particular neural basis.

29. The eyes of birds

Birds depend more on their eyes than on the other senses; they are perhaps more fully visual than are any other animals. The eyes are extremely large: those of hawks and owls, for instance, may be absolutely larger than in man. The shape is not spherical, the lens and cornea bulge forwards in front of the posterior chamber, this form being maintained by a ring of bony sclerotic plates (Fig. 292). In most birds the whole eye is thus broader than it is deep, but in those with very acute sight it is longer, and in some eagles and crows

FIG. 290. Pintail ducks (*Anas acuta*). Males displaying dark brown feathers of neck with white bands on either side. (From Tinbergen, after Lorenz.)

FIG. 291. The red tuft of feathers is attacked by male robins holding territory, but the complete juvenile bird (without red) is left alone. (After Lack, from Tinbergen.)

becomes almost tubular. The great distance between lens and retina allows broadening of the image, thus improving the possibility of the fine two-point discrimination needed by these diurnal birds. The shape of the back of the eye is such that 'the retina lies almost wholly in the image plane, so that all distant objects within the visual angle are sharply focused on the photosensitive cells, whereas in the human eye this is only true of objects lying close to the optic axis' (Pumphrey; Fig. 293). The lens is usually soft and accommodation is effected by changing its shape, and especially the curvature of its anterior surface, by the pressure upon it of the ciliary muscles behind. These, like the iris muscles, are striated, presumably allowing for the quick accommodation necessary in a rapidly moving bird, though it must not be forgotten that these muscles are also striated in lizards. The ciliary muscle is characteristically divided into 'anterior' and 'posterior' portions, the muscles of Crampton and Brücke (Fig. 292). The latter draws the lens forward into the anterior chamber so that, the

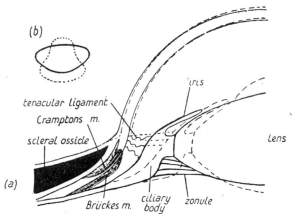

FIG. 292. *a*. The mechanism of accommodation in a bird's eye; the positions during near vision are shown dotted. *b*. The lens of the cormorant's eye at rest (full line) and fully accommodated (dotted line). (From Pumphrey, after Franz and Hess.)

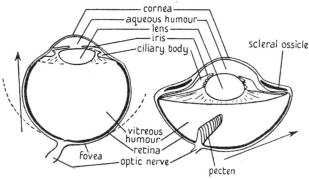

FIG. 293. Diagrams of right eye of man and left eye of swan to show the difference in shape. The position of the image plane in man is shown dotted; it lies behind the retina except near the centre. The arrows point forward. (From Pumphrey.)

shape of the eye being fixed by the sclerotic plates, the lens becomes more curved and hence accommodated for near vision, contraction of the iris sphincter assisting in the process. Crampton's muscle is so arranged as to pull on the cornea, shortening its radius and further assisting in accommodation. This double method of active accommodation for near vision is most fully developed in diurnal predators, such as the hawks, less so in night birds. In aquatic birds Crampton's muscle is reduced, the cornea being of little importance in image-formation. Special arrangements are found in diving birds, for instance in the cormorants Brücke's muscle is large and there is a very powerful iris muscle, which assists the ciliary muscles to give the great change in shape of the soft lens, allowing accommodation of 40–50 diopters (about 10 in man). The kingfishers are said to possess

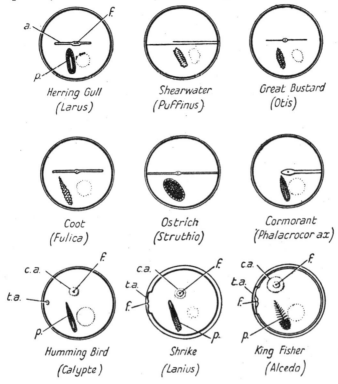

FIG. 294. The appearance of the retina of various birds as seen with an ophthalmoscope through the pupil.

c.a. central area; *f.* fovea; *p.* pecten; *t.a.* temporal area. (After Wood, from Pumphrey.)

an amazing arrangement of double foveas, placed at different distances from the lens, so that as the bird dives under water the image is transferred from one fovea to the other without any change in the dioptric apparatus. These details of the visual system show, like so many other features of bird anatomy, how readily the structure conforms to special habits of life.

The retina of day birds consists largely but not wholly of cones; these animals are more fully diurnal than is man. The very high resolving power and hence high powers of discrimination and of movement-detection depend on the great density of the cones, as many as 1,000,000 to each square millimetre in the fovea of a hawk, three times denser than in man. Nocturnal birds, on the other hand, have retinas composed mainly or completely of rods, and the differences between the behaviour of these two types of eye, found in birds as in mammals, have been a powerful support for the duplicity theory of vision. There are usually one or more areae, regions of the retina consisting of tightly packed rods. In birds that live on the sea, in the desert, or other open spaces the area often has the form of an

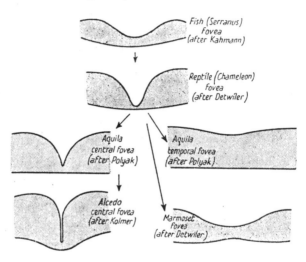

FIG. 295. Forms of the fovea in various vertebrates, showing the development from moderately to sharply convexiclivate types in foveas adapted for detection of movement, but flattening of the fovea where there is binocular vision. (From Pumphrey.)

elongated horizontal band (Fig. 294), whereas in tree-living birds it is circular. Some birds have two areae, a central one in the optic axis and a second placed on the temporal surface of the eye, so that the image of objects in front of the head falls on the temporal areae of both eyes. This arrangement is common in birds that follow moving prey (shrike, *Lanius*) or for some other reason require accurate perception of distance (swallows, humming-birds; the latter feed their young on insects caught on the wing). The density of the cones is so high in diurnal birds, even outside the areae, that they probably obtain a good detailed picture in all directions. They do not, therefore, scan the world with the central area of the retina as we do; indeed, the eyes move relatively little. Instead the bird is able to detect very small movements anywhere in its surroundings. The bird's-eye view usually lacks stereoscopic solidity and it is possible that in compensation for this the animals appreciate distance by movements of the intrinsic eye-muscles. The familiar cocking of the head of a bird before pecking may be its means of judging distance.

As in man there is often within the central area of the eye a fovea

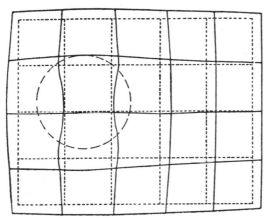

FIG. 296. Effect of refraction produced by the curvature of the fovea of the golden eagle. An image of the form shown with dotted lines is distorted by the fovea to the form shown in solid lines. The circle represents a radius of 10μ at the centre of the fovea. (From Pumphrey.)

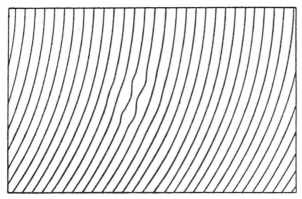

FIG. 297. Distortion by the fovea. The lines represent the successive images at equal time-intervals of the boundary of a regular object when the object moves steadily across the visual field. If this picture is viewed at 7 m. the area of irregularity subtends an angle about equal to the angle subtended by the central part of the hawk fovea. It will be found that the irregularity is very evident to the human eye at this distance though the lines are resolvable with difficulty. (From Pumphrey.)

or pit, and in many birds the sides of this pit are steeply curved (Fig. 295). Walls has suggested that since the vitreous humour and retina differ in refractive index this curvature serves to magnify the image and increase acuity. Pumphrey points out that any such advantage would be counteracted by the aberration introduced and he makes the suggestion that this disturbance of the picture by the 'convexiclivate' fovea is itself an advantage, improving the power of fixation and sensitivity to movement, at the sacrifice of acuity. Such an arrangement would serve to emphasize angular displacements, transforming a radially symmetrical image into an asymmetrical one, except when there is coincidence between the axes of symmetry of the fovea and of the object (Figs. 296 and 297). Foveas with steep sides are found in

FIG. 298. Tracing of the shadow of the pecten on the retina in various birds. (After Pumphrey and Menner.)

birds of prey, kingfishers, and others that have very high powers of detecting movement; a similar but less pronounced arrangement is found in fishes and reptiles. It is probable that the primitive functions of the eyes were fixation and detection of movement, rather than resolution of detail and recognition of patterns. Some birds have one convexiclivate and one flatter fovea (Figs. 294 and 295), the latter being on the temporal surface of the retina and used in binocular vision. The fovea is also flat in the retinae of primates with binocular vision; evidently the optical errors of a curved fovea cannot be tolerated where there is fusion of the two retinal images.

Birds undoubtedly discriminate colours, apparently on a trichromatic basis similar to that of mammals. No other animals, except perhaps primates, show such signs of awareness of colour in their surroundings, including the food and other members of the species. In animals that move so freely recognition and attraction of the sexes is much more efficiently performed in this way than by touch or odour. The cones of birds often contain red and yellow droplets, which may heighten visual acuity by reducing the effects of chromatic aberration. The droplets in the central area are always yellow. The presence of droplets of various colours in adjacent cones may also increase powers of discrimination. Sometimes the droplets are so arranged as to allow accentuation of different contrasts in the parts of the visual field. The lower part of the pigeon's retina contains red, the upper yellow filters, increasing the contrast of blues and greens respectively, as required for vision against the sky in the one case and the ground in the other. There have been many investigations of the distribution of sensitivity in the retina; probably many birds are rather insensitive to the blue end of the spectrum. There is no truth in the suggestion that the eyes are sensitive to infra-red radiation.

Although the eyes of birds are directed forwards, so that their fields overlap, they do not have binocular vision and decussation of the optic tracts is complete. Perception of distance, a very important function for the bird, must be performed in some other manner. Very many functions have been suggested for the most enigmatic organ of the bird's eye, the pecten, a pleated highly vascular fold, projecting from the retina into the vitreous. It is possible that the irregular shadow cast by this organ provides, as it were, numerous small blind spots and hence by a stroboscopic action increases the number of on-and-off effects produced by a very small object in the visual field, increasing contrast and allowing detection of its movement. This, however, is only one of the numerous suggestions about the function of the pecten, and the only real support for the idea is that the body is large and much pleated in predatory birds, which detect minute movements at great distances and is small and smooth in nocturnal birds (Fig. 298). However, it is almost certain that the original function of the pecten was to bring nourishment to the vitreous and retina. It has often been suggested that the body is in some way connected with accommodation; it is not likely that the pecten actually assists in focusing, for instance, by pressing forward the lens, and no changes have been seen in it during accommodation. However, it might possibly assist by adjusting the intra-ocular pressure, which must be increased by the extensive changes in the lens during accommodation.

FIG. 299. Labyrinths of various vertebrates, to show varying development of cochlea (C) and lagena (L).

S, saccule; U. utricle. (From v. Frisch.)

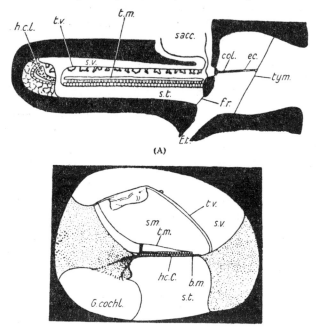

(A)

(B)

FIG. 300. A. Diagram of section of bird's ear.

b.m. basilar membrane; *col.* columella; *e.c.* extra-columella; *E.t.* Eustachian tube; *f.r.* round window; *h.c.C.* hair-cells of Corti's organ; *h.c.l.* hair-cells of lagena; *sacc.* sacculus; *s.t.* scala tympani; *s.v.* scala vestibuli; *t.m.* tectorial membrane; *t.v.* tegmentum vasculosum; *tym.* tympanic membrane.

B. Diagram of section across cochlea of a bird.

G.cochl. cochlear ganglion; *s.m.* scala media; other lettering as in A. (From Pumphrey, after Satoh.)

30. The ear of birds

Both vestibular and auditory parts of the ear are well developed in birds. The former are not known to possess special peculiarities, but the large connexions with the cerebellum suggest great importance in the operations of flight, presumably especially by the semicircular canals. It has been suggested that the receptors in the canals might provide the bird with a special sense of direction by response to the 'Corioli's forces' generated by the earth's rotation. There is no experimental evidence of this effect and probably the forces are not of the necessary magnitude; however, birds show most striking orientation during migration and we must not too easily dismiss any reasonable suggestions about their sense-organs, nor suppose that they impose the same limitations as do our own. There is a distinct cochlea, slightly curved and especially well developed in owls and in parrots (Fig. 299). In this there is a basilar membrane, with fibres increasing in length towards the tip and carrying hair-cells in contact with a tectorial membrane (Fig. 300), very much as in mammals. At the tip of the cochlea is a special sensory region, the lagena, similar to that of lower vertebrates and perhaps responsible for reaction to lower notes, the basilar membrane responding to the higher frequencies. Birds are known to be sensitive to distant gunfire and other low-frequency vibrations inaudible to man. Transmission of vibration from the tympanum to the inner ear is effected by the columella auris, derived from the cartilages of the hyoid arch. The inner portion of the columella is rod-like ('stapes'), but the outer end makes contact with the tympanum by means of three processes, of somewhat irregular shape.

Hearing is, of course, acute and the song birds must be able to discriminate between simple tunes; some of them are surprisingly good mimics. Ability to localize sound is high and owls and other night birds probably find their prey largely by ear. For the purpose of direction-finding they have developed an asymmetrical arrangement of the ear cavities (*Strix*) or asymmetrical external ears (*Asio*).

XVII

BIRD BEHAVIOUR

1. Habitat selection

The success of bird life has been very largely due to the great variety and ingenuity displayed in finding situations suitable for providing food and allowing reproduction. It is often said that birds are creatures of stereotyped habits, yet compared with other animals they have certainly exploited their mobility to the full; they obtain the means of life in most various ways. This mobility makes it difficult to specify the 'environment' of a bird. For instance, a swallow may pass part of its life in the tropics, part near the Arctic Circle. A gull may nest on a rock, eat grain in a field, and then fish in the sea, all within a few hours. Observation of the familiar birds of town and country soon shows that they are at home in a much greater variety of situations than could be supported by most animals, and that within limits they can adapt their behaviour to each situation. Birds show, therefore, in a marked degree, two of the features most commonly used as criteria for the recognition of a higher animal, namely, freedom to move to different conditions and ability to obtain a living in unpromising circumstances.

In recent years ornithologists have claimed that 'habitat selection' is of first importance in determining the distribution of birds. It is still not clear exactly what process is involved, but the conception implies that the activity of the bird moulds the circumstances of its own life rather than vice versa. This is, of course, true to an extent of all animals—they are active, seeking creatures and the degree to which they show this character is a measure of their liveliness. Though the birds certainly have considerable powers of this sort it is probable that the situations in which they live, eat, and breed are quite strictly determined by their heredity. In spite of the appearance of freedom the bird which deviates from the 'normal' habits and habitat of its species can only survive under unusual conditions, when predators and competitors are absent (p. 509). With all the adaptability each individual bird species yet maintains a very definite set of habits—the ornithologist knows well enough the conditions under which any one type is likely to occur. For example, food will be sought by means of the particular devices available to any given species, a cormorant can fish, and a woodpecker eats insects, but their roles cannot be reversed. Where the food is very specific substitutes will only be accepted under unusual conditions of starvation, but many birds are more catholic in tastes and some of these are among the most common, for instance, rooks, starlings, thrushes, blackbirds, and gulls, to name only a few. Both field observation and experiment suggest that birds very quickly learn from experience where and how food may be obtained. They will remember to visit an abundant source of supply and there are numerous stories of the ingenuity of such birds as the jackdaws in obtaining it. This short-term memory is probably of very great importance in allowing the bird to establish an effective routine for each part of its life, especially as it is combined with the power to explore elsewhere when conditions change.

The main provision for defence made by birds is their swift escape in flight, and here too they show considerable ingenuity and ability in learning to avoid undesirable situations.

2. Recognition and social behaviour

Great mobility has made it necessary for birds to develop elaborate means for recognizing their fellows, their enemies, and their competitors; from this power an elaborate social life has developed in many species. In spite of their freedom many birds are not individualists, they live much of their lives together in flocks; the unit of life is larger than the 'individual' body. Species feeding on the ground, such as rooks, starlings, and partridges, commonly move about in groups during the winter and obtain the advantage that the alertness of each single bird serves to warn for many. The lack of procryptic coloration in some of these social birds is a measure of the effectiveness of the protection afforded by the society; indeed, it may be advantageous that the birds should be conspicuous to their fellows. Starlings carry the communal life further by collecting together in very large numbers each night to roost. As many as 100,000 may be found in one roost, the birds flying home from their feeding-grounds every night for distances of many miles. Possibly in this way the disadvantage of the conspicuous outline is minimized while roosting. Rooks show somewhat similar behaviour, but it is not found in the protectively coloured partridge.

Many different means are adopted by birds for recognition of other members of the species and of the same and opposite sex; bird-life contains elaborate social and sexual rituals for many occasions. For example, relief of the one bird by the other at the nest is accompanied by a peculiar wing-flapping ceremony in herons and other birds. Greeting ceremonies are common in many species, and there is a host of sexual recognition and courtship rituals, to be considered later, serving to prevent attempted copulation with the same and to ensure it with a member of the opposite sex and of the right species.

Apart from sexual behaviour birds show many complex mutual and social reactions. Thus in communities of hens or pigeons there is quickly established a rank or 'pecking order', such that each bird is submissive to the one above it, the order changing, however, when age, moulting, or experiment (e.g. sex-hormone injection) alters the state of the birds. More pleasing communal habits are the dances and corporate flights, which are well known in cranes and other species. It is not always possible to see obvious biologically practical advantages of these aspects of bird behaviour, nor indeed of many others. Observation of birds gives an impression that their life is so full that it spills over, as it were, into actions that might be called play. An interesting suggestion is that these actions, like those of human play, are the expressions of an 'instinct' in the absence of its correct external stimulus. In other words, in these animals with complicated nervous systems elaborate patterns of action are produced when touched off by some biologically irrelevant stimulus, or perhaps without any external stimulus at all.

3. Bird migration and homing

Among the remarkable devices of birds is their habit of seasonal movements to obtain the advantage of the favourable conditions offered in more northerly regions only during the summer. The most familiar migrations are those north and south (sometimes north-east and south-west) over the land masses of the northern hemisphere, but there are similar movements also in the southern hemisphere, though they are of lesser extent. Some tropical birds migrate to breed in the rainy season in the outer tropics, removing to the central tropics in the dry season. Marine birds also may make extensive migrations. Thus the great shearwater (*Puffinus*) breeds on Tristan da Cunha, but comes as far north as Greenland or Iceland in May, returning again after months of wandering at sea, apparently without making a landfall. The Arctic tern (*Sterna*) breeds on the American coast, crosses to Europe, and migrates to the Antarctic down the east side of the Atlantic. Penguins make migrations by swimming.

Distances up to 6,000 miles from north Europe to South Africa have been recorded, for instance, for swallows and storks, and even farther for the Arctic tern. It is still not known what determines the direction and course of migration. Soaring birds migrate with the help of up-currents and hence tend to use short sea-crossings. Many birds

FIG. 301. Direction of migration of the stork (*Ciconia*). The black spots represent points of recovery of birds ringed in Germany. The dotted areas show the pathways produced by ecological and geographical factors. (After Schülz and Streseman.)

follow coastlines, or at least migrate overland, and this produces the appearance of 'routes' of migration (Fig. 301). Small birds migrate south-west in western Europe until they reach the coast, where they then turn south. They also avoid mountain ranges. It is sometimes difficult to avoid the conclusion that the birds possess some sense of 'general direction'. For instance, juvenile hooded crows, on their first journey south-west in Europe, if transported westwards at right angles to their line of flight reach a winter quarters at the usual absolute distance, but shifted by the movement. Next spring they return to a position west of their birthplace. Chaffinches crossing from Holland with a tail-wind come over direct to England, but if they meet a head-wind continue down the coast to Cap Gris-nez and then turn northwards to cross.

Birds certainly do not learn the routes from their elders, indeed the young often leave first. However, juveniles return only approximately to their birthplace, whereas older birds return to their old nesting-sites. Individual memory therefore certainly plays a large part in the phenomenon. Probably the clues by which the longer migrations take place are mainly the simple coastal outlines. It is not improbable that more subtle clues may be used, for instance, wind directions or gradients of temperature or other climatic factors, but in spite of many interesting suggestions (p. 467) there is no reliable evidence for a magnetic or other esoteric direction sense.

Powers of 'homing' are remarkable in birds, altogether apart from migration. It is probable that these feats are performed by the use of visual clues, combined with a tendency to follow coastal outlines and other conspicuous geographical features. Pigeons are trained to 'home' by release at progressively increasing distances and can acquire the ability to return from more than 500 miles. Pigeons not trained, or re-leased over unfamiliar country, often return home, and may do so also across the sea. However, in these cases the proportion returning and the speed decrease with the distance from familiar country. Thus pigeons released over the Atlantic at distances of 200, 300, and 500 kilometres returned to France at rates of 100, 60, and 40 kilometres per hour re-spectively. Many failed to return; some were found in England, Por-tugal, Spain, Cape Verde Islands, Algeria, Egypt, and the Caucasus.

The habit of the pigeon is to ascend, presumably to seek for clues; should it find none it will explore in one direction, or perhaps several, until familiar country is met. It is not easy for earth-bound man to realize the opportunities made available in this way by free mobility and wide range of vision. Birds do not usually fly very high, but even at 1,000 feet the horizon is 40 miles away. Such wide fields, together with the high speed of birds, make accurately controlled experiments very difficult; it cannot be said that we have full certainty about the methods used in homing. Further significant facts are that pigeons cannot 'home' well on moonless nights or in foggy weather, and that they are confused by a snowfall.

Other birds are also able to return home from spectacular distances, an instance being the Manx shearwater removed from its nest (burrow) on Skokholm Island off the Welsh coast and sent to Venice by air: it returned in 14 days, the distance being 900 miles direct or 3,700 miles by the coastal route. In another experiment three out of ten untrained terns returned to their nests from a distance of 855 miles, in about 6 days. There are many peculiar and unexplained features about such long journeys.

4. The stimulus to migration

It is probable that the north-to-south migrations of birds in the northern hemisphere take place under some stimulus provided by the internal condition of the gonads, these being themselves affected by the seasonal change. Rowan has made extensive experiments with juncos, birds that are summer visitors to Alberta, Canada. If the birds are caged in the autumn and illuminated to compensate for the shortening day the gonads do not regress as they normally do at that season, so that full breeding song continues on into the middle of winter. The light perhaps does not work directly, but by the stimulus it provides to activity of the bird. Rowan had the interesting idea of releasing these birds in the winter and found that they immediately moved away, perhaps northwards, conditions being now appropriate if anything for that direction. On the other hand, control birds, which had been kept in Alberta but without extra light, showed no tendency to move away if released in mid-winter. Since the gonads of these controls had, of course, by then undergone reduction, the stimulus to migrate south was not felt. This would agree with the fact that only some individuals of species such as the thrush and blackbird migrate. These experiments suggest that seasonal changes in illumination may be an important factor determining migration. However, they leave many points unsettled. For instance, is there a stimulus that starts the bird migrating north again if it has 'wintered' near the equator, where there is little or no seasonal change? It cannot be excluded that once alteration of the gonads has been started, say, by reduction in light, a cycle will be set up, the gonads developing again with the longer days in the south and thus driving the bird north again, and so on.

5. The breeding-habits of birds

The complexity and variety of bird behaviour shows especially in their breeding; perhaps in no other creatures except men is such elaborate behaviour involved in bringing the birds together and caring for the young. In order to ensure adequate provision for the development of a warm-blooded animal and its nourishment until it can fend for itself it is necessary either to keep it within the mother or to provide a means of incubating the eggs. In either case a long period of care is necessary after birth; the young animals, having a large surface area, require a great amount of food to keep warm. Thus young starlings and crows may eat as much as their own weight of food each day.

Mammals and birds set about providing for this warmth and food in different ways. Since a female mammal can move about and get food while pregnant the father can desert her altogether, though frequently he does not do so. In birds the eggs and young cannot be left cold for long and it is therefore especially desirable that the father should help. In birds, therefore, perhaps even more than in mammals, the breeding-habits involve the development of elaborate systems of mutual relations, serving not only to bring the parents together but also to keep them together throughout the period of incubation and while feeding the young. The actual building of the nest may be an intricate business in which both birds collaborate and a further factor is that the pair occupies a territory around the nest, which they defend against others of the same species.

The type of association of the sexes varies greatly. In the ruff and certain game birds (blackcock) there is no pair formation: display and copulation occur at communal display grounds. The wren (*Troglodytes*) and a few other birds are polygamous, each male forming continuous association with several females. The great majority of birds form pairs throughout a single season, occasionally they change mates for the second brood. The same pair may mate in successive years (crows, swifts) and in a few cases the birds remain together throughout the year (ducks).

6. Courtship and display

The breeding of birds is nearly always seasonal, even in the tropics where conditions are apparently almost uniform throughout the year. In temperate latitudes breeding begins in spring as the gonads develop, probably under the influence of increasing illumination. The changes in behaviour with ripening of the gonads vary, of course, greatly with the species. Birds which have been social through the winter, for instance buntings, begin to leave their flocks, and in many cases the voice of the male changes from the simple winter notes to the more complex breeding song.

The song is one feature of the elaborate business of display and courtship, which is used by different birds for various combinations of purposes. In the simplest case the display serves to bring the sexes together, to enable recognition, and at a later stage as a stimulus to copulation. Since a male bird cannot grasp the female, copulation can occur only with her fullest co-operation and one reason for elaborate display is probably to ensure that this is forthcoming. Moreover, in some cases at least (doves and budgerigars), the display serves as part of the stimulus to ovulation. Involved in the display actions, however, is often a threat to ward off other males who may attack during copulation, and this leads on to the establishment of a territory, within which the mated birds operate while rearing the young. Finally, some forms of courtship, especially those that are mutual, seem to serve to keep the partners together for the period of incubation and feeding.

We may recognize in courtship, therefore, three elements, first sexual stimulation, secondly threat to other males, and thirdly mutual stimulation while rearing a family, but the various types of display are combined in so many different ways that any classification or analysis is bound to be arbitrary and only a few examples that have been thoroughly studied can be given.

Song and displays that bring the sexes together are responsible in part at least for many of the pronounced secondary sexual characters in which the male and female differ. The beautiful plumage of the cock pheasant or peacock and the more bizarre combs and wattles of turkeys are displayed before the female in a manner which is clearly an excitant to copulation. The secondary sexual characters by which the sexes are differentiated may affect features as different as the colour, length, and structure of the feathers, the colour of the iris and size of the pupil, the shape and size of the body, the voice, the ornamentation of the head, and the spurs on the feet. The importance of species recognition in leading to differentiation of male plumage is shown by Darwin's finches (p. 500) which, in the isolation of the Galapagos Islands, where there are few other passerine birds, have abandoned the highly coloured male plumage found in other finches. The recognition of individuals of the same species in this case is based on the characteristics of the beak; a male will begin to attack an intruder only when the face is seen.

Display takes place either by one bird to the other or mutually, and has the effect of bringing the animals together and keeping them together for periods varying from a few days to several years. Long unions are common in the large birds of prey and are often a result as much of mutual association with the nest as with display by the other bird. Some birds pair in the winter long before the gonads are ripe (ducks), but more usually after two birds pair off the display produces a gradual heightening of tension, leading to nest-building, copulation,

FIG. 302. Incidents in the courtship of the great crested grebe. 1. Mutual head shaking. 2. The female is displaying before the male who has dived and shoots out of the water in front of her. 3 and 4. Further views of the male rising from the water. 5. Both birds have dived and brought up weeds. (From Huxley, *Proc. Zool. Soc.*, 1914, by permission of the Zoological Society.)

and ovulation within a few days. Probably the process of bringing the birds together and ensuring coition requires even more elaborate stimulation in birds than other animals because of their great mobility and the fact that the male cannot grasp the female. Before he can tread her in such a way as to ensure coition she must be brought into a suitably receptive state. The function of the display is certainly very largely to induce this state in the female, though much more is involved in addition. The processes of sexual stimulation, nest-building, incubation, and caring for the young necessitate a particular state of excitability that must last a long time, and the display serves to provide this condition in both birds. The reproductive process

FIG. 303. Display of various birds of paradise.
1 and 4, *Paradisea*; 2, *Diphyllodes*; 3, *Cicinnurus*.
(From Stresemann, after Seth Smith.)

may be interrupted at any time if the stimuli are inadequate. Thus laying begins only after the female has been suitably stimulated and the eggs are very readily deserted if the birds are interfered with in any way, or if they fail to stimulate each other.

The actual procedure of display is as varied as any other feature of bird life. When the sexes are alike in colour and shape the performance is usually mutual, as in the great crested grebes (*Podiceps*), which approach each other over the water and go through various actions such as the head-shaking ceremony (Fig. 302). Where the male is more strongly coloured, provided with a special comb, &c., he often displays before the female who adopts a more passive role. A very common element in the procedure of courtship is the sudden revelation of some feature or pattern, serving as it were to arrest and awaken the female and at the same time almost to hypnotize her into passiveness. The actual movements involved are very various. An excellent example is the peacock, who approaches showing his dull-coloured back and then suddenly turns on his hen, revealing the pattern of spots (which we have noted elsewhere to be an arresting shape),

FIG. 304. Display of the pheasant, *Centrocercus*. 1. Beginning of inflation. 2. Complete display with cervical air-sacs inflated. (From Streseman, after Horsfall.)

shaking his 'tail' with a rustling noise and himself emitting a scream, in a way that can easily be believed both arresting and fascinating. It is a common characteristic of all bird displays that they involve sights and actions which seem strange and exaggerated to us and probably also to the partner (Figs. 303, 304). Watching the effects of such appearances on the female one has the impression that this vision acts as it were as a key or 'releaser', opening in her the appropriate course of behaviour. Under its influence she acts as if 'mechanically', moving towards the male and adopting the receptive position, while his display activity passes over into that of mounting and coition. This sort of behaviour we have seen elsewhere in bird life; there must be somewhere in the nervous organization a receptive matrix ('the lock') ready to be actuated by the appropriate 'key', which may be the display of structures as bizarre as the wattles and tippets of a turkey.

Very many displays are modified versions of everyday actions of the birds and some at least of these seem to be symbolic; they awaken the desired interest by recalling to the bird some phase of its life other than sex. Thus, in many birds courtship and coition include ritual feeding of the female by the male. Involved in this is a reversion by the female to an infantile condition. She may beg for food, often with actions very similar to those she used as a nestling. The prime significance of this feeding is not in the nourishment provided but, in many cases at least, in the fact that it is the male who provides it. This is proved by the fact that the female (robin, for instance) will not feed herself when food is all around, but will beg the male to give it to her. Female herring gulls bringing back fish may even beg to be fed by the male, who has not left the rock! There are, of course, many cases of practical feeding of the sitting female by the male, but it is possible that these have been derived from the ritual feeding, rather than vice versa.

The various forms of billing and gaping ceremony probably represent a further degree of abstraction from ritual feeding. A variety of birds touch bills during courtship, for instance, gulls, ravens, great crested grebes, and some finches. The inside of the mouth is sometimes brilliantly coloured in adults, as it is in so many nestlings; it is green in some birds of paradise, yellow in many birds. During display it may be opened suddenly, producing an obvious effect on the mate, who approaches fascinated into a state of passive acceptance by this surprising revelation, perhaps recalling a possibility of satisfaction remembered from childhood.

Other aspects of the courtship may show this reversion to infantile behaviour. Thus, in female sparrows and many other birds one or both wings are held drooping and fluttering during display, as they are by the chick craving food or by the frightened adult; a behaviour known as injury feigning or distraction display. The female hedge-sparrow may quiver with one wing and open her bill to the male at the same time. There is abundant evidence that this injury-feigning, though originating perhaps in a reversion when frightened to infantile behaviour, has survival value in distracting the attention of a predator from the nest, as can be well seen in plovers and other ground-nesting birds. Some plovers have different displays for use against different types of nest enemy.

The effects of bird display are by no means restricted to ensuring mutual recognition of males and females and stimulating them to coition, especially important though such functions must be in 'flighty' creatures. The element of threat and even fighting with other males is very common. It is seen in its purest form in such birds as the blackcock and ruff, which are promiscuous. The male ruffs congregate on a chosen 'courting ground' and go through an elaborate series of ritual fights. The females ('reeves') do not take part in this procedure, but at intervals one of them will 'select' a male by fondling him with her bill and then adopt the receptive attitude for copulation. Selous, who observed this display, noted that males with large ruffs were chosen especially often. Such selection of males by females was the basis of Darwin's theory of sexual selection, the supposition being that the males chosen would be the most gorgeous, victorious, and hence most vigorous and effective breeders. Selous recorded that in one area, during a period of $3\frac{1}{2}$ hours, there were 12 copulations, 10 of them with a single male. It must be very difficult when observing birds to establish exactly the actions and relationships of males and females and hence to distinguish between the 'stimulation' of female by male and 'selection' of male by female. Perhaps there is only a verbal difference between the two.

7. Bird territory

The element of threat in singing and display has a further importance in connexion with the territories which many birds establish around their nests. Eliot Howard especially has developed the concept of bird territory, as a result of observation mainly of warblers and buntings. For instance, in the warblers (Sylviidae) the males, returning from migration some days earlier than the females, establish themselves on a certain area, singing often from a tall tree or other headquarters near its centre. As other males arrive boundaries develop, so that the region becomes divided up into a number of areas, at first each of about 2 acres, later reducing to 1. When the females arrive they pair off with the males and throughout the whole season the two birds occupy a single territory, driving off other birds that encroach and in this way establishing quite definite boundaries to their area.

Howard supposed that this arrangement was universal in birds and that it has four desirable effects for the species.

1. Uniform distribution over the habitable area is ensured.

2. Females are assisted to find unmated males.

3. The two birds are kept together and are not distracted by wanderings far from home.

4. It is possible to find adequate food without travelling far from the nest, this being especially important during the period of incubation and rearing of the young. There is no doubt that many birds do remain mostly in the area around their nest and that they may resist invasion. It is probable, however, that in most cases the territory is

less rigid than Howard implied, and there is certainly much variety between different species. According to Lack the territory is often mainly associated with the sexual display of the male; it is his area, part, as it were, of the method he adopts to stimulate the female and to keep the pair together. By establishing a territory he ensures the opportunity to display and copulate without disturbance, a very necessary precaution since he is vulnerable at these times and other individuals may attack a copulating male, trying to displace him. The complicated song characteristic of so many male birds at the breeding-season is, on this view, partly an attraction to the female, but largely also a threat to warn off other males. We cannot exclude that it serves as a stimulus to the male himself. The impression is strong when one hears a thrush 'singing for joy' at his headquarters or a lark soaring above his patch of ground.

Territory is therefore, according to Lack, put to various uses in different species. It may be either (1) a mating arena only, as in the ruff and blackcock mentioned above, or (2) it may be a mating station and nest as in the plover and swallow, which birds will not allow others near the nest, although all mix freely for feeding. (3) In sparrows and herring gulls the nest is likewise defended, but is not a mating station. (4) In the warblers investigated by Howard the territory, besides being a mating station, is also a feeding-ground. The significance of this in spacing out the birds remains, however, very doubtful. (5) In still other birds, such as the robin, it is a feeding-ground mainly, and therefore it is kept throughout the winter. Examination of the territory concept therefore shows that birds have a very strong sense of place and that they associate this in various ways with their life, especially during the breeding-season. It is certain that the occupation of territory helps in the initiation and maintenance of the pair, but not yet proved that it serves to limit the breeding density and ensure a food-supply for the young.

8. Mutual courtship

In many birds courtship displays do not necessarily end in coition and may continue long after the eggs have been laid. A classic example of this sort is the great crested grebe, a water-bird watched by J. H. Huxley (Fig. 302). The male and female birds do not differ greatly and the ceremonies are mutual. One bird may dive and come up close to the other and they then approach with necks stretched out on the water, giving a curious ripple pattern that Huxley called the plesiosaur appearance. When they meet the birds come together neck to neck and a period of swaying ensues and may sometimes end by the mounting of one bird by the other, not necessarily the female by the male. At other times the diving bird comes up with pieces of nest-building material and elaborately presents them to its mate. This is apparently a symbolic act; the material is not actually used to make the nest and it is not far-fetched to suppose that such behaviour is an expression of the mutual activity in which the birds are engaged. In so far as it has a biological function it serves, like the rest of the ritual, including post-ovulatory copulation, to keep the two individuals together while rearing the young.

Other types of courtship include ritual feeding of the other sex during display and often before coition, for instance, in pigeons and gulls, and this again may have a symbolic or reassuring function. It is perhaps not fantastic to find analogies between behaviour of this sort and the elaborate and prolonged courtship and frequent copulation of man, continuing without cyclical breeding-seasons for as long as the pair remain together and rear their young. In birds, as in man, the 'procreation of children' is not fully accomplished by a single act of fertilization.

9. Nest-building

As in every other aspect of their life we find the nests of birds varied in many ways to suit different manners of life. It is suggested that the habit of making a nest may have arisen from the 'sex-fidgeting' that is commonly seen before, during, and after copulation. This fidgeting may take various forms, including making a 'scrape' in the soil or picking up pieces of grass, &c., after copulation. Whether or not such nervous outlets were the origin of nest-building there is certainly, in many birds, a close connexion between this process and copulation. Ritual offering of nest-material is an important element in many courtship displays and in some species (e.g. magpie) male birds may build extra nests as if for an outlet for their energy.

The nest is therefore often at first a sex site and its position may be chosen by the male. The actual building of the nest is done very variously. Sometimes the male brings the material and the female uses it. She may do the fetching as well, perhaps accompanied by the lazy male; or he may have nothing to do with the whole business.

The complicated forms of nest are found only in passerine birds; in others it is usually simply a hollow in the ground or a heap of sticks. The more elaborate nests show many protective devices; in temperate regions, where predators come largely from below, the nests are often open, but where there are many snakes they are mostly domed or actually hung from branches or provided with a long tubular entrance (weavers).

In building the nest the bird follows a set pattern, laid down in some way by the method of working of its brain and showing no foreknowledge of the result. Young birds, however, build rougher nests

FIG. 305. Process of nest-building by a weaver bird (*Quelea*). The arrows show directions in which the piece is pulled. A, the points of holding by the beak; 4, 5, and 6 show successive stages of co-operative weaving by the foot and beak. (From Streseman, after Friedmann.)

than mature ones. Weaver birds reared by hand for four generations made perfect nests of a type which, of course, they had never seen. On the other hand, it has been claimed that canaries deprived of nest-building materials for some generations then build clumsily at first, though they quickly improve.

The methods used, of course, vary with the materials. Many of them involve most elaborate tying of grasses to the branches, which is done with the beak or the feet or both (Fig. 305). The shape and construction of the nest varies with the habits of the bird. Many sea-birds, nesting safely on the cliffs, make only very simple nests or none at all. In such birds as the plovers or larks the nest is a cup in the earth, the eggs being procryptically coloured with a blotched green and brown pattern, so that it is very difficult to see them on the spring ploughland or partly green earth. Nests constructed in trees vary from the simple sticks of rooks or pigeons to the elaborate domed and lined nests of many passerines. The nest is woven from materials brought in with the beak and often lined with moss or in ducks with feathers from the breast of the bird. The thrush lines its nest with mud moistened with saliva and the swift makes nearly the whole nest of saliva. Many birds build roughly and often use the old nests of others, for instance, kestrels are often found using the nests of crows. Others build in burrows, either accidental or, as in the case of the kingfishers, made by the bird itself. Similarly, holes already in trees may be used (titmice), but the woodpeckers drill their own holes. The female hornbill walls herself into a hole in a tree with the help of mud brought by the male and for the three months of incubation she is fed by the male through a small aperture. In the brush turkeys (Megapodes) the eggs are not incubated by the bird but are buried in a mound of decaying material, which provides the necessary heat; the young bird is independent from the moment it hatches.

10. Shape and colour of the eggs

Eggs are as varied as the rest of bird structures. The shape is determined by the pressure of the oviducal wall and the blunt end always emerges first. With lesser pressure from behind the egg approaches a spherical shape. The pointed end may serve to prevent the eggs rolling away (guillemot) or to help the eggs to fit together (plover). The pigment is laid down at the end of the travel along the oviduct and is derived from the bile pigments. The coloration is usually procryptic in eggs laid on the ground, whereas those laid in holes are white and birds like the pigeons which do not attempt to protect themselves or their nests by concealment also have light-coloured eggs. The significance of the varied colours of eggs that are not procryptic is obscure. It is likely that they serve as a stimulus to the brooding bird, who will sometimes leave a nest when a wrong-coloured egg is inserted. A further sign of this is that there are various races of cuckoo, each laying eggs appropriate to the nest it parasitizes; but the genetics and behaviour of cuckoos are still very obscure subjects.

11. Brooding and care of the young

Usually it is the hen who broods the eggs, but the cock may assist and in a very few species he does all the brooding. Brooding is not a mere sitting on the eggs, but depends on the development of a vascular response in a part of the skin, the brood spots, produced by a local moult of the feathers. At hatching the parents may assist the action of the caruncle of the young. The care of the nestlings is a very elaborate business in most birds, involving many separate actions. The young are warmed, fed, and occasionally watered, and in many cases the nest is kept clean by careful removal of their faeces, which are produced as pellets enclosed in a skin of mucus. In warm climates the parents may shield the nestlings from the sun during the heat of the day.

The work of caring for the young birds is often performed by both parents and there are various adaptations to ensure this. The young react strongly to the return of the parents to the nest, usually by opening the beak and displaying the coloured inside of the mouth, an action that strongly stimulates the parent, releasing the feeding behaviour, which varies with the species. The young pigeon thrusts its bill into the throat of the adult to collect the milk secreted by the crop. The inside of the mouth of many nestlings is brightly coloured to guide the parents and release their feeding behaviour. It is probable that this careful attention by the parents is ensured by a series of some- what simple stimulus reactions. For example, Eliot Howard showed that a female linnet responds to its own nest rather than to its own young. When its young were put into an abandoned nest and the latter placed near to its own the hen usually returned to its nest and neglected the young, though the male gave them some food. Cuckoos similarly make use of the undiscriminating 'instinctive' behaviour; birds will feed any young that provide the appropriate stimulus and if no young appear they make little effort to find them.

While the young are in the nest the parents often resort to special devices to protect them. A hen thrush will sit especially tight at this time. Plovers when disturbed lead an invader away by a distraction display of cries at a distance from the nest; other birds will actually simulate injury, drawing off the attacker.

XVIII

THE ORIGIN AND EVOLUTION OF BIRDS

1. Classification

Class Aves.

*Subclass 1. Archaeornithes. Jurassic
  Archaeopteryx, *Archaeornis*
Subclass 2. Neornithes
*Superorder 1. Odontognathae. Cretaceous
  Hesperornis, *Ichthyornis*
Superorder 2. Palaeognathae. Ratites. Cretaceous–Recent
  *Struthio, Rhea, Dromiceius, Casuarius, *Dinornis, *Aepyornis,*
  Apteryx, Tinamus
Superorder 3. Impennae. Penguins. Eocene–Recent
  Spheniscus, Aptenodytes
Superorder 4. Neognathae. Cretaceous–Recent
  Order 1. Gaviiformes. Loons
    Gavia (loon)
  Order 2. Colymbiformes. Grebes
    Colymbus (= *Podiceps*) (grebe)
  Order 3. Procellariiformes. Petrels
    Fulmarus (petrel), *Puffinus* (shearwater), *Diomedea* (albatross)
  Order 4. Pelecaniformes. Cormorants, Pelicans, and Gannets
    Phalacrocorax (cormorant), *Pelecanus* (pelican), *Sula* (gannet)
  Order 5. Ciconiiformes. Storks and Herons
    Ciconia (stork), *Ardea* (heron), *Phoenicopterus* (flamingo)
  Order 6. Anseriformes. Ducks
    Anas (duck), *Cygnus* (swan)
  Order 7. Falconiformes. Hawks
    Falco (kestrel), *Aquila* (eagle), *Buteo* (buzzard), *Neophron*
    (vulture), *Milvus* (kite)
  Order 8. Galliformes. Game birds
    Gallus (fowl), *Phasianus* (pheasant), *Perdix* (partridge),
    Lagopus (grouse), *Meleagris* (turkey), *Numida* (guinea
    fowl), *Pavo* (peacock), *Opisthocomus* (hoatzin)
  Order 9. Gruiformes. Rails
    Fulica (coot), *Gallinula* (moorhen), *Crex* (corn-crake), *Grus*
    (crane), *Phororhacos*, *Diatryma*

Order 10. Charadriiformes. Waders and Gulls
   Numenius (curlew), *Capella* (snipe), *Calidris* (sandpiper), *Vanellus* (lapwing), *Scolopax* (woodpecker), *Larus* (gull), *Uria* (guillemot), *Plautus* (little auk)
Order 11. Columbiformes. Pigeons
   Columba (pigeon), **Raphus* (dodo)
Order 12. Cuculiformes. Cuckoos
   Cuculus (cuckoo)
Order 13. Psittaciformes. Parrots
Order 14. Strigiformes. Owls
   Athene (little owl), *Tyto* (farm owl), *Strix* (tawny owl)
Order 15. Caprimulgiformes. Nightjars
   Caprimulgus (nightjar)
Order 16. Micropodiformes. Swifts and humming-birds
   Apus (swift), *Trochus* (humming-bird)
Order 17. Coraciiformes. Bee-eaters and kingfishers
   Merops (bee-eater), *Alcedo* (kingfisher)
Order 18. Piciformes. Woodpeckers
   Picus (woodpecker)
Order 19. Passeriformes. Perching birds
   Corvus (rook), *Sturnus* (starling), *Fringilla* (finch), *Passer* (house-sparrow), *Alauda* (lark), *Anthus* (pipit), *Motacilla* (wagtail), *Certhia* (tree-creeper), *Parus* (tit), *Lanius* (shrike), *Sylvia* (warbler), *Turdus* (thrush), *Erithacus* (British robin), *Luscinia* (nightingale), *Prunella* (hedge-sparrow), *Troglodytes* (wren), *Hirundo* (swallow)

2. Origin of the birds

Many characteristics of birds show close resemblance to those of reptiles and in particular to the archosaurian diapsids. Already in the early Triassic period the small pseudosuchians such as **Euparkeria* (p. 395) showed the essential characteristics of the bird group, especially those associated with a bipedal habit. From some such form the birds have almost certainly been derived, by a series of changes parallel in many cases to those found in other descendants of the pseudosuchians, such as the crocodiles, dinosaurs, and pterosaurs.

3. Jurassic birds and the origin of flight

We have no detailed evidence of the stages by which cold-blooded terrestrial reptiles were transformed into warm-blooded flying birds, but two fossil specimens from the upper Jurassic rocks of Bavaria

FIG. 306. Restored skeleton of *Archaeornis*, compared with the skeleton of a
pigeon drawn on a more reduced scale.

c. carpal; *cl.* clavicle; *co.* coracoid; *d.* digits; *f.* femur; *fi.* fibula; *h.* humerus; *i.* ilium;
is. ischium; *mc.* metacarpals; *mt.* metatarsals; *p.* pubis; *py.* pygostyle; *r.* radius; *s.* scapula;
st. sternum; *tm.* tarso-metatarsus; *tt.* tibiotarsus; *u.* ulna; *v.* ventral ribs; *I–IV*, toes.
(From Heilmann, *The Origin of Birds*, H. F. & C. Witherby, Ltd.)

show us one intermediate stage on the way (Fig. 306). The two fossils
are not identical and are usually given distinct generic names,
Archaeopteryx and *Archaeornis*, but the differences between them
are not considerable.

These animals certainly had achieved some powers of flight or
gliding, but they were less specialized for the purpose than are modern

birds. The whole body axis was still elongated and lizard-like. The dorsal vertebrae were not fixed and only about five went to make up the sacrum. There was a long tail, with feathers arranged in parallel rows

FIG. 307. Skulls of A, *Euparkeria*; B, *Archaeornis*; C, *Columba*.

A. angular; Al. adlachrymal; Ar. articular; Bo. basi-occipital; C. condyle; D. dentary; E. eye with sclerotic ring; F. frontal; J. jugal; L. lachrymal; Mx. maxilla; N. nasal; O. occipital; Op. opisthotic; P. parietal; Pa. palatine; Pf. post-frontal; Pm. premaxilla; Po. post-orbital; Pt. pterygoid; Q. quadrate; Qj. quadratojugal; S. squamosal; Sa. sur-angular; Sp. splenial. (From Heilmann, *The Origin of Birds*, H. F. & C. Witherby, Ltd.)

along its sides, probably an important organ, as in other animals that live in trees and jump and glide. The fore-limb ended in three clawed digits, with separate metacarpals and phalanges; it was used as a wing, for the fossils show feathers on the back of the ulna and hand, but the wing area was small and the shape rounded, like that of the wing of birds that fly for short distances only. There was no sternum (at least none is preserved in the fossils). The ribs were slender and had no uncinate processes. The pelvic girdle and hind

Fig. 308. Restoration of hypothetical proavian. (From Heilmann, *The Origin of Birds*, H. F. & C. Witherby, Ltd.)

limb resembled those of archosaurs, with elongated ilium and backwardly directed pubis. The fibula was complete and the proximal tarsals were free, but the distal ones were united with the metatarsals.

In the skull of *Archaeopteryx* (Fig. 307) there were teeth in both jaws. The shape was more reptilian than bird-like, with rather small eyes and brain, and premaxillae and frontals much smaller than in modern birds. There was a large vacuity in front of the eye and probably there were post-frontal and post-orbital bones. The condition of the temporal region is unfortunately not clear on account of the crushing of the material. The brain-case was large and many of the bones were united, as in modern birds. The bones were not pneumatized.

These very interesting fossils suggest that the birds arose from a race of bipedal arboreal reptiles, living in forests and accustomed to running, jumping, and gliding among the branches (Fig. 308). There has been much controversy about the origin of flight, some maintaining that the earliest birds were terrestrial and used the wings to assist in running, leading eventually to a take-off, perhaps at first for short distances. The claws and long tail of *Archaeopteryx* speak definitely against this view and in favour of a gliding origin for flight.

4. Toothed birds in the Cretaceous. Superorder Odontognathae

These Jurassic fossils are so distinct from other birds that they are placed in a distinct subclass *Archaeornithes. All other known living and extinct birds have a short tail, reduced hand, a sternum, and other characteristics of the subclass Neornithes. A few fossils are known from the upper Cretaceous in which certain reptilian characteristics are still preserved. *Hesperornis* and *Ichthyornis* both possessed teeth, and are placed in a superorder *Odontognathae; they were aquatic birds, and the former was a diver that had lost the power of flight.

Already in the Cretaceous there were some birds that had lost the teeth and can be referred to orders found alive to-day. Birds are not commonly found as fossils, however, and it is not possible to give a detailed history of the evolution of the various orders which are recognized. We do not even know whether bird life first became abundant after the Cretaceous, at the same time as the mammals began to be numerous.

5. Flightless birds. Superorder Palaeognathae

Among the birds alive to-day there is a group placed as the superorder Palaeognathae that shows more 'primitive' characters than the rest, especially in the palate, which lacks the special arrangement of other birds (the Neognathae) by which the palatine bones articulate with the brain-case and the pterygoids are able to move on the palatines. All of the palaeognathous or ratite birds are flightless and they are often large, with reduced wings and sternum, long legs, and curly feathers. This association of failure to fly and primitive condition of the palate has been used to support the contention that these birds have never passed through a flying stage. More probably the ratites represent a population that diverged early from the main stock of flying birds. It is not even certain that they constitute a single phyletic group.

The various ratite birds are placed in eight distinct orders, but the orders of the ornithologist generally represent lesser degrees of difference than are usual elsewhere in the animal kingdom. The ostriches (*Struthio*) are the largest living birds, now limited to Africa and southwest Asia. The rhea (*Rhea*) occupies the same ecological position in South America and the emu (*Dromiceius*) and cassowary (*Casuarius*) in Australasia. The moas (**Dinornis*) were another type; several species lived in New Zealand until recent times. The elephant-birds (**Aepyornis*) were similar, with several species in Madagascar in the Pleistocene. Some were larger than ostriches, with eggs estimated to weigh more than 10 kg., presumably the largest single cells that have existed!

The kiwis (*Apteryx*) of New Zealand are smaller, terrestrial birds whose relationship to the ratites is doubtful. They are nocturnal and insectivorous or worm-eating, with a very long beak and small eyes. The sense of smell and the parts of the brain related to it are better developed than in other birds; it is not clear whether this is the retention of a primitive feature. The palate shows large basipterygoid processes. There is a penis, as in other ratites.

Still more doubtful is the position of the tinamus (*Tinamus*), terrestrial birds rather like hens, of which about fifty species are found throughout South America. They show similarities to the ratites in the palate and other features and may be placed among the Palaeognathae. Probably they are, like the more typical ratites, an early offshoot that has long developed independently.

6. Penguins. Superorder Impennae

The penguins (*Spheniscus*) are birds that early lost the power of flight and became specialized for aquatic life. Unlike most other water-birds they swim chiefly by means of the fore-limbs, modified into flippers; the feet are webbed. The penguins are confined to the southern hemisphere. They come ashore to breed, many make no nests, the one or two eggs being sometimes carried on the feet throughout the incubation period. The emperor penguin breeds in winter on the Antarctic ice and is the only bird that never comes on land. The egg is supported on the feet.

7. Modern birds. Superorder Neognathae

All the remaining birds have the characteristic palate, sternum, and other features already described and are placed in a single group as the superorder Neognathae. Birds of this type probably existed in the Cretaceous and many of the orders are known from Eocene times, but the fossil evidence is not adequate for us to be able to say when they became numerous and differentiated as they are now. The existing types, as has already been suggested, show very great variety of details of structure and habits, superimposed on the basic plan. Classification of the vast number of genera involves recognition of over forty distinct orders and even then one of the orders, the Passeriformes, contains about half of all the species. Unfortunately, little can be done in a short space towards describing the great variety of bird life. We can only list the important orders, mentioning a few of the characteristics of some of the more interesting types. Birds are so conspicuous that their species have been very fully described. The arrangement of the orders adopted for the survey, *Birds of the World*, by J. L. Peters has been used.

Order 1. Gaviiformes. Loons

The divers are aquatic birds retaining some primitive characteristics. They are birds of open waters, feeding mainly on fishes. Various species of *Gavia* live mostly on the sea, but breed by lakes throughout the holarctic region.

Order 2. Colymbiformes. Grebes

The grebes (*Colymbus = Podiceps*) are also aquatic birds, resembling the divers in some ways, but perhaps not closely related to them. They nest on lakes, laying a small number of white eggs, in a floating nest.

Order 3. Procellariiformes. Petrels

The petrels (*Fulmarus*), shearwaters (*Puffinus*), and albatrosses (*Diomedea*) are birds highly modified for oceanic pelagic life, some of them very large. They lay one white egg, often in burrows. Their very long narrow wings are specialized for soaring flight (Fig. 272).

Order 4. Pelecaniformes. Cormorants, Pelicans, and Gannets

This is another order of aquatic birds, mostly very fully modified for diving and fishing and including the cormorants (*Phalacrocorax*), pelicans (*Pelecanus*), and gannets (*Sula*). They nest in colonies on rocks or trees; the eggs are usually unspotted and covered with a rough chalky substance. These birds make spectacular dives when fishing; gannets may plunge from more than 50 feet.

Order 5. Ciconiiformes. Storks and Herons

The storks (*Ciconia*), herons (*Ardea*), and flamingos (*Phoenicopterus*) are large, long-legged birds, living mostly in marshes and feeding mainly on fish. They are strong flyers and some of them perform extensive migrations. Nests are usually in colonies and may be used year after year; there are elaborate display ceremonies. Eggs are few and unspotted (Fig. 273).

Order 6. Anseriformes. Ducks

The ducks (*Anas*) and swans (*Cygnus*) represent yet another group of birds specialized for aquatic life. The characteristic flattened bill is used to feed on various diets. Some are vegetarians, a few filter-feeders; some eat molluscs, others fish. The numerous eggs are usually white or pale and the nest is built on the ground.

Order 7. Falconiformes. Hawks

This order includes the birds of prey that hunt by day, having sharp, strong, curved bills and powerful feet and claws. The retina contains mainly cones. Many different types are found throughout the world. Most feed on birds or mammals, some on carrion, and a few on fish or reptiles. Typical examples are the kestrel (*Falco*), eagle (*Aquila*), buzzard (*Buteo*), and vulture (*Neophron*). The eggs, few in number, are usually spotted and the nests are generally made on cliffs, tree-tops, or other inaccessible places, some, however, on the ground.

Order 8. Galliformes. Game birds

These are mainly terrestrial, grain-eating birds, capable only of short, rapid flights; some of their structural characters and habits are certainly primitive. The palate differs from both that of ratites and of most modern birds, suggesting an early divergence. There is often a marked difference in plumage, and sometimes in size, between the sexes. The nest, usually made on the ground, is simple and the eggs numerous, white, or spotted. The young develop very quickly after birth. The order contains many successful types and is of world-wide distribution. It includes *Gallus*, the jungle-fowl of India, and all its domesticated descendants, also *Phasianus* and other pheasants,

Perdix (partridge), *Lagopus* (grouse), *Meleagris* (turkey), *Numida* (guinea-fowl) and *Pavo* (peacock). The Megapodes or mound-builders of the Australasian and east Indian regions lay their eggs in mounds of decaying leaves and earth. In *Opisthocomus*, the hoatzins of tropical South America, one of the few tree forms, the young possess well-marked claws on the digits of the wing (Fig. 308*a*), which they use for climbing. These claws are usually considered to be a

Fig. 308*a*. Claws on hand of the hoatzin (*Opisthocomus*), I, in nestling; II, adult. (After Parker and Heilmann.)

secondary development; their resemblance to the claws of *Archaeopteryx* is remarkable.

Order 9. Gruiformes. Rails and Cranes

The rails are mostly secretive, terrestrial birds, compressed laterally and often living in marshy country and having an omnivorous diet; common British members are the coots (*Fulica*) and moorhens (*Gallinula*). They run, swim, and dive easily, but are poor flyers; they build rather simple nests and lay numerous, often dark-spotted eggs. *Crex* (the corn-crake) and other landrails are of more terrestrial habit. The cranes (*Grus*) are long-legged birds found in swamps and probably allied to the rails rather than to the waders as is still often supposed.

Probably related to the rails are the cariamas of South America, carnivorous birds with very long legs, hardly able to fly, living largely on reptiles. The Miocene *Phororhacos* was a similar bird reaching 6 feet high; evidently the group was successful in a region free of mammalian carnivores. *Diatryma* was an even larger carnivorous bird, found in the Eocene of Europe and North America and perhaps also related to the early ancestors of the Gruiformes, though usually classified in a separate order.

Order 10. *Charadriiformes. Waders and Gulls*

This is a large order including the wading birds and the gulls, terns, and auks, which have evolved from them. The typical waders are birds that live mainly on the ground, often inhabiting open watery places or marshes. They are usually gregarious out of the breeding-season and are often very numerous on the sea-shore. They often have long legs and long bills and feed chiefly on small invertebrates. The curlews (*Numenius*), snipe (*Capella*), and sandpipers (*Calidris*) are well-known examples. The lapwings (*Vanellus*) and related plovers are birds found on drier land than is usual among other waders; the woodcocks (*Scolopax*) inhabit swampy woods.

The gulls (e.g. *Larus*) are a very important group of birds derived from the waders and adapted to life by and on the sea. Usually they have a grey or white colour, often with black head and wing-tips. The young are usually darker than the adults and mottled with brown. The guillemots (*Uria*) and little auks (*Plautus*) are more fully marine animals, breeding in very large colonies on the cliffs.

Order 11. *Columbiformes. Pigeons*

The pigeons are tree-living, grain- or fruit-eating birds, mostly good flyers but retaining some primitive features. They are of world-wide distribution. There is little sexual dimorphism; the nest is usually simple and the eggs normally one or two and white. The young are born very little developed and are nourished by the 'milk' secreted by the crop (p. 446). The dodo (*Raphus* = *Didus*) was a pigeon that adopted a terrestrial habit in the island of Mauritius and grew to a large size, but was exterminated by man in the seventeenth century.

Order 12. *Cuculiformes. Cuckoos*

The cuckoos include some species that build nests but many lay their eggs in those of other birds. In the common cuckoo (*Cuculus*), any one individual female lays mostly in the nests of a single foster species, in England often the meadow-pipit or hedge-sparrow. She watches the building of the nest and lays her egg on the same day as the foster parent, removing one of the clutch before she does so. Often about twelve eggs are laid in this way, each in a different nest; even more have been recorded. The eggs are usually strongly mimetic with those of the host, variable in colour, more so when varied host nests are available. The young hatch before the host eggs, which are then ejected from the nest by the young cuckoo.

Order 13. *Psittaciformes. Parrots*

The parrots are birds found mainly in warm climates, living among the trees and having many special characteristics. With the crows, they are usually reckoned to be the most 'intelligent' birds and certainly have considerable powers of memory. They are predominantly vegetarian and some, though by no means all, make use of the beak for breaking open hard shells. The eggs are usually laid in holes and are white and round. The period of parental care after hatching is unusually long (2–3 months).

Order 14. *Strigiformes. Owls*

The owls, specialized for hunting at night, resemble the hawks, by convergence, in their beaks, claws, and in other ways. The food is swallowed whole. They probably detect their prey mainly by sound, and show various specializations in the ears. The eyes contain mostly rods and are directed forwards; they are very large and they cannot be moved in the orbits, the movements of the neck compensating for this restriction. The feathers are so arranged as to allow very little noise in flight. The eggs are white and laid in holes or in the old nests of other birds, some on the ground. Many genera are recognized from all parts of the world, examples being the farm owls (*Tyto*) and the eared owls (*Asio*).

Order 15. *Caprimulgiformes. Nightjars*

The nightjars (*Caprimulgus*) are a rather isolated group of crepuscular birds, feeding on insects taken on the wing. Two mottled eggs are laid on the bare ground.

Order 16. *Micropodiformes. Swifts and Humming-birds*

The swifts (*Apus*) and humming-birds (*Trochus*) are perhaps more fully adapted to the air than are any other birds. The wings are very long, composed of a short humerus and long distal segments. The swifts are insectivorous and have very large mouths, adapted for feeding on the wing. The nests are made in holes, the eggs are white, and the young helpless at birth.

Order 17. *Coraciiformes. Bee-eaters and Kingfishers*

This is a large group of birds including the bee-eaters (*Merops*), mainly tropical and often brightly coloured. The three anterior toes are united (syndactyly). The nests are usually made in holes and the eggs are white. The kingfishers (*Alcedo*) are modified for diving into the water to catch fish.

Order 18. Piciformes. Woodpeckers

The woodpeckers (*Picus*) are highly specialized climbing, insectivorous, and wood-boring birds. The bill is very hard and powerful and the tongue long and protrusible and used for removing insects from beneath bark. The tail feathers are used to support the bird as it climbs the tree-trunk. The nest is made in a hole in a tree and the eggs are white.

Order 19. Passeriformes. Perching birds

The great order of perching birds contains about half of all the known species. They are birds mostly living close to the ground, rather small, and of very varied habits. There are always four toes arranged to allow the gripping of the perch. The display and nesting behaviour is usually complicated, with a very well-developed song in the male. Many species build very elaborate nests and the eggs are often brightly coloured and elaborately marked. The young are helpless at birth. Only a few of the many and very varied types can be mentioned here.

The rooks and jackdaws (*Corvus*) are the largest passerines, mostly colonial and differing from the rest of the order in many ways. The starlings (*Sturnus*) are colonial and nest in holes. The finches (*Fringilla*, &c.) are seed-eating birds with a short, stout, conical bill. The house-sparrows (*Passer*) are closely related to the finches and have become commensals of man all over the world. The larks (*Alauda*) make their nests on the ground. The pipits (*Anthus*) and wagtails (*Motacilla*) are somewhat like the larks, largely terrestrial birds with slender bills. The tree-creepers (*Certhia*) are tree-living, insectivorous birds with long bills, showing some convergent resemblance to woodpeckers. The tits (*Parus*, &c.) are a large group of woodland birds; they chiefly eat insects, also buds and fruits. The shrikes (*Lanius*) are peculiar among passerines in being mainly carnivorous, using their strong bills to eat other birds, amphibia, reptiles, and large insects.

The warblers (*Sylvia*, &c.) make a very large group of woodland birds, living in trees or scrub. Related to them are the thrushes and blackbirds (*Turdus*), the British robins (*Erithacus*), and nightingales (*Luscinia*), mainly eating small invertebrates, also fruits. They have a very wide distribution and are among the most recently evolved and successful members of the whole class. The hedge-sparrows (*Prunella*) are small omnivorous passerines, possibly related to the thrush group. The wrens (*Troglodytes*) are small and mainly insectivorous.

The swallows (*Hirundo*) form a very distinct family of passerines, suited for powerful flight and feeding on insects caught in the air. The very long pointed wings and 'forked' tail allow rapid manœuvring in the air and the insects are taken in a wide mouth. These features, together with the elaborate migrations, mark the swallows as among the most specialized of all birds.

8. Tendencies in the evolution of birds

The bird plan of structure, originating in the Jurassic period, perhaps 150 million years ago, has become modified to produce the great variety of modern birds. In trying to discover the factors that have influenced this modification we are handicapped by the poverty of fossil remains; it is not possible to trace out individual lines as it is in other vertebrate groups. It is clear that the process of change has been radical, the later types often completely replacing the earlier ones: no long-tailed or toothed birds remain to-day.

Our knowledge of direction of the change is largely dependent on study of the variety of birds existing to-day, which is perhaps more thoroughly known than in any other group of animals. In the reports of those who have studied this variation there are two distinct, indeed opposite, tendencies. Many have observed that adaptive radiation has occurred; birds are found occupying a wide variety of habitats, with modifications appropriate to each way of life. Other workers, recording minor differences between races occurring in different areas, have found difficulty in believing that these have adaptive significance. The existence of such 'subspecies' with a geographical limitation is a very striking characteristic, especially conspicuous in widely distributed species such as the chaffinch (*Fringilla*). On continental areas such subspecies usually grade into each other (making 'clines') and are interfertile at the areas where they meet. On the other hand, where a group of individuals becomes isolated on an island, or by some other geographical barrier, it may become infertile with the 'parent' species. If the two groups again come to occupy a common area, then either one eliminates the other or slight modifications of habits enable the two to survive side by side as two distinct 'species'.

Definite cases of formation of new species in this way have been recorded in birds, which are especially suitable for such study. Thus in the Canary Islands, besides a local form of the European chaffinch (*Fringilla coelebs*) there is the blue chaffinch (*F. teydea*), which was probably originally an offshoot from the European form. On the mainland *F. coelebs* inhabits both broad-leaved and coniferous forests, but in Grand Canary *F. teydea* occupies the pine woods, *F. coelebs* the chestnut and other woods. On the island of Palma, however, the blue chaffinch is absent and the European form occupies both habitats. It is presumed that the blue form is more suited to the coniferous woods, but this could not be deduced from its specific characters as recorded by a systematist. The adaptive significance of the differences between groups of animals may not be easy to discover, but it is most unwise to assume that they do not exist until a very thorough study has been made. Detailed observation generally shows small differences in habits and behaviour between animals occupying what seems at first to be a single 'habitat'. As Lack, who has studied this question in detail, puts it, 'A quick walk through the English countryside might suggest that there is a wide ecological overlap between the various song-birds. In fact, close analysis shows that there are extremely few cases in which two species with similar feeding habits are found in the same habitat'. The differences may be in the breeding habitat, as in the case of the meadow, tree, and rock pipits (*Anthus pratensis*, *A. trivialis*, and *A. spinoletta*). The spotted and pied flycatchers (*Muscicapa striata* and *M. hypoleuca*) catch their food in slightly different ways and the chiff-chaff (*Phylloscopus collybita*) feeds higher in the trees than the willow warbler (*P. trochilus*).

A complicating factor is that birds that occupy similar habitats for one part of the year may migrate to different regions, for instance, the tree and meadow pipits and the chiff-chaff and willow warbler.

Birds are able to get their food and to breed in many different ways, and when a race finds a situation occupied it perhaps often survives by slight change of habits, creating a new 'habitat' not previously occupied. This presumably results from the action of certain individuals whose constitution differs from the mean of the race, enabling them to pioneer. It is not certain to what extent individual birds are able to 'adapt themselves' in this way to new habitats. Probably the majority of the members of any population are limited by their structure and behaviour pattern to a rather narrow habitat range.

9. Darwin's finches

A remarkable example of evolution and adaptive radiation is provided by the birds of the Galapagos Islands. It was these birds and the giant tortoises (after which the islands are named) that started Darwin on his study of evolution. 'In July opened first note-book on "Transmutation of Species". Had been greatly struck from about month of previous March on character of S. American fossils—and species on Galapagos Archipelago—These facts origin (especially latter) of all my views' (Darwin's Diary 1837).

These islands are volcanic and probably of Tertiary (? Miocene) date. They lie on the equator, 600 miles west of Ecuador, the only other nearby land being the island of Cocos, 600 miles north-west

FIG. 309. Position of the Galapagos Islands. (From Lack, *Darwin's Finches*, Cambridge University Press.)

(Fig. 309). Though it has been suggested that the islands were connected by a land bridge with South America, it is much more probable that their limited stock of plants and animals has arrived across the sea. Of hundreds of species of land birds on the mainland, descendants of only seven species are found in the Galapagos. The only land mammals are a rat and a bat. The land reptiles include giant tortoises, iguanas, a snake, one lizard, and one gecko. There are no amphibians and only a limited number of land insects and molluscs. There are large gaps in the flora; for instance, no conifers, palms, aroids, or Liliaceae. This fragmentary flora and fauna strongly suggests that the islands have been colonized by chance transportation across the sea, and that, once arrived, the animals and plants have proceeded to settle not only in the habitats they occupied on the mainland but also in others, not filled, as in their homeland, by rivals. Thus the tortoises and iguanas, arriving presumably by chance, have grown to large size, to occupy the ecological position usually taken in other faunas by mammalian herbivores. The composite plant *Scalesia* and the prickly pear, *Opuntia*, have become tall trees in the Galapagos. We have here, therefore, an example of the results of evolution over a relatively limited period of time (perhaps less than 20 million years) from a limited number of initial creatures, and this provides an excellent opportunity for trying to discern the forces that have been at work.

FIG. 310. Suggested evolutionary tree of Darwin's finches. (From Lack.)

There are thirteen larger islands in the Galapagos group, the largest 80 miles long. They are separated by distances of up to 100 miles and several of the peculiar Galapagos animals have formed island races. The land birds present perhaps the most interesting features of the whole strange fauna. Besides two species of owls and a hawk they consist of five passerine types and a cuckoo, all very close to others found on the South American mainland, and a group of fourteen species of finches, placed in a distinct subfamily, Geospizinae. These finches are related to the family Fringillidae, which is represented in South America, but they cannot be derived from any single species now existing there. Like the other animals in the islands the birds tend to become differentiated into distinct island races, but this process has gone to varying extents. The cuckoo, warbler, martin, and tyrant flycatcher are similar in all the islands and it is significant that they are all very close to species occurring in South America. Presumably they are recent arrivals. The vermilion flycatcher, also a

South American species, has three island races. The mocking-bird,
Nesomimus, is placed in a genus distinct from that on the mainland and
has different races on each island, some of them being reckoned as
separate species. The extreme of island differentiation is shown by
the finches, now reckoned to belong to fourteen species, classed in

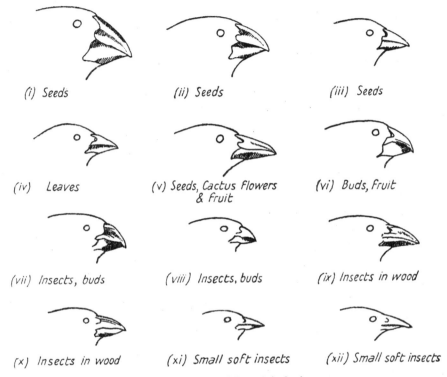

FIG. 311. Beaks of Darwin's finches.

(i) *Geospiza magnirostris*; (ii) *Geospiza fortis*; (iii) *Geospiza fuliginosa*; (iv) *Geospiza difficilis debilirostris*; (v) *Geospiza scandens*; (vi) *Camarhynchus crassirostris*; (vii) *Camarhynchus psittacula*; (viii) *Camarhynchus parvulus*; (ix) *Camarhynchus pallidus*; (x) *Camarhynchus heliobates*; (xi) *Certhidea olivacea*; (xii) *Pinarolaxias inornata*. (After Swarth, from Lack.)

four genera (Fig. 310), one of these being found on the distant Cocos
Island.

Evidently these finches have been in the archipelago for a considerable time and the specially interesting feature is that not only have
they formed races recognizably distinct, but they have radiated to
form a series of birds, which have quite varied habits, many of them
very un-finchlike. The main differences are in the form of the beak,
which varies greatly with the food habits (Fig. 311). The central
species, which are also the nearest to the presumed Fringillid ancestor,
are the ground-finches, *Geospiza*, of which there are five species,

feeding mainly on seeds. Two further species of *Geospiza* have left
the ground and taken to eating cactus plants. The tree-finches, placed
in a distinct genus *Camarhynchus*, include one vegetarian and five
mainly insectivorous species, one of the latter, *C. pallidus*, having
acquired the habit of climbing up the trees like a woodpecker and
excavating insects with a stick (Fig. 279). A third group of this
remarkable subfamily has acquired a convergent likeness to warblers:
Certhidea has a long slender beak and eats small soft insects; by many
it has been regarded as distinct from the other Galapagos finches, but
it has now been shown to resemble them, not only in structure but
also in breeding-habits. Nevertheless it probably diverged some time
ago and is found on all the islands. Presumably its success is due to
the absence of other warbler-like birds, the true Galapagos warbler
being a recent arrival. The fourth genus of the Geospizinae is
Pinaroloxias, the Cocos-finch, found on Cocos Island 600 miles away,
and also having warbler-like characteristics.

These birds provide a remarkable example of adaptive radiation
'with seed-eaters, fruit-eaters, cactus-feeders, wood-borers and eaters
of small insects. Some feed on the ground, others in the trees—
originally finch-like, they have become like tits, like woodpeckers and
like warblers' (Lack). This is interesting enough, but more can be
learned from this extraordinary natural experiment than from other
examples of adaptive radiation. Another most striking feature is that
the birds are very variable, and are by no means uniformly distributed
over the islands. The outlying islands lack certain species and their
place is then taken by variants of others, with corresponding modification of the beak. In some such cases the local subspecies can be
clearly seen to have an adaptive significance, but this is by no means
always so. Some races found on one or more islands differ in minor
features of colour or size. It remains to be shown whether these are
themselves significant or connected with other significant factors.

The striking feature is that so many distinct races should appear,
even in birds, which could easily cross the distances, mostly less than
50 miles, between the islands. Evidently the birds tend to remain at
home, and there is no doubt that degree of geographical separation is
a main factor in producing the races. Thus the central islands of the
group, lying close together, have no endemic subspecies, whereas the
forms in the outlying islands are mostly distinct (Fig. 312). It is
evident that isolation is tending to break up the population into a
number of distinct units and it is remarkable that, in spite of the large
amount of variation, intermediates are rare between species and even

between subspecies. The species, of course, do not cross in nature, and such as have been tested in captivity mate only with their own species.

It is still not possible to give an entirely clear idea of the factors responsible for the development of varied animals, even in this much

FIG. 312. Percentages of endemic forms of Darwin's finches on each island, showing the effects of isolation. (From Lack.)

simplified case. There is no clear line between subspecific differences, say, of the beak, with not obviously adaptive and with clearly adaptive character. Since favourable mutations will spread through a population the easiest assumption is that all these differences are in fact adaptive, or linked with unseen adaptive characters. The easiest assumption is not necessarily correct, but the demonstrably adaptive character of many of these differences certainly constitutes a case for considering that the others are also of this nature. In very small

populations (< 1,000) unfavourable characteristics may become established by chance (Wright, 1940), and this factor may be responsible
for some of the island races.

It is especially interesting that in the case of the Galapagos animals

·Fig. 313. Development of distinct forms from a single one in the Galapagos
finch *Camarhynchus*. Charles Island has two forms derived independently from
the central form *C. affinis*. (From Lack, partly after Swarth.)

special reasons have made it possible for variety to arise. If, as seems
likely, the earliest *Geospizas* were among the first birds to arrive in the
archipelago, they found there neither competitors nor enemies. Because of the distance from the mainland this condition has remained
with little change ever since. Even to-day the six passerines not belonging to the Geospizinae do not provide serious rivals, and the local
owls and hawks are apparently not serious. predators on the finches.

Susan Williams-Ellis

0" 1" 2"

Fig. 314. Adaptive radiation of sicklebills in Hawaii. (From Lack, after Keulemanns.)

The other great factor that has led to differentiation is the splitting up of the area into a number of isolated units. This has allowed slightly different races to emerge, and we may suppose that if these again came into contact with each other they would find slightly different optimal conditions, and therefore, with partial or complete inter-sterility, would continue as distinct species. This has almost certainly happened with the Canary chaffinch (p. 499), and in Galapagos there is a similar case in that two species of the large insectivorous tree-finch *Camarhynchus* occur together on Charles Island. Both are derived from a single population, offshoots from which have independently colonized the island (Fig. 313).

10. Birds on other oceanic islands

While the case of Darwin's finches is very striking it is important to recognize that similar radiation from a few species is not found on all oceanic islands. For instance, there are numerous birds on the Azores and they differ little from those of Europe. Whereas migrants are frequent in the Azores they are rare in the Galapagos; evidently there are special factors producing the isolation of the latter.

A radiation similar to that of the Galapagos has, however, occurred in Hawaii, where there are only five passerine forms and one of these, a finch-like bird the sicklebill, has produced an even greater variety than Darwin's finches (Fig. 314). Some of these sicklebills feed on insects, others on nectar, fruit, or seeds, and the beaks have developed accordingly. One species climbs like a woodpecker, digs for beetles with a short lower mandible and probes them out with a long curved upper one.

11. The development of variety of bird life

This and similar evidence from the study of the relatively recent evolution of birds might be summarized by saying that the production of variety of animal types is largely due to the interplay of biotic factors. The particular characteristics that each population acquires depend partly on physical and geographical conditions, but the stimulus to change, or the check on change, comes from the interaction of the animals and plants with each other.

It has already been suggested that the tendencies to increase and to vary are important among these factors influencing animal evolution and there is evidence that both have been at work in the development of the population of Galapagos finches and other animals. It is safe to say that there are more and varied finches, tortoises, iguanas, and

mocking-birds than there were when each arrived. The other factors
that we are now able to isolate, by their absence in this case, are the
competitors and the predators. In more fully developed continental
populations these probably tend to limit the development of variety,
allowing only those individuals of a population showing the mean or
'normal' structure and behaviour to survive. Extreme variants that
venture to brave the enemies and seek new habitats are eliminated.
Variation will arise when these checks are weak. In a crowded habitat
this may occur as a result of some peculiar swing of the elaborately
balanced interacting system of biotic factors, or by some external
physical change. We still do not know which of these is the more
important in producing the changes of these complicated mainland
populations, but the evolutionary laboratories provided by the vol-
canoes of the Galapagos and other islands suggest that evolutionary
change does not follow only on climatic or other physical changes. A
single population will become divided into several distinct ones by its
own tendencies to growth and variation, given absence of competitors
and predators and some means of isolating the animals in different
parts of the range.

XIX

THE ORIGIN OF MAMMALS

1. Classification

Class Reptilia

  Subclass *Synapsida

    Order 1. *Pelycosauria (= Theromorpha). Carboniferous–Permian *Varanosaurus, *Edaphosaurus, *Dimetrodon

    Order 2. *Therapsida. Permian–Jurassic

      Suborder 1. *Dromosauria. Permian   *Galepus

      Suborder 2. *Dinocephalia. Permian   *Moschops

      Suborder 3. *Dicynodontia. Permian–Trias *Dicynodon

      Suborder 4. *Theriodontia. Permian–Trias

        *Scymnognathus, *Cynognathus, *Bauria

      Suborder 5. Ictidosauria. Trias–Jurassic

        *Dromatherium.

Class Mammalia

  Subclass 1. Prototheria

    Order Monotremata. Pleistocene–Recent. Australasia

      Tachyglossus (= Echidna), spiny anteater, Australia. Zaglossus (= Proechidna), New Guinea. Ornithorhynchus, platypus, Australia

  *Subclass 2. Allotheria

    *Order 1. Multituberculata. Jurassic–Eocene. Europe and N. America

      *Plagiaulax, Jurassic, Europe.

      *Ptilodus, Palaeocene, N. America

    *Order 2. Triconodonta. Jurassic. Europe and N. America

      *Amphilestes. *Triconodon

  Subclass 3. Theria

    *Infraclass. Pantotheria

      *Order 1. Pantotheria. Jurassic. Europe and N. America

        *Amphitherium

      *Order 2. Symmetrodonta. Jurassic. Europe and N. America   *Spalacotherium

    Infraclass 2. Metatheria

     Order Marsupialia

    Infraclass 3. Eutheria (= Placentalia)

2. The characteristics of mammals

The idea that the mammals include the highest of animals can easily be ridiculed as a product of human vanity; we shall find, however, that in many aspects of their structure and activities they do indeed stand apart as animals which are 'higher' than others, in the sense in which we have used the word throughout this study. The mammals and the birds are the vertebrates that have become most fully suited for life on land; among them are many species in which the processes of life are carried on under conditions most remote from those in which life first arose. The mammalian organization includes a great number of special features that together enable life to be supported under conditions which seem to be extravagantly improbable or 'difficult'. For example, the surface of the body is waterproofed, and elaborate devices for obtaining water are developed. A camel and the man he is carrying through the desert may perhaps contain more water than are to be found in the air and sandy wastes for miles around. This is only an extreme example of the 'improbability' of mammalian life, which is one of its most characteristic features.

The faculty of maintaining a high and constant temperature has opened to the birds and mammals many possible habitats that were closed to the reptiles. Besides making life possible under extremely cold conditions, such as those of the polar regions, the warm blood vastly extends the opportunities for life in more temperate climates. Mammalian races, which can feed all through the winter, can of course expand more rapidly than their reptilian cousins, which must hibernate for much of the year, during which period they consume rather than produce living matter.

The success of the mammals in maintaining life in strange environments is very largely due to the remarkable powers they possess of keeping their own composition constant. All living things tend to do this, but it seems probable that the mammals maintain a greater constancy than any other animals, except perhaps the birds. Claude Bernard's famous dictum 'La fixité du milieu intérieur c'est la condition de la vie libre' may be doubtful of vertebrates in general, but it can certainly be applied to mammals. They have a life which is more free than that of other groups, in the sense that they can exist and grow in circumstances which other forms of life would not tolerate, and they can do this because of the elaborate mechanism by which their composition is kept constant. Besides the regulation of temperature there is also a regulation of nearly all the components of the blood, which are kept constant within narrow limits. Barcroft has pointed out that the achievement of this constancy has enabled the mammals to develop some parts of their organization in ways not possible in lower forms. For instance, an elaborate pattern of cerebral activities requires that there shall be no disturbances by sudden fluctuations in the blood.

We shall expect to find in the mammals, therefore, even more devices for correcting the possible effects of external change than are found in other groups. Besides means for regulating such features as those mentioned above we shall find the sense-organs especially sensitive and the motor mechanisms able to produce remarkable adjustments of the environment to suit the organism, culminating in man with his astonishing perception of the 'World' around him and his powers of altering the whole fabric of the surface of large parts of the earth to suit his needs.

Such devices for maintaining stability often take very peculiar and specialized forms in particular cases. The activity and 'enterprise' of mammals has led many of them to make use of particular structures and tendencies to develop very odd specializations, which enable them to occupy peculiar niches. What could be more bizarre than the development of the muscles of the nose until a huge mobile trunk appears, so that the heaviest of four-footed beasts, while using its legs for support, can also handle objects more delicately than almost any other animal?

The mammals have developed along many special lines and many of these have already become extinct; others, especially among rodents and primates, remain among the dominant land-animals to-day. Warmth, enterprise, ingenuity, and care of the young have been the basis of mammalian success throughout their history. The most characteristic features of the modern mammals are thus seen to be very largely in their behaviour and soft structures. Mammalian life is above all else active and exploratory. Mammals might well be defined as highly percipient and mobile animals, with large brains, warm blood, and a waterproofed, usually hairy skin, whose young are born alive. Since it is difficult to recognize such characters as these in fossils we cannot say exactly when they arose, and our technical definition of a mammal must be made on the basis of hard parts.

The whole series of mammal-like forms from Carboniferous anapsids onwards forms a natural unit, and it is only by an arbitrary convention that we separate the reptilian subclass Synapsida from the class Mammalia. The present-day mammals form a very distinct group of animals, which we identify superficially by their possession of hair. For instance, the duck-billed platypus is immediately referred because of its hair to the mammalia, and we class it apart from reptiles or birds, even though its internal organization and the fact that it lays eggs show it to have many similarities with reptiles, and its bill is like that of a duck. The technical characteristic of the class Mammalia is, however, given by the presence of a single dentary bone in the lower jaw, the articular and other bones forming, with the quadrate, part of the mechanism of the middle ear. All the descendants of the Synapsida from the Jurassic onwards have these characteristics and we may assume that the full mammal-like condition was already established in the late Jurassic period, about 130 million years ago. The reduction of the jaw bones may perhaps have been associated with the habit of chewing the food, in order to obtain the large amounts necessary to maintain a high temperature.

It would not be very rash to suggest that by Jurassic times the synapsids had developed the other mammalian characters, such as active habits, large brain, warm blood, hair, and perhaps also a diaphragm, four-chambered heart, and single left aortic arch. They may even have been viviparous, for the surviving monotremes, which lay eggs, probably diverged at a still earlier period, perhaps the Trias or even Permian (p. 575).

3. Mammals of the Mesozoic

In spite of all the uncertainties of the fossil record it is now possible to follow the history of the Mammalia back to their origin from cotylosaurian reptiles of the Permian, more than 200 million years ago. Sufficient information is available for us to be quite sure that some population of early anapsid reptiles, such as *Seymouria* of the Carboniferous and Permian times, besides giving rise to all the modern reptiles, to the dinosaurs, and to the birds, also produced the mammals. The evidence for this connexion rests on a most interesting series of fossils, together with some 'living fossils' such as the monotremes of Australia. The fossil history is not at all times equally clear. The mammalian stock first became distinct in late Carboniferous times, as a special type of cotylosaurian reptile, with a tympanum placed behind the jaw and later a lateral temporal aperture. This stock quickly became very abundant and successful as the theromorphs and therapsids of Permian and Triassic times, but then nearly died out in the Jurassic, during which period we know of the mammals only from fragmentary remains of a few small animals. Then, in the Cretaceous, some of these small forms became more numerous and from them arose, before the Eocene, a variety of different types of mammal, from which the histories of the modern orders can be followed in some detail.

We have, therefore, abundant evidence of the earliest stages of mammalian evolution, say, 20 million years, from fossils in the Permian Red Beds of Texas. For the next following 40 million years or so we have also a very rich material, from the Upper Permian and Triassic Karroo beds of South Africa. In these early times the mammal line was a very flourishing one, more so indeed than the diapsids or any other of the descendants of the cotylosaurs. The animals were mostly carnivorous, though there were also herbivorous types. Many of these early mammal-like forms became quite large and numerous, in fact this stock dominated the land scene in the Permian. In the later Trias, however, if our fossil evidence is a safe guide, their numbers became reduced, perhaps the carnivorous dinosaurs took their place. However, already at this time many of the essential features of mammalian organization had been developed, so far as these can be judged from the bones. Possibly the soft parts of these Permian forms were also mammal-like, the animals may have been active and 'intelligent', have possessed hair and warm blood. However, their brains were very small and reptilian in structure.

Throughout the succeeding 90 million years of Jurassic and Cretaceous times our knowledge of the mammalian stock is dim. Mammals of a somewhat rodent-like type, the multituberculates, became quite numerous and produced some large forms, but then became extinct in the Eocene. Unless we have been singularly unlucky in the preservation of mammalian remains, no other mammal-like animals larger than a lizard existed throughout this very long period. Since we possess detailed information, based on numerous fossils, about scores of larger diapsid reptilian types, it can hardly be only an accident that mammal-like fossils are so rare.

We must conclude that the mammalian organization, after an initial success in the Permian and Triassic, was almost supplanted in the Jurassic and Cretaceous by the various diapsid creatures. However, a few very rare fossils, mostly lower jaw bones, give us some idea of the nature of the animals that carried our type of organization through the Jurassic period. Then from the Cretaceous, about 100 million years ago, come the first fossil remains of mammals similar to those alive to-day; rare, insectivorous creatures, not widely different from modern shrews but larger. This was the time of the beginning of an astonishing revolution, which completely altered the life on the face of the earth. The descendants of these shrew-like animals multiplied exceedingly in the new conditions, and by the earliest Palaeocene times, 60 million years ago, they had produced recognizable ancestors of the modern orders of mammals.

Our knowledge about this 'Laramide' revolution is still very dim, but it was undoubtedly one of the major geological crises, a period in which the surface of much of the earth became unstable, there were great volcanic outflows and the building of vast mountain chains. It is possible that these upheavals led to the disappearance of the swampy conditions, which had been so suitable for large reptiles, and to the appearance of dry uplands on which the mammals and birds flourished, especially where the climate was cold. We must be careful here, however, not to argue in a circle. Our evidence about the climate is derived from the changes in the populations, as revealed by the fossils. Study of the plant remains, however, confirms the supposition that conditions became drier during this time.

Our knowledge of the origins of mammals derived from fossils is supplemented by certain surviving mammals, whose structure shows them to have diverged rather early from the main stock, especially the monotremes (duck-billed platypus and *Echidna*) and the marsupials (kangaroos, opossums, &c.). Unfortunately it is still not clear exactly how these survivors are related to the main stocks as revealed by the fossils. The monotremes are unknown except as Pleistocene fossils; tantalizingly enough we know only little about the affinities of this very ancient group. The characteristics of their bony skeleton show that they must have diverged from other mammals well back in Mesozoic times. For instance, the pelvic and pectoral girdles are very 'reptilian' in structure. Such features suggest that it is not wild speculation to use the characters of the soft parts of monotremes to deduce those of the mammalian stock in late Triassic or early Jurassic times, say, 150 million years ago. The marsupials appear as fossils in the late Cretaceous. Some of the earliest forms are very like modern opossums, and we may conclude that the condition of modern marsupials throws some light on the probable condition of the soft parts of mammals 70 or 80 million years ago. However, it has been realized in recent years that many features in marsupial organization are special developments, not 'primitive' characteristics carried over from the ancestral condition.

The piecing together of all this evidence to give a reliable picture of the history of mammals is a valuable exercise in zoological and geological method, as well as a means of becoming familiar with a fascinating story. We may now return to the Carboniferous times to examine the evidence more in detail (see Fig. 222).

4. Mammal-like reptiles, Synapsida

All our evidence about the origin of mammals must of course be based upon the study of hard parts, which can become fossilized, and in particular on the skull. The characteristic feature of the skull in the populations that lead to the mammals is the development of a hole in

Dimetrodon   *Varanosaurus*

FIG. 315. Skulls of two early synapsids. (After Romer, *Vertebrate Paleontology*, University of Chicago Press, and Abel.)

the roof, low down on the side of the temporal region, the lower temporal fossa (Fig. 224). This hole was at first bounded above by the post-orbital and squamosal bones, below by the jugal and squamosal. It was at one time supposed that this single fossa was formed by union of the two present in diapsid reptiles, and thus the whole group acquired the inappropriate name Synapsida. Animals having this characteristic appear in the rocks at the same time as the cotylosaurs, with no hole in the skull roof (Anapsida), from which they were presumably derived. We have only fragmentary knowledge of anapsids from the Carboniferous; most of our information comes from lower Permian forms, such as *Seymouria; yet there are quite well-preserved synapsids of Upper Carboniferous date. Therefore we have no complete series of successive types to show how the earliest mammal-like types arose; nevertheless we can see something of the probable stages of this progress within the Permian Anapsida. One of the characteristics of the skull of *Seymouria was the presence of an 'otic notch', in which lay the tympanic membrane, at the back of the skull (Fig. 221). In *Captorhinus and similar anapsid fossils from the Lower Permian this notch has disappeared (Fig. 223). The tympanum apparently lay behind the quadrate in these forms, leaving the whole side of the skull as a rigid support for the jaw. This arrangement was accompanied by an elongation of the columella auris to articulate with the quadrate, a modification that led to one of the most characteristic features of the skeleton of mammals, namely, the conversion of the hinder jaw bones (quadrate and articular) into ossicles for the transmission of vibrations to the ear (p. 526).

Captorhinus and its allies were a foot or more in length and showed some development of the limbs towards the mammalian condition, in that the bones were moderately elongated and slender and the limbs perhaps tended to be held vertically under the body. However, there was no great development of a backwardly directed elbow and forward knee. The teeth were considerably specialized, possibly for eating molluscs, and there were several rows of crushing teeth on the edge of the jaw, and long overhanging ones in the premaxillae.

5. Order *Pelycosauria (= Theromorpha)

The synapsid line began when an early offshoot from some such anapsid as *Captorhinus* developed a temporal fossa. This must have occurred in the middle of the Carboniferous, nearly 250 million years ago, producing in the later part of that period, and in various Pennsylvanian and Lower Permian strata, especially in North America, these earliest synapsid populations, classified together as pelycosaurs or Theromorpha. *Varanosaurus* (Fig. 315), from the Texas Red Beds, is a typical example, a carnivore, about 3 ft. long, showing a lizard-like appearance little different from that of anapsids or primitive diapsids. Intercentra were found all along the vertebral column, as in anapsids, and there were abdominal ribs. The teeth showed the beginnings of the mammalian differentiation in that one or more near the front of the series were elongated as 'canines'. The skull of pelycosaurs also showed tendencies in the direction of that of mammals in having a long anterior region and a relatively high posterior part, giving a large brain-case and deep jaw.

Other pelycosaurs developed very characteristic neural spines, whose function is not clear. This seems to have occurred in more than one line, *Edaphosaurus* and its allies being herbivores, some of them as much as 12 ft. long, whereas *Dimetrodon* (Fig. 315) was a carnivore. These animals were important in the late Carboniferous and early Permian fauna, presumably preying on the other early reptiles and on rhachitomous amphibia. They did not survive long, however, being apparently replaced by their descendants. From some form similar to *Dimetrodon* (but without the elongated neural spines) a whole series of lines arose, classed together as Therapsida.

6. Order *Therapsida

The early pelycosaurs were very like early parapsids, such as *Araeoscelis*, or diapsids such as *Youngina*, but their descendants soon showed characteristic tendencies. There was never any trace of the bipedalism that developed in the Archosauria; the fore-limbs were always at least as long as the hind, tended to be turned under the body and to carry it off the ground. The skull became deeper and its brain-case enlarged; a bony secondary palate developed from flanges of the premaxillae, maxillae, palatines, and pterygoids. The teeth became differentiated for various functions and the bones of the lower jaw, except the dentary, were gradually reduced.

These features seem to have developed in several different lines descended from pelycosaur ancestors; the sorting out of the various genealogies is not yet complete. It is therefore still difficult to decide for certain the interesting question whether parallel evolution occurred, and especially whether similar features appeared independently in animals of different habits. The fossils giving us information about this stage in the evolution of the mammals are nearly all found in South Africa and have been studied in great detail by R. Broom.

Much of the surface of the southern part of Africa is covered by rocks known as the Karroo system. These consist partly of shales and mud-stones formed by the matter brought down by a large Mesozoic river, and the remainder are sandstones composed of blown sand. Both sorts of rock were particularly favourable for the preservation of the remains of terrestrial animals. Unfortunately the absence of marine fossils makes it very difficult to give dates for these rocks. Altogether the strata present a thickness of some 15,000 ft., laid down over a period corresponding probably to that from the Middle Permian to the Upper Trias in Europe, that is to say, from 195 to 160 million years ago.

The reptiles in the lowest of these beds, *Galepus* and others, classed as the suborder *Dromasauria, are little known, but seem to have resembled the pelycosaurs. The temporal opening was small, the teeth all alike and the bones at the hind end of the jaw large. The *Dinocephalia, 'giant heads', such as *Moschops*, were large animals, some carnivorous, others herbivores; they were numerous in the later Permian. They retained many primitive features, but the legs were turned under the body and the phalanges became reduced to the mammalian formula of 2.3.3.3.3. The roof of the head was expanded into a large dome, giving the name to the group. The dicynodonts

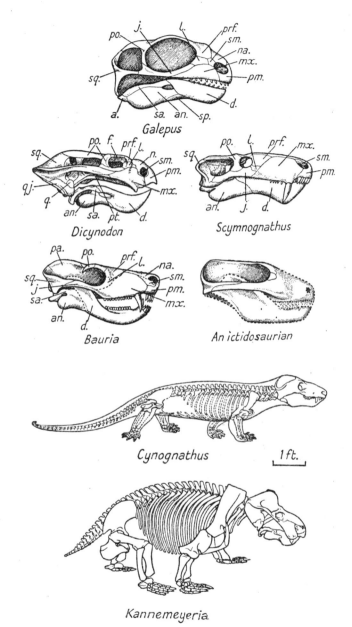

FIG. 316. Skull and skeleton of various synapsid reptiles, abbreviations as Fig. 215. (After Romer, *Vertebrate Paleontology*, University of Chicago Press, from Broom, Watson, Gregory, & Pearson.)

were a still more specialized and successful offshoot, they became the commonest of all reptiles in the later Permian. They were large creatures (*Kannemeyeria*, Fig. 316), probably living in marshes, and were herbivorous. The margins of the jaws were covered with a horny beak and the teeth reduced to a single pair of upper 'canine' tusks, even these being absent in the female.

The most interesting of the therapsid reptiles are, however, those placed in the suborder *Theriodontia, which, by the early Trias, had produced a very mammal-like type of organization, apparently in several independent lines. The temporal opening became progressively wider, presumably for the accommodation of larger jaw-muscles, so that the parietal bone entered into the margin of the fossa and post-orbital and squamosal bones no longer met above it. Eventually the post-orbital bar itself became incomplete, leading to the typical mammalian condition, with the orbit and temporal fossa confluent. The brain-case was high and large and the animals were presumably active and 'intelligent' creatures. The limbs came to support the body off the ground, and the dorsal parts of the girdles were developed accordingly, the scapula becoming large and bearing an acromial spine for muscle attachments, the coracoids being reduced. The anterior portion of the ilium became large and a hole appeared between the pubis and ischium. The head of the femur lay at the side, and a special knob, the great trochanter, appears on it for the attachment of muscles running from the front part of the ilium. In the hands and feet the toes show a reduction of the formula to 2.3.3.3.3. The teeth became differentiated into incisors, canines, and cheek teeth, the latter having several cusps in place of the cone of a typical reptile tooth. In some forms there was almost certainly a single replacement of 'milk' by permanent teeth, as in mammals.

These features were little developed in the earliest theriodonts, such as *Scymnognathus* and other Permian forms, and these are grouped as Gorgonopsia (Fig. 316). The temporal fossa still resembled that of pelycosaurs, there was a single condyle, no secondary palate, and a phalangeal formula of 2.3.4.5.3. *Cynognathus* and other Triassic forms, classed as Cynodontia, were typical theriodonts, showing the above 'mammalian' features. They were carnivores, of distinctly dog-like appearance, although still retaining many signs of a heavy reptilian build. *Bauria* and others classed as Therocephalia were of another type, still more advanced than *Cynognathus* in that the orbit and temporal fossa were confluent (Fig. 316).

These *Theriodontia were the dominant carnivores of the early

Trias, but by the end of that period they had almost disappeared. The latest members of the Therapsida are placed in a separate sub-order, the *Ictidosauria, such as *Dromatherium* of the Upper Trias (Fig. 316). They are rare fossils, showing almost completely mammal-like structure. There was no post-orbital bar and no prefrontal, post-frontal, or post-orbital bones. A well-developed secondary palate was present. The bones at the hind end of the lower jaw had become very

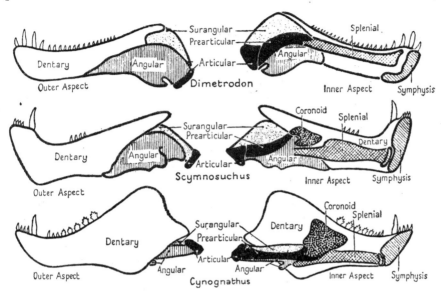

FIG. 317. Reduction of the articular and other bones and increase in the dentary in therapsid reptiles. (From Neal and Rand, *Comparative Anatomy*, The Blakiston Company, after Watson.)

small, but angular, surangular, articular, and prearticular are still recognizable (Fig. 317).

Study of these fossils, mainly from the Karroo system, shows us, therefore, a series of types, of which the earliest were very like the first reptiles and the latest very like the earliest true mammals. There can be no doubt of the general tendency, but the series is not complete enough to enable us to follow the details of the evolution of the populations. These fossils are revealed by denudation and can be given only approximate dates. They are grouped into orders and suborders by their structure and we cannot say from definite stratigraphical evidence that any one type has given rise to any other. It is certain that some of the mammal-like features appeared independently in lines whose evolution proceeded separately from a common ancestor. Thus the dinocephalians, dicynodonts, and later theriodonts all had the mammalian phalangeal numbers, but each of these lines has certainly evolved independently from pelycosaur-like ancestors having a greater number of phalanges.

The influences that produced the evolution of these populations must have been quite complex, since they did not affect all parts of the body at once. For instance, the *Dinocephalia, in spite of their mammalian phalangeal formula, still showed pelycosaur features in the absence of a secondary palate, and presence of a single occipital condyle and small dentary. We still know too little to be able to specify clearly the conditions controlling such evolutionary changes, but it seems likely that the gradual appearance of terrestrial life and of large herbivores led other animals of a suitable structure and disposition to a carnivorous life. For this purpose certain changes of the ancestral structure would be suitable, leading to parallel evolution in related stocks. However, at present we can hardly do more than pose questions about such matters and resolve to be rigorous in interpretation of the available evidence.

7. Mammals from the Trias to the Cretaceous

The types classified as synapsid reptiles, which we have been considering, are not found later than the Triassic, 160 million years ago; mammals of approximately the modern type appear in the late Cretaceous. For the enormous time of more than 80 million years between these dates the mammalian organization must have maintained itself in the form mostly of small insectivorous animals, perhaps arboreal and nocturnal; very few remains of these are found as fossils. No doubt many types existed of which we have no fossil remains, but the Mesozoic mammals which we know can be divided into four orders, *Multituberculata, *Triconodonta, *Symmetrodonta, and *Trituberculata (or Pantotheria). The last of these may perhaps be directly related to the animals which gave rise to the modern mammals, the other three lines are specialized offshoots. All of them were true mammals in that the lower jaw consisted of a single dentary bone, the articular and other bones being presumably incorporated in the middle ear. The brain-case (where known) was high and the temporal fossa joined with the orbit. The post-cranial skeleton is almost unknown and indeed many forms are known only from lower jaws. There is reason to think that the monotremes have preserved to the present day many of the features which characterized the mammalian stock during the Mesozoic period. Some of the 'Mesozoic mammals' had indeed advanced beyond the stage of the monotremes, for instance the limb girdles of multituberculates resemble those of modern mammals rather than reptiles. For purposes of classification we can most conveniently divide the class Mammalia into three sub-classes, the Prototheria for the monotremes, Allotheria for the multituberculates and triconodonts (though it is probable that these two are not closely related), and the Theria for the modern mammalian line. This latter sub-class can then be subdivided into three infra-classes, Pantotheria

FIG. 318. A, triconodont (*Priacodon*) from the Jurassic; B, pantothere (*Docodon*) from the Jurassic; C, multituberculate (*Ptilodus*) from the Palaeocene. (After Lull, *Organic Evolution*, copyright 1917, 1929 by The Macmillan Company and used with their permission. A and B after Marsh, C after Gidley from Scott.)

for those 'Mesozoic mammals' that probably led to the rest, Metatheria for the marsupials, and Eutheria for the placentals. This is approximately the classification provided by G. G. Simpson of the American Museum of Natural History, who has not only greatly increased our knowledge of many orders of mammals but also provided a complete systematic review of the group.

The multituberculata were much the most numerous and long-lasting group of Mesozoic mammals, surviving from the early Jurassic period to the lower Eocene. They were herbivorous animals, sometimes of quite large size (Fig. 318). The incisors were rodent-like, and between the incisors and the molariform teeth there was a gap (diastema), as in other mammals which chew large amounts of vegetable matter. The cheek teeth carried longitudinally arranged rows of cusps, presumably used for grinding the food. The relationship of these animals to earlier and later types is quite uncertain, and it may be that animals not very closely related have been included in the order. It has been suggested that the multituberculates gave rise to the monotremes or marsupials, but the features which they have in common with these are mostly those common to all primitive mammals.

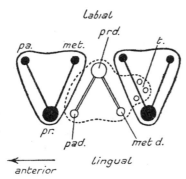

FIG. 319. Arrangement of occlusion of cusps of tritubercular teeth. Upper molars continuous outline, lower dotted.

met. metacone; *metd.* metaconid; *pa.* paracone; *pad.* paraconid; *pr.* protocone; *prd.* protoconid; *t.* talonid (heel). (After Osborn.)

Still less is known about the other three orders existing in the Mesozoic. They occur only as teeth and occasional lower jaws, from Jurassic strata. The triconodonts (**Amphilestes*) possessed teeth with three cusps arranged in a line, and were presumably a separate offshoot from one of the earlier synapsid stocks (Fig. 318). The symmetrodonts and panthotheres are very imperfectly known and may include a mixture of unrelated types. The lower jaw was formed of a single dentary bone, the hinder jaw bones having presumably already formed ear ossicles.

In **Amphitherium* there were four pairs of incisors on each side of the lower jaw, one canine and eleven cheek teeth, four of these being preceded by milk teeth and hence classed as premolars. Several different sorts of pantotherian are known from the Jurassic and could have given rise to the earliest placental insectivores, which appear in the late Cretaceous (p. 559). The reason for believing in this relationship is the cusp-pattern of the teeth.

8. Original cusp-pattern of mammals

In the symmetrodonts and pantotheres the cusps were arranged approximately in a triangle (Fig. 318) and this is believed to have been the plan from which the modern mammalian condition is derived. The apical cusp, which lies on the inner side of the upper molars and the outer side of the lower, was at one time believed to represent the original reptilian cone and was therefore called the protocone in the upper and protoconid in the lower molars. The other two cusps are called the paracone (paraconid) in front and metacone (metaconid) behind. The separation between these latter cones is not sharp in the pantotheres, especially in the upper jaw, and we shall find this condition again in the earliest placental mammals, which were also insectivorous. There have been various theories about how the triangular plan was reached. The original tritubercular theory supposed that there was a 'rotation' into a triangular position from the three cusps in line of a triconodont. Even if this could be shown to have happened in a series of fossil teeth, we should still require a knowledge of the change of morphogenetic process by which the 'rotation' was produced.

FIG. 320   FIG. 320 A

FIG. 320. Duck-billed platypus (*Ornithorhynchus*). (From photographs.)
FIG. 320 A. Five-toed Echidna (*Tachyglossus*). (From photographs.)

There have also been attempts to explain the many-cusped mammalian tooth as due to the 'fusion' of a number of reptilian tooth germs, either those making one series on the gum or the teeth of successive series. It is plausible that changes in relative time and/or place of tooth development could occur in this way, leading to a partial 'fusion' and the production of many-cusped structures. At present there is too little information to decide how the reptilian became changed into the mammalian tooth, but there can be little doubt that the tritubercular theory shows us approximately the nature of the earliest mammalian cusp patterns.

9. Egg-laying mammals. Sub-class Prototheria (Monotremata)

The duck-billed platypus (*Ornithorhynchus*) and spiny ant-eater, usually called *Echidna* but strictly *Tachyglossus* (Fig. 320), are Australian mammals, basically similar to each other, but so different from other mammals that it is certain that they left the main stock far back in the Mesozoic, possibly before the Mesozoic mammals we have been discussing. Unfortunately the monotremes are not only very remote from the other modern mammals but are also unknown as fossils before the Pleistocene. The details of their ancestry are therefore obscure, but their organization possibly shows us many of the characteristics of mammalian populations of the Mesozoic.

Since we are comparing the platypus and echidna chiefly with Mesozoic reptiles we shall deal first with their hard parts, examining the living animals as if they were fossils. The lower jaw consists of a

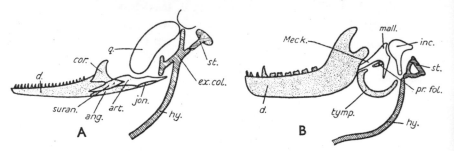

FIG. 321. Diagram of arrangement of jaw and auditory ossicles. A, in a reptile; B, in a mammal.

ang. angular; *art.* articular; *cor.* coronoid; *d.* dentary; *ex.col.* extracolumella; *hy.* hyoid; *inc.* incus (quadrate); *jon.* gonial; *mall.* malleus (articular); *Meck.* Meckel's cartilage; *q.* quadrate; *st.* stapes; *suran.* surangular; *tymp.* tympanic (angular). (After Ihle, from Gaupp.)

FIG. 322. The temporary upper teeth of the duck-billed platypus. (From British Museum Guide.)

single dentary bone. The quadrate, articular, and tympanic have entered the ear, but the malleus is large, the incus small, and the stapes elongated, all three less clearly suited to their new functions than are the ossicles of modern mammals (Fig. 321). The tympanic bone forms a partial ring around the tympanum, and the whole apparatus is not enclosed in a bony 'bulla' as it is in modern mammals. Neither animal possesses true teeth in the adult, the platypus having a flattened bill covered with soft skin and used for 'paddling' for the small aquatic animals, especially mussels and snails, on which it lives. *Tachyglossus* and the related New Guinea form *Zaglossus* have long 'beaks' for eating ants. However, in the young platypus flattened, ridged teeth are present, unlike those of any other mammals (Fig. 322). These true teeth are replaced by horny structures, formed by an ingrowth of epidermis beneath them and apparently used for breaking the shells of the molluscs. It is particularly unfortunate, since most

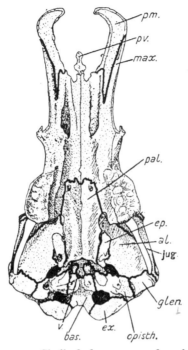

FIG. 323. Skull of platypus seen from below.

al. alisphenoid; *bas.* basioccipital; *ep.* epipterygoid; *ex.* exoccipital; *glen.* glenoid facet of squamosal; *jug.* jugal; *max.* maxilla; *opisth.* opisthotic; *pal.* palatine; *pm.* premaxilla; *pv.* prevomer; *sq.* squamosal; *v.* 'vomer'—basisphenoid. (From Ihle, after van Benneden.)

of our knowledge of early mammalian affinities comes from their teeth, that we can deduce so little from those of the monotremes.

The skull (Fig. 323) is specialized in both genera, particularly at the front end, and many of the bones fuse early. There is a wide communication between the orbit and temporal fossa. There are many 'reptilian' features; for instance separate pterygoid bones and the reptilian prevomers, still present as a pair of 'dumb-bell-shaped bones', though these often drop off from dried skulls. The side of the skull is like that of a reptile in that the dermal bones do not cover the whole of it, so that an epipterygoid, or ossification in the ascending process, can be recognized. In the temporal region there is a narrow canal which apparently represents the posterior temporal fossa of anapsida.

The vertebrae are very reptile-like, especially the cervicals, which bear separate ribs, as in the synapsid reptiles. There are seven cervical vertebrae, but in the dorsal region differentiation has proceeded less far than in other mammals, there being 16 ribs in the

FIG. 324. Skull and skeleton of a female platypus.

at. atlas; *c.* coracoid; *cl.* clavicle; *ep.* epipubic bone; *f.* femur; *fib.* fibula; *h.* humerus; *icl.* interclavicle; *is.* ischium; *j.* jugal; *m.* maxilla; *pc.* precoracoid; *pm.* premaxilla; *pub.* pubis; *pv.* prevomer; *r* radius; *sc.* scapula; *st.* sternum; *sq.* squamosal; *t.* tooth; *ti.* tibia; *u.* ulna. (Modified after Owen.)

spiny ant-eaters and 17 in the platypus, with 3 or 4 lumbars in the former and only 2 in the latter. The ribs articulate only with the bodies of the vertebrae, not with the transverse processes. The tail is vestigial in *Zaglossus*, but forms a flattened swimming-organ in the platypus. The limbs and their muscles and girdles are remarkably reptilian. They tend to be held laterally rather than beneath the body and in general the ventral parts are far better developed than in modern mammals, and this is sometimes spoken of as a 'plate-like' condition. In the pectoral girdle there are separate clavicles and a median interclavicle. The coracoid region includes two quite large and separate bones, the coracoid and 'precoracoid'. There is no spine on the scapula. The ventral portion of the pelvic girdle is enlarged by the development of epipubic bones, presumably partly for the support of the marsupial pouch. The limbs show a very large and broad humerus in both animals. In *Ornithorhynchus* the fibula is expanded at its upper end like the ulna of other mammals, for the attachment of the large muscles that produce the swimming action. The tarsus carries a spur in both animals, more highly developed in the male and having a poison gland attached.

The condition of the skeleton is therefore quite sufficient to establish the early divergence of the monotremes from other mammals and we are justified when looking at the soft parts in supposing that many of the characters were possessed by the synapsid reptiles. However, it must always be borne in mind that many of the 'mammalian' characters could conceivably have been produced by parallel evolution, subsequent to the divergence of the two lines. Perhaps the outstanding non-skeletal feature is the egg-laying habit. The large yolky eggs have a whitish shell and in the spiny ant-eater are transferred by the mother to a special marsupial pouch, which develops at the breeding season. Monotremes are unique in possessing a caruncle as well as an egg-tooth, suggesting that both were present in the ancestor of Amniotes. After incubation and hatching the young enter the pouch and are fed by milk. The post-natal care of the young therefore developed before the egg-laying habit was lost. Both species produce milk from specialized sweat glands on the ventral abdominal wall of the female, but the ducts of these are not united to open on nipples.

The presence of hair again gives us a valuable clue. Unless this feature has been separately evolved on several lines we may conclude that the Mesozoic mammals and perhaps even the synapsids had made some progress in temperature regulation. The mechanism is still imperfect in monotremes, whose temperature is lower and more variable than that of other mammals. The platypus has a fine short fur of dark brown colour; in the spiny ant-eater the back carries a mixture of spines and hairs, the belly carries hairs alone.

The rectum and urinogenital system open to a common cloaca, a 'reptilian' feature found also in marsupials (Fig. 325). The penis of the male is a simple groove in the cloacal floor and is used only for the passage of sperm, the urine entering the cloaca by a special urinary canal.

The brain is relatively large and arranged essentially on the mammalian plan (Fig. 326). The pallial portion of the cerebral hemispheres is well developed, not the striatal portion as in reptiles, and the surface is actually convoluted in spiny ant-eaters, though smooth in the platypus. These features suggest that the large brain and active, memorizing habits appeared early in the Mesozoic, but an interesting feature is that there is no corpus callosum joining the hemispheres.

FIG. 325. Comparison of the cloaca and penis of tortoise (A) with monotreme (B and C). The penis is shown erect in B, withdrawn in C. (From Ihle.)

bl. bladder; *cl.* cloaca; *fibr.* corpus fibrosum; *p.s.* preputial sack; *spong.* corpus spongiosum; *sp.d.* sperm duct; *urogen.* urogenital canal; *u.c.* urinary canal; *v.d.* vas deferens; *w.* ureter.

The soft parts also show mammalian features. The diaphragm is fully developed and the heart and single left aortic arch resemble those of other mammals. These animals have therefore advanced in their circulatory system beyond the anapsid condition, such as is probably shown to-day in Chelonia (p. 377).

With all their archaic features the monotremes also show many specializations. The platypus is highly modified for aquatic life. Apart from its bill there are the webbed feet, dorsal nostrils, long palate, short fur, thick tail, and perhaps absence of external ears. The animals burrow actively in the banks, making nests in which the young are reared. They are not uncommon in the rivers of southern and eastern Australia and Tasmania and fortunately are difficult to catch and therefore in no danger of extinction, though their fur and flesh are both useful.

Several species of spiny ant-eater are known and they occur in New Guinea as well as Australia. They show specializations for

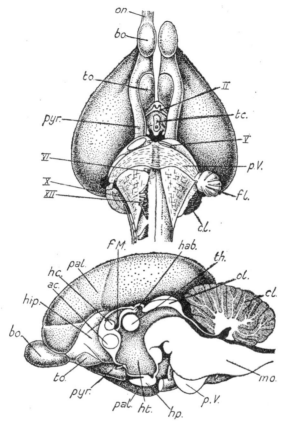

FIG. 326. Brain of the platypus.

ac. anterior commissure; *bo.* olfactory bulb; *cl.* cerebellum; *fl.* flocculus; *fM.* foramen of Munro; *hab.* habenula; *hc.* hippocampal commissure; *hip.* hippocampus; *hp.* hypophysis; *ht.* hypothalamus; *mo.* medulla oblongata; *ol.* optic lobe; *on.* olfactory nerve; *pal.* pallium; *pV.* pons Varolii; *pyr.* pyriform lobe; *tc.* tuber cinereum; *th.* thalamus; *to.* tuberculum olfactorium; *II–XII.* cranial nerves. (From Kingsley, *Comparative Anatomy of Vertebrates*, The Blakiston Company. After Elliot Smith.)

ant-eating similar to those of *Myrmecophaga* (p. 571), namely, long snout, long tongue, and large salivary glands. The clawed feet are used to make burrows for the young, as well as for digging up the nests of ants. It is perhaps significant that both of these very early mammals burrow and make nests to assist in the protection of their young.

The Monotremata thus show a peculiar mixture of mammalian and reptilian characteristics. In their brain, hair, warm blood, heart, and diaphragm they are mammalian, but in skeleton and egg-laying habit they resemble reptiles. A large part of their interest is that they suggest an intermediate stage, in many features, between the two groups. Thus the pectoral girdle appears to be that of a reptile partly changed to a mammal. Further study of such features may help considerably to reveal the changes in morphogenetic process which produced the mammals. It would be especially interesting to discover how the changes in the various parts are correlated, so that we might see how variation of a single growth process has produced apparently disconnected alterations of various parts of the body. In this way it may become possible to replace such diffuse accounts as the present by more general statements.

There are certainly many things to be discovered from these extraordinary creatures, which have remained in their isolated part of the world with little change in fundamental organization for possibly nearly 150 million years. The characters they show literally provide us with a view of the past, yet the facts that these two alone have survived and that they show special features of their own remind us sharply that evolutionary change is almost universal: new types replace the old almost if not quite completely.

XX

MARSUPIALS

1. Marsupial characteristics

The pouched mammals, though essentially very similar to placentals, are primitive in many characters and undoubtedly they diverged from some early stage of the main mammalian stocks; with the insectivora

FIG. 327

FIG. 328

FIGS. 327–8. Skulls of thylacine (327), and rat kangaroo (*Bettongia*) (328). (From Flower and Lyddeker, *Mammals, Living & Extinct*, A. & C. Black, Ltd.)

they show us what mammals were like in the late Cretaceous period. They are, however, very varied in habits (there are some 230 living species), paralleling, in the isolation of Australasia, the adaptive radiation accomplished in other parts of the world by the placentals. Many of their features are specialized, so that they do not so much represent a stage on the way to placental evolution as a specialized side branch, which has remained in some respects at a different level of organization. To-day they are found mainly in the Australasian region, with a few representatives in North and South America, but in Eocene times they occurred in Europe and they have presumably become restricted by the competition which has been imposed by the placentals.

The skull shows many characters found also in insectivora and other early mammalian groups (Figs. 327–8). The brain-case is small and the top of the skull therefore rather flat. The orbit and temporal fossa remain fully confluent and there is no post-orbital bar. The bony palate is incomplete posteriorly, there being large holes in the palatine

FIG. 329. Teeth of the upper jaw of the opossum (*Didelphys*) showing the last premolar whose place is occupied in the young by a molariform tooth. (From Flower and Lyddeker.)

portion of it. The jugal bone always reaches back to the glenoid articulation of the jaw. The lower jaw, consisting of course of a single dentary, has a characteristically inturned or 'inflected' inner 'angle'. Other special features of the skull, not usually found in placentals, are that the foramen for the optic nerve and that for the eye-muscle and trigeminal ophthalmic nerves are not separated from each other and that the lachrymal bone extends outside the orbit. More interesting than these apparently trivial and unconnected diagnostic features is the fact that the auditory region is not protected by the formation of a bulla of the petrous bone as it is in other mammals; instead the alisphenoid bone sends a wing over the middle ear.

The teeth are not very easy to interpret (Fig. 329). The incisors are more numerous than in placentals, as many as 5 on each side in the upper and 3 in the lower jaw. Of the cheek teeth only one, the third of the series, is replaced in modern forms, and if this is regarded as the last premolar we have a dentition of 3 premolars and 4 molars, as against the 4 and 3 of a typical placental. However, fossil marsupials with three replacing teeth have been found and the significance of the peculiar condition of the modern forms remains obscure; it may be connected with the specialization of the mouth of the young for life in the pouch. The cusps of the teeth of many marsupials (e.g. opossum) show a close approach to the presumed primitive plan (p. 524), but in addition to the main triangle other cusps, especially on the outside, are clearly marked. As in placentals the herbivorous types of marsupial develop grinding surfaces on the teeth.

The general plan of the muscles and backbone is essentially that found in placentals and has been greatly changed from the reptilian or monotreme condition. There are no cervical ribs. The thoracic region consists of about 13 rib-bearing vertebrae, as in placentals, and there are about the usual 7 lumbars. The pectoral girdle shows no interclavicle, but the clavicle remains large. The coracoid is reduced, as in placentals, and the scapula enlarged and provided with a spine. In fact all the developments of the dorsal region of the girdle which are typical

FIG. 330.   FIG. 331.

FIGS. 330-1. Hind foot of A, *Trichosurus*, and B, *Macropus*, showing elongation of the toes of the latter and reduction of the 1st, 2nd, and 3rd toes. (From Zittel, *Text-book of Palaeontology*, Macmillan, after Dollo.)

of the mammalian method of locomotion have taken place. In the pelvic girdle there are epipubic bones, reminiscent of those of monotremes; they take the special stresses produced by the abdominal muscles and pouch, but are reduced in the very fully terrestrial and quadrupedal Tasmanian wolf. The hands usually carry five digits, armed with claws, but the number of toes is often reduced and they may bear hoof-like structures.

The reproduction of marsupials shows a very simple viviparous condition not closely similar to any found in placentals. The egg is rather yolky and covered with albumen and a membrane; cleavage is very unequal. The only connexion between the foetus and the mother is by the contact developed in some forms (*Dasyurus*) of the vascular wall of the yolk sac with the somewhat hypertrophied uterine wall (omphaloidean placenta). Only in the bandicoot, *Perameles*, does the allantois develop a nutritive function to some extent. In most marsupials no placental arrangement develops at all, instead, uterine milk may be taken up by the yolk sac. The embryos are born very young, as little as 8 days from conception in the opossum, and only 39 days in the kangaroo (Fig. 332). They crawl to the pouch, where they become attached to the teats and remain for a long time, as much as 65 days, even in the opossum.

This is not by any means a primitive plan of development, it

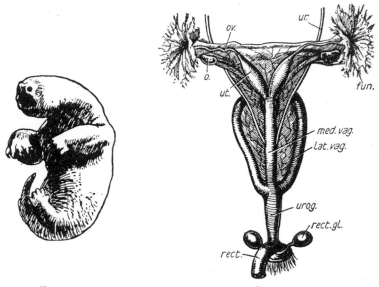

FIG. 332   FIG. 333

FIG. 332. Newborn opossum, showing large clawed hands and round mouth. (From *American Mammals*, by W. J. Hamilton, McGraw Hill Book Company.)

FIG. 333. Genital ducts of female kangaroo (*Macropus*).

fun. fallopian funnel; *lat.vag.* lateral vagina; *med. vag.* median vagina; *o.* ovary; *ov.* oviduct; *rect.* rectum; *rect.gl.* rectal gland; *ur.* ureter; *urog.* urogenital duct; *ut.* uterus. (From Ihle, after Brass.)

involves many specializations. To make the journey to the pouch the fore-limbs and their nervous centres are precociously developed, being fully functional at birth, when the hind-limbs are mere buds. The method of suckling also involves special developments of both mother and foetus, so that milk is injected into the latter without choking it. The sides of the lips grow together round the teat, which is thrust far back in the pharynx, the larynx extending forwards into the nasal passage. Milk is pressed out by a special muscle attached to the epipubic bones.

The reproductive tract is in a very interesting condition in that the two oviducts remain distinct along their whole length, including a pair of vaginae (Fig. 333); but in some forms the two passages come into contact at a point along their length to form a sac, the median vagina or birth passage, which acquires an opening to the urinogenital sinus before the young are born, often closing again thereafter. As in monotremes the rectum and urinogenital sinus open together at a common cloaca (Fig. 334), though this is not very long, more so in the female than the male. In the male there is a well-developed penis (Fig. 334), often bifid at the tip, in which case the clitoris is also

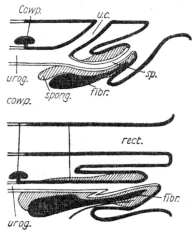

FIGS. 334–5. Diagrams of arrangement of genital ducts of male *Perameles* and *Macropus*.

Cowp. Cowper's gland; *fibr.* corpus fibrosum; *rect.* rectum; *sp.* spermatic duct; *spong.* corpus spongiosum; *u.c.* urinary canal; *urog.* urogenital canal. The part shown in black develops from ectoderm. (From Ihle, after V. d. Broek.)

double, the arrangement presumably ensuring fertilization of both oviducal tubes.

The brain shows many reptilian features. The cerebral hemispheres are small for a mammal, and the olfactory bulbs very large. The hemispheres are not prolonged backwards over the cerebellum, which is itself small and simple. The commissures between the cerebral hemispheres are very much simpler than in placentals and there is no corpus callosum. The cochlea of the ear is spirally coiled.

2. Classification of marsupials

Marsupials are often divided into two suborders, the more primitive insectivorous or carnivorous polyprotodonts, formerly of world-wide distribution and still found outside Australasia, and the diprotodonts, more specialized and restricted. The distinction is based on the presence of more than three pairs of incisors in each jaw in the first group and three or less pairs in the other, but a further interesting feature is that in most diprotodonts the second and third digits of the hind-limb are fused to make a comb for cleaning the hair (Fig. 336). This character is absent in nearly all polyprotodonts, which are hence said to be didactylous, and this is no doubt the primitive condition. However, the comb-like condition (syndactyly) is found not only in diprotodonts but also in the polyprotodont bandicoots;

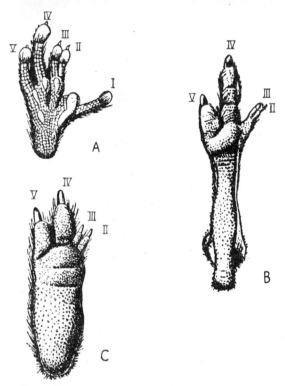

FIG. 336. Hind feet of marsupials. A, opossum, with grasping hallux, arboreal; B, kangaroo, without hallux, digits II and III syndactyl, cursorial; C, tree kangaroo, without hallux, arboreal (secondarily). (After Bensley, from Lull, *Organic Evolution*, copyright 1914, 1929 by The Macmillan Company, and used with their permission.)

conversely the curious South American opossum-rat (*Caenolestes*), though didactylous, has diprotodont teeth.

The fact is that marsupials, having radiated perhaps over 60 million years ago, present us to-day with a number of separated types of organization. Simpson groups them into six superfamilies and it is perhaps better not to attempt any higher grouping of these. The absence of Australian Tertiary deposits before the Pleistocene increases the difficulties of study of marsupial phylogenesis.

Infraclass 2. Metatheria

Order Marsupiala

Superfamily 1. Didelphoidea. Upper Cretaceous–Recent, Europe and America

Didelphodon. Upper Cretaceous, N. America. *Didelphis*, opossum, Pliocene–Recent, N. and S. America. *Chironectes*, water opossum, Central and S. America

*Superfamily 2.

Borhyaenoidea. Palaeocene–Pliocene, S. America

Prothylacinus. Miocene. *Borhyaena*. Oligocene–Miocene

Superfamily 3. Dasyuroidea. Pleistocene–Recent. Australasia *Dasyurus*, native cat. *Sarcophilus*, Tasmanian devil. *Thylacinus*, Tasmanian wolf. *Myrmecobius*, banded ant-eater. *Notoryctes*, marsupial mole. *Sminthopsis*, pouched mouse

Superfamily 4.

Perameloidea. Pleistocene–Recent. Australasia *Perameles*, Bandicoot

Superfamily 5. Caenolestoidea. Eocene–Recent, S. America *Palaeothentes* (= *Epanorthus*), Oligocene–Miocene. *Caenolestes*, opossum-rat, Ecuador, Columbia, Peru

Superfamily 6. Phalangeroidea. Pliocene–Recent, Australasia *Trichosurus*, Australian opossum. *Petaurus*, flying opossum. *Phascolarctos*, koala bear. *Phascolomis*, wombat. *Macropus*, kangaroo. *Bettongia*, rat kangaroo. *Diprotodon*, Pleistocene

3. Opossums

The opossums (Didelphoidea) were the earliest group to appear and the other families have probably evolved from them, syndactyly appearing twice independently. They are arboreal, mainly insectivorous animals, with a prehensile tail, occurring over the southern United States and Central and South America (Fig. 337). The pouch is generally absent. Similar forms are found back to the Upper Cretaceous (*Didelphodon*) and the American opossums are certainly the closest of living marsupials to the ancestors of the group, perhaps they are the least modified of all therian mammals. *Chironectes* is a related South and Central American aquatic form, with webbed feet. Perhaps related to the opossums is *Perameles*, the bandicoot of Australia and New Guinea, a rabbit-like herbivore with polyprotodont dentition, quadritubercular grinding molars, syndactyly of the hind toes, and an allantoic placenta.

4. Carnivorous marsupials

The Dasyuroidea include some carnivorous polyprotodonts, show-ing remarkable convergence with placental carnivores, the teeth

FIG. 339. Tasmanian devil (*Sarcophilus*). (From photographs.)

FIG. 340. Tasmanian tiger cat (*Dasyurus*). (From photographs.)

FIG. 337. American opossum (*Didelphis*). (From photographs.)

FIG. 338. Tasmanian wolf (*Thylacinus*). (From photographs.)

being modified for cutting flesh in a way similar to the carnivore carnassial. *Thylacinus* (Fig. 338), the Tasmanian wolf, is now nearly or quite extinct. *Sarcophilus*, the Tasmanian devil (Fig. 339), is rare, but *Dasyurus* (native cat) (Figs. 340 and 341) includes several species of cat-like creatures common in Australia and New Guinea. A line of carnivorous marsupials also existed in South America but is now extinct. They are interesting because two or several milk teeth were replaced, suggesting that the modern condition is secondary. Their affinities are obscure and they are best left in a separate superfamily Borhyaeno dea.

FIG. 341. Eastern native cat (*Dasyurus*). (From photographs.)

FIG. 342. Banded anteater (*Myrmecobius*). (From photographs.)

FIG. 343. Marsupial mole (*Notoryctes*). (From photographs.)

FIG. 344. Pouched mouse (*Sminthopsis*). (From photographs.)

FIG. 345. Kangaroo (*Macropus*). (From photographs.)

5. Marsupial ant-eaters and other types

Myrmecobius is an ant-eating form, with elongated snout (Fig. 342). *Notoryctes*, the marsupial mole (Fig. 343), is a remarkable type from South Australia, having reduced eyes, well-developed fore-limb, fused cervical vertebrae, and many features suiting it for burrowing and feeding upon ants. Its pouch opens backwards. *Sminthopsis*, the pouched mice (Fig. 344), are small marsupials occupying the niche taken in other parts of the world by the shrews.

Caenolestes, the opossum-rat of the forests of Ecuador, is an interesting shrew-like creature with the polyprotodont number of incisors but procumbent lower incisors, resembling those of diprotodonts. There is no syndactyly. Related fossil forms are found throughout the Tertiary of South America.

6. Phalangers, wallabies, and kangaroos

The diprotodont marsupials form a compact group (leaving out *Caenolestes*) of Australian forms, here included as the superfamily Phalangeroidea. Their fossil history is little known, but they have become specialized for various modes of life, mainly as herbivores, in Australia and the neighbouring islands. The kangaroos and wallabies (Macropodidae) (Fig. 345) have become terrestrial and developed a bipedal method of progression, involving modification of the ilia and thigh muscles, for whose attachment the tibia bears a marked anterior crest. The foot gains increased leverage by elongation of the metatarsal of digit 4, which is larger than the others. Digits 2 and 3 are very small and syndactylous. There are several modifications for a herbivorous diet; the single pair of lower incisors is directed forwards and their sharp inner edges can be moved in such a way as to cut grass. This condition recalls that of Rodentia (p. 620) and, as in that group, a special transverse muscle is developed (m. orbicularis oris), but in this case it is part of the facial musculature and innervated from the seventh nerve, whereas the analogous muscle of the rodents is a part of the mylohyoid and innervated from the trigeminal. The molar teeth are modified for grinding, by the fusion of the cusps to make two transverse ridges, recalling those of ruminants. The stomach has a special sacculated non-glandular chamber, presumably allowing digestion by symbionts. *Bettongia* and other 'rat kangaroos' are terrestrial and bipedal jumpers, they also have a prehensile tail (Fig. 346).

The Australian opossums or phalangers are less modified than the kangaroos and are arboreal animals, with a prehensile tail and various special modifications, mostly for herbivorous diets; *Trichosurus* is the common phalanger, with 4-cusped upper molars. *Phalanger*, the cuscus (Fig. 347), eats mainly leaves. The koala or native bear, *Phascolarctos* (Fig. 348), is arboreal and has cheek-pouches, an enlarged caecum, and a reduced tail. Three distinct genera of phalangers have developed extensions of the skin for purposes of soaring; *Petaurus* (Fig. 349) is the best known of these flying phalangers. *Phascolomis*,

FIG. 346. Rat kangaroo
(*Bettongia*).
(From photographs.)

FIG. 347. Cuscus (*Phalanger*).
(From photographs.)

FIG. 349. Flying opossum (*Petaurus*).
(From photographs.)

FIG. 348. Koala bear (*Phascolarctos*).
(From photographs.)

FIG. 350. Wombat (*Phascolomis*). (From photographs.)

the wombat (Fig. 350), is a large, burrowing, tailless animal, with rodent-like grinding teeth; it eats roots. *Diprotodon* was a very large marsupial, as much as 12 ft. long, living in Australia in the Pleistocene.

7. Significance of marsupial isolation

The marsupials have evidently retained many features of the life of mammals of the late Cretaceous period, more than 70 million years ago. Their relatively simple, macrosmatic brain presumably limits their behaviour and powers of adaptation to circumstance and they have lost such beginnings of the development of an allantoic placenta as may have been present in the Cretaceous mammals, retaining the yolky eggs and developing special means of caring for the young. Even those members that have become highly specialized retain features throughout the skeleton and other parts that recall Cretaceous mammalian organization and resemble conditions in modern insectivorous placentals. However, the general organization of the muscular and skeletal system so closely resembles that of modern placentals that we can be confident that this plan of life had already been arrived at in the Cretaceous, along with many other mammalian features, such as warm blood and hair, though the temperature of marsupials is lower and more variable than in placentals.

The fact that the marsupial type of organization, once found all over the world, has hardly survived outside Australia is a good proof that later animal types are often in some way more efficient and come to replace the earlier ones. In this case we have indeed a controlled experiment, since the placentals were unable to cross to Australia and the marsupials flourished there, becoming differentiated into numerous types, arboreal, fruit-eating, grazing, gnawing, digging, burrowing, ant-eating, insectivorous or carnivorous, in each case with appropriate structure. It will be interesting to see how this assemblage stands up to competition with placentals in the future. Carnivores, ruminants, lagomorphs, rodents, and primates have recently become firmly established in Australia and it can hardly be an accident that some of the corresponding marsupial types are already becoming rare or extinct.

XXI

EVOLUTION OF PLACENTAL MAMMALS AND ITS RELATION TO THE CLIMATIC AND GEOGRAPHICAL HISTORY OF THE CENOZOIC

1. Eutherians at the end of the Mesozoic

Several different lines of evidence converge to show that all the eutherians (placentals) have been derived from small, perhaps nocturnal, insectivorous animals living in the Cretaceous period, about 100 million years ago. Many features of marsupials and placentals alike suggest origin from a small Cretaceous shrew-like form, perhaps itself descended from some animal like the Jurassic pantotheres. It is especially interesting, therefore, that fossil evidence is now available to show that both opossums (p. 539) and placental insectivora (p. 559) existed in the Cretaceous. We may be reasonably sure that the population from which those groups were derived resembled both of these animals, which are indeed basically similar. At this Cretaceous period the arrangements for nourishing the young were presumably not yet fully developed and in the marsupials (Metatheria) they have remained at a simple level, little above ovo-viviparity, though the condition in *Perameles* makes it doubtful whether an allantoic placenta has been lost by the other marsupials.

The stock that was to give rise to the eutherians was therefore already differentiated in the Cretaceous; as the Laramide revolution proceeded these animals began to flourish and to develop into several divergent populations. The only placental types known to have lived during Cretaceous times were insectivores; yet by the very beginning of the Cenozoic period, in the formations known as the Palaeocene, several different types of placental are found.

2. The end of the Mesozoic

It is not easy to discover any close connexion between the climatic changes and this early flowering of the placentals. Throughout the period of the Cretaceous earth movements the land gradually became higher and the climate probably in general colder. Indeed, this process had been going on intermittently throughout the Mesozoic. In the Permian there was a series of glaciations even more profound than those of the Pleistocene and it has been suggested that these may have been responsible for the production of mammal-like characteristics among the synapsids (p. 521). It is tempting to make similar suggestions about the development of placental mammals at the end of the Cretaceous. The presence of cold uplands may indeed have been responsible for such success as the multituberculates and other Mesozoic mammals achieved during the Cretaceous. But this slow revolution does not explain, by itself, the success of the placentals, because they only become differentiated into varied groups towards the end of the Cretaceous. There is some evidence that this latter time was not very cold, and it will be remembered that some dinosaurs persisted to the very close of the Mesozoic. On the other hand, pterodactyls had died out earlier and so had some groups of the dinosaurs.

Although there were large climatic changes at the end of the Cretaceous period it is certainly very unwise to make simple statements about their relation to the evolution of the mammals. The whole Cretaceous period lasted for more than 50 million years and we cannot trace in detail the numerous changes of climate that must have taken place, probably in different directions in different parts of the world. Even the marine faunas were affected; for instance, the ichthyosaurs and plesiosaurs died out before the end of the Cretaceous and were followed by the mosasaurs (p. 385), which had a sudden period of success lasting for some millions of years.

There is no doubt that towards the end of the Cretaceous period, about 60–70 million years ago, there were very great climatic changes, even more marked, perhaps, than any that had occurred during previous phases of the period of unrest that had been going on throughout the Cretaceous. The change of fauna was as remarkable for the animals that appeared as for those that were lost. The remaining dinosaurs died out on land, as did the mosasaurs, and incidentally, ammonites and belemnites, in the sea. At the same time not only did numerous placental mammals appear, but also a great variety of true birds, and in the seas teleostean fishes.

The apparent suddenness of the change may be deceptive. Our knowledge of the conditions at the beginning of the Cenozoic period is very fragmentary. It was a time when the land stood high, a great part of the continental shelf being above water, and therefore producing few fossils. Most of our information about the fossils laid down at this time comes not from marine beds, but from the 'Palaeocene' continental deposits, known chiefly in America. These deposits lie on top of undoubted Cretaceous, dinosaur-containing beds, and they contain a variety of placental mammals. At the upper end these

Palaeocene deposits are continuous with beds that can be correlated with the previously known Eocene marine beds in other parts of the world, at which level there is a still wider variety of placentals.

It is clear, therefore, that there was a period of time of unknown duration following the disappearance of the dinosaurs during which the placentals were becoming differentiated. The old belief in the sudden appearance of various types in the Eocene was, therefore, perhaps chiefly an artefact of the conditions of fossilization at the time.

3. Divisions and climates of the Tertiary period

The whole Tertiary or Cenozoic period is now divided as follows:

Epoch	Time from beginning of epoch to present (millions of years)	Per cent. modern species
Recent	..	100
Pleistocene ('most recent') .	1	90
Pliocene ('more recent') . .	10	50
Miocene ('less recent') . .	25	20
Oligocene ('few recent') . .	35	10
Eocene ('dawn recent') . .	50	5
Paleocene ('ancient recent') .	60	0

The names were originally given by Lyell to indicate the percentages of modern species of shells; for curiosity these latter are given (approximately) in the third column. The Cenozoic period is a peculiar one in comparison with earlier phases of geological history, and although, being recent, we know more about it than of earlier periods, it remains difficult to fit into the rhythmical system of cycles (p. 18).

The whole Cenozoic is longer than the characteristic earlier periods of about 30 million years, and there is good reason to think that it represents two of these cycles. The Palaeocene, Eocene, and Oligocene was a relatively quiet time, during which the mountains raised during the Laramide revolution were eroded. The climate was cold early in the period, but it later became warmer and damper and there were probably extensive forests during the later Eocene and Oligocene. Palms then grew over much of Europe and there were forests where are now immense areas of steppe. The climate probably showed marked seasonal changes, at least in many parts of the world, and deposits of the time often show a lamination ('varving') that indicates an alternation of wet and dry seasons. During this first part of the Cenozoic there was some invasion of the land by water, but this was on a much smaller scale than during the inundations of earlier periods; indeed, the main land-masses have remained approximately constant throughout the Tertiary.

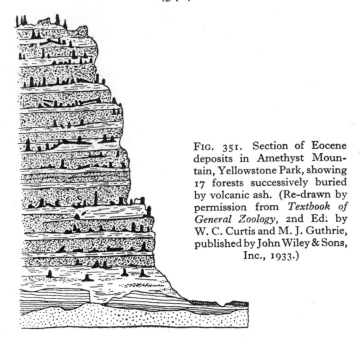

FIG. 351. Section of Eocene deposits in Amethyst Mountain, Yellowstone Park, showing 17 forests successively buried by volcanic ash. (Re-drawn by permission from *Textbook of General Zoology*, 2nd Ed: by W. C. Curtis and M. J. Guthrie, published by John Wiley & Sons, Inc., 1933.)

FIG. 352. Polar projection, showing the zoogeographical realms. (From Lull, *Organic Evolution*, copyright 1917, 1929 by The Macmillan Company, and used with their permission.)

During the early Miocene there was a time of intense crustal disturbance, the Cascadian revolution, in which many of the earth's main mountain chains, the Rockies, Andes, Alps, Himalayas, as well as humbler ranges such as the English chalkdowns, were raised into their present form. This revolution marks the subdivision of the Cenozoic into two periods. After it there was a further denudation during the Miocene and Pliocene, with some renewed sea invasion. The uplifting of the land during the Miocene probably produced arid conditions unfavourable to the growth of forests, and at this time there emerged several types of animal suitable for life on open prairies. Conditions probably became gradually colder throughout the Pliocene, and the Pleistocene epoch was characterized by the very extensive glaciations of the 'Ice Ages', occurring in at least four peaks of maximum cold, during each of which the ice caps advanced over large parts of the continents (p. 614).

Study of the history of the Cenozoic therefore gives us some idea of the climatic changes that have taken place, and we can try to correlate these with the succession of types of animal life. On the other hand, it is very important not to be over-impressed with any simple account of climatic changes. The periods of time involved are enormously long and it is unsafe to assume that conditions remained constant for any length of time that can be easily imagined, or even that conditions varied at a constant rate. For example, in Yellowstone Park, U.S.A., there are exposures of the remains of Eocene tree-trunks and these are arranged in layers, showing that at least twenty forests grew up and were covered by volcanic ash one after the other (Fig. 351). Each of these eruptions presumably produced a major revolution for the animals and plants in the area concerned; we do not know how wide that area may have been. Obviously no broad generalization about the presence of 'humid conditions and forests' throughout the Eocene can give us any clear picture of the ecological conditions even in one area. The geological history shows us that conditions were continually changing, though perhaps often at a rate very slow in comparison with the duration of animal lives. We can well imagine that these slow changes were responsible for producing new conditions and hence new types of life, but the data of the rocks are too obscure to show us the detailed circumstances of the emergence of any particular type.

4. Geographical regions

Although the main land-masses have varied little during the Tertiary period, there have been considerable changes in the opportunities for communication between them, both by the making and breaking of narrow land-bridges and by the development of sharp temperature gradients and desert areas. Zoogeographers divide the land into six regions (Fig. 352), Palaearctic (Central and N. Asia, Europe), Nearctic (N. America), Neotropical (Central and S. America), Ethiopian (Africa), Oriental (S. Asia and E. Indies), and Australasian. The Palaearctic and Nearctic have similar climates and have been connected several times during the Tertiary by an Alaska–Siberian bridge; they are therefore often grouped together as Holarctic. The Ethiopian region is now separated from the Palaearctic by the sudden change of temperature and desert conditions of North Africa, but in earlier times the animals of the two regions mixed freely. The same is true of the Palaearctic and Oriental regions. South America was connected with the Nearctic region in the Eocene, but the bridge was then broken until the Pleistocene; the Neotropical land faunas therefore differ considerably from the others. Australasia east of Wallace's line has been separated since the late Cretaceous.

The land masses have therefore been connected, in the main, in the north and separated in the south. In other words, America, North and South Africa, and the Oriental regions are capes projecting into the sea from the central Palaearctic (Eurasian) land-mass. In many cases there is evidence that animal life has evolved in this central area and migrated away towards the extremities. In several cases the types that evolved earlier remain as vestiges at these 'ends of the world', long after newer types have replaced them nearer to the centre. The lung-fishes are a conspicuous example of this and at another extreme it is perhaps no accident that Australian Aborigines and South African Bushmen are among the more primitive of men. This is the most probable explanation of the similarity in the fauna between these southern continents, but many suggestions of Antarctic land bridges have been put forward, in particular one connecting South Africa and South America in the early Tertiary. Opinion now inclines to the view that similarities of fauna can be explained by migration from a central land-mass, together with occasional chance crossings of the ocean, which might, for instance, explain the appearance of porcupine-like animals (p. 624) in Africa and South America at the same time (Oligocene). To explain the distribution of animals and plants it is not wise or necessary to *postulate* special land bridges, still less large floating movements of whole continents. The question whether such connexions and movements have existed must be decided primarily on geological evidence.

5. The earliest eutherians

Fossil placentals found in the Cretaceous period have all been insectivorans (p. 559). Those of the Palaeocene include also members which can be referred to the primates and to the carnivora, but they are very unlike modern members of those groups and could almost equally well be classed as Insectivora. Similarly, the ungulates and various other types that appeared in the Palaeocene could have had an insectivoran ancestry. Evidently, therefore, during the late Cretaceous and Palaeocene, the original placental stock was branching out into very varied habitats, and the branching was rapid. Simpson's careful classification recognizes twenty-six order of placentals (p. 554), and nearly all of these had become established by the Eocene. Ten of them have since become extinct. Evidently the great period of mammalian expansion was in the earlier part of the Cenozoic and the group may be considered to have passed its peak for the present. Only the bats, rodents, lagomorphs and perhaps the primates and carnivores can be considered really successful land animals at the present time; to these we may add the whales in the sea. The Artiodactyla are also abundant, but most of the remaining placental orders are to-day only very poorly represented in numbers.

In order to gain a comprehensive general understanding of the great placental history during its 80 million or so years duration, we will first give a technical definition of a placental, then the characteristics of the earlier types, and finally try to list some of the tendencies to change that are widely found in different groups. For simplification we can then attempt some grouping of the great list of orders, before dealing with them individually.

6. Definition of a eutherian (placental) mammal

The distinguishing characteristics of placentals are often listed somewhat as follows: The young are retained for a considerable time in the uterus and nourished by means of an allantoic placenta; there is no pouch or epipubic bones. In the skull there is usually a separate optic foramen, no palatal vacuities, and no inturned angle of the jaw. The tympanic bone is either ring-like or forms a bulla, there is never an alisphenoid bulla. The brain has large cerebral hemispheres connected by a corpus callosum. There is no cloaca. The dental formula is $\frac{3.1.4.3}{3.1.4.3}$, or some number reduced from this.

Many of these are obviously small points of formal definition, artificially abstracted for the purpose of classification. They are not really satisfactory as a definition of the life of a placental, such as we may hope to have in a more developed biology. The early population of Cretaceous insectivores presumably possessed most of these features, and in addition showed certain characteristics that are common to all the earlier mammals. Among these we may list (1) small size; (2) short legs with a plantigrade type of foot, having five digits; (3) the full eutherian number of teeth $\frac{3.1.4.3}{3.1.4.3}$, the molariform teeth being based on the tuberculo-sectorial pattern (p. 524); (4) the face was long and the skull tubular, enclosing a relatively small brain.

7. Evolutionary trends of eutherians

In the descendants of these early mammals we can recognize changes in each of these four sets of characters; changes occurring, independently, in some members at least of all the later lines. (1) Many of the mammals became larger. Increase in size seems to be advantageous to many animal types, but is presumably especially so for warm-blooded animals in cold climates, since it reduces the relative area of heat loss, though also introducing new problems of obtaining adequate amounts of food, if this has to be finely ground by tooth-surfaces whose increase with size is less rapid than that of the weight of tissue they must support. (2) The limbs became longer and specialized in various ways for locomotion, often by raising the heel off the ground, so that the animals came to walk on the digits instead of the sole of the foot (Fig. 353) and the number of toes became reduced. (3) The number of teeth became reduced and their shape specialized, often by the addition of cusps and their fusion to make transverse or longitudinal grinding ridges in herbivorous animals or cutting blades in carnivores. (4) The brain of the earlier mammals resembles that of reptiles (Fig. 354) and later forms show increasing development of the non-olfactory part of the cortex, increase of the frontal lobes, and other changes probably correlated with more complicated behaviour. It has often been supposed that the brain becomes relatively larger in later forms, but Edinger has shown by study of fossil horse brains that as the body size increases the brain-body ratio decreases.

8. Conservative eutherians

Much of this change was the result of adopting a fully terrestrial and often herbivorous mode of life, in place of the earlier arboreal and

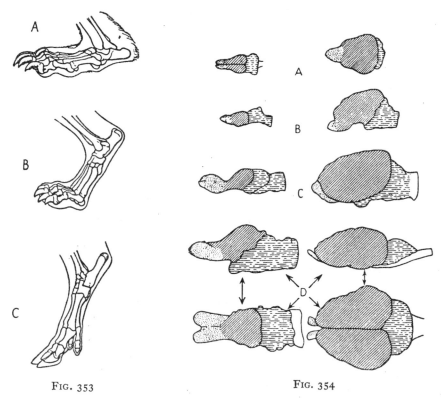

FIG. 353   FIG. 354

FIG. 353. Postures of the foot in mammals. A, plantigrade (bear); B, digitigrade (hyaena); C, unguligrade (pig). (From Lull, after Pander and D'Alton.)

FIG. 354. Comparison of pairs of brains of archaic (left) and modern (right) mammals of similar size. Olfactory lobes dotted, cerebral hemispheres oblique lines, cerebellum and medulla, dashes. A, *Arctocyon* and *Canis*; B, *Phenacodus* and *Sus*; C, *Coryphodon* and *Rhinoceros*; D, *Uintatherium* and *Hippopotamus*. (After Osborn, from Lull, *Organic Evolution*, copyright 1917, 1929 by The Macmillan Co., and used with their permission.)

insectivorous or carnivorous one. Changes in these four directions have taken place in many separate mammalian lines, but the evidence contradicts the thesis that they are the result of some force of orthogenesis, driving the animals infallibly along. In nearly every group there are examples of some animals that have remained nearly unchanged for long periods, e.g. the opossums and shrews since the Cretaceous (70 million years), lemurs and tarsiers since the Eocene (50 million years), pigs and tapirs since the Oligocene (35 million years), and deer since the Miocene (20 million years), to name only a few.

It is important to study such cases where there has been no change; they form the 'controls', and may enable us to decide the factors inducing change when it does occur. Moreover, in many further cases there has been change in some but not all of the above directions, for instance, many of the most successful mammals have remained small. There may even be changes in directions opposite to those listed, for instance, some edentates and whales have more than the original number of teeth. This, however, seems to be rare, and still rarer is a reversal of the usual directions. Mammals do not commonly decrease in size during evolution, and they probably never reacquire lost digits, though in a few cases claws have reappeared after they had been lost (p. 593).

9. Divisions and classification of Eutheria

Infraclass 3. Eutheria
    Cohort 1. Unguiculata
        Order 1. Insectivora
        Order 2. Chiroptera
        Order 3. Dermoptera
       *Order 4. Taeniodonta
       *Order 5. Tillodontia
        Order 6. Edentata
        Order 7. Pholidota
        Order 8. Primates
    Cohort 2. Glires
        Order 1. Rodentia
        Order 2. Lagomorpha
    Cohort 3. Mutica
        Order Cetacea
    Cohort 4. Ferungulata
      Superorder 1. Ferae
        Order Carnivora
      Superorder 2. Protungulata
      *Order 1. Condylarthra
      *Order 2. Notoungulata
      *Order 3. Litopterna
      *Order 4. Astrapotheria
        Order 5. Tubulidentata

Infraclass 3 (cont.)

    Superorder 3. Paenungulata
        Order 1. Hyracoidea
        Order 2. Proboscidea
      *Order 3. Pantodonta
      *Order 4. Dinocerata
      *Order 5. Pyrotheria
      *Order 6. Embrithopoda
        Order 7. Sirenia

    Superorder 4. Mesaxonia
        Order Perissodactyla

    Superorder 5. Paraxonia
        Order Artiodactyla

For purposes of phylogenetic study as well as classificatory convenience it is very desirable to attempt to discover how the original
eutherian population became divided at its Cretaceous origin, and
whether there were main trunks of the placental tree. By Eocene
times most of the existing orders were already well established (Fig.
355) and it is often stated that the branching of the population occurred
relatively rapidly, though it is doubtful if we may use this term for a
process occupying perhaps 30 million years during the late Cretaceous
and Palaeocene! This early expansion into varied branches, occurring
at a time when few fossils were being formed, makes it difficult to
discover the outlines of the main divisions. Nevertheless, careful
piecing together of evidence suggests grouping of the twenty-six
eutherian orders into four main cohorts, and the division corresponds
in the main to the classification originally proposed by Linnaeus in
1766 on a basis of the foot structure. The Unguiculata include orders
in which the original characteristics of the mammalian type have been
largely preserved, the Insectivora themselves and the Chiroptera (bats),
the Primates and the Edentata (sloths, ant-eaters, and armadilloes),
all of which can be easily and directly derived from the insectivores.
Here also probably belong the scaly ant-eater, *Manis* (Pholidota)
and the extinct *Taeniodontia and *Tillodonta, which survived only
for a short time and of which little is known and they will not be
mentioned further. The Rodentia and the rabbits and hares (Lagomorpha) are often also considered to belong here, but they appear
fully developed in the Eocene and must have diverged very early and
are therefore placed alone in a separate cohort Glires. Similarly the
whales (Cetacea) have certainly been distinct since the Eocene and,

their affinities being quite obscure, they are classed as a separate cohort Mutica.

All the remaining mammals show signs of a common origin and Simpson suggests grouping them together as a cohort Ferungulata. It has long been realized that the hoofed animals include two distinct types, those with an uneven number of toes, Perissodactyla, and even toes, Artiodactyla. The former can be derived from the Palaeocene and Eocene animals known as *Condylarthra. The Carnivora seem at first sight to have no similarity to either of the ungulate types, but it has been suspected for some time that the ancestral Carnivora, the *Creodonta, resembled the earliest artiodactyls. Further study has shown that creodonts and condylarths are often so alike as to be hardly separable (they are also very like Insectivora). Simpson's suggested cohort Ferungulata recognizes the existence of this common creodont-condylarth stock, perhaps in early Palaeocene times. The cohort may then conveniently be subdivided into five superorders, Ferae for the Carnivora, Protungulata (= 'first ungulates') for the condylarths, the extinct South American ungulates (*Litopterna and *Notoungulata), the obscure *Astrapotheria and Tubulidentata (*Orycteropus*, the Cape ant-eater). The third superorder Paenungulata (= 'near ungulates') includes the elephants (Proboscidea), conies (Hyracoidea), and sea cows (Sirenia), as well as the extinct *Pantodonta, *Dinocerata, *Pyrotheria, and *Embrithopoda. The fourth superorder Perissodactyla is then made to include only the horses, tapirs, and rhinoceroses; and the fifth superorder Artiodactyla the pigs, camels, and ruminants. This system gives us a means of grouping that is both phylogenetically accurate and conveniently close to the usually accepted uses of familiar names.

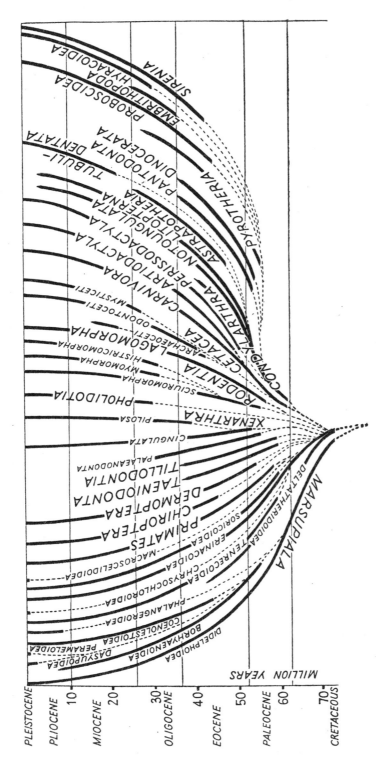

Fig. 355. Chart showing the probable affinities of the orders of Mammals (large capitals) and the lesser divisions of some of the more primitive orders (smaller capitals).

XXII

INSECTIVORES, BATS, AND EDENTATES

1. Shrews, hedgehogs, and moles; order Insectivora

Infraclass 3. Eutheria
  Cohort 1. Unguiculata
    Order 1. Insectivora
      *Superfamily 1. Deltatheridioidea. Upper Cretaceous–
        Eocene. Asia and N. America
        *Deltatheridium. Cretaceous. Asia

      Superfamily 2. Tenrecoidea. Palaeocene–Recent
        Solenodon, alamiqui, W. Indies;
        Tenrec (= Centetes), tenrec, Madagascar;
        Potamogale, otter shrew, W. Africa

      Superfamily 3. Chrysochloroidea. Pleistocene–Recent
        Chrysochloris, golden mole, S. Africa

      Superfamily 4. Erinaceoidea. Upper Cretaceous–Recent,
        Holarctic and Africa
        *Zalambdalestes, Upper Cretaceous, Asia;
        Erinaceus, hedgehog, Old World, Miocene–Recent

      Superfamily 5. Soricoidea. Palaeocene–Recent
        Family Soricidae. Holarctic, Africa, Oligocene–Recent
          Sorex, shrew, Miocene–Recent;
          Neomys, water shrew, Eurasia
        Family Talpidae. Holarctic, Upper Eocene–Recent
          Talpa, mole, Miocene–Recent;
          Myogale, desman, water mole

      Superfamily 6. Macroscelidoidea. Oligocene–Recent
        *Family. Anagalidae. Oligocene. Asia
          *Anagale
        Family 2. Macroscelididae. Recent. Africa
          Macroscelides, elephant shrew
        Family 3. Tupaiidae. Recent. Asia
          Tupaia, tree shrew;
          Ptilocercus, pen-tailed tree shrew

Modern insectivores are mostly nocturnal animals, maintaining in some special habitat the primitive mammalian features, which have persisted with little change since the Cretaceous. Thus the hedgehog has his spines and the mole his retiring habits. The shrews are perhaps the most successful members of the order.

The characteristics of insectivores are mostly those of a primitive placental. The full dentition of $\dfrac{3.1.4.3}{3.1.4.3}$ is usually preserved, and the cusps have diverged very little from the tritubercular-tuberculo-sectorial pattern. The skull (Fig. 356) shows many primitive features, such as an incomplete bony palate and an open tympanic cavity, in

FIG. 356. Skull of hedgehog (*Erinaceus*).

which the tympanic bone (the old angular) forms a partial ring. In the post-cranial skeleton there is usually found a clavicle, five digits with claws in both limbs, and a plantigrade method of locomotion.

The soft parts are correspondingly primitive. The brain has large olfactory bulbs and small cerebral hemispheres, composed mainly of large pyriform lobes (rhinopallium) and usually not covering the corpora quadrigemina or cerebellum, and with little convolution. The neopallium and corpus callosum are very small. Some insectivores retain the cloaca. The uterus is bicornuate and the testes are never fully descended into a scrotum. Many insectivores hibernate in winter and are provided with special reserves of fat for this purpose.

*Deltatheridium is a fossil insectivore found in the Upper Cretaceous of Mongolia and having characters very close to those of the ancestor not only of insectivores but of all placental mammals. The skull was tubular and elongated, but without the special snout of some modern forms. The zygomatic arch, reduced in many later insectivores, was complete and strong. The teeth are of special interest in that in the upper molars the central cusp (amphicone) shows only partial division into paracone and metacone. Other insectivores found in similar beds (**Zalambdalestes*) were more like hedgehogs, though of primitive type.

Classification of the various lines of insectivores has been difficult, as might be expected in a group containing surviving ancient as well as modified types. It is not feasible here to discuss the possible affinities of the various groups.

Tenrec (Fig. 357) from Madagascar and *Solenodon*, the alamiqui (Fig. 358), from the West Indies are remarkably similar animals, resembling hedgehogs. The teeth have a tritubercular pattern, by which they are sometimes distinguished as 'zalambdodont' from the remaining or 'dilambdodont' insectivores. The resemblance of the alamiqui and the tenrec has often been cited as evidence of a land bridge, but is probably a result of retention of primitive features. *Potamogale* (the otter shrew) is a related aquatic African form, feeding on fish.

The golden moles (*Chrysochloris*) of Africa are burrowing animals, with interesting features of similarity to the marsupial and true moles. The hedgehog (*Erinaceus*) (Fig. 359) is a mainly nocturnal creature, feeding on a mixed animal diet of insects, slugs, small birds, and snakes or even fruit. The type is very ancient and there are many species, restricted to the Old World. The shrews (Soricidae) are mouse-like, insectivorous, and omnivorous animals of various types, some terrestrial, others aquatic, found throughout the world. *Sorex* (Fig. 360) is a very ancient type, found from the Miocene onwards without change. Moles (*Talpa*) (Fig. 361) are related to shrews and are found throughout the Holarctic region. They are highly specialized for burrowing, with rudimentary eyes (sometimes covered with opaque skin) and no external ears, smooth fur, fused cervical vertebrae, massive pectoral girdle, including a procoracoid, and broad digging claws on the hands. They feed mainly on earthworms. *Myogale*, the desman, of south Europe is an aquatic mole, with webbed feet.

Apart from these familiar forms the Insectivora includes the interesting oriental tree shrews (*Tupaia*) (Fig. 362) and African jumping shrews or elephant shrews (*Macroscelides*) (Fig. 363), sometimes placed together in a separate sub-order ('Menotyphla'). This group can be traced back to the Oligocene and its special interest is that it shows in several ways indications of primate organization. The brain is larger than in the remaining insectivores, which we have already considered ('Lipotyphla'). There are various genera and species of elephant shrews in Africa, all with long trunk-like snouts. They are diurnal and proceed by a series of jumps with their long back legs. There are five digits in hand and foot. The tree shrews, *Tupaia* and its allies, are arboreal squirrel-like creatures with a long tail. They feed on insects or fruit and show many lemuroid characters. For

FIG. 357. *Tenrec.*
(From photographs.)

FIG. 358. *Solenodon*, alamiqui.
(After *Cambridge Natural History*.)

FIG. 360. *Sorex*, common shrew.
(From photographs.)

FIG. 359. *Erinaceus*, hedgehog.
(From photographs.)

FIG. 361. *Talpa*, common mole.

FIG. 362. *Tupaia*, tree shrew.
(From photographs.)

FIG. 363. *Macroscelides*, elephant
shrew. (From a photograph.)

instance, there is a complete post-orbital bar, and the brain shows
larger hemispheres than in *Macroscelides* or other insectivores, and
less development of the olfactory regions. These animals, though
they are like insectivores, have a life very like that of lemurs and they
are often classified with the primates; they show how narrow is the
gap between the two groups, but we need not worry unduly whether
they 'really' belong in one group or the other.

FIG. 364. Little brown bat (*Myotis*). (After *American Mammals*, by W. J. Hamilton, McGraw Hill Book Company.)

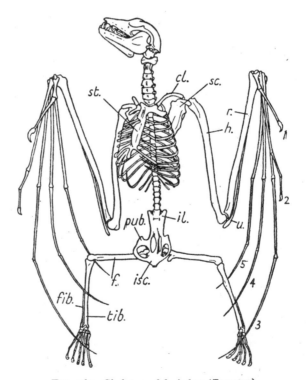

FIG. 365. Skeleton of fruit bat (*Pteropus*).

cl. clavicle; *f.* femur; *fib.* fibula; *h.* humerus; *il.* ilium; *isc.* ischium; *pub.* pubis; *r.* radius; *sc.* scapula; *st.* sternum; *tib.* tibia; *u.* ulna. (From Reynolds, *The Vertebrate Skeleton*, after Shipley and MacBride.)

2. Order Chiroptera. Bats

Cohort Unguiculata
 Order 2. Chiroptera
  Suborder 1. Megachiroptera. Oligocene–Recent
   Family Pteropidae. Asia, Australia, Africa
    Pteropus, fruit bat
  Suborder 2. Microchiroptera. Eocene–Recent
   18 families, including:
   Family Rhinolophidae
    Rhinolophus, horse-shoe bats, Europe, Asia, Australasia
   Family Phyllostomatidae
    Desmodus, vampire bats, S. America
   Family Vespertilionidae
    Vespertilio, European bats, Palaearctic
 Order 3. Dermoptera. Palaeocene–Recent
   Cynocephalus (= *Galeopithecus*), colugo or flying lemur, Asia
 *Order 4. Taeniodonta. Palaeocene–Eocene. N. America
  *Psittacotherium
 *Order 5. Tillodontia. Palaeocene–Eocene. Europe, N. America
  *Tillotherium

Except for their specializations for flight the bats stand very close to the insectivores. They diverged early, however, and their characteristics were already developed in the Eocene. They are the only mammals that truly fly by flapping the wings, as distinct from the soaring of flying phalangers, colugos, and others. The wing (Fig. 364) is a patagium or fold of skin, involving all the digits of the hand except the first, and extending also along the sides of the body to include the legs (but not the feet) and, usually, the tail. The chief skeletal modification is therefore a very great elongation of the arm, and especially of its more distal bones (Fig. 365). The sternum carries a keel for the attachment of the large pectoral muscles and the clavicle is stout, often fused with the sternum and with the scapula. Since the thorax is used as a fixation point for the flight muscles the ribs move relatively little on each other and respiration is mainly by the diaphragm. The ribs are flattened and may indeed be fused together and with the vertebrae. The characteristics of the arms and thorax are rather similar in these flying animals to those found in brachiating arboreal creatures, such as gibbons, which also have very long arms and large, fixed thoracic cages.

The humerus is very long and carries a much-enlarged greater tuberosity, which may acquire a special articulation with the scapula. The flight movements occur mostly at the shoulder, with the rest of the limb held stiff. The radius is very long and the ulna reduced and fused with the radius; the elbow joint allows only flexion and extension. The carpus is much specialized by fusion of bones, allowing

FIG. 366. Temperature chart of greater horseshoe bat. Manipulation during attachment of thermocouple to back has caused warming at beginning of experiment. Bat stimulated at points marked *s*. The black rectangles mark periods during which the animal was shivering or moving. Room temperature 15·5° C. (From Burbank and Young.)

flexion-extension and spreading of the digits. Of the five fingers the first is stout and free of the wing; it bears a claw in Microchiroptera, as does the second also in fruit bats. The remaining metacarpals and proximal phalanges are enormously elongated to support the wing, the distal phalanges being relatively short.

The pelvis is rotated so that the acetabulum lies dorsally and the limb is held outwards and upwards. The ventral portions of the girdle are thus drawn apart and are often not united in a symphysis. The hind legs are weak and carry five clawed digits, by which the animal is suspended upside down when at rest.

The great development of the arm and patagium makes it impossible for bats to walk actively, but they can climb and crawl. When not flying they usually hang head downwards. The temperature varies

with the activity: they become cold every time they go to sleep and
warm up by jerking the legs when they awake (Fig. 366).

The typical microchiropteran is an insectivore, often with molars
of the ancestral tritubercular type.   Insects are caught on the wing
with the very large mouth and either swallowed at once or stored in a
pocket formed by the tail end of the wing. Diets differ considerably:
many members of the Phyllostomatidae of South America drink blood,
and this is the sole diet of *Desmodus* and *Diphylla*, which pierce the skin

FIG. 367. Big-eared bat (*Plecotus*).
(After *American Mammals*, by W. J. Hamilton, McGraw Hill Book Company.)

with special pointed incisors and then lick or suck the blood. Other
Microchiroptera eat fruit or flesh, and the Megachiroptera or flying
foxes of the tropics are wholly fruit-eaters and have flattened grinding
teeth. The skull of flying foxes retains many primitive features such
as an annular tympanic bone and absence of a post-orbital bar.

In the soft parts the bats resemble the insectivores in many ways.
Thus the cerebral hemispheres are small and do not cover the cerebellum. As in birds the olfactory portion of the brain is reduced,
especially in the insectivorous bats. The placenta is of a discoidal
form and haemochorial, at least in some types. A very peculiar feature
is that copulation occurs in the autumn and the sperms remain alive
(but presumably not active) within the female until fertilization takes
place in the spring. The young are well formed at birth and have then
already cut the milk dentition of special teeth with sharp, backwardly
directed hooks, which, with the claws, enable the baby to remain
attached to the mother in flight.

The Megachiroptera, fruit bats or flying foxes, are quite large animals (with wing span up to 5 ft.) living in Asia, the Pacific, Australia, and Africa. In spite of their diet they are in some ways the less-specialized group, having a snout, head, and ears of normal mammalian form.

The Microchiroptera are highly modified for flight at night and find their way without the aid of the eyes. It has been shown that they are able to avoid obstacles in complete darkness and they do this mainly by a system of echo-sounding, using the very high-pitched sounds that they emit. It has long been supposed that bats possess a high development of the sense of touch, but there is no experimental evidence as to the function of the peculiar areas on the nose and ears, which may be tactile organs. The nose folds are well developed in the horse-shoe bats (*Rhinolophus*), two species of which are found in Great Britain. The ears are very large in all bats and sometimes extremely long and with a very marked tragus (Fig. 367). The high squeak of the bat is the lower range only of a series of sounds sent out for purposes of direction-finding by reflection from objects.

The Microchiroptera is one of the most successful groups among modern mammals, including a large number of families, genera, and species, with differing habitats. As would be expected, the families often have wide geographical ranges, vespertilionids, for instance, are found all over the world. It is interesting, however, that the genera mostly have a rather restricted range. For instance, *Vespertilio* is limited to the Palaearctic, though *Pipistrellus* is found also in North America. The vampire bats (Phyllostomatidae) are restricted to Central and South America. The fact that even flying mammals should be so restricted is good evidence that the simple problem of communication is one of the least of the difficulties standing in the way of the dispersal of an animal type.

3. Order Dermoptera

The colugo or flying lemur of the orient, correctly called *Cynocephalus*, though the name *Galeopithecus* has long been used, is a very early offshoot from the insectivoran stock, with a patagium developed for parachuting. The wing differs from that of bats in that the fingers are not elongated and the wing is not flapped in flight; otherwise the animals are like insectivores. They are nocturnal and feed on leaves and fruit. A peculiarity is the forwardly projecting lower incisors with tips divided to form a comb as in lemurs. A related Palaeocene form shows that this line has been separate for more than 50 million years.

4. Order Edentata

Cohort Unguiculata

    Order 6. Edentata

      *Suborder 1. Palaeanodonta. Palaeocene–Oligocene. N. America

        Metacheiromys, Eocene

      Suborder 2. Xenarthra. Palaeocene–Recent. Central and S. America

        Infraorder 1. Cingulata. Palaeocene–Recent

          Superfamily 1. Dasypodoidea, armadilloes

            Dasypus, nine-banded armadillo

          *Superfamily 2. Glyptodontoidea, Upper Eocene–Pleistocene

            Glyptodon

        Infraorder 2. Pilosa. Upper Eocene–Recent. Central and S. America

          *Superfamily 1. Megalonychoidea. Ground sloths. Upper Eocene–Pleistocene

            Megatherium, *Mylodon*

          Superfamily 2. Myrmecophagoidea. Ant-eaters. Pliocene–Recent

            Myrmecophaga, giant ant-eater; *Tamandua*, tamandua; *Cyclopes*, two-toed ant-eater

          Superfamily 3. Bradypodoidea. Sloths. Recent

            Bradypus, three-toed sloth; *Choloepus*, two-toed sloth, unau

    Order 7. Pholidota

      Family Manidae. Oligocene–Recent

        Manis, scaly ant-eater (pangolin), Asia, Africa

The reduction or loss of the teeth with adoption of a diet of soft invertebrates and especially ants has occurred independently at least five times among mammals; this habit is indeed to be expected, since the whole mammalian stock was at first insectivorous. We have already noticed the occurrence of ant-eating characteristics in the echidnas and in *Myrmecobius*, the marsupial ant-eater. Among eutherians the habit is well developed in animals of three different types, (1) the ant-eaters of South America, *Myrmecophaga* and its allies, (2) the pangolins of Africa and Asia, *Manis*, and (3) the aardvark or Cape ant-eater (*Orycteropus*). These ant-eating animals have many features in common, for instance, they all possess a long snout and tongue, very well-developed salivary glands, and reduced teeth; because of these similarities they were for a long time classed together as Edentata. It has gradually become apparent, however, that the three groups of placental ant-eaters have evolved separately. The aardvark was probably an early offshoot from the ferungulate stock, though we know little of its history (p. 663). The pangolins are placed in the Unguiculata, but they represent a separate line, diverging from the insectivore stock very early (p. 575). The South American ant-eaters form a natural group with the armadilloes and sloths, having, like the South American ungulates and other animals, proceeded along several courses of evolution of their own during the long isolation of their continent throughout the Cenozoic period. The term Edentata is now technically reserved for this South American group.

In many ways the Edentata remain close to the basic eutherian condition. The characteristic feature has been a simplification of the teeth, which are absent altogether in the ant-eaters themselves. In sloths and armadilloes the front teeth are absent and the hinder ones present as a row of similar pegs, with no covering of enamel. Except in sloths, there is considerable elongation of the snout and the whole cranium is of tubular form, with a low brain-case, containing a small brain with poorly developed hemispheres, having a large olfactory region. The jugal bar is often incomplete, but the hind end of the jugal carries a large downward extension in sloths and ground sloths. A characteristic common to all the Edentata is the presence of extra articulations between the lumbar vertebrae, a striking feature in view of many different modes of locomotion in the group. From these articulations the group gets its name, Xenarthra. Several other peculiar features of the skeleton are common to most or all these animals, such as a fusion of the coracoid with the acromion to enclose a coraco-scapular foramen and a union between the ischium and the caudal vertebrae. The feet have well-developed claws, often used for digging, and the animals may walk on the outside of the claws, though other species are arboreal and use the claws for hanging.

Many of the characteristics of the group are obviously those of all generalized eutherians, the edentates having departed little from the original mammalian plan. Their features are mostly the result of special ways of life, often leading to very bizarre external appearances, such as the long snout of the great ant-eater or the carapace of the armadillo.

The order Edentata is divided into two suborders, the first *Palaeanodonta for a few Palaeocene and Eocene types such as *Meta-chèiromys*, which were like armadilloes, but lacked the carapace and had not yet acquired the structure of the vertebrae found in all the remaining edentates (suborder Xenarthra). The palaeanodonts are found in North America and presumably they represent survivors of the original stock, existing before the separation of the continents.

FIG. 368. Hairy armadillo, *Dasypus*. (From photographs.)

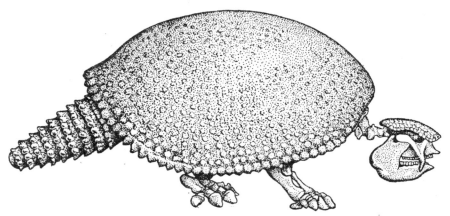

FIG. 369. *Glyptodon*. (From a reconstruction lent by the Trustees of the British Museum.)

The xenarthrous population itself split up very early and we can recognize two main groups (infraorders), the Cingulata for the armadilloes and glyptodons, and Pilosa for the ant-eaters, sloths, and ground sloths.

5. Armadilloes

The armadilloes (Dasypodidae) (Fig. 368) have departed least from the ancestral plan and are a very ancient group, already differentiated in Palaeocene times. They are nocturnal and fossorial and obtain protection by the development of bony plates in the skin, these being covered by horny scutes. The plates are usually arranged in rings round the body and in some genera allow the animal to roll up into a ball. The vertebrae tend to be fused to support the shield, and many unite in the sacrum. The teeth are simple uniform pegs, without enamel, and with open roots and continuous growth. They are often more numerous than in other mammals (as many as 25 in each jaw); with simplification of the system of tooth morphogenesis, repetition becomes possible, as we see also in whales. The armadilloes are insectivores and omnivorous scavengers, feeding on dead carcasses and the like in tropical central and South America; there are many different genera and species; *Dasypus*, the nine-banded armadillo, is a common form, about 16 in. long, found as far north as Texas.

FIG. 370. Skeleton of ground-sloth (**Scelidotherium*) from Pleistocene of Argentina. (From Woodward, *Palaeontology*, after Lydekker.)

During the Pleistocene and earlier periods, besides the modern armadilloes, there were also giant armadilloes, and in addition the glyptodonts (Fig. 369) were a related type, diverging as early as the Upper Eocene, with a skull composed of many fused small pieces and sometimes the well-known 'battle-axe' tail.

6. Ant-eaters and sloths

The modern soft-skinned edentates (ant-eaters and sloths) are very specialized and not superficially like the armadilloes. The ground sloths (Fig. 370), of which there were several families living between the Oligocene and Pleistocene, were in some respects intermediate between the two types. They were quadrupedal animals, but the fore-limbs acquired very long claws and it is often suggested that the ground sloths used them to bend down branches in order to reach the leaves. The teeth were few and used for grinding. Nearly fifty genera of ground sloths have been recognized and they were evidently very successful in the South American forests. **Megatherium* was larger than an elephant and a similar form, **Neomylodon*, persisted very nearly to the present day; pieces of skin have been found, and these, even in the favourable conditions, can hardly have maintained their appearance for more than a few hundreds or at the most thousands of years.

The ant-eaters are placed in the family Myrmecophagidae and have the characteristic elongated snout, without teeth. There are three

FIG. 371. Great ant-eater, *Myrmecophaga*, from life.

FIG. 372. Lesser ant-eater, *Tamandua*. (From photographs.)

FIG. 373. Tree ant-eater, *Cyclopes*, showing one of the peculiar attitudes adopted. (From a photograph.)

genera, differing in size, and the larger species have relatively much the longer snouts. The great ant-eater *Myrmecophaga* (Fig. 371) has an enormously elongated face, but this is much shorter in the smaller *Tamandua* (Fig. 372), and the very small tree-living *Cyclopes* (Fig. 373) has a head of normal mammalian shape. Analysis shows that there is little difference between the relative rate of growth of the face in these three genera, and the differing final forms result mainly, though not wholly, from the differences in absolute size (Figs. 374 and 374*a*). In all ant-eaters the face becomes relatively longer as the animal increases in size, and the enormous snout of the great ant-eater is produced by a relative growth-rate only slightly higher than that found in *Tamandua* and *Cyclopes*. This is an excellent example of the way in which the proportions of an organ will vary in animals of different sizes if its growth is heterogonic, that is to say, relatively faster or slower than that of the body as a whole.

The hard palate is prolonged backwards in *Myrmecophaga* by union of the pterygoids, a condition found also in some armadilloes (*Dasypus*).

The great ant-eater is a fine animal over 6 ft. long, with a long hairy coat, including a very bushy tail and with a black stripe edged with brown at the shoulder. It has a very long thin tongue for collecting

FIG. 374. Side views of adult skulls of A, *Myrmecophaga*; B, *Tamandua*; C, *Cyclopes*. *Tamandua* and *Cyclopes* are approximately 1½ and 3 times the scale of *Myrmecophaga*. T.L. measurement of total length; M.L. of maxilla length. (From Reeve.)

ants, and enormous submaxillary salivary glands. The claws of the front legs are very large and used for defence as well as for digging. *Tamandua* and *Cyclopes* differ from *Myrmecophaga* in other features besides the length of snout. Although perhaps the most striking differences are due to the greater size, and hence face length, of the larger forms, it must not be supposed that the populations have been changed into each other by a simple change in size, though this might appear to be so from looking at the skulls alone. Each genus has many special characteristics of colour, pelt, and other features. Thus *Tamandua* is yellow with black sides, *Cyclopes* golden yellow all over, and both have soft fur. Whereas *Myrmecophaga* is terrestrial the others are arboreal and have prehensile tails; in *Cyclopes* the hind foot is specially adapted for climbing.

The sloths (Bradypodidae) (Fig. 375) are very fully adapted for arboreal life and indeed show, as do the bats, how the mammalian skeleton can be used with surprisingly little change to support weight by hanging, the limbs being used as tension members rather than as pillars. In marked contrast to the ant-eaters the face is short and the

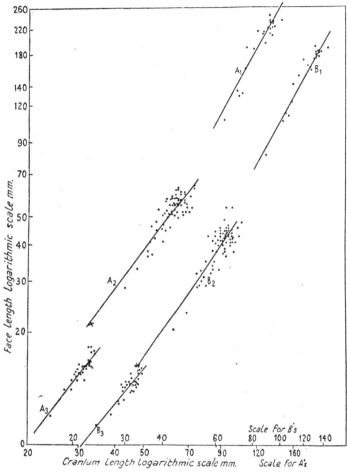

FIG. 374a. Logarithmic plots of lengths of maxillae (A's) and nasals (B's) against cranium.

The suffixes represent: 1, *Myrmecophaga*; 2, *Tamandua*; 3, *Cyclopes*. Scale for B graphs is shifted to the right compared with A's. Crosses at bottom of lines for A₂ and B₂ represent a very young *Tamandua*. The lines were fitted to each sample by least squares. (From Reeve.)

head rounded, with large frontal air sinuses. The neck is peculiar for the presence of nine or ten cervical vertebrae in the three-toed sloth, *Bradypus*. This might be supposed to provide a flexible neck for an animal that must often face backward, were it not that in the two-toed sloth *Choloepus* there are but six cervical vertebrae.

The limbs are very long, especially the fore-limbs, and the digits carry hooked claws for hanging (Fig. 376). In the pectoral girdle the clavicle articulates with the coracoid, a unique condition among mammals. As in ant-eaters the acromion is connected with the coracoid,

FIG. 375. Two-toed sloth, *Choloepus*. (From a photograph in Scott, *Land Mammals*, copyright 1913, 1937 by the American Philosophical Society and used with the permission of the Macmillan Company.)

FIG. 376. Skeleton of *Bradypus*. (After Blainville.)

enclosing a coraco-scapular foramen. The significance of these special features is not clear, but the habit of hanging upside down has produced some obvious modifications, for instance all the vertebral neural spines are low and the pelvis is short. Even here, however, we find peculiar similarities to the ant-eaters, in the union of the ischium with caudal vertebrae, a feature whose adaptive significance is obscure.

The sloths live on foliage, but this herbivorous diet is secondary to a long period of inseetivorous life, during which there was a reduction of the teeth and loss of enamel. On adoption of the new way of life the enamel could not be restored, but a grinding surface is provided by the presence of cement and continuous growth of the teeth. The stomach is large and divided into several chambers.

The sloths live in the forests of South and Central America, moving very slowly among the branches, which they come to resemble closely by the growth of blue and green algae in special grooves in the hairs. Their upside-down posture has led to many changes from the typical mammalian organization, including, it is said, a reversal of the usual mechanism for maintaining posture. When a normal mammal is decerebrated its legs assume a pillar-like extensor rigidity, because of the overaction of the reflexes of standing. A decerebrate sloth is said to show the opposite, flexor, rigidity.

FIG. 377. Black-bellied tree pangolin, *Manis*. (From photographs.)

7. Order Pholidota: pangolins

The pangolins or scaly ant-eaters, *Manis* (Fig. 377) of the Old World (Africa and Asia) have many features superficially like those of the New World ant-eaters and the groups may be remotely related. Unfortunately nothing is known of the fossil history of *Manis* and its position among the unguiculates is therefore provisional. The body is up to 5 ft. long, covered with horny epidermal scales, interspersed with hairs. The absence of teeth, the elongated snout, long thin tongue, simple stomach, reduced ears, and long claws are all features found in the other ant-eaters and are presumably produced by convergence. Other common features, such as reduction of the jugal bone, have been suggested as signs of affinity, but may also be convergent, in this case by reduction of the muscles of mastication. There are very peculiar rods of cartilage extending backwards from the xiphisternum. These have been compared with the abdominal ribs of reptiles, but are probably a special development, connected with the protrusion of the enormous tongue, which is carried in a special sac and operated by muscles attached to the xiphisternal processes. There are various species of *Manis*; some live in open savannah, others are able to climb trees. All are nocturnal and eat ants and termites.

XXIII

PRIMATES

1. Classification

Order 8. Primates

  Suborder 1. Prosimii. Palaeocene–Recent

    Infraorder 1. Lemuriformes. Palaeocene–Recent

      *Family 1. Plesiadapidae. Palaeocene–Eocene. Europe, N. America
        Plesiadapis, Palaeocene

      *Family 2. Adapidae. Eocene. Europe, N. America
        Notharctus

      Family 3. Lemuridae. Pleistocene–Recent. Madagascar
        Megaladapis, Pleistocene; *Lemur*, common lemur

      Family 4. Indridae. Pleistocene–Recent. Madagascar
        Indri, indris

      Family 5. Daubentoniidae. Recent. Madagascar
        Daubentonia (= *Cheiromys*), aye-aye

    Infraorder 2. Lorisiformes. Pliocene–Recent. Asia and Africa

      Family. Lorisidae.
        Loris, India, slender loris; *Galago*, Africa, bush baby; *Perodicticus*, Africa, potto

    Infraorder 3. Tarsiiformes. Palaeocene–Recent. Holarctic, Asia

      *Family 1. Anaptomorphidae. Palaeocene–Oligocene
        Necrolemur, Eocene. Europe

      Family 2. Tarsiidae. Recent. E. Indies
        Tarsius, tarsier

  Suborder 2. Anthropoidea. Oligocene–Recent

    Infraorder 1. Platyrrhina. Miocene–Recent. S. America. New World monkeys

      Family 1. Callithricidae. Recent
        Callithrix (= *Hapale*), marmoset

      Family 2. Cebidae. Miocene–Recent
        Homunculus, Miocene; *Cebus*, capuchin; *Ateles*, spider monkey; *Alouatta*, howler monkey

Infraorder 2. Catarrhina. Oligocene–Recent
  *Family 1. Parapithecidae. Oligocene. Africa
    *Parapithecus
  Family 2. Cercopithecidae. Oligocene–Recent. Africa,
    Asia, Old World monkeys
    Macaca, rhesus monkey, macaque, Asia, N. Africa; Papio,
    baboon, Africa; Mandrillus, mandrill, Africa; Cerco-
    pithecus, guenon, Africa; Presbytis, langur, E. Asia;
    Colobus, guereza, Africa
  Family 3. Pongidae. Oligocene–Recent. Apes
    *Propliopithecus, Lower Oligocene. Egypt; *Pliopithecus,
    Lower Miocene. Europe, Africa; *Dryopithecus, Mio-
    cene. Africa, Asia; *Australopithecus, Pleistocene. S.
    Africa; *Proconsul, Miocene. Africa; Hylobates, gibbon,
    SE. Asia; Pongo, orang-utan, E. Indies; Pan, chimpan-
    zee, Africa; Gorilla, gorilla, Africa.
  Family 4. Hominidae. Pleistocene–Recent. Man
    *Pithecanthropus (= *Sinanthropus), Java and Pekin man,
    Pleistocene. E. Asia; *Eoanthropus, Piltdown man,
    Pleistocene. England; Homo, Pleistocene–Recent. man
    (all living races)

2. Characters of primates

Linnaeus reserved his order Primates for the monkeys, apes, and men, distinguishing them thus from the other mammals, Secundates, and all other animals, Tertiates. The term primate carries with it to our minds the implication that the animals in the group are not only the nearest to ourselves but are also in some sense the first or most completely developed members of the animal world. We shall try to examine this belief in accordance with the principles adopted earlier and to inquire whether we and our relatives can be said to be the highest animals in the sense that we possess a system of life able to survive under the most varied and unpromising conditions.

The earliest eutherians of the Cretaceous were probably arboreal; the primates have continued this habit and with it they retain many of the features present at the beginning of mammalian history, for instance the five fingers and toes and the clavicle. It is not surprising, therefore, that it is difficult to separate the primates from the insecti-vores; the tree shrews for instance (p. 560) have been several times transferred from the one order to the other. The primates have be-come perfected for life in the trees by the development of many special features. Their characters are those of animals raised up from the ground; the opportunities offered in the trees for the use of hand and brain have no doubt been important influences in the shaping of man.

The general plan of primate life has thus been to retain the original eutherian conditions, with emphasis on those features important for tree life. In such an existence continual quick reaction to circumstances is likely to be necessary, the environment is very varied, and the mechanical supports it offers are often precarious. Under these conditions safety is achieved by quick reactions rather than by stability; thus primate more than any other life tends to be a matter of continual exploration and change. Awareness of the surroundings is obviously of first importance, but in the tree-tops one cannot hunt by smell; the eyes and ears therefore became developed, at the expense of the nose. Primates are microsmatic, with reduction of the number and length of the turbinal bones and hence of the long snout that houses them. Consequently the eyes come to face forwards, so that their fields overlap, binocular vision becomes possible, and central areas appear in the retinae. Monkeys are certainly more dependent on vision than are most animals and for this reason they approach the birds in the adoption of colour patterns for sexual recognition and excitation.

The changes in the sense-organs were accompanied by conspicuous changes in the brain, which becomes very large in later primates, with cerebral hemispheres reaching far backwards. The olfactory bulbs and rhinopallium become small and the neopallium very large, differentiated into areas and provided with a very large corpus callosum. The occipital pole, concerned with vision, and the frontal areas become especially developed in the apes and man. Stereoscopic eyes with numerous cones would be of no value without a central analyser to allow the animal to discriminate shapes, retain the impression of past situations, and otherwise make use of the available information. The marked differences in the rate of growth of the brain of different primates are shown in Fig. 378, from Schultz's careful measurements. At very early stages of development all the primates studied have the same (high) relative brain weight, but in the adults the marmosets have relatively the smallest brains, followed by those of other New World and Old World monkeys. The brain is even larger in the great apes and very much larger still in man (see p. 579).

The special developments of the sense-organs and brain have marked effects on the skull, whose facial portion becomes shorter and brain-case relatively larger and rounder; the foramen magnum comes to face downwards, rather than backwards. As the eyes are directed forwards the orbits become closed off from the temporal fossae behind. The head is more clearly marked off from the body than is usual

FIG. 378. The relative cranial capacity as a function of body-weight in various primates. The brain grows relatively faster in man than in either monkeys or apes. The curves are constructed by measuring cranial capacity and body-weight of individuals of differing ages. The monkeys included various Cercopithecidae, the apes only gorillas, chimpanzees, and orangs. (Modified after Schultz, *Am. J. phys. Anthropol.* **28**.)

in mammals and the neck is very mobile, allowing the eyes to be turned in all directions.

The skeletal and muscular systems become arranged to allow jumping, swinging, and grasping. The pentadactyl plan is retained, without the loss of digits or fusion of bones found in most mammals, but the hand and foot are made suitable for grasping by development of adduction movements of pollex and hallux. The digits mostly have sensitive pads and the original claw is replaced by a flat nail. The clavicle remains very well developed, which is a retention of a primitive mammalian feature, specially developed in primates to allow great mobility of the fore-limb, the muscles being arranged to allow rotation of the scapula on the clavicle, increasing the range of movement. Still further mobility is provided by improving the joints between radius and ulna and humerus at which movements of pronation–supination take place.

The primates early ceased to feed only on insects, and took to a mixed diet; the teeth have not become so specialized as in ungulate mammals. The hands are frequently and ingeniously used to obtain food. Omnivorous or frugivorous diets are common, and the molars have become quadritubercular (Fig. 379), the upper adding a hypocone and the lower losing the paraconid of the original pattern, leaving the meta-conid and protoconid, while the hypoconid and entoconid become raised to make a posterior pair, some-times with addition of a fifth cusp, the hypoconulid, posteriorly. The cusps are usually not of the sharp insectivorous type, but are low (bunodont) cones and extra ones may be added, or the cusps joined to make ridges. These changes are associated with the adoption by many primates of a diet of fruit or leaves, requiring treatment by biting and grinding.

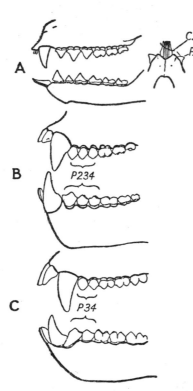

FIG. 379. Dentition of A, *Lemur*, B, *Cebus*, and C, *Macaca*. In A the letter *C* shows the incisiform canine, the first premolar (*P*) being caniniform. (Slightly modified from Le Gros Clark, *B.M. Guide*.)

The reproduction is one of the most characteristic of primate fea-tures. The uterus retains signs of its double nature in the earlier types, but later becomes a single chamber. The arrangements for placentation involve very elaborate changes in the uterine mucosa in preparation for reception of the embryo, followed by breakdown at regular intervals (menstruation). This special nature of the uterine mucosa makes possible the efficient haemochorial form of placentation. Besides these arrangements for nutrition of the young the primates also extend parental care for a long time after birth, often by the formation of family groups.

In many features of their life, therefore, the primates show to a very high degree that adjustability and power to obtain sustenance from an unfriendly environment which is characteristic of all life.

The sense-organs, brain, and hand provide means for doing this in more elaborate ways than are used by any other animals. The monkeys and apes have exploited these powers to a considerable extent and are successful animals, living, as we might say, by their wits, in a wide variety of circumstances. Man has made still better use of his talents and manages to support a population of more than 2,000 million large individuals, scattered all over the globe.

3. Divisions of the primates

Fortunately many of the changes of habit characteristic of primates involved changes in the skull and these can be followed in the fossils. Our knowledge of the evolutionary development of primate life, though very far from complete, is less so than might be expected from the rarity of preservation of arboreal skeletons. During the 50 million years since the Eocene the various primate stocks have, of course, divided and subdivided many times, and invaded many special habits. The forms at present known, living and as fossils, are placed by Simpson in 150 genera, two-thirds of them extinct. Bitter controversy still rages around the question of the best means of classification of the members of this evolutionary bush. Earlier zoologists tended to postulate a series of stages successively closer to man, the latest product of evolution. There has been increasing awareness of the unwisdom of this procedure. Recognition that many of the surviving stocks have been separate for a long time has led systematists to emphasize the distinction between their groups more sharply. Thus lemurs, far from being regarded, as they were formerly, as rather primitive monkeys, are now often placed in a distinct order, having in common with other primates only 'the retention of certain primitive characters and an adaption to arboreal life' (Wood Jones). There is no general agreement about the best means of classification; the more traditional schemes, such as that adopted here, probably give an oversimplified idea of a progression of forms. A classification on more 'natural' or phyletic lines could probably be devised, but would necessitate the postulation of a large number of distinct categories, unless these were simplified by admitting speculations about the affinities of the lines.

We shall, as usual, in the main follow Simpson. His arrangement retains the order Primates and recognizes two great sub-orders Prosimii and Anthropoidea. The division is 'horizontal' rather than 'vertical'; the two groups are not separate and divergent lines, rather they contain respectively the ancestral and the 'developed' forms.

Two primate stocks are indeed known to have existed in the Palaeocene and these are both included in the prosimians, whereas no anthropoids are known before the Oligocene. The Prosimii includes three sorts of primate, all 'primitive' in the sense of retaining insectivoran characters, such as long face, lateral eyes, and small brain; they

are grouped here as three infraorders: Lemuriformes for the lemurs of Madagascar and their fossil allies; Lorisiformes for the rather similar animals outside Madagascar; and Tarsiiformes for the living tarsier and its Eocene relatives. The suborder Anthropoidea includes two distinct types, first the New World monkeys, infraorder Platyrrhina, secondly the Old World monkeys, apes and man, grouped together as Catarrhina.

FIG. 380. Ring-tailed lemur, *Lemur.*
(From life.)

We propose, therefore, to arrange our examination of primates around the idea of three main stocks diverging in the Palaeocene, lemurs, lorises, and tarsiers, with an anthropoid stock arising from one of these, probably the tarsioid, in the Eocene, and itself early becoming separated into two lines, the New World monkeys on the one hand, and Old World monkeys and apes on the other (Fig. 402).

4. Lemurs and lorises

The lemurs (Fig. 380) living in Madagascar to-day resemble certain fossils, known as plesiadapids and adapids, found in various parts of the world in Palaeocene and Eocene times. We are therefore safe in assuming that they show us the characters of part at least of the primate stock more than 50 million years ago. Lemurs show their 'primitive' nature in their habits and appearance, as well as in the details of their structure. They are nocturnal, arboreal, insectivorous, omnivorous, or fruit-eating animals; the name means 'ghost', but it is more interesting that they are often said to be rather like squirrels in behaviour. The brain (Fig. 381) shows relatively small cerebral hemispheres, not overlapping the cerebellum, but with olfactory regions large for a primate, though smaller than in insectivores or other primitive mammals. The nose had numerous well-developed

FIG. 380a. Skeleton of ring-tailed lemur.

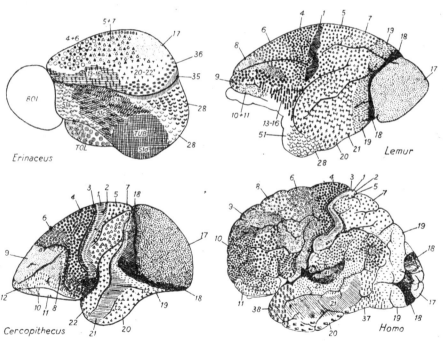

FIG. 381. Brains of hedgehog and various primates to show the relative development of various parts. The numbers refer to the areas recognized by Brodmann on a basis of their structure. 4 and 6 are the precentral motor areas, 8–12 the frontal and prefrontal areas, lacking in the earliest forms. 1–3 are the end station of skin sensations, and 5 and 7 are also concerned with these. 17 is the visual end station, and 18 and 19 are also concerned with this sense. 22 is the auditory end station. BOL, bulbus olfactorius; TOL, tuberculum olfactorium. (From Brodmann.)

turbinal bones (Fig. 387a). The cerebral sulci tend to run longitudinally, rather than transversely as in anthropoids. The whole behaviour is not like that of a monkey; the animals move from branch

Tarsius

Lemur

Notharctus

FIG. 382. Skulls of early primates. (After Gregory and Flower and Lydekker, *Mammals, Living and Extinct*, A. & C. Black, Ltd.)

A B C D

FIG. 383. Tympanic ring and tympanic bulla.

A, Primitive mammalian condition, floor of cavity unossified. B, Lemuriformes, ring enclosed within bulla. C, Lorisiformes and platyrrhines, ring part of bulla. D, *Tarsius* and catarrhines, bony meatus. (After Le Gros Clark, *Early Forerunners of Man*.)

to branch by sudden leaps, balancing with the long, bushy tail, which is not prehensile.

The snout is long, with a cleft and moist upper lip, the eyes are directed sideways, the retina contains only rods, there is no central area and no binocular vision. The external ears may be large, as in other nocturnal animals. In the skull (Fig. 382) there is a post-orbital bar, but the temporal fossa opens widely to the orbit. The tympanic region shows several peculiar features, the tympanic bone forms a ring, lying within a petrosal bulla, but not fused with it (Fig. 383), a condition like that in *Tupaia*, but not found in higher primates. The pollex and hallux are used for grasping; most of the digits have nails, but the second digit of the foot has a toilet claw. The fourth digit is usually the longest, whereas in anthropoids the whole symmetry of the hand and foot is arranged about a long third digit. The teeth show the typical primate number $\frac{2.1.3.3}{2.1.3.3}$, but the upper incisors are very small and the lower incisors and canines are procumbent, that is to

FIG. 384. Aye-Aye, *Daubentonia*. (From a photograph.)

say directed forwards and are used for combing the fur; the first lower premolar is caniniform. The molars are triangular in some genera, in others a hypocone gives them a square shape. The lower molars are of typical tuberculosectorial type, with a heel. The reproduction shows several primitive features; the uterus is bicornuate and the placenta of a diffuse and epitheliochorial type, the allantois being large and filled with fluid. These conditions are remarkably similar to those of other primitive mammals, such as the pig.

There are several variants of this type of animal in Madagascar. *Indri* is the largest lemur, nearly 3 ft. long, arboreal and able to walk on the hind legs. *Daubentonia* (= *Cheiromys*), the aye-aye (Fig. 384), has rodent-like incisors and a very long and thin third finger, which it uses, with its teeth, to find insects deep in the bark. It also eats the inside of bamboo and sugar canes among which it lives. Evidently the lemurs have flourished in the isolation of the island throughout the Tertiary. Some of the animals became quite large, the skull of the Pleistocene *Megaladapis* was nearly a foot long.

The Palaeocene and Eocene *Adapidae (*Notharctus, *Adapis, *Pronycticebus) were like the modern lemurs, but they were closer to the insectivore stock in several respects, such as the presence of four premolars and lack of procumbent incisors. The skull (Fig. 382) was very low and long and the brain small, the foramen magnum pointed backwards. Large crests were often present for muscle attachment, perhaps because of the small expanse of the skull. The tympanic region already showed the special features found in modern lemurs

FIG. 385. Slender loris, *Loris*.
(From life.)

FIG. 386. Bush-baby, *Galago*.
(From photograph.)

FIG. 387. Spectral tarsier, *Tarsius*.
(From life.)

and it therefore seems unlikely that any member of the Lemuriformes could have been directly ancestral to the other primates. The upper molars of some early types were tritubercular, but others later became quadritubercular, by development of a special extra cusp, the pseudo-hypocone. *Plesiadapis* and its relatives were similar to the Adapidae, but with some signs of rodent-like specializations, perhaps ancestral to those of the aye-aye.

The Lorisiformes (Fig. 385) include the slow lorises and other lemur-like animals that are found outside Madagascar. They are known as fossils only back to the Pliocene. The slow lorises of India are quite like lemurs and are plainly a slightly different line of descent from the Eocene forms. They are arboreal and nocturnal, proceeding by remarkably slow and deliberate movements. They eat fruit or small animals. Lorises also show some features that recall the higher primates, for instance the tympanic ring is fused to the petrosal bulla. In some of them the face is shorter and the brain-case rounder than in true lemurs. It is therefore possible that they are survivors of an earlier stock, closer to our own than are the lemurs, and some of the features, such as procumbent incisors, may have developed independently in the two groups. On the African mainland there are also two specialized survivors of this type of animal, *Galago*, the bush baby (Fig. 386), and *Perodicticus*, the potto. The former are jumping animals and can leave the trees; their elongated tarsus somewhat recalls that of *Tarsius*.

5. Tarsiers

The third group of the Prosimii, the Tarsiiformes, includes one living form, *Tarsius*, and a number of early Tertiary forms, placed in a separate family *Anaptomorphidae. The whole group could be described by saying that its members show many characteristics similar to those of Insectivora and lemurs, but also others suggestive of the anthropoid primates. Yet there are present specializations which rule out the possibility that these animals are in the direct line of descent of the higher forms, and we must therefore regard them as an early offshoot, showing us something of the characteristics possessed by the anthropoid stock in Palaeocene or early Eocene times.

Tarsius itself (Fig. 387) is an arboreal, nocturnal, insectivorous creature, the size of a small rat, living in the East Indian islands. The dental formula is $\frac{2.1.3.3}{1.1.3.3}$; the molars retain a very simple tritubercular pattern and the incisors and canines do not show the specializations found in lemurs (Fig. 379). The head is much more like that of a monkey than of a lemur; it is set on a mobile neck, indeed the animal has the uncanny power of turning its head through 180° so that it faces backwards, the eyes, like those of owls, being so large that they are little movable. The foramen magnum opens downwards. The eyes face much more nearly forwards than in lemurs, the snout being shortened and the turbinals of the nose reduced. The nose thus resembles that of a monkey (Fig. 387a), and there is neither a cleft in the upper lip nor a moist rhinarium, such as is present in most mammals and in lemurs, but absent in anthropoids; this reduction of the snout as a tactile organ perhaps goes with the development of the hand for that purpose.

The eyes, though large, are suited only for night vision, the retina containing only rods. There is a curious thickened spot in the region where in anthropoids a thin macula of cones is found. The external ears are large and mobile and the sense of hearing is very keen. The

FIG. 387*a*. The nasal passages of various mammals.

cp. choanal passage; *mt.* maxillo-turbinal; *nt.* naso-turbinal; *I–IV*, endo-turbinals.
(From Cave, *B.M.A. Ann. Proc.* 1948.)

orbit is partly divided off from the temporal fossa (Fig. 382). The tympanic bone is not only fused to the very large petrosal bulla but also somewhat drawn out into a spout, as in anthropoids (Fig. 383).

The brain is relatively large and its olfactory part is reduced, while the cerebral hemispheres overhang the cerebellum on account of a great development of the visual centres of the occipital region. The midbrain is very large and the cerebellum simple, both these being primitive features. The uterus is double, as in lemurs, but the placenta itself is of discoidal shape and haemochorial organization, with a much reduced allantois, almost like that of apes and men.

These are all characters indicating a type of organization so similar to that of anthropoids that the resemblance can hardly be entirely due to convergence. Many of the monkey-like features of the head could, however, be due to the very large size of the eyes. The reduction of the turbinals has taken place differently in *Tarsius* and anthropoids.

In its legs (Fig. 388) *Tarsius* shows considerable specialization for its remarkable jumping method of progression, the fibula being fused

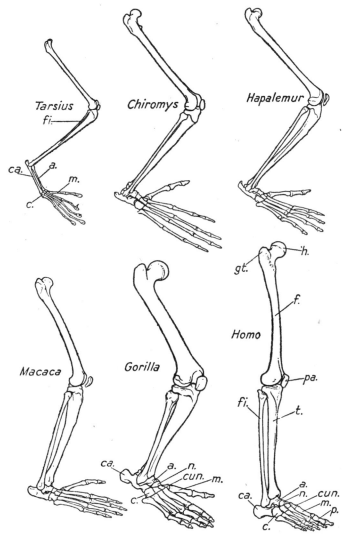

FIG. 388. Bones of hind leg and foot of various primates (not to the same scale).

a. astragalus (talus); *c.* cuboid; *ca.* calcaneum; *cun.* medial cuneiform; *f.* femur; *fi.* fibula; *gt.* greater trochanter; *h.* head; *m.* first metatarsal; *n.* navicular; *p.* proximal phalanx; *pa.* patella; *t.* tibia.

with the tibia and the calcaneum and navicular elongated so as to provide an extra leg segment while retaining the grasping foot. Both first digits can be used for grasping and the digits bear adhesive pads;

all have nails except the second and third in the hind limb which carry claws used for cleaning the fur. As in other jumping animals the ilium is very long.

The *Anaptomorphidae are found from Palaeocene to Oligocene in Europe and America. Many genera are known, mostly from skulls and teeth; where limb bones are found they already have the tarsioid specializations. Some had a short face like *Tarsius*, but in *Necrolemur* the snout was elongated and the molars possessed a hypocone. Some of these animals may have been very close to the primate ancestry, but it must be recognized that the tarsioids show more similarity to the anthropoids than to the lemurs. We are ignorant of tarsioid history from the Oligocene to recent times, but it seems likely that they have remained an isolated stock, their relationship to higher primates being one of common ancestry in very early Tertiary times, when all of these primates were so alike that it is best to class them together as Prosimii, some of which went on to develop into anthropoids (Fig. 402).

6. Characteristics of anthropoids

The monkeys, apes, and men form a natural group, almost certainly of common descent from some Eocene population. They first appear as fossils in the Oligocene and have flourished greatly since; Simpson lists 66 genera in the suborder, of which only 30 are extinct; evidently the type has been successful and is expanding. The outstanding characteristic of the anthropoids might be said to be their liveliness and exploratory activity, coming perhaps originally from life in the tree-tops necessitating continual use of eye, brain, and limbs. With this is associated the development of an elaborate social life, based not, as in most mammals, on smell, but on sight. Monkeys show more bright colours than do other mammals, especially the curious reds and blues worn on the head and rear. Moreover, the sphincter colli muscle of the face becomes divided into a set of muscles used by the animals to influence their fellows by the expression of their emotions.

Many of the characters of the group are those of *Tarsius*, listed already, but the anthropoids are mostly diurnal and microsmatic, with a short snout, large forwardly directed eyes, many cones, a well-marked central area in the retina and partial decussation in the optic tract, features associated with binocular vision and large powers of visual form discrimination. The external ears, no longer serving as tactile organs or for direction-finding, are small and the edge is usually rolled over. The orbit is closed off behind. The tympanic bone is fused to the petrosal and in later forms drawn out to a spout. The brain (Fig. 381) is relatively much larger than in lemurs or *Tarsius* and its cerebral hemispheres are especially developed, overhanging the cerebellum and medulla. The olfactory parts of the brain are reduced and the pyriform lobe becomes displaced on to the medial surface by the extension of the neopallium. The surface of the neopallium is usually highly fissured, showing a characteristic form of Sylvian fissure, and a well-marked central sulcus, separating the motor and sensory areas, a lunate sulcus delimiting the visual area, and other special features. The occipital (visual) and prefrontal regions are especially large.

The head is rounded to fit the brain, with the foramen magnum below, so that the head is carried up on a mobile neck. The gait of monkeys is typically quadrupedal and plantigrade, but they also tend to use their hands for feeding. The pollex and hallux are opposable and the digits all carry nails. The characteristic of the tooth row is a tendency to shortening, presumably connected with the shortening of the face. There are three premolars in the earlier anthropoids, later reduced to two (Fig. 379). In the line leading to man there is a tendency to still further reduction, the last molar becoming smaller than the others. The cusp-pattern is tritubercular in earlier anthropoids, but later the molars become square and have four or more bunodont cusps in higher anthropoids (Fig. 379). The incisors become spatulate, rather than pointed, and the premolars bicuspid. The reproduction is characterized by development of a single uterus, with very efficient placenta and by care of the young for a long period after birth.

7. New World monkeys, Platyrrhina

The continent of South America houses a special type of monkeys, as of so many other mammalian groups. These platyrrhine (flat-nosed) monkeys have presumably been isolated since Eocene times and they therefore show us something of the condition of the anthropoid stock nearly 50 million years ago, perhaps some ten million years after its divergence from the tarsioids. They could not have been a post-tertiary immigration from North America because, so far as we know, no cercopithecids or hominoids reached that continent until man came. The differences from the Old World monkeys are not very profound, however; therefore either the characteristic monkey organization had appeared in the Eocene or the platyrrhines and catarrhines have evolved on parallel lines.

In the teeth the second premolar is retained $\left(\dfrac{2.1.3.3}{2.1.3.3}\right)$, whereas it is lost in all Old World forms; the molars are quadritubercular. The brain is relatively small, and the nasal apparatus, though smaller than

FIG. 389. Common marmoset, *Callithrix*. (From life.)

FIG. 390. Spider monkey, *Ateles*. (From life.)

in lemurs, is larger than in Old World monkeys, producing the wide separation of the nostrils, from which the name platyrrhine derives. The pattern of the cerebral fissures is similar to that of Old World monkeys and this, with other features, suggests parallel development in the two groups, since the earliest platyrrhines have smooth hemispheres and the lemurs show a distinct pattern. However, convolution of the hemispheres is largely a matter of size, larger animals having more convolutions than smaller. In the ear the tympanic bone is a ring fused with the petrosal, but is not drawn out into a tube as it is in catarrhines, and there is a large bulla, which is absent in the latter. The coecum is relatively large. The reproductive system does not show the full 'anthropoid' pattern; for instance, there is at most only a slight sign of menstrual bleeding at the end of the follicular phase of the oestrus cycle.

The New World monkeys are divided into two families, the marmosets, *Callithrix* (= *Hapale*), being more primitive than the remainder (Cebidae). The marmosets (Fig. 389) are very small insect- and fruit-eating animals, of somewhat squirrel-like appearance and habits, living in tropical South America. They have a thick non-prehensile tail and there are claws on all the digits except the first, allowing the animals to run up trunks they cannot grasp. It is possible that these are not primary claws but secondarily modified nails. Three premolars are present, but the molars are reduced to two, a condition found in no other anthropoid. The cusp-pattern is tritubercular. Unlike other anthropoids the marmosets give birth to two or three young and there are signs of ancient conditions in the placenta, where the yolk sac becomes larger than in most primates.

The cebids, the characteristic monkeys of the New World, are now grouped into twelve genera. *Ateles*, the spider monkey (Fig. 390), is a typical example, with a prehensile tail, three premolars, and three molars. *Cebus*, capuchin monkey, will eat insects or fruit, but other cebids (*Lagothrix*, the woolly monkey) are frugivorous. These New World monkeys are very well adapted for arboreal life, with long limbs, delicate hands, and tail for balancing or seizing. They swing along very freely among the branches and may make jumps in which they advance by as much as 15 ft. while falling 50 ft.

Unfortunately very little is known of the evolutionary history of the New World monkeys; fossils are found only back to the Miocene. In view of the isolation and compactness of the group we may feel reasonably confident that it has evolved independently since the Eocene.

XXIV

MONKEYS, APES, AND MEN. CATARRHINA

1. Common origin of Old World monkeys, apes, and men

The Old World monkeys and apes and men are usually classified together as Catarrhina, because of the common characteristics in which they contrast with the New World monkeys. Probably this union is justified and the Catarrhina is a monophyletic group, with a common ancestor in the late Eocene. However, the Old World monkeys proper, the family Cercopithecidae, probably diverged very early from the apes (Pongidae) and men (Hominidae) and some would therefore distinguish between the monkey and ape-man branches of the stock; others regard all three groups as widely separate. However, the earliest catarrhine known, *Parapithecus* of the Oligocene, could have given rise to all three groups, so we may reasonably keep them together.

2. Old World monkeys, Cercopithecidae

The cercopithecid or Old World monkeys do not differ very strikingly in general habits and organization from the monkeys of the New World. We must conclude either that the two groups have made many changes in parallel or that already in the Eocene there were animals with the good senses, active brains, and skilled movements of the monkeys. The distinguishing features of the Old World types are rather trivial, for instance they sit upon ischial callosities, surrounded by naked and often highly coloured skin that becomes enlarged in the female before ovulation. There are often cheek pouches in which to store food, usually complicated laryngeal sacks, a bony tympanic tube, and never a prehensile tail. The great reduction of the olfactory turbinals leaves the nostrils close together and pointing downwards.

The diet of the more generalized cercopithecids is omnivorous, including insects, lizards, eggs, and fruit, but many monkeys are specialized fruit-eaters, with the molar teeth quadrangular and the cusps united to make transverse ridges used for grinding, somewhat as in ungulates. These specialized molars show that the modern cercopithecids could not have been ancestral to the apes or man. The colon usually has a sigmoid flexure and a small coecum. The reproduction is very similar to that of apes and man; there is a menstrual bleeding and haemochorial placenta.

The Cercopithecidae include a number of variant types, many very common and well known. *Macaca*, the macaque (Fig. 391), has many species in Asia and North Africa, one reaching Gibraltar. *Cercopithecus*, the guenons, are similar animals in Africa, many highly coloured. The baboons, *Papio* (Fig. 392), of Africa and

FIG. 391. Macaque, *Macaca*.
(From life.)

FIG. 392. Sacred baboon, *Papio*. (From life.)

FIG. 393. Drill, *Mandrillus*. (From life.)

related forms in Arabia, and mandrils, *Mandrillus* (Fig. 393) of West Africa have become secondarily terrestrial and quadrupedal and the face has become elongated ('dog-face'), allowing for a long tooth-row of grinding molars. The Colobinae are a distinct, vegetarian group within the family, without cheek pouches but with the stomach sacculated; the guerezas (*Colobus*) live in tropical Africa and the langurs or leaf monkeys (*Presbytis* = *Semnopithecus*) in south Asia. *Apidium* and other genera of cercopithecids are found back to the Oligocene.

The monkey type thus shows us something of the condition of catarrhines in late Eocene or early Oligocene times, perhaps 40 million years ago. A lower jaw from the lower Oligocene of Egypt, *Parapithecus* (Fig. 399), is that of an animal like a modern catarrhine, but with four cusps on the molars, not joined to form ridges, and a fifth cusp, the hypoconulid, which is present on the molars of apes and men, but only on the last molar of monkeys. Some such animal could have given rise not only to the Cercopithecidae but also to the apes and men.

FIG. 394. Gibbon, *Hylobates*. (From life.)

3. The great apes: Pongidae

The question of the exact degree of affinity between the existing apes and man remains unsettled. There were plenty of fossil apes in Miocene times and man-like creatures are found in the early Pleistocene, but we have no evidence of human remains from the Pliocene and it is therefore impossible to say whether the human stock was derived from apes after Miocene times or whether it separated much earlier, either from the ancestral catarrhine stock, say, in the Oligocene, or, as a few believe, even earlier still, from some *Tarsius*-like prosimian. Evidence of definitely man-like creatures that can be placed in a family Hominidae is found only back to less than 1 million years ago, whereas the longest of the above estimates would say that our stock has been distinct and evolving separately for nearly 60 million years, without leaving any remains. Although the view that men have descended from apes is probably the more widely held, we shall first survey the structure of the great apes by treating them as members of a separate family Pongidae.

Fig. 395. Orang-utan, *Pongo*.
(From life.)

Fig. 396. Chimpanzee, *Pan*.
(From life.)

Fig. 397. Gorilla, *Gorilla*. (From life.)

FIG. 398. Skeletons of gibbon and man.

a. astragalus (talus); *car.* carpus; *cl.* clavicle; *ca.* calcaneum; *co.* coracoid; *fi.* fibula; *h.* femur; *hu.* humerus; *il.* ilium; *is.* ischium; *mc.* metacarpals; *pu.* pubis; *pa.* patella; *r.* radius; *sc.* scapula; *st.* sternum; *t.* tibia; *u.* ulna.

The living apes include the gibbon, *Hylobates* (Fig. 394), and orang-utan, *Pongo* = *Simia* (Fig. 395), from east Asia and the chimpanzee, *Pan* (Fig. 396), and *Gorilla* (Fig. 397) from Africa. They and related fossil forms are marked off from the cercopithecids by their teeth and methods of locomotion. All apes are rather large animals and this has

FIG. 399. Mandibles of A, *Parapithecus*; B, *Propliopithecus*; C, *Pliopithecus*, D, *Hylobates*. Dental arches of E, *Gorilla*; F, *Dryopithecus*; G, *Plesianthropus*; H, *Homo*.

(A–D after Le Gros Clark, *B.M. Guide*, and Gregory; E–H after Howells, *Mankind so Far*, Doubleday and Company, Inc.)

made it impossible for them to walk along the branches as monkeys do. They therefore swing by the arms, which are longer than the legs and are provided with very powerful muscles, the hands and feet being efficient grasping organs. These brachiating habits have affected the entire skeleton. All the apes and men differ from the cercopithecids in having wider chests, longer necks, longer limbs, and larger heads (Fig. 398). The cervical and sacral regions are longer in apes than in the monkeys and the lumbar region shorter. When proceeding on the ground the apes cannot balance on two legs (except the gibbons for short distances); instead, the long forearms prop up the front of the body and produce a semi-erect position. The plantigrade gait is difficult for them and they tend to proceed on the outside of the hands and feet. The tail is short.

The teeth (Fig. 399) are of a rather generalized type, with the trigon still present in the upper molar, the hypocone being small. The lower molars have a hypoconulid, making five cusps, as contrasted with the four of monkeys. The canines are often very large. All the apes are mainly vegetarians, but they may eat meat occasionally. The canines are used for attack and defence. In the digestive system apes and man differ from other primates in the presence of a vermiform appendix. Ischial callosities and sexual skin are present only in the gibbon.

The gibbons are the most primitive of the four apes and, perhaps because of this, in some ways also the nearest to man. They are fully arboreal, swinging rapidly with their extremely long arms. They eat mainly fruit and leaves. Gibbons are numerous throughout south Asia and the type is certainly the most successful among modern great apes. The orang-utan of Borneo and Sumatra is larger and also has very long arms and is vegetarian. The chimpanzees (*Pan*) and gorillas (*Gorilla*), living in the forests of tropical Africa, are so alike that it is doubtful if the generic separation is justified. The chimpanzee is the smaller and less muscular animal, lacking, for example, the very large parietal and occipital crests found in the male gorilla. There is a corresponding difference of temperament, the chimpanzee being lively and sometimes tameable, the gorilla gloomy, ferocious, and unafraid. Both animals live in families and make temporary nests for resting in the trees. They are mainly herbivorous, but the chimpanzee will eat insects or birds.

The similarities and differences between these animals and man will be discussed later. Their relationship with the other catarrhines is more clear. The lower jaw *Parapithecus* of the Egyptian Oligocene contained teeth of a pattern that could have given rise to those of the Pongidae as well as the Cercopithecidae. In the same beds was found another jaw, which is definitely that of an ape, *Propliopithecus*. Here the molars have a distinctly five-cusped pattern, with protoconid and metaconid in front and a large heel, carrying a hypoconid laterally and entoconid medially, and also a posterior hypoconulid. Some such animal could have given rise to *Pliopithecus* of the Miocene and Pliocene, an animal very similar to the gibbon, which lived in the woods of Europe. Great apes were found quite widely in the Old World during the Miocene and Pliocene. The earliest of these, such as *Proconsul* from the early Miocene of Africa, were probably not brachiators and could have given rise both to the great apes and to the human stock. Fragments referred to *Dryopithecus* and related genera have been collected from Africa, Europe, and India. They had large canines and a dental arch shaped in a U, like that of other apes. The lower teeth showed the five cusps found in *Pliopithecus*, and recognizable in the gorilla and chimpanzee, animals which could well have descended from these Miocene apes.

4. The ancestry of man

In order to discover the position of man in relationship to the living and fossil ape populations we may try to specify the characters distinctive of the family Hominidae and then discuss whether they could have been derived from those of monkeys or apes. The American anatomist Schultz, who has made careful measurement of a great many features of primates, lists the following as the chief specializations of man: (1) elaboration of the brain and behaviour, including communication by facial gestures and speech; (2) the erect posture; (3) prolongation of post-natal development; and (4) the great rise in population in recent years. Others might make up the list differently, but we may use it as a basis for discussion of the differences between men and other creatures.

5. Brain of apes and man

The brain is very much larger absolutely and relatively in man than any living ape; Fig. 378 shows that man stands farther apart from the apes in this respect than they do from other anthropoids. The cranial capacity for males of modern (Caucasian) man may be taken as 1,500 c.c., whereas chimpanzees are given as 410, gorillas as 510, and orangs at 450. The general arrangement of function within the brains seems to be similar in man and apes, but the parts especially well developed in man are the frontal and occipital lobes. The latter are concerned with the sense of sight and are related to our intensely visual life. The frontal lobes, so far as is known, serve to maintain the balance between caution or restraint and sustained active pursuit of distant ends, which, above all else, ensures human survival in such a great variety of situations, and makes possible the social life by which so great a population is maintained. The difference of behaviour between men and apes exceeds all the structural differences; our lives are so widely different from theirs that any attempt to specify the divergences in detail is apt to seem ridiculous. Perhaps the more striking of them are related to the powers of communication by speech which, besides its obvious social advantage, gives to man the power of abstract thought. Whatever we may think about the consciousness of animals there is no doubt that our own awareness of life, being expressed in words, is widely different from that of all other creatures.

6. The posture and gait of man

The gait of man differs from that of any ape in that the body can be fully and continuously balanced on the two legs. This involves considerable modifications throughout the skeleton and musculature (Fig. 398). The backbone, instead of the single thoracic curve of quadrupeds, has an S shape, being convex forward in the lumbar, backward in the thoracic, and again forward in the cervical region. The thoracic curve develops before birth, but the cervical only as the baby holds its head up and the lumbar as it begins to walk. The vertebral column, which in quadrupeds is a horizontal girder, in man becomes vertical, carrying bending and compression stresses along its length. This entirely alters the arrangement of its secondary struts and ties. The bodies of the vertebrae carry much of the weight and are massive, tapering in size upwards. They are separated by well-developed intervertebral disks, acting as elastic cushions. The weight of the head is balanced on the backbone through the neck, and the thorax acts as a bracket from which the viscera are suspended. The muscles of the back, the ties of the vertebral girder, though arranged on the same general morphological plan as in quadrupeds, now carry very different stresses and no long neural spines or large transverse processes develop, since the girder is not now of cantilever type. For the same reason there is no sharp change in the direction of the neural spines at the hind end of the thoracic region, the girder is now one unit, with bending stressing along its whole length.

The balancing of the body on the legs also involves many changes. The muscles around the hip joint achieve this balance, and the changes to allow this affect especially the gluteal muscles and the ilium to which they are attached, these being the extensor and abductor muscles, which raise the body from the quadrupedal position and prevent it falling medially when the weight is on one leg. The buttocks are therefore a characteristic human structure. The adoption of a bipedal position imposes entirely new requirements on the musculature of the limbs. In quadrupedal progression the retractor muscles are the main means of locomotion, drawing the leg backward at the hips while straightening the knee. In man these muscles are small and the propulsive thrust is obtained mainly from the calf muscles and in particular from the soleus, which runs from the tibia to the heel, the gastrocnemius, since it tends also to bend the knee, being reduced. The quadriceps femoris becomes very large, serving to keep the knee extended both while the calf muscles develop their thrust and, as a check to the forward momentum, when the foot touches the ground.

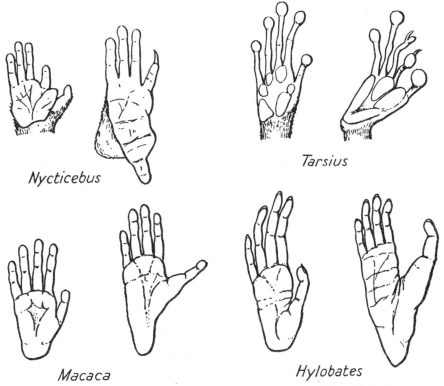

Nycticebus

Tarsius

Macaca

Hylobates

FIG. 400. Manus and pes of various primates. (After Le Gros Clark, *Early Forerunners of Man.*)

The ilium is very broad in man, increasing the surfaces for attachment of the glutei, iliacus (a flexor of the hip), and for the abdominal muscles, which are attached along its crest and have an important part to play in carrying the weight of the viscera.

7. The limbs of man

Many changes would be needed to convert an ape-like leg and foot to the human condition (Fig. 388). The femur of man is straight and the articular surface at its lower end set at an angle to the shaft. This allows the lower legs and feet to be as nearly as possible below the centre of gravity in standing, in other words, for the knees to be held together although the femoral heads are wide apart. At the ankle joint, on the other hand, the articular surface is at right angles to the tibia in man, at an oblique angle in apes, since in the latter the foot is turned outwards. In ourselves the weight is transferred from the tibia

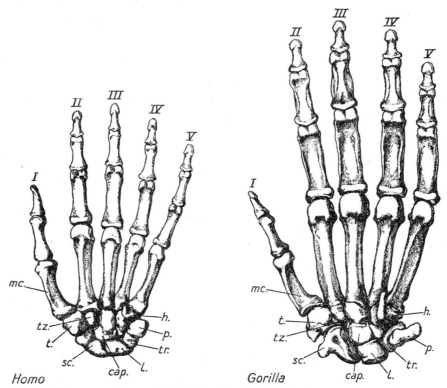

FIG. 400a. Bones of the left hands of man and gorilla, palmar view.

cap. capitate; *h.* hamate; *l.* lunate; *mc.* metacarpal; *p.* pisiform; *sc.* scaphoid; *t.* trapezium; *tr.* triquetral; *tz.* trapezoid.

Notice the large bony points of attachment of the flexor muscles of the gorilla on the trapezium, scaphoid, hamate, and proximal phalanges.

to the talus and then partly backwards to the calcaneum and partly forwards through the tarsus to the metatarsal heads. The calcaneum is modified for this weight-bearing and the tarsus and digits even more so, the whole foot being converted into an arched system, no trace of which is found in apes. With this arrangement the hallux is not used for grasping and is very large. It is held in line with the other digits and the whole forms a compact wedge with a joint at the metatarsal heads. In walking, when the foot is raised by the calf muscles, the toes remain on the ground, to prevent slipping forwards. The condition in which the first toe is the longest is peculiar to man, but in some monkeys and apes the axis tends to shift from the third digit medially and the human condition is an accentuation of this change, the meta-tarsal and first phalanx of the first digit becoming long and strong. Even in modern human populations the second toe as a whole is often longer than the first; this condition was perhaps commoner in historical antiquity (the 'Grecian toe'), and may be a cause of foot trouble, the long second digit being unsuited to the stresses it is made to bear.

The differences between apes and men in the arms and hands (Fig. 400) are marked, though perhaps less striking than in the feet. The human forelimb is, of course, relatively very much shorter than that of any ape and its muscles far less powerful. In order to carry the whole weight of the large body an ape needs enormous muscles all along the limb. Thus the serratus anterior, which pulls the body up on the scapula, is very large and the ribs to which it is attached have large flattened surfaces, are very long, and extend far caudally; the chest of man is much more lightly built. Similarly the muscles of the shoulder and the flexor muscles of the elbow, wrist, and hand are all much larger in apes, as are the ridges to which they are attached, for instance on the palmar surfaces of the phalanges (Fig. 400a).

In the hand itself the thumb is characteristically long in man and moved by powerful muscles. In fact in the hand, as in the foot, the human condition involves development of the medial rather than the lateral part. Man is the only animal in which the thumb can be in the fullest sense opposed to the other digits, so that the pads face each other. This is achieved by special development of the joint between the first carpal and metacarpal. The third digit is the longest in apes, as in men, but the second digit (index) of man is generally at least as long as the fourth, often longer (the 'Napoleonic finger'). In lower primates the digits of the ulnar side are relatively much longer. Apart from proportions and skeletal features the human hand also has a very well developed sensory supply, which is essential for its use as a handling organ.

8. The skull of man

Comparisons between the skulls of apes and men have attracted special attention because so many of the finds of early human types have been of skulls (Fig. 401). The differences are mainly referable to changes in the brain, dentition, and method of balancing the head upon the neck. The enlargement of the brain has been in the occipital and especially in the frontal region (p. 601), giving a high forehead and the characteristic upright face. At the same time the jaws have receded, so that the human tooth-row is unusually short. Moreover, the dental arcade is characteristically rounded in front, that of apes is U-shaped, with large canines at the bend (Fig. 399). In man the canines are small and incisiform and the premolars and molars show

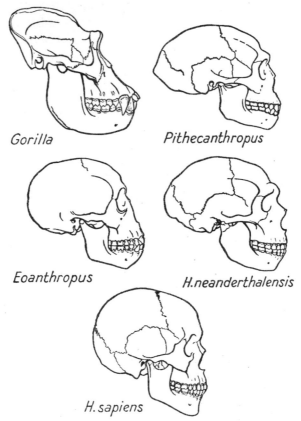

Gorilla   Pithecanthropus

Eoanthropus   H.neanderthalensis

H. sapiens

FIG. 401. Skulls of apes and man. The face and back of jaw of *Pithecanthropus* and the face and other parts of *Eoanthropus* have been restored. (Partly after Romer, *Vertebrate Paleontology*, University of Chicago Press.)

a characteristic pattern that may be regarded as based on four cusps above and five below, but is not easily derived from the *Dryopithecus* type of molar. The last molar (wisdom tooth) is smaller than the others in man, but not in modern apes. There are, however, many signs of possible ape-like ancestry in our teeth; for instance the canine has a long root and erupts late.

The lower jaw of man is less shortened than the upper; whereas in apes it is strengthened by a 'simian shelf' of bone on its inner side in man this strengthening is on the outside, making the chin. The jaw is less massive in man than in apes, especially its posterior ramus; the muscles for moving it are less powerful. Correlated with this weakening of the jaw has been a rounding of the surface of the skull. Occipital ridges for the attachment of the neck and jaw muscles are well developed in the male gorilla, suggested in other apes, but absent in man. The brow ridges, also characteristic of the apes, are large masses of bone above the eyes, probably produced to meet the compression stresses set up by the powerful action of the jaw-muscles. Their absence, together with the large forehead, produces the human type of face. The large external nose is presumably another corollary of the shortened face; it provides some extension of the nasal cavity, necessary for warming and filtering the air.

The balancing of the head on the neck is a result of the adoption of the upright position. Movement of the foramen magnum to a position beneath the skull has been noted as a primate characteristic and it reaches its extreme in man, allowing considerable reduction of the musculature at the back of the neck; the splenius and semispinalis capitis muscles are much smaller in man than in apes. The small size of the trapezius is partly a consequence of the good balance of the head, partly of the absence of brachiating habits. Reduction of these muscles leads to simplification of the bones at both ends of them. The area of their attachment to the occipital surface of the skull becomes very much reduced and remains smooth, instead of being roughened and even raised into ridges as in apes. At the same time the spines of the cervical vertebrae, very long in the gorilla, are short and almost vestigial in man. When the head is properly balanced on the backbone it can be freely turned around, and for this purpose the sternomastoid muscles are well developed and the large mastoid ('breast-like') swellings where they are attached to the base of the skull provide a characteristic human feature.

9. Rate of development of man

One of the most striking differences between man and apes is the slow rate of our own growth and development; there is a strong suspicion that many of our features are due to retardation of the time of onset of maturity. Schultz has shown that in the apes growth ceases between the ages of 10 and 12 and that the epiphyses finally close between 12 and 14. Many of the features of man, such as the reduction of hair and the large head, are those to be found in foetal apes, and it is therefore suggested that one of the main changes leading to our development has been delay in the rate of differentiation and onset of maturity. This might well depend on the endocrine balance, perhaps particularly on the action of the anterior lobe of the pituitary. It is only possible to guess at the process of habit change and selection by which the appropriate genetic change has occurred. It may well be that those family organizations were more efficient in which individuals developed late and were therefore better behaved, in early years because of immaturity, and later by the great development of the 'inhibitory' or balancing functions made possible by growth of the frontal lobes (p. 601). Families composed of such slow-developing and restrained individuals would therefore survive and the genetic factors involving delay of maturity be selected.

10. Growth of human populations

This increase of the post-natal developmental period may well be connected with the appearance of the fourth outstanding feature of man noted by Schultz (p. 601), the great population increase in recent times. No exact figures are available, but it is probable that a first increase occurred when the Neolithic agricultural civilization developed, perhaps 10,000 years ago. This development presumably depended on factors making for orderly and restrained behaviour, such as we have been discussing; it is no accident that family customs are closely linked with those of tribes and nations in all stages of society. A further great increase of human population, probably at least a doubling, has occurred during the past 200 years, and we may associate this with the further extension of habits of thought and restraint in the conduct of affairs, making possible the development of logic and science and their application to human productivity.

11. Time of development of Hominidae

Thus there are seen to be very profound differences between man and the existing apes, and it must be remembered that we have considered mainly skeletal features and hardly touched on the details of the inner life of the animals, or their mental powers or social organization. The most profound difference between man and all other animals is in the size of the brain (Fig. 378) and the difference of life and behaviour that goes with this. In studying the documents of our history, however, we can discover only little of the brains and less of the behaviour of our ancestors; we must rely mainly on study of the skeleton.

Many of the differences in skeletal structure between apes and men may be expressed by saying that the former are brachiators and the latter bipedal: one of the greatest problems of hominid ancestry is to decide whether men have ever passed through a stage of brachiation. If they have not done so we must assume that the dryopithecines (p. 599), though ancestral to the apes, are not in the line of human descent, which must therefore have proceeded from some *Parapithecus*-like early catarrhine of the late Eocene, or even, as is maintained

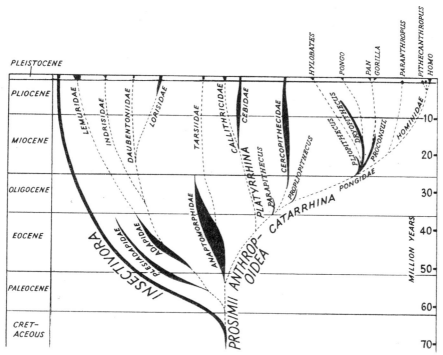

FIG. 402. Evolutionary tree of primates.

by Wood-Jones, from a still earlier *Tarsius*-like form. The differences between man and ape make such views attractive; it is impossible not to be impressed with the extensive changes that would be necessary to convert an ape into a man. On the other hand, it is important not to minimize the difficulties of the opposite, or ancient-ancestry, view. First of all it is almost a truism to say that apes are much more man-like than are any monkeys. Anyone who has looked in the eyes of a gorilla or chimpanzee and watched their behaviour must be impressed with their almost human nature. On the view that our descent has been separate since the Eocene we must assume that this characteristic appearance and manner has been evolved twice independently and with it the characters of the large brain and its organization, not to mention those of many other soft parts. This parallel evolution is not impossible, but it would require strong evidence to convince us that it occurred and it must be recognized that such evidence is not available.

The suspicion that man is not closely related to the modern apes comes from consideration of their present structures, not from the study of series of fossils. The evidence of the latter is admittedly very imperfect and incomplete but the facts must be very seriously considered. In particular it is striking that no undoubted human remains are found before the beginning of the Pleistocene, less than one million years ago. They are not common until 500,000 years later, but their total absence from the Pliocene, Miocene, and Oligocene epochs must certainly be considered suspicious. During those periods we have admittedly only few remains of apes, but they do occur and men do not; there is therefore a prima-facie case for considering that apes have become men.

A survey of the evidence about the affinities of man and apes will probably lead the unprejudiced to the conclusion that we do not know enough to make any detailed statement. Probably most zoologists and anthropologists would incline to the view that the human stock diverged from that of the apes in the early Miocene times, perhaps from a form like *Proconsul*, before the brachiating habit had become fully developed. Fig. 402 shows the possible relationship based on this hypothesis, but we shall remain uncertain of the exact course of our descent until Pliocene and Miocene fossils that could have been our ancestors are found.

12. The Australopithecinae

A peculiar piece of evidence is the finding in South Africa, embedded in lime deposits probably of middle Pleistocene date, of the remains of creatures, the australopithecines, with a curious combination of the characters of man and ape (Fig. 403). The exact position of these fossils in the series is still in doubt, but they may be described as having human gait, posture, and hand, but ape-like brain (Fig. 403). The cranial capacity was only about 650 c.c. but the other characteristics showed some resemblances to man. The palatal arcade was rounded, arm short, leg long, with straight tibia, having man-like facets at its lower end and probably a human type of foot. It may be that these were Pleistocene descendants of Pliocene types that gave rise to man, but some anthropologists regard them as specialized bipedal apes.

13. Early Hominids, *Pithecanthropus, and *Eoanthropus

Fossil remains that are beyond doubt those of creatures close to man have been found from the first interglacial period of the Pleistocene onwards. The most primitive type, *Pithecanthropus*, was first named from fossils found in Java, but very similar bones have since

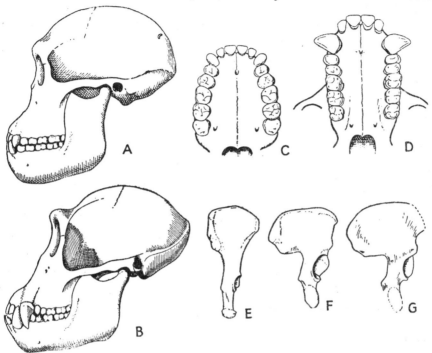

FIG. 403. A and C, diagrammatic reconstructions of skull and palate of an australopithecine for comparison with those of gorilla, B and D. Right side of pelvis of chimpanzee, E, modern man, F, and an australopithecine, G (not to the same scale). The missing part of the front of the ilium of G extended farther forward than the dots show. (After Le Gros Clark, *B.M. Guide*.)

been found near Pekin, however although named *Sinanthropus* by some investigators Pekin man is best included in the same genus as the Java man. These creatures had a long, low brain-case, with low forehead, large brow ridge, and a very thick skull (Fig. 401). The cranial capacity was about 900–1,000 c.c., much less than in modern men, but more than in any known ape. The face was rather prognathous, the lower jaw long and strong, but with a receding chin. The teeth were in general of human type, but with rather large canines. The foramen magnum pointed more backwards than in modern man, but the head must have been quite well balanced on the neck, for the mastoid processes were large. Further evidence that the creature walked erect is found in the straight and very modern femur, but the post-cranial skeleton is not well known.

The differences between these people and modern man are sufficient to make the use of a separate generic name a convenience, yet they must have been in many ways very like ourselves. There is evidence from the Pekin caves of the use of fire and pottery, and also the bones there show clear signs of being broken open for their marrow. There is, however, a slight possibility that the fire, the instruments, and the cannibalism were all the work of later invaders, of a still more human type!

Another set of remains which, though man-like, show great differences from *Homo sapiens* are those found in Sussex, possibly from the first glacial period and named the Piltdown man, **Eoanthropus* (Fig. 401). In this case the skull was larger (capacity 1,200 c.c.) and of human shape without brow ridges, though made of very thick bone. The peculiar feature of these remains is that the lower jaw was very ape-like, with receding chin and a very massive ramus, showing little separation between the coronoid and condyloid processes. Moreover, the canine teeth were rather large. The jaw was found within a few feet of the skull, but many have doubted whether the two belong to the same creature; since no other fossil primates are known in England it is reasonable to suppose that these two should belong to a single species, but they may be of relatively late date.

14. Man

All the remaining finds are usually referred to the genus *Homo*. All living races of man are included in a single species *H. sapiens*, but some of the fossils are placed in other species, *H. heidelbergensis*, *neanderthalensis*, and *rhodesiensis* being the better known. The first of these is the name given to a jaw of the first interglacial period. It is of a very heavy type, rather like that of **Pithecanthropus*, but with a chin and without a simian shelf. The teeth are not far from the modern type. The true position of this Heidelberg man is uncertain and so therefore the true age of the type which we call *Homo*. Much more abundant remains are found in the third interglacial and last glacial period and are referred to as Neanderthal man (Fig. 404). The brain-case was larger than that of many modern men (nearly 1,600 c.c.), but was long and low and especially prominent behind. The brow ridges are large, the face rather prognathous, and the chin receding. The whole structure of the skull was stouter than our own, with a thick jugal bar, thick roof bones, and very large mandibular ramus.

The foramen magnum pointed rather backwards and there is no doubt that Neanderthal man did not walk fully upright. The post-cranial skeleton is well known and shows long spines on the cervical vertebrae, bent femora, and other features indicating a slouching gait.

FIG. 404. Skeletons of Neanderthal and modern man. (After Howells, *Mankind so Far*, Doubleday and Co. Inc.)

15. Human cultures

Our knowledge of the exact history of these early races of men remains imperfect, but it can be supplemented by study of the instruments they used, which are well known throughout the Pleistocene

(Fig. 405). All of these early men were hunters, living apparently in
small families, in caves. They used fire, but their only known instruments were of wood or stone. Chipped flints found from the time of
the first glaciation and following warm period are so crude as to be
hardly recognizable as artefacts and these 'eoliths' are said to be signs
of a pre-palaeolithic culture. More definitely shaped flints, used as

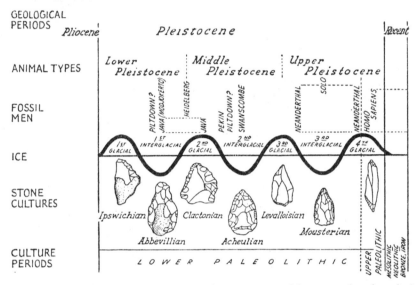

FIG. 405. Diagram of Pleistocene time and some stages of human cultural evolution.
(From Howells, *Mankind so Far*, Doubleday and Co. Inc.)

axes, are found during the second ice age, second interglacial, and
third ice advance and are referred to the lower Palaeolithic (Chellean
and Acheulian) stages. The third interglacial and last glacial period
constitute the middle Palaeolithic (Mousterian) with well-made flints,
probably made by Neanderthal man. The recession of the last main
glaciation began about 50,000 years ago and at that time there were
a series of upper Palaeolithic cultures (Aurignacian, Solutrean, and
Magdalenian) in which besides wonderfully chipped flints there were
also fine bone and ivory needles, blades and other instruments. These
were probably made by men of *H. sapiens* type, whose skulls first
become recognizable in caves and deposits of the last glacial period.

    The details of the replacement of these species and races by each
other remain very obscure. Probably invading races often took over
parts of the cultures of their victims, as well as bringing in their own
culture, so that the whole story becomes very confused. It is generally
considered that *H. neanderthalensis* did not evolve into *H. sapiens*, at

least in Europe, but was replaced by a wave of invaders coming from central Asia. Similarly, at the end of the Palaeolithic period, about 14,000 years ago, the hunters of that time gave place first to a series of little-known Mesolithic invaders, builders of the lake-dwellings found in various parts, and then to the Neolithic people, who were farmers and city-builders and from about 9000 B.C. onwards dominated the Middle East and south Mediterranean region and thence spread outwards, developing the series of cultures known as the Bronze and Iron Ages.

The history of man, like that of so many other mammals, has therefore been of a series of invasions from the central Asiatic land-mass, and it is not surprising that remnants of earlier types should be found surviving to-day on the tips of the continents, towards the south. The most conspicuous of these are the Australian Aborigines, who show several primitive features, both of structure and of culture. The brow ridges are better developed than in any other men and the forehead and chin recede. These Blackfellows are nomadic hunters, without fixed abode, and their social organization and instruments are those of a Palaeolithic stage of life.

In something the same way the Bushmen of South Africa, though not physically of a very primitive type, preserve traces of Palaeolithic culture, including art conventions similar to those used by the Aurignacian people who painted bison and mammoths in the caves of Altamira in Spain 50,000 years ago.

Study of the gradual mixing and changing of human populations, besides its personal interest, is of value in calling the process of evolution to our imagination and showing us its complexity and slowness. Without undue difficulty we can have in mind a picture of great populations of human beings, composed of individuals differing slightly in structure and habits, warring and competing with each other, so that one group comes to dominate another, the invader taking over some of the genes and the gods of its victims. We can at least guess how such a process would lead the population of any area to change, either if one set of individuals arises that is more active or in some way more efficient than another, or following a change in conditions that gives preference to a particular set of structures or habits. Though evolution is a very slow process it is always going on before us, and the best way to see it is to look at our own species, vastly more familiar and revealing than any other. All sheep or shrews look to us much alike, but we can more readily tell what sort of man or woman we are meeting and what they are likely to do in the world. In this way we may get some faint picture of the very slow and confused changes that constitute evolution. Even with such a slow breeding species as our own the effort of thought is very great. Allowing only so few as four generations per century we may conclude that we are separated from *Pithecanthropus* by 40,000 generations. If we ever had a brachiating hairy ancestor it was perhaps our great-grandfather 500,000 times removed, counting back only to the beginning of the Pliocene. Yet men and apes are zoologically much alike.

XXV

RODENTS AND RABBITS

1. Characteristics of rodent life

The animals loosely known as rodents are certainly the most successful of modern mammals; they live in all parts of the world, from the tropics nearly to the poles. Three thousand species are known, as many as are found in all other mammalian orders put together. They inhabit a considerable variety of ecological niches, mostly on the land, often in burrows, but many in the trees and some in the water. This most successful type of mammalian life is, however, in several ways untypical of the rest and indeed has been isolated since the early Tertiary. One striking point is that the animals have never become large in size, although such increase is a tendency found in almost all other mammalian groups. The South American capybara, the largest living rodent, is the size of a small pig, and few fossil forms were much larger. Rodent life has specialized in rapid breeding and this system of production of large numbers of small animals has been very successful. The total rodent biomass to-day may well be greater than that of the whales, which are at the other extreme, and have all the advantages of aquatic life. The rapid reproduction presumably brings considerable evolutionary advantages, enabling the population to make the adjustments necessary to meet changing circumstances. One of the characteristics of rodent populations to-day is their great fluctuations (p. 627), especially notorious in the case of the voles, mice, and lemmings, but very marked also in rats and other forms. The pressure of rodent life is such that no stable equilibrium is reached with the environment and extreme oscillations occur, often with results of great importance to man and to his crops.

In spite of the similarities of all these animals with gnawing teeth, zoologists consider that the rabbits and hares are not very closely related to the others and are therefore to be placed in a distinct order Lagomorpha, the order Rodentia being retained for all other 'rodents'. It is not even certain that the two orders are in any way related. Fossil rodents (in the strict sense) certainly occurred in the late Palaeocene period and a probable lagomorph is reported from the same time. Both groups retain many primitive mammalian characters, for instance, a long, low skull, with small brain and small cerebral hemispheres, temporal fossa widely open to the orbit, pentadactyle limbs, separate radius and ulna, and so on. These features, being found in all early mammals, indicate no closer affinity of the two orders than depend on evolution from a common stock. It is not even clear exactly how the two groups are related to the ancestral eutherians, and separate evolution from marsupials has been suggested. We must be content to say that it is probable that animals with rodent specializations diverged from the insectivoran eutherian stock in the late Cretaceous or Palaeocene and then rapidly became differentiated into lagomorphan and rodent types. The two orders are therefore placed together in an isolated cohort Glires.

2. Classification

Cohort 2. Glires

Order 1. Rodentia (= Simplicidentata)

Suborder 1. Sciuromorpha
Thirteen families, including
*Family Ischyromyidae. Palaeocene–Miocene. Eurasia, N. America
Paramys. Palaeocene–Eocene
Family Aplodontidae. Eocene–Recent
Aplodontia, sewellel. N. America
Family Sciuridae. Squirrels. Miocene–Recent
Sciurus, squirrel, Holarctic; *Marmota*, marmot, woodchuck, Holarctic; *Tamias*, chipmunk, N. America; *Sciuropterus*, flying squirrel, Eurasia
Family Geomidae. Gophers. Oligocene–Recent. N. America
Geomys, pocket gopher
Family Castoridae. Beavers. Holarctic. Oligocene–Recent
Castor, beaver

Suborder 2. Myomorpha
Nine families, including
Family Dipodidae. Jerboas. Palaearctic. Pliocene–Recent
Dipus, jerboa, Eurasia
Family Cricetidae. Voles. World-wide (except Australasia). Oligocene–Recent
Peromyscus, deer mouse, N. America; *Lemmus*, lemming, Holarctic; *Microtus*, vole, Holarctic

Family Muridae. Rats and mice. Native to Old World. Pliocene–Recent

Apodemus, field mouse; *Rattus*, rat; *Mus*, house mouse; *Glis*, dormouse; *Notomys*, jerboa-rat

Family Zapodidae. Jumping mice. Oligocene–Recent. Holarctic

Zapus, jumping mouse

Suborder 3. Hystricomorpha

Nineteen families, including

Family Hystricidae. Oligocene–Recent. Palaearctic, Africa

Hystrix, porcupine, Asia, Africa; *Erethizon*, N. American porcupine, N. America

Family Caviidae. Pliocene–Recent. S. America

Cavia, guinea-pig

Family Hydrochoeridae. Pliocene–Recent. S. America

Hydrochoerus, capybara

Family Dasyproctidae. Recent. S. America

Cuniculus, agouti (pacas)

Family Chinchillidae. Oligocene–Recent. S. America

Lagostomus, vizcacha

Family Bathyergidae. Pleistocene–Recent. Africa

Bathyergus, mole-rat

Order 2. Lagomorpha (= Duplicidentata)

Family 1. *Eurymylidae. Palaeocene

*Eurymylus, Asia

Family 2. Ochotonidae. Upper Oligocene–Recent

Ochotona (= *Lagomys*), pika (cony), N. America

Family 3. Leporidae. Upper Eocene–Recent

Lepus, hare, Palaearctic, N. Africa, Pleistocene–Recent; *Oryctolagus*, rabbit, Europe, N. Africa, Pleistocene–Recent; *Sylvilagus*, cotton-tail, N. and S. America, Pleistocene–Recent

3. Order Rodentia

The characteristic features of rodents are, of course, in their teeth, and especially the incisors, one pair only of which persists in each jaw; hence they were the sub-order 'Simplicidentata' of the older order Rodentia, which included also the rabbits and hares. These latter have a second pair of upper incisors, hence 'Duplicidentata'. The incisor has enamel only on its interior surface and thus maintains a cutting edge. It is worn away at the rate of perhaps several millimetres a week and is replaced by continual growth, for which it has a very wide open pulp cavity, or in the conventional term is said to be a 'rootless' tooth. The incisors are often very large and curved and their gnawing action against each other gives them chisel edges. If one incisor is lost the other continues to grow round in a spiral, until it enters the skull.

The remaining incisors, canines, and anterior premolars are missing, leaving a large diastema in front of the cheek teeth. Folds of skin can be inserted into this gap to close off the front part of the mouth, so

FIG. 406. Diagrams of lower jaws of *Sciurus*.

A, at rest; B, opened for seizing; C, closed for gnawing or to prise open a nut. *mlp.* deep part of lateral masseter; *mls.* superficial part of the same; *tm.* transversus mandibuli. (From Weber after Krumbach.)

that material bitten off during gnawing is not necessarily swallowed. The teeth are not used only for obtaining food; rats will eat their way through a lead pipe.

The premolars are reduced to two above and one below in the more primitive squirrels; even fewer are present in other rodents. The molars and premolars are usually alike in pattern and show modifications similar to those found in the grinders of other herbivorous mammals. The cusps of the original eutherian molar can still be recognized in the squirrels, but they are arranged in transverse rows, paracone and protocone in front, metacone and hypocone behind. The cusps become joined in pairs to form ridges, giving a bilophodont grinding tooth. In most of the rodents further ridges are then added in front, behind, and between the original ones, and these are also joined by cross-ridges, giving a multi-lophodont molar. Similar changes occur in the lower teeth. The teeth also become very high-crowned or 'hypsodont' and the enamel, dentine, and bone ('cement') wear at differing rates. The roots remain wide open and the teeth grow continually. All of these features are very like those arrived at in ungulates by a convergent process of evolution. A further feature of the rodents is that the upper tooth-rows are set closer together than the lower and bite inside the latter, often giving an oblique grinding surface.

The lower jaw and its muscles show many modifications. The articulation is very long, so that the lower jaw can move backwards and forwards on the upper; indeed the lower incisors are thrust so far

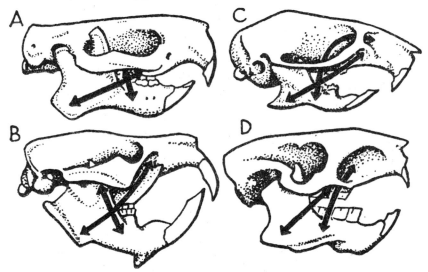

FIG. 407. The masseter of rodents.

A, primitive sciuromorph: the muscle takes origin from the zygomatic arch; B, advanced sciuromorph: the superficial masseter is attached to the skull in front of the orbit; C, myomorph: the deep masseter passing through the orbit is also attached to the face; D, hystricomorph: superficial masseter unspecialized, large foramen for deep portion. (From Romer, *Vertebrate Paleontology*, University of Chicago Press.)

forward that while gnawing the molar surfaces no longer occlude. A very curious feature is that the mandibles are not united in a symphysis but are freely movable, with a joint cavity between them. A special portion of the mylohyoid muscle, known as the m. transversus mandibuli, draws the two mandibles together, causing the lower incisors to separate (Fig. 406). The action of the lateral portions of the masseters then brings the two teeth together again with a scissor action.

The jaw-muscles are not only very large but also specialized to produce the backward and forward motion of the jaw (Fig. 407). In the more primitive condition, found in squirrels (Sciuromorpha), the masseter is attached to the zygomatic arch as it is in other mammals, but is divided into a more lateral portion with simple up and down action, and a medial part that pulls the jaw forward. In more advanced rodents both of these parts of the muscle obtain extra insertions. In rats and mice (Myomorpha) the lateral part extends forward on to the face and the medial passes out of the orbit through the much-enlarged infra-orbital canal. In the porcupines and their allies (Hystrico-morpha) the lateral portion remains simple and the medial proceeds

FIG. 408   FIG. 410

FIG. 408. Marmot, *Marmota*. (From photograph.)
FIG. 410. Beaver, *Castor*. (From photographs.)

FIG. 409. Flying squirrel, *Petaurista*. (From a photograph.)

to a large insertion on the face below (but not through) the infra-orbital canal. The lower jaw often carries a large flange, for the attachment of the masseter muscle. The pterygoid muscles and their attachments are also often large, but the temporal muscle is usually small.

Apart from their gnawing mechanism the rodents remain rather unspecialized mammals. The gait is plantigrade, the fore-limbs often shorter than the hind and used for handling the food. In some cases this tendency is carried to the extent of producing a hopping, bipedal gait. The gut shows a very large coecum, as in other herbivores, but a division of the stomach is found only in mice, which have a horny cardiac region. The uterus is usually double; the placentation shows a considerable variety, but is often of the discoidal and haemochorial type.

No thoroughly satisfactory scheme for grouping the very varied types of rodent has been devised; the best that we can do is to keep to the classical division of the order into three suborders, Sciuromorpha, Myomorpha, and Histricomorpha. The first includes besides the more primitive surviving forms also the most ancient (Palaeocene) fossil rodents and some families of uncertain affinities.

FIG. 411. Lodge and food store of the beaver. (From *American Mammals*, by W. J. Hamilton, McGraw Hill Book Company.)

The characteristics of the suborder are that there are two upper premolars and one lower and a masseter muscle that does not pass through the infra-orbital canal. The suborder includes the squirrels (Sciuridae) found in all major regions except Australasia. They are diurnal, but the related flying squirrels, *Petaurista* (Fig. 409) of the Holarctic region are nocturnal. The gophers, Geomyidae, of North America are burrowers, whereas the beavers, Castoridae, found throughout the Holarctic, are aquatic rodents (Fig. 410) that show remarkable habits in preparing a house and store of food for the winter (Fig. 411). The house ('lodge') is built on a mass of debris or on a bank close to deep water. Sticks are built up to make a wall round the platform and the whole finally closed by a dome of sticks and mud, which is carried by the beavers with their fore-paws. When this damp structure freezes it makes a strong protection against bears and other enemies, and the beavers keep warm inside it. Food is obtained from the bark of branches kept in a store under water and brought up to the lodge through a plunge hole. The beaver dams are made by the beavers during the summer in order to deepen the streams; they may reach a height of 12 feet and a length of several hundred. *Aplodontia*, the sewellel or mountain beaver of North America, is a primitive rodent with a very simple masseter, similar to *Paramys* and many other known fossil forms from the Eocene.

The Myomorpha is a very large group, including the rats, mice, voles, jerboas, and many other types, all having the medial portion of the masseter running through the infra-orbital canal. They include many families and genera, with specializations for individual ecological niches. The jerboas, Dipodidae (Fig. 412), are members of this group, with very specialized hopping limbs, but in other respects somewhat primitive characteristics. There has been a great elongation of the metatarsals of the three central digits, which alone are well developed. The Muridae (Fig. 413) are perhaps the most successful of all mammals and are an ancient family, recognizable back to the Pliocene and invading all parts of the world, including in relatively recent times South America and Australasia, reaching the latter before man. They are the only mammals indigenous to New Zealand. The family includes an enormous variety of mice, rats, dormice, field mice, and so on, and also some special forms such as the jerboa-rat (*Notomys*) of Australia, which has paralleled the true jerboas in its jumping habits. The rats and mice may be considered as parasites of man and are still changing their distribution.

The voles (Cricetidae) are a related family, including partly aquatic as well as terrestrial forms. The field vole (*Microtus agrestis*) is apt to increase very greatly in numbers, producing notoriously destructive plagues. *Lemmus*, the lemming, is a mouse-like form living on grasses and roots on the Norwegian mountains. At irregular intervals of 3–5 years the population increases greatly by increase in the numbers in the litters and in the number of litters in the season. The population becomes too great for the area to support and large numbers emigrate to the lowlands and die of starvation or from predators. Others reaching the sea-shore swim out and are drowned.

The histricoid rodents are also a large group, with the infra-orbital canal enlarged for the medial part of the masseter, but with the lateral part attached to the zygoma. They include the porcupines (*Hystrix*) of Africa and Asia (Fig. 415) and the somewhat different porcupines of North America, but all the rest of the group occurs in South America, an area invaded by hardly any other rodents. Fossil histricomorphs are found in South America from the Oligocene.

FIG. 412. Jerboa, *Dipus*.
(From life.)

FIG. 414. Lemming, *Lemmus*.
(From a photograph.)

FIG. 413. Common brown rat,
Rattus. (From photographs.)

FIG. 415. Porcupine, *Hystrix*.
(From a photograph.)

FIG. 418. Vizcacha, *Lagostomus*.
(From a photograph.)

FIG. 416. Capybara, *Hydrochoerus*.
(From a photograph.)

FIG. 417. Agouti, *Dasyprocta*. (From life.)

The Hystricidae all have long spines, used for attack by a rapid
backward movement as well as for defence. The cavies and capybaras
(Fig. 416) are closely related South American forms, the latter being
a very large semi-aquatic animal with a greatly enlarged and folded

last upper molar. The agoutis (Fig. 417) are also rather large, for
rodents, and are terrestrial, often burrowing forms. The vizcachas,
Lagostomus (Fig. 418), also burrow underground, often making large
colonies.

Possibly related to the hystricomorphs are still more modified
digging animals, the Bathyergidae or African mole-rats, which have
lost most of the hair and developed very long claws on the fore-
limbs.

4. Order Lagomorpha

The rabbits and hares are nowadays considered to be a very isolated
offshoot of the early eutherian stock, whose similarities to the Rodentia
may be only superficial. The two orders are kept together in one
cohort Glires, more as a convenience than because of characters they
have in common. The arrangements for gnawing found in the lagomorphs have indeed a superficial similarity to those of rodents, but
on inspection the differences appear profound. Continually growing
incisors are present in both groups, but in lagomorphs the upper pair
is accompanied by a small second pair ('Duplicidentata'). The
diastema is common to the two groups, and both have cheek pouches
with similar functions. The similarity of the molariform teeth is only
very superficial, however; in the lagomorphs three premolars remain
in the upper jaw and two in the lower. The premolars and the molars
all acquire sharp transverse ridges, usually two each, used for cutting
rather than grinding, the upper teeth biting outside the lower ones,
not inside as in rodents. The masseter is powerful, but simpler than
in rodents, and it does not extend into the infra-orbital canal. The
temporalis muscle is reduced in both groups, but the lagomorphs
lack the power of movement between the two halves of the lower jaw.

Taken all together, therefore, the differences are as great as the
similarities, even in the gnawing mechanism, which the rabbits share
with the other rodents. In the remaining parts there are few points of
close similarity, other than those due to the fact that neither set of
animals has departed very far from the original eutherian condition.
Rabbits and hares have characteristically developed the hind legs for
a jumping method of locomotion and there has been a reduction of
the tail. The rabbits show a number of specializations for burrowing
life. They are among the most successful of all mammals, especially
in the Holarctic region, but have made relatively little progress in
Africa or South America. Their enormous spread in Australia since
introduction by man in the eighteenth century shows how accidental

limitations of access, and their alteration, affect the distribution of animal life.

Fossil lagomorphs, quite like modern hares and rabbits, are found back to the Oligocene. Few remains are known from the Eocene, but there is evidence that the type was already distinct in the Palaeocene and has persisted with relatively little change ever since.

5. Fluctuations in numbers of mammals

Fluctuation in numbers is characteristic of many rodents and other small mammals. The phenomenon is usually first recorded as a

FIG. 419. Fluctuations in numbers of varying hares (above), and lynx (below). Estimated from the Hudson Bay Company's fur returns. (From W. J. Hamilton, *American Mammals*, McGraw Hill Book Company. After MacLulich.)

'plague' of the rats, mice, voles, or rabbits, and these may be cases of local and sporadic abundance. Study of several species has shown, however, that there are rather regular cyclical fluctuations in numbers, extending over many years. Thus figures for the furs collected by trappers for the Hudson Bay Company enable the variations in numbers of the varying hare to be followed back to 1850 (Fig. 419). The cycle is surprisingly regular, with a period of 9·7 years. During the periods of abundance of the hares the mammal and bird predators of these also increase and fall off a little later than the herbivore populations, changes in food taken by the predators producing all sorts of secondary effects on the animals of the area.

The existence of these fluctuations is very striking evidence that animal populations are not maintained in any stable equilibrium. It is often suggested that the cycles depend on changes in the physical conditions, for instance, on the sunspot cycles, but no close correspondences have been discovered. The sunspot cycle has a period of 11·1 years, whereas rodent and lagomorph cycles varying from the 9·7 years for the hares to 5 years for lemmings and 3 for voles have been recorded. Changes in the amount of solar radiation no doubt produce considerable effects on the animals, but it seems likely that the cycles of numbers depend on the particular balances set up within the animal communities. These presumably depend on the interactions of the reproductive pressures of the plants, herbivores, carnivores, and parasites, and it is easy to believe that in some conditions these factors, either alone or in association with cycles of solar radiation or other climatic factors, would produce a rhythmic system.

Such phenomena are probably not peculiar to small mammals, but appear markedly in them because the rapid breeding and short life provide cycles of relatively short period. The facts are all consistent with the interpretation already reached (p. 509) that the control of animal populations depends very largely on the interaction of biotic factors. This continual pressure of the animals on each other is probably the main factor responsible for the great variations in the characteristics of animal populations in different parts of their range, which is found wherever sufficiently careful study is undertaken. This variation in turn leads to the phenomenon of organic evolution and the continual replacement of types by their descendants, which appears so clearly as one follows the history of the vertebrates.

XXVI

WHALES

Cohort 3. Mutica
Order Cetacea
　*Suborder 1. Archaeoceti. Eocene–Miocene
　　Protocetus, Eocene; *Basilosaurus* (= *Zeuglodon*), Eocene
　Suborder 2. Odontoceti. Toothed whales. Eocene–Recent
　　*Superfamily 1. Squalodontoidea. Eocene–Miocene
　　Squalodon, Miocene
　　Superfamily 2. Platanistoidea. River dolphins. Miocene–
　　　Recent
　　Platanista, Ganges dolphin. Recent
　　Superfamily 3. Physeteroidea. Miocene–Recent
　　Hyperoodon, bottle-nosed whale, N. Atlantic, Antarctic;
　　　Physeter, sperm whale, all oceans
　　Superfamily 4. Delphinoidea. Miocene–Recent
　　Monodon, narwhal, Arctic; *Delphinus*, dolphin, all oceans;
　　　Phocaena, porpoise, all oceans
　Suborder 3. Mysticeti. Whalebone whales. Oligocene–
　　Recent
　　Balaenoptera, rorqual, all oceans; *Balaena*, right whale,
　　Arctic

The whales are a very successful set of populations of aquatic, carnivorous mammals that diverged from the eutherian stock, possibly from the creodont branch, at an unknown but certainly very remote date. Their specializations for aquatic life involve divergences from the typical mammalian plan greater than those found in any other order, and their organization shows in a remarkable way the effects of habit of life and environment. In many respects the whales have reverted to the characteristics of a fish form of life, most noticeably in the body shape, with elongated head, no neck, and tapering 'streamlined' body. In terrestrial mammals the air resistance is not a serious factor and the body shape does not conform to it, but in water this factor becomes of first importance.

The swimming mechanism depends on up-and-down oscillations of the body and tail, and the efficiency of the system is shown by Gray's demonstration that the power necessary to drag a wooden model of a dolphin through the water with the speed of the animal would necessitate a horse-power in the muscles several times greater than that of any known mammal. Presumably in life the movements of the water over the surface reduce the skin friction. The surface is completely smoothed off by the loss of all hair, except for a few sensory bristles round the snout in some species. There is a thick layer of dermal fat (blubber), which, besides acting as a heat insulator (if this is necessary in such large animals), may also provide a reservoir of food and perhaps, when metabolized, of water (p. 636). The fat also serves to reduce the specific gravity of the animal and perhaps provides an elastic covering to allow for changes in volume during deep diving. There are no glands in the skin.

The propulsive thrust comes largely from the horizontally placed tail flukes, which constitute a cambered aerofoil that is moved up and down by the tail muscles. These consist of upper and lower sets of longitudinal fibres, originating on the vertebrae and inserted by means of long tendons either into the skin or on to the hinder vertebrae. The arrangement allows the whole tail to be bent up and down on the body, while the fluke is bent relative to the tail and produces the thrust. Stability is provided by the paddle-like fore-limbs, and there is often a large dorsal fin, especially in fast swimmers such as the killer-whales (*Orcinus*). The plasticity of animal form is shown by the fact that the flipper is a modification of the ambulatory fore-limb, whereas the dorsal and tail fins are 'neomorphs', folds of skin with no skeletal support, radical innovations indeed: it is not easy to imagine by what alterations of habit an early eutherian could come to develop fins out of such folds of skin. Equally remarkable has been the disappearance of the hind limb, leaving no external trace and internally only a pair of bony rods, not connected with the vertebral column. These rods serve as attachments for the corpora cavernosa of the penis and may therefore be regarded as ischia.

The vertebral column (Fig. 420) carries no weight; the zygapophyses between the vertebrae are reduced, but the centra are well developed to make a compression strut, as in fishes. The vertebral epiphyses remain separate to a late age. The neural spines and transverse processes are well developed for the attachment of muscles; there has not been a return to the segmental myotome arrangement of fishes. The neck is very short and the cervical vertebrae partly or wholly fused together. The ribs, as in other aquatic vertebrates, are rounded and very mobile; they are the chief agents of respiration, the diaphragm containing little muscle.

In the fore-limb the humerus is short, the elbow-joint hardly mobile, and the hand expanded, with fingers not increased in number but provided with numerous extra segments (hyperphalangy). The scapula is of peculiar flattened form and there is no clavicle.

Some most striking modifications are seen in the head. The pressure of the water has led to shortening of the structures at the front end of the body; thus the anterior part of the skull and the cervical vertebrae show a 'telescoping', only the middle of the skull remaining large to contain the brain and support the enormous jaws. A further curious feature is that the skull in the toothed whales is asymmetrical,

FIG. 420. Skeleton and outline of the right whale (*Balaena*).
(After *British Museum Guide*.)

the vertex being shifted over to the left side, presumably because of some asymmetrical stresses set up while swimming. The jaws are always greatly elongated, in the whalebone whales they make up a third of the length of the body. Whales are microsmatic or even in some species anosmatic (with no olfactory nerve) and the brain-case is therefore short and rounded. This has allowed the nostrils to move backwards and open upwards, with very great elongation at the pre-maxillary and maxillary bones. The process has proceeded somewhat differently in the toothed and in the whalebone whales. In the former the nasal region is very asymmetrical.

The supra-occipital is well developed and therefore also the central bones of the skull, while the frontals and especially the parietals are very much reduced on the top of the head. The auditory region is much modified and the whole petrosal bone is free from the rest of the skull; there is a large tympanic bulla, fused with the petrosal. The Eustachian tube forms large pneumatic sacs below the base of the skull, serving to lift the head and bring the nostril to the surface.

The respiratory system shows many special developments in the air passages, lungs, and muscles. There are valves for closing the nostrils during diving, and special cartilaginous rings and muscles in the bronchioles. The epiglottis forms a tube and is pushed up in such a way as to make a complete airway leading from the internal nostril to the larynx. The very elastic and extensible lungs can thus be quickly filled with large volumes of air and breaths are taken only at intervals of several minutes. Some whales can remain submerged for more than 30 minutes, perhaps for an hour. The whole arrangement ensures the taking down of a maximum of air and of rapid ventilation while on the surface, followed by slower heart-beat and presumably reduced tissue respiration while below surface, so that the whale can take down enough oxygen to last throughout its dives.

Besides the air in the lungs there is also some provision for storage of extra oxygen in the large blood-volume of the retia mirabilia, networks of blood-vessels, which abound throughout the body; there is much haemoglobin in the muscles. No doubt the metabolism is also arranged to allow accumulation of a high oxygen debt, but the special metabolic peculiarities that allow for this are not known. It is not necessary for the whale to have a special defence against caisson sickness; there is no continuous addition to the nitrogen dissolved in its blood which could lead to the formation of bubbles such as occur when miners or divers rise suddenly after breathing air at great depths.

The brain is absolutely larger in whales than in any other animals, and the hemispheres are elaborately folded. Little is known in detail about the sensory equipment or powers of the animals. The eyes are small (vestigial in *Platanista*) and in all whales much modified for aquatic life and diving. The cornea is more flattened than in subaerial mammals, and the lens rounded; in these respects the whales have returned to fish-like conditions. The whale eye is enclosed in a very much thickened sclera and further protected by special lid muscles, derived from the four rectus muscles. The tear glands and their duct are absent; instead, the surface of the eye is protected by a special fatty secretion of the Harderian glands.

The ear shows reduction of the apparatus concerned with reception of air-borne vibrations. The external opening is very small and the long meatus is often filled with secretion. The tympanum is very thick and the ossicles are fused together and with the foramen ovale. The petrosal bone is not united with the skull and vibrations are presumably therefore not conducted from the latter; the cochlea has only $1\frac{1}{2}$ turns and the whole acoustic system is reduced. Even the labyrinth is not well developed, the semicircular canals being very narrow.

The reproduction shows various modifications for aquatic life. The testes do not descend into sacs, but to a position just below the body surface. The penis is very long, and curled when not erect. The uterus is bicornuate, but only one young is carried and is retained for a long time (more than a year in large whales), so that it is as much as a third the length of the mother at birth. The placenta is diffuse but the yolk-sac and allantois are small. There is a pair of teats in the inguinal region and the mammary glands are provided with a special receptacle and muscle so that milk is pumped into the mouth of the young. Many species migrate to shallow protected water at the time of parturition.

The feeding arrangements provide further special features. Many of the toothed whales, such as the porpoises and dolphins, eat mainly fish and the teeth form a row of numerous (65/58), similar peg-like structures, usually in both jaws. With elongation of the jaws the masticatory function of the teeth has been reduced and they probably serve to hold the prey or prevent its escape. In *Orcinus*, the killer whale, however, the jaws and teeth are strong enough to eat the flesh of other whales, birds, and seals. In whales that feed chiefly on cephalopods the teeth are reduced, for instance, to a single lower pair in the bottle-nosed or beaked whales, *Hyperoodon*, and to the enormous upper horn in the male narwhal, *Monodon*. In whalebone whales (Mysticeti), however, there are teeth only in the foetus; the food is plankton, collected by the baleen, consisting of rows of transverse plates of keratin hanging from the roof of the mouth and serving as strainers on which plankton is caught as the whale moves through the water with the mouth open. These ridges may be derived from the transverse folds of the palate found in other mammals. The tongue is raised against the palate, forcing water from the mouth; the shrimp-like 'krill' and other organisms are then swallowed through the narrow oesophagus to a special four-chambered stomach. This complication of the stomach is found in carnivorous as well as plankton-feeding whales and is related to the simplification of the dentition, which makes it necessary for the unchewed food to remain for a long time in the stomach.

Both types of nutrition are evidently efficient and the whales are abundant and of course very large. It is more easy to see the advantage of large size for aquatic than for land animals. There are no problems of support of weight, and on the other hand a great premium is placed on large size by the fact that skin friction is thereby relatively reduced, and this, which forms but a small element in the work to be done by a land animal, must be a very important factor in the water. Further, the heat loss is greatly reduced by the large size, though is difficult to believe that heat retention presents a serious problem in such large animals, even in water with its high heat conductivity. After death

FIG. 421. Blue whale, *Balaenoptera*. (After Mackintosh and Wheeler.)

FIG. 422. Killer-whale, *Orcinus*. (After *British Museum Guide*.)

FIG. 423. Porpoise, *Phocaena*. (After *British Museum Guide*.)

FIG. 424. Dolphin, *Delphinus*. (After *British Museum Guide*.)

whales lose heat so slowly that fermentation keeps the temperature high and they decompose very rapidly, with formation of much gas.

It is clear that many factors have collaborated to concentrate the biomass of whale life into large units. Some forms are larger than have ever existed in any other animal group; the blue whale, *Balaenoptera* (Fig. 421) reaches to nearly 150 tons, with a length of 100 feet. This is one of the whalebone whales, which are in general larger than the odontocetes, perhaps because of the immense sources of food directly available in the plankton; they have grown fat by eliminating the 'middle-men' upon which all toothed whales must feed. The Mysticeti appeared in the Oligocene and radiated in the Miocene and since into a relatively small number of types, all of very large size, now mostly restricted to the Arctic and Antarctic seas. *Balaena*, the right whale, gained its name from the fact that it gives a large yield of oil and has long fine plates of elastic baleen, whereas that of other forms is shorter and therefore less suitable for the manufacture of corsets.

The odontocete whales are a more varied group; their history can be traced back to the late Eocene. The squalodonts of the Oligocene

FIG. 425. Narwhal, *Monodon*. (After Norman and Fraser.)

FIG. 426. Sperm whale, *Physeter*. (After Flower and Lydekker, *Mammals, Living and Extinct*, A. & C. Black, Ltd.)

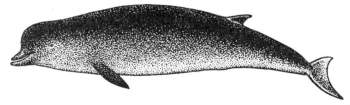

FIG. 427. Bottle-nosed whale, *Hyperoodon*. (After Norman and Fraser.)

and Miocene were like the porpoises, but with triangular teeth. Most of them disappeared in the Miocene, but the river-porpoise *Platanista* of the Ganges, and related forms in the Amazon and in China may be descendants. The modern porpoises (Delphinoidea) are a very successful and numerous group of mostly small whales, with a dorsal fin and teeth in both jaws. They are all active predators, but the habits vary from those of the killer whale *Orcinus* (Fig. 422), which is a fierce and cunning hunter, attacking even the largest whales, to the omnivorous porpoise *Phocaena* (Fig. 423), whose food includes crustacea and plants as well as fishes and cephalopods. This is the commonest and smallest British cetacean, the largest individuals reaching 6 feet; the jaws are rather short, especially the upper one.

The true dolphins, *Delphinus* (Fig. 424), are larger animals (8 ft.), living mostly on fish and having long, many-toothed jaws, the upper forming a beak. They are very fast swimmers, reaching 30 knots or more. The narwhal *Monodon* (Fig. 425) is a large delphinoid (15 ft. long) with a single tooth, usually the left upper incisor, remaining in the male and growing continually to make the spirally twisted horn,

FIG. 428. Change in position of the blowhole (*nos.*) during the evolution of whales. The two upper figures show the condition in the Eocene *Basilosaurus*, the lower figures a modern toothed whale.

f. frontal; *m.* maxilla; *n.* nasal; *p.* parietal; *pm.* premaxilla; *sq.* squamosal. (Modified after Romer, *Man and the Vertebrates*, University of Chicago Press.)

up to 9 ft. long, whose use is not known. The female retains a pair of small incisors buried in the premaxillae.

The sperm whales, Physeteroidea (Fig. 426), are odontocetes that have developed an enormous square snout, filled with sperm oil, presumably a reservoir of food or water (p. 530). Either this, or some other feature, enables them to reach a larger size than other toothed whales (60 ft.). Sperm whales have teeth only in the lower jaw, and they feed on cephalopods, the remains of whose jaws, combined with solid secretions to make stones in the intestine, form the substance ambergris. The bottle-nosed whales, such as *Hyperoodon* (Fig. 427), common in the North Atlantic, are also cephalopod feeders and reach 30 ft. in length.

The whales known from the Eocene were different from either of the modern groups and are placed in a separate suborder *Archaeoceti

(Fig. 428). The body was very long (up to 70 ft.) and apparently thinner than in modern whales, suggesting a sea-serpent form, probably of low swimming efficiency. The hind legs had already disappeared, the skull was long, the nostril had moved some way back. The teeth are very interesting in that they were of the normal mammalian number, 44, and show some signs of the heterodont arrangement. The molars had sharp crenated edges, as in other fisheaters, and the animals were obviously carnivorous, suggesting a possible creodont ancestry. These animals, such as *Basilosaurus* (= *Zeuglodon*), had already developed very far from the main eutherian stock by middle Eocene times. This is an example of relatively rapid evolutionary change; it may be presumed that their ancestors had been in the condition of small insectivora not much later than the end of the Cretaceous, at the most 20 million years earlier. The basilosaur type persisted to the Miocene, but the exact connexions with the two modern sorts of whale are not clear. Whales have been abundant throughout the Tertiary, but there is not yet sufficient evidence available to reconstruct their full phylogenetic history. In broad outlines, however, it is clear that there has been a progressive adoption of features suitable for aquatic life, the long-bodied, heterodont basilosaurs giving place to the shorter, stream-lined modern whales, provided with suitable stabilizing fins and with the mouth highly specialized for eating fish, cephalopods, or plankton. It is very interesting that such change goes on in the water, where fluctuation in solar radiation and other cyclical phenomena are perhaps felt less than on dry land. It is impossible to say whether the changing of the populations is due to indirect influences of such climatic changes or to factors within the animal populations themselves. The course of whale evolution, like that of teleosts, appears to have produced increasing efficiency within a single habitat, rather than a progressive colonization of new fields; but this appearance may be only a reflection of our ignorance and lack of imagination of the varied and changing condition of the sea.

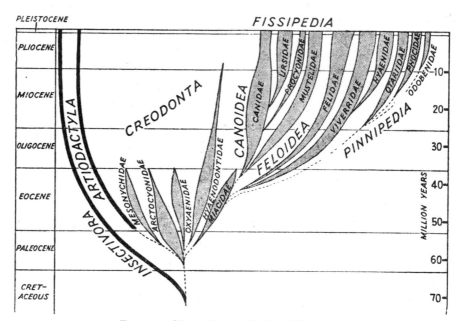

FIG. 429. Chart of the evolution of Carnivora.

1. Affinities of carnivores and ungulates: Cohort Ferungulata

The union of the modern carnivores and hoofed animals in a single cohort Ferungulata is based on palaeontological work that has shown how both groups, together with some isolated surviving types such as the elephants and sea-cows, and many other forms now extinct, all arose from a common population in Palaeocene times. The ungulates have been grouped together for a long time because of their obvious common characteristics of herbivorous diet and hoofed feet, but it is clear that 'ungulates' include two very different sorts of creature, the even-toed artiodactyls, such as the pigs, sheep, and cows, and the uneven-toed perissodactyls, the rhinoceroses and horses. The latter can be traced backwards to a very ancient group, the Condylarthra of the Palaeocene and Eocene, and they were therefore for some time placed rather widely apart from the Artiodactyla, whose origin was mysterious. It has now been shown, however, that there is a close resemblance between the Eocene artiodactyls and some of the creodonts, animals which were also the ancestors of the modern Carnivora. The creodonts and condylarths are themselves very alike, and it now seems probable that the whole group makes a single unit, diverging first from the insectivoran eutherian ancestral population in the late Cretaceous or Palaeocene, probably as a carnivorous stock. Some members then diverged almost at once to make the condylarths, perhaps from a stock which already possessed hoofs and then proceeded later to produce the Artiodactyla (Fig. 705).

It is a convenience to use these relationships as a basis for classification, but it must be recognized that modern carnivores have little more in common with ruminants than with, say, monkeys or rats. The three great groups that make up the Ferungulata diverged from each other only a short time after their common stock had diverged from that of the other mammals; at that time all eutherians were so alike that we should probably place them in a single order if they had left no descendants.

The Ferungulata have become much more diversified than the other cohorts into which we have divided the Eutheria and we have to recognize no fewer than fifteen orders in the group. It is therefore convenient to make further subdivision into five superorders. The first of these, Ferae, makes the central group, including the Carnivora. The second superorder, Protoungulata, includes the earliest ungulates, the condylarths, and it is convenient to place here also certain early offshoots, such as the South American ungulates. The third superorder is known as Paenungulata ('near ungulates') and includes a group of orders with rather primitive organization, most of them extinct. The elephants, hyraxes, and sea-cows remain as isolated vestiges of this great group, which included the huge pantodonts and dinocerates, formerly classed together as amblypods, also the pyrotheres, elephant-like animals from South America, and the embrithopods, large, horned animals from Africa. The fourth superorder, Mesaxonia, includes only the Perissodactyla, descended from the condylarths, while the fifth superorder, Paraxonia, contains the artiodactyls, derived a little later, perhaps from the part of the creodont stock that had earlier produced the condylarths.

Of all this assembly of varied types only the carnivores and ruminant artiodactyls remain successful types at the present day, abundant in species and individuals, the remaining orders are either extinct or are represented only by few species.

2. Classification

Cohort 4. Ferungulata

  Superorder 1. Ferae

    Order Carnivora

      *Suborder 1. Creodonta. Palaeocene–Pliocene. Holarctic

        *Family 1. Arctocyonidae. Palaeocene–Eocene
          Arctocyon, Paleocene; *Tricentes*, Palaeocene

        *Family 2. Mesonychidae. Palaeocene–Eocene
          Mesonyx, Eocene

        *Family 3. Oxyaenidae. Palaeocene–Eocene
          Oxyaena, Palaeocene–Eocene

        *Family 4. Hyaenodontidae. Eocene–Pliocene
          Hyaenodon, Eocene–Oligocene; *Apataelurus*, Eocene

      Suborder 2. Fissipeda. Palaeocene–Recent

       *Superfamily 1. Miacoidea. Palaeocene–Eocene, Holarctic
        *Family Miacidae
          Miacis, Eocene; *Vulpavus*, Eocene

       Superfamily 2. Canoidea

        Family 1. Canidae. Dogs. Eocene–Recent
          Canis, world wide, but not originally wild in S. America or Australia; Pliocene–Recent, wolves, dogs, jackals; *Vulpes*, fox, Holarctic, N. Africa, Miocene–Recent

        Family 2. Ursidae. Bears. Miocene–Recent
          Ursus, bear. Pliocene–Recent, Holarctic

        Family 3. Procyonidae. Raccoons. Miocene–Recent
          Procyon, raccoon, N. and S. America, Pliocene–Recent; *Ailurus*, panda, Asia, Recent; *Ailuropoda*, giant panda, Asia, Recent.

        Family 4. Mustelidae. Weasels. Oligocene–Recent
          Mustela, weasel, ferret, stoat, Holarctic, S. America, N. Africa, Miocene–Recent; *Meles*, badger, Eurasia, Pliocene–Recent; *Taxidea*, American badger, N. America, Pliocene–Recent; *Mephitis*, skunk, N. America, Recent; *Lutra*, otter, Holarctic, S. America, Africa, Pliocene–Recent; *Martes*, marten, Holarctic, Pliocene–Recent

Superfamily 3. Feloidea
　　Family 1. Viverridae. Civets and mongooses. Oligocene–Recent
　　　　Viverra, civet, Asia, Miocene–Recent; *Herpestes*, mongoose, Eurasia, Africa, and introduced to W. Indies, Oligocene–Recent
　　Family 2. Hyaenidae. Miocene–Recent, Eurasia, Africa
　　　　Hyaena, hyena, Asia, Africa. Pliocene–Recent
　　Family 3. Felidae. Cats. Upper Eocene–Recent
　　　　Felis, cats, pumas, ocelots, leopards, lions, tigers, jaguars, world-wide, Pliocene–Recent; **Hoplophoneus*, sabre-tooth, Oligocene–Miocene; **Smilodon*, sabre-tooth, Pleistocene

Suborder 3. Pinnipedia
　　Family 1. Otariidae. Eared seals. Miocene–Recent
　　　　Eumetopias, sea lion, Atlantic and Pacific
　　Family 2. Odobenidae. Walruses. Miocene–Recent
　　　　Odobenus, walrus, Arctic
　　Family 3. Phocidae. Seals. Miocene–Recent
　　　　Phoca, seal, Atlantic and Pacific; *Halichoerus*, grey seal, N. Atlantic.

3. Order Carnivora

The earliest Cretaceous mammals were probably insectivorous and it is not therefore surprising that some of their descendants became flesh-eating; indeed it is curious that a single stock has provided nearly all the hunters found among the mammals ever since. The marsupials have produced carnivorous types in Australasia, but other parts of the world to which the main carnivore stock could not penetrate were not plagued by mammalian predators. Madagascar and South America have few to this day, and the latter was quite free of them during the long period of its isolation from the other continents. It is difficult to see why carnivores have not developed more often from the insectivoran or some other stock; that they have not done so may remind us that very special circumstances are necessary for the origin even of a type for which a means of life would seem to be readily available.

4. The Cats

The changes that convert a mammal into an effective hunter occur in many parts of the body, without, as it were, radically distorting any. We may illustrate this by considering the most specialized members of the group, the cats (Fig. 430). The head is large, with very well developed sense-organs, large eyes, long ears, long whiskers,

FIG. 430. Skeleton of the cat (*Felis*).

and keen nose with many turbinals. The brain is large, the cerebral hemispheres overlap the cerebellum; the olfactory centres are large. As is usual with carnivores, the behaviour is complicated; in order to continue pursuit of prey that cannot be seen, or perhaps even smelt, the animals learn to associate the presence of food with obscure clues such as footmarks, and to make use of these clues they must lie in wait for the prey, all of which involves an elaborate balance of internal motivation with activity and restraint. This power of 'abstraction' of ultimate satisfaction from the immediate situation may perhaps be associated with the familiar play of the kitten or the less edifying treatment of a captured mouse by an adult cat.

Social or family groups are commonly well marked in carnivores and there are usually characteristic odours for recognition, often associated with large anal glands, especially well known as producers of civet and the 'poison' of the skunks. The back of the head is enlarged to take the brain and there is a well-developed snout for the nose, but the face is nevertheless short, and it is characteristic of the specialized carnivores that the tooth-row is shortened, developed especially at the front end, producing the incisors for piercing, canines for tearing, and premolars and anterior molars for cutting. In contrast to the ungulate type of dentition the hinder molars, not being needed for grinding, are reduced. In the cats, as in all modern carnivores, the teeth most favourably placed for biting by their position relative to the jaw muscles, namely, the last upper premolar and first lower molar. are specially developed into cutting-blades, the carnassials. This is done by formation of a ridge along the outer side of the upper molar, the paracone and metacone making a single cutting-edge. The protocone remains as an inwardly projecting ridge at the front of the tooth, which otherwise makes a single blade, shearing outside a similar blade formed by the paraconid-metaconid of the lower molar. This restriction of dentine production to long sharp ridges also affects the teeth in front of the carnassials, but behind them the molars are so reduced that in true cats they are represented only by a single vestige in each jaw. More of the posterior molars remain in some of the primitive carnivores (dogs), and in some, such as the bears, they may acquire a bunodont surface and hence the power of grinding.

The jaws are, of course, powerful in carnivores, the articulation being a tight, transverse hinge, allowing none of the rotatory movements found in other mammals. The jaw-muscles include especially powerful temporals, for whose attachment there is a large coronoid process on the jaw and often large sagittal crests on the top of the skull. The temporal fossa is very wide and never closed off from the orbit, since there is no need for specially increased surfaces for the masseter, which is only moderately strong. The pterygoid muscles (and their fossa) are reduced, as would be expected since the jaw has no rotary action.

The post-cranial skeleton shows a generalized mammalian build, with specializations for sudden leaping movements. There are five digits in the hand and four in the foot in cats; in other carnivores the number is never less than four. The toes are armed with the characteristic claws, which are held drawn back by elastic ligaments and pulled out when needed by the action of the flexor digitorum profundus muscles on the terminal phalanx, to which the claw is attached. The weight of the body is carried on special pads on the second interphalangeal joints and the metatarsal heads. A curious feature of the carpus of all modern carnivores is the fusion of the scaphoid and lunate bones. The arrangement of the limbs and back-bone is that of a quadruped able to proceed over uneven surfaces and also steeply upwards and downwards, especially in the carnivores that are arboreal. This involves a long body, with much of the weight carried on the fore-limbs; the thoracic neural spines are therefore high. On the other hand, the vertebral girder has to take the strain of powerful sacrospinalis muscles for leaping; the transverse processes are broad in the lumbar region, and again in the neck for the muscles that move the head. The tail, well developed for the maintenance of balance in wild cats, tends to become reduced under domestication, the extreme being the Manx variety, with only three caudal vertebrae.

As in so many carnivores, the alimentary canal is short and the stomach never complex or the coecum large. The uterus retains the primitive mammalian bicornuate form. The placenta is of a special endothelio-chorial type and the villous portion of the chorion is restricted to a characteristic band around the embryo (hence 'zonary' placenta).

5. *Suborder Creodonta

Besides animals such as the cats, adapted in this very detailed way for hunting live prey, the order Carnivora contains a variety of less-modified forms, such as the dogs and their offshoot the bears, which are partly scavengers. Others are suited for special types of carnivorous life, such as the weasels, mongooses, and other small animals. The seals and walruses are carnivores very much changed by aquatic life.

Great numbers of fossil carnivores are known and we can trace much of the history of the order. The *Creodonta (= 'flesh-tooth') of the Palaeocene and Eocene included four distinct families, one, the *Arctocyonidae, very close to the ancestry of the whole Ferungulate stock, the other three more specialized. The earliest carnivores, such as *Tricentes of the North American Palaeocene were small creatures, very like the contemporary small insectivores, which were the prototype of all eutherian mammals. The skull was long and low, with a small brain, but already having sagittal crests for the temporalis muscle. The dentition included the full number of teeth and these carried sharp cusps, arranged in the tritubercular pattern, with the beginning of the development of a hypocone in the upper molar. There was no carnassial, however; animals of this type could therefore well have given rise to non-carnivorous forms, such as the ungulates. Other differences from modern carnivores were that the scaphoid and lunate were not fused and there was no ossified auditory bulla.

It is not surprising that these early creodonts were for a long time classed as Insectivora. Their descendants soon began to show various specializations. Thus *Arctocyon* of the Upper Palaeocene of Europe was a large animal, like a bear. Some Eocene descendants of this type, such as *Mesonyx* (Fig. 431), retained the triangular molars and became very large, perhaps they were scavenging creatures. Their toes carried hoofs, and this, together with their very simple dentition

FIG. 431. The skulls of some early carnivores.

A, *Mesonyx*; B, *Oxyaena*; C, *Sinopa*; D, *Vulpavus*. A–C are creodonts, D is a miacid fissipede. (After Romer, A after Scott, B and C after Wartmann, and D after Matthew.)

and other features, suggests that smaller members of the group may have been ancestral to the Artiodactyla. Other Eocene creodonts, however, became more typical carnivores, with shearing carnassials, developed from various teeth, often the upper first and lower second molar. These early carnivores radiated into various types, paralleling those found to-day. Thus *Dromocyon* resembled a dog, *Oxyaena* an otter, *Dissacus* a cat, and *Sinopa* a weasel. *Hyaenodon* and its allies were very abundant hyena-like animals of various sizes; they survived until the Eocene. *Apataelurus* was an Eocene sabre-tooth. By their similarities to later carnivores these arrays of early carnivore types constitute a very remarkable example of convergent evolution.

After their abundance in the Eocene the creodonts declined, although a few genera survived until the Pliocene. Perhaps the type, though able to catch the cumbrous early herbivores, was unable to make a living from the later, faster-moving ungulates.

6. Suborder Fissipeda

Towards the end of the Eocene a new type of carnivore became abundant. The earliest of these, the *Miacidae, were so like creodonts

FIG. 432. Wolf, *Canis*. (From a photograph.)

FIG. 433. Brown bear, *Ursus*. (From life.)

that they are sometimes classified in that group, sometimes with the Fissipeda. Thus miacids of the Eocene (Fig. 431) were small animals, perhaps arboreal, very close to the *Arctocyonidae and still with triangular molars, unossified bulla, and separate carpal bones. There was, however, a sign of the beginning of the fissipede carnassials, the fourth upper premolar and first lower molar being elongated, the cusps partly united to form a ridge. At the end of the Eocene and beginning of the Oligocene early representatives of the various fissipede families appeared and were presumably derived from these miacids. The dogs (Canidae) (Fig. 432) appeared very early and have since changed

relatively little, the modern *Canis* being practically a survivor showing us the Eocene stage of carnivore evolution. Numerous fossil dogs
are known and the type has been a very successful one. The diet is
varied and partly herbivorous. The European red fox, for instance,
feeds on mice, hares, rabbits, and chickens, but also on snails, insects,
and berries. The type is not suited for climbing but for running in
open country, for which purpose long legs and a digitigrade habit

FIG. 434. Carnassial teeth of carnivores.

The top row shows the last left upper premolar from the labial side; middle row
the same from below; bottom row the first left lower molar from the labial side.
h. heel (talonid); *me.* metacone; *md.* metaconid; *pa.* paracone; *pd.* paraconid; *pr.*
protocone. (Partly after Flower and Lydekker.)

have been developed, the pollex and hallux being reduced (Fig. 353).
The teeth have remained unspecialized, with at least two post-
carnassial grinding molars and still distinct signs of the triangular
form in the carnassial (Fig. 434). Dogs, wolves, and foxes are found
throughout the world, including South America, but not in Madagascar or New Zealand. So many types are known that the exact
ancestry of the various wolves and foxes has not been fully dis-
entangled. This population provides yet another example of the great
variety of animal life that appears on close inspection.

The bears (Ursidae) (Fig. 433) were a Miocene offshoot from this
dog stock and here the tendency to non-carnivorous diet became

accentuated; there are no carnassials and the molars acquire bunodont grinding surfaces. The gait is plantigrade. Various types are found through the Holarctic region and South America. The raccoons

FIG. 435. Raccoon, *Procyon*.
(From a photograph.)

FIG. 436. Giant panda, *Ailuropoda*.
(From a photograph.)

FIG. 437. Badger, *Meles*.
(From photographs.)

FIG. 438. Stoat, *Mustela*.
(From a photograph.)

FIG. 439. Common skunk, *Mephitis*.
(From photographs.)

(Procyonidae) (Fig. 435) are a rather similar though smaller type of animal, with dentition suited to an omnivorous diet, the upper carnassial having developed (? redeveloped) a hypocone. They are all American, except *Ailurus* and *Ailuropoda*, the panda and giant panda (Fig. 436), large, herbivorous creatures living in Asia. The latter has a special bone near the pollex, making a grasping organ for holding bamboo shoots.

These families of rather primitive carnivores are united in a super-family Canoidea, and with them we may associate the weasels (Mustelidae), which are the typical small carnivores found throughout the world retaining many primitive characters. They have well-developed

FIG. 440. Otter, *Lutra*. (From photographs.)

FIG. 441. Indian mongoose, *Herpestes*.
(After a photograph by F. W. Bond.)

FIG. 442. Hyena, *Hyaena*. (From photographs.)

carnassials and never more than one post-carnassial molar. They can be recognized back to the Eocene and now include the stoats and weasels, *Mustela* (Fig. 438), that live on rats and mice, rabbits, and other small herbivores; *Meles* the badger (Fig. 437), which is omnivorous and has a hypocone; *Mephitis* the skunk (Fig. 439), a burrowing animal that ejects a stream of foul-smelling liquid from special anal glands; and the otters, *Lutra* (Fig. 440) with webbed feet, short fur, small ears, and other features suited for life in the water.

The most-modified Carnivora are placed in the superfamily Feloidea. The civets and mongooses (Viverridae) (Fig. 441) are survivors which show us many of the characters possessed by this type in the Oligocene. They are the small carnivores that occupy in the Old World tropics the position taken farther north by the weasels. In general they are very like the ancestral miacids, with long skull, small brain, and short legs. *Herpestes*, the mongoose, is abundant throughout Africa and Asia.

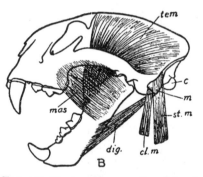

The hyenas (Fig. 442) have become large running creatures, with massive teeth specialized for crushing, and hence allowing a scavenging life. The true cats (Felidae) were already differentiated from the miacid ancestry in the Eocene, but at that early period they all had the very great development of the upper canines as cutting and piercing sabre-teeth (Fig. 443). There were numerous genera with this characteristic between the Eocene and Pleistocene (*Smilodon, Fig. 444); probably the animals fed on large thick-skinned herbivores and disappeared when their prey became rare. The jaw could be opened to a right angle to allow the fang to strike, and there were such associated developments as large mastoid processes for the sternomastoid muscles that pulled the head downwards and forwards in

FIG. 443. Neck and jaw muscles of A, sabre-tooth, *Smilodon*, compared with those of a modern cat B, to show modifications for striking with the whole head and biting, respectively.

c. condyle; *cl. m.* cleidomastoid; *dig.* digastric; *m.* mastoid process; *mas.* masseter; *st. m.* sternomastoid; *tem.* temporalis. (From Lull, *Organic Evolution*, copyright 1917, 1929 by The Macmillan Company and used with their permission, after Matthew.)

the strike. The closing muscles of the jaw and the coronoid process were, however, small in the sabre-tooths.

The cats themselves, with smaller canines, appeared suddenly in the Oligocene. They are very successful carnivores, partly arboreal and hence most common in tropical regions, where there are large forests. There is much difference in detailed habits between the many species of the family, but they are all very alike in bony structure. Numerous attempts have been made to divide the group into genera and subgenera, but all may reasonably be retained in a single genus *Felis*. Lions (*F. Leo*) have many distinct races in Africa and Asia and

FIG. 444. Sabre-tooth, *Smilodon*. (After Scott.)

FIG. 445. Tiger, *Felis*. (From photographs.)

are mainly terrestrial, hunting in open country. Tigers (*F. tigris*) (Fig. 445) occur throughout Asia to Siberia, are usually solitary, and often frequent damp places. They also have many races, and in captivity lions and tigers can be crossed. As in so many other cases close examination shows that the attempt to describe the characters of animal populations by referring them to species and subspecies breaks down: variety and gradation is the rule in all animal life. Various other sorts of cats are found, usually smaller and more fully arboreal than the lion and tiger. The leopard (*F. pardus*) of Africa and Asia reaches 5 ft. in body length. *Felis catus*, the wild cat, formerly common, still exists in Britain and has a Palearctic distribution. The domestic cat probably arose in Egypt from the caffre cat, *F. ocreata*. The jaguar (*F. onca*), puma (*F. cougar*), and ocelot (*F. pardalis*) are large Central and North American cats, which have recently invaded South America.

FIG. 446. Sea-lion, *Eumetopias*. (From a drawing belonging to the Zoological Society.)

FIG. 447. Skeleton of the seal, *Phoca*. (After Blainville.)

Felis is thus one of the most widespread of all mammalian genera, occurring in all main parts except Australasia, Madagascar, and oceanic islands. Because of their striking and familiar characteristics we can form a vivid picture of all these slightly different sorts of cat, pursuing varying prey in the different regions. In order to visualize past evolution properly we should need to have an equally detailed knowledge of past populations. It is difficult enough to classify and describe a modern population of this sort and we need not be surprised that the palaeontologist, who has to consider also variations with time, finds that the growth of his material introduces intolerable problems of classification.

7. Suborder Pinnepedia

The seals and walruses (Fig. 446) have become large and highly successful marine carnivores. Their exact affinities are very doubtful;

they first appear in the Miocene, and show some similarities to otters, perhaps due to common ancestry but possibly to convergence, and also a remote likeness to the bears. The swimming is performed entirely by the paddle-like limbs, the hind pair being turned backwards (Fig. 447). The basal segments of the limbs are shortened and the hand and foot lengthened, without any increase in the number of digits and little increase of phalanges. These animals superficially resemble the whales in many respects, for instance, the microsmatic brain, large auditory ossicles, flat cornea, and round lens; the closure of the eyelids by special fibres of the rectus muscles is a specially remarkable convergence. The ribs are rounded and the vertebral column is somewhat simplified, but retains complicated articular facets, transverse processes, and neural spines. All the seals, of course, leave the water to breed, and therefore need some support for their large bodies.

Various modifications are present in the nostrils and lungs and there are special blood sinuses to allow increased time of submergence. The scaphoid and lunate bones are fused, as in Fissipeda. The teeth have lost the carnassials (if indeed they ever had them) and are reduced to a series of similar prongs. They sometimes have three cusps in a row, a reversion to 'reptilian' conditions, which serves to prevent escape of the fish prey. In the sea-lions (Otariidae) the legs can still be turned forward for use on land, and there are other primitive features, including external ears. The family dates back to the Miocene. The walrus, *Odobenus*, is a related form, highly specialized for eating bottom-living crustaceans and molluscs, which it digs up with its enormous canines. The Phocidae are the modern seals, found in all seas and very well suited to life in water, the hind limbs being attached to the tail. They come ashore only for short periods in isolated places to breed, and can only just drag themselves along the beaches. Many seals migrate for long distances to particular breeding-places, such as the Pribilof Islands in the case of the fur seals (*Callorhinus*). The males, arriving first, fight furiously with each other, the victors then collecting harems of twenty or more females, who give birth to their young and are soon afterwards again impregnated. The bulls remain on shore guarding the family, while the females feed in the sea and return to suckle the young.

XXVIII

PROTOUNGULATES

1. Origin of the ungulates

No herbivorous eutherians are known from the Cretaceous period, but during the Palaeocene epoch a number of animals abandoned the insectivorous habit and began to eat plants. These condylarths rapidly radiated into numerous types, so that by the end of the Palaeocene several distinct orders descended from this stock can be recognized. In North America and elsewhere there appeared large, clumsy animals, the *Pantodonta (Amblypoda) and *Dinocerata, while in South America a special fauna, the *Notoungulata and *Litopterna, developed. Further types then arose in the Eocene, including the early elephants and Perissodactyla. The Artiodactyla first appeared in the lower Eocene, as rather pig-like creatures; their origin is uncertain but, as already suggested, they may have come from some form not very distinct from the *Creodonta.

During the Eocene and Oligocene there were, therefore, numerous large, heavy-bodied herbivorous mammals, perhaps mainly suited to forest life and living upon relatively soft green food, since their teeth were mostly not highly developed for grinding. They were, however, gradually replaced during the Miocene by swifter, grazing animals suited to the plains of that period.

Following Simpson we shall classify the numerous orders of herbivorous (ungulate) mammals into four superorders. The Protoungulata, including *Condylarthra, *Litopterna, *Notoungulata, *Astrapotheria, and Tubulidentata, include the oldest forms, together with various early offshoots and one living creature the aardvark or Cape ant-eater, which is difficult to place elsewhere. A second superorder, Paenungulata, includes a number of descendants of the condylarths that early achieved success, the *Pantodonta and *Dinocerata of the Holarctic region, *Pyrotheria of South America, and *Embrithopoda in Africa. With these are placed the Proboscidea, which succeeded them as large herbivores in the Miocene. The conies (Hyracoidea) are an isolated group that still shows some of the Eocene characteristics of this Paenungulate group, and the sea-cows (Sirenia) are an early offshoot that took to aquatic life. Finally, the orders Perissodactyla and Artiodactyla occupy two separate superorders, Mesaxonia and Paraxonia.

FIG. 448. Skeletons of horse and cow. (After Ellenberger and Sisson.)

a. astragalus; *at.* atlas; *ax.* axis; *c.* calcaneum, *c2–4,* distal carpals; *cb.* cuboid; *cn3.* 3rd cuneiform; *D1.* 1st thoracic vertebra; *f.* femur; *fib.* fibula; *h.* humerus; *i.* intermedium; *il.* ilium; *is.* ischium; *L1.* 1st lumbar vertebra; *n.* navicular; *r.* radius, *rad.* radials; *sc.* scapula; *t1–3.* distal tarsals; *tib.* tibia; *u.* ulna; *ul.* ulnae, *II–IV,* metatarsals.

2. Ungulate characters

When mammals adopt a herbivorous diet they assume certain characteristics, which it is convenient to recognize, before dealing with the individual groups (Fig. 448). In many cases the animals become large, but it must be remembered that, outside the ungulates, the rodents include many successful small herbivores, and that conversely among the ungulates the hyraxes are small. The problem of security often leads an unaggressive animal to the development of a swift gait. For this the limbs are lengthened by raising up on the toes (p. 553), producing first digitigrade and then unguligrade locomotion. When this happens the more lateral digits, failing to reach the ground, become reduced and may disappear, leaving finally the characteristic one or two. The movement of the limb becomes

FIG. 449. Skeletons of feet of horse and cow.
Lettering as Fig. 448.

restricted to a fore-and-aft direction, and the joints assume a pulley-like form, especially characteristic in the trochlea of the talus, deeply grooved in Artiodactyls but markedly so also in perissodactyls (Fig. 449). The carpal and tarsal bones of these swift-moving animals become arranged on the so-called interlocking plan, by which each elongated metapodial thrusts up against two carpals or tarsals. No movements of pronation occur, and the ulna and fibula tend to be reduced and fused with the radius and tibia. The hoofs themselves are a characteristic development, in which the terminal phalanx is broadened, and the claw becomes modified to surround it, while a pad forms below. The elongation of the limbs is mainly in the lower sections, the humerus and femur being short. Locomotion is by movement of the whole limb by the action of its proximal muscles, the hind limbs being the main propellants and the fore limbs weight-bearers, with corresponding modification of the vertebral girder (p. 671). The neural spines are very high above the fore-legs and the ribs are numerous, so that the girder has large compression struts above and below and it balances largely on the fore-legs and is pushed from behind. The ilium is broad and raised vertically, providing large attachments for the glutei, which are the important locomotor muscles, and for the abdominal muscles, which carry the weight of the belly. This arrangement of the column is essentially preserved even in the very large animals, such as elephants, rhinoceroses, and many extinct types, which are said to be 'graviportal'. In these latter, however, the legs are arranged on a different plan, since the great weight can only be carried by very massive struts of large cross-section. The proximal parts are therefore enlarged and several digits

FIG. 450. *Hyracotherium.* Upper (A) and lower (B) premolars and molars. (After Wortmann from *Outlines of Vertebrate Palaeontology*, Cambridge University Press.)

are retained to make broad supports for the pillars, as is well seen in the elephant's foot.

In many ungulates the neck becomes considerably lengthened, probably both in order to reach up or down for food and also to give a good look-out for the head. The ears are long, so that the direction of sounds may be more easily detected.

Perhaps the most significant modifications are in the means of obtaining and digesting the food. The triangular molar pattern gives place to a square one, by development of a hypocone on the posterior interior side of the upper molar. The lower molar also becomes square, by loss of the paraconid and raising of the heel, whose outer hypoconid and inner entoconid make a pair, behind the metaconid and protoconid (Fig. 450). Even more characteristic is the change in the cusps themselves. Instead of the original sharp points they develop first low cones, giving so-called bunodont grinding surfaces. Then, in later evolutionary stages, ridges or lophs appear between the cusps; an ectoloph between paracone and metacone, transverse protoloph at the front of the tooth (between protocone and

U u

protoconule), and metaloph behind between hypocone and metaconule. All sorts of further developments and cross-connexions may then take place in such lophodont molars; moreover, the whole tooth becomes surrounded by 'cement' (bone), so that the ridges are supported as they wear away and continually maintain a rough surface for grinding. Short (brachydont) molars, which would wear away too quickly, are replaced by deep (hyposodont) ones, which grow continually from open roots in extreme instances.

In these animals that need to increase the grinding surfaces the whole set of teeth is usually retained and the molar structure extends forwards to the premolars. This molarization may be said to be the opposite of the condition in carnivores, where the tooth row is shortened and the hinder teeth come to have cutting edges like the front ones. The incisors of ungulates become specialized for cropping the food; in artiodactyls the upper ones are lost and the lower work against a horny upper lip. The canine is often absent, leaving a diastema. The cropping and grinding mechanisms involve various modifications of the lips, palate, tongue, and, of course, the jaws and their muscles. The articulation of the jaw with the skull is usually made by a flattened facet, allowing rotatory action of the lower jaw. The pterygoid and masseter muscles are well developed, the temporal less so (in contrast with carnivores). To provide lateral attachment for these muscles there is a tendency for a redevelopment of the postorbital bar.

In the digestive system of ungulates there is usually some chamber in which bacterial action upon cellulose can take place, but this has evidently evolved independently in the different groups, being in the stomach of artiodactyls but in the coecum of perissodactyls.

This set of 'ungulate' characteristics has developed independently many times in descendants of the insectivoran eutherian ancestor, and shows very strikingly how the adoption of a particular method of life leads to selection of variations of structure tending in similar directions. There is no special difficulty in understanding how this has happened if we imagine that each part varies genetically in its dimensions. A herbivorous diet will be easier for animals with ridged teeth and long legs, whereas those with sharper teeth can become carnivores. Those types are selected which combine a nervous organization leading to certain habits with other features that make these habits successful. In the evolution of all populations there is evidently a very elaborate interplay between variations in different directions and changes in the environmental circumstances.

3. Classification

Superorder 2. Protoungulata

*Order 1. Condylarthra, Palaeocene–Eocene

*Family 1. Hyopsodontidae. Palaeocene–Eocene. N. America
*Mioclaenus, Palaeocene. *Hyopsodus, Eocene

*Family 2. Phenacodontidae. Palaeocene–Eocene. Holarctic
*Tetraclaenodon, Palaeocene; *Phenacodus, Palaeocene–Eocene

*Family 3. Didolodontidae. Palaeocene–Eocene. S. America
*Didolodus, Eocene

*Family 4. Periptychidae. Palaeocene. N. America
*Periptychus

*Family 5. Meniscotheriidae. Palaeocene–Eocene
*Meniscotherium, Holarctic

*Order 2. Notoungulata. Palaeocene–Pleistocene
*Palaeostylops, Palaeocene, Asia; *Notostylops, Eocene, S. America; *Toxodon, Pleistocene, S. America; *Homalodotherium, Miocene, S. America; *Hegetotherium, Oligocene–Miocene, S. America

*Order 3. Litopterna. Palaeocene–Pleistocene. S. America
*Thoatherium, Miocene; *Macrauchenia, Pleistocene

*Order 4. Astrapotheria. Eocene–Miocene. S. America
*Astrapotherium, Oligocene–Miocene

Order 5. Tubulidentata. Pliocene–Recent
Orycteropus, aardvark, Cape ant-eater, Africa

4. Superorder Protoungulata

*Order Condylarthra

This group includes animals so close to the central eutherian stock that it is still disputed whether some of them should be classified as insectivores, primates, or creodonts. Five families are recognized, all from the Palaeocene and Eocene periods. The more 'primitive' in structure, such as the Eocene *Hyopsodus, had a complete row of bunodont, quadritubercular teeth, and also short legs with clawed digits. They were small (1 ft. long) and perhaps arboreal and therefore could be classified with lemurs or insectivores. *Mioclaenus is an even older type, which possessed sharp-cusped teeth. *Phenacodus (Fig. 451) is perhaps the best-known condylarth. It was an Eocene form with ungulate characters already present, including hoofs and square bunodont molars. The build was, however, still that of a generalized carnivorous or insectivorous mammal, with small brain-case, sagittal crests, rather short limbs with slightly elongated meta-podials, the central digit the longest, complete ulna and fibula, carpus and tarsus not interlocking, and a long tail. The animal was, however, rather large (4 ft. long). Smaller Palaeocene phenacodonts, such as *Tetraclaenodon*, still possessed claws and may have been very close to the ancestry of all protoungulate types. Evidently some 10 million

FIG. 451. Skeleton of *Phenacodus* as found in the rock.
(Simplified after S. Woodward and Cope.)

years of herbivorous life in the Palaeocene produced only suggestions of the 'ungulate' facies. Other condylarths became more specialized in the Eocene. Thus *Meniscotherium* had lophodont grinders, though retaining the clawed digits. *Didolodus* and similar forms from South America are condylarths that may perhaps have given rise to some of the characteristic South American ungulates.

5. South American Ungulates

*Order Notoungulata

The ungulate fauna of South America provides a case of geographic isolation as striking as that of the marsupials in Australia. In Palaeo-cene times there were ungulates common to South America and the rest of the world. Besides the condylarths, considered above, there was the animal *Palaeostylops*, which was abundant in the Palaeocene of Asia, and is closely similar to fossils (*Notostylops*) found in North and South America. These earliest notoungulates showed only a

Palaeosyops

Toxodon

Astrapotherium

Thoatherium

Macrauchenia

Thoatherium

Macrauchenia

FIG. 452. Various ungulates. (After Zittel, K. A., *Text-book of Palaeontology* (revised A. S. Woodward), Macmillan & Co., Romer, *Vertebrate Paleontology*, Chicago University Press, and Scott, *Land Mammals*, The Macmillan Co.) Lettering as Fig. 448.

slight advance in size and other features from the basal condylarth condition. The teeth possessed simple ridges. From some such beginnings there quickly developed, after the isolation of South America in the Eocene, a very rich fauna, including many large animals. Specimens of these peculiar animals were first collected by Darwin during the voyage of the *Beagle* and were later described by Owen. Darwin records that their characteristics were among the earliest stimuli that turned his thoughts to evolution (see p. 500). As many as nine families of notoungulate can be recognized in the Oligocene; after this period they became less numerous. Some of them persisted throughout the Tertiary, but all became extinct in the Pleistocene, when the connexion with North America was re-made and competition was felt from more modern types, both ungulates and carnivores.

The notoungulates known as toxodonts were very large and numerous animals, the teeth being bent into a bow, from which the group takes its name. The limbs were massive, with as few as three digits, the middle the longest, bearing hoofs. *Toxodon* itself (Fig. 452) survived to the Pleistocene and was a creature nearly 10 ft. long, with enormous head, short front and long hind legs. Variants of the type were developed, often with peculiar front teeth, such as *Homalodotherium*, which had claws, and *Hegetotherium* with rodent-like dentition. Most, but not all, toxodonts were large and for many millions of years they were the dominant herbivores of the South American forests.

6. *Order Litopterna

Some descendants of the condylarths in South America developed along lines astonishingly similar to those of the horses. The Didolidae already show tendencies in this direction and are, indeed, sometimes removed from the condylarths and placed with the South American horse-like forms in the *order Litopterna. A series of fossils shows that members of this order became first digitigrade and then unguligrade, the central metapodials elongating and the lateral ones reducing, first to three and then, in *Thoatherium* (Fig. 452), to a single one, with even smaller splint bones than remain in our horses. The general appearance of the limbs was very horse-like, for instance in the grooved talus, but the carpus never became interlocking. Other respects in which these litopterns developed less far than the horses were that the tooth row remained nearly complete and the molars low-crowned, though provided with ridges. A post-orbital bar was developed. These differences from our horses are as interesting as the similarities, and they show that the features of the ungulate facies do not necessarily all evolve together. It is impossible to say what difference in conditions was responsible for forming horse feet on an animal whose head was only partly horse-like.

These animals were presumably evolved to meet conditions on the South American plains in the Miocene. It is interesting that the three-toed types outlived the one-toed *Thoatherium*, lasting into the Pliocene. *Macrauchenia* (Fig. 452), a creature looking like a camel but perhaps living in swamps, was the only Pleistocene survivor.

Fig. 453. *Orycteropus*, the aardvark. (From life.)

7. *Order Astrapotheria

This order includes some very aberrant Oligocene and Miocene South American ungulates, with a short skull, long canines, and massive molar teeth (Fig. 452). There was probably a proboscis. The legs were weak and the vertebral spines and transverse processes small, suggesting that the animals may have been aquatic.

8. Order Tubulidentata

The aardvark ('earth-pig') or Cape ant-eater, *Orycteropus* (Fig. 453), is a zoologically very isolated form, of unknown affinities, placed by Simpson with the Protoungulata, because it is possibly not very remote from the condylarths. It is the size of a small pig, with a highly curved back, and is much given to digging, both for protection and to obtain the termites which are its main food. It occurs from South Africa to the Sudan. There is an elongated snout, round mouth, and long tongue, as in other ant-eaters. The peglike teeth, with tubes in the dentine, are unlike those in any other mammal; it has been suggested that they represent a redevelopment of teeth for biting the termites, when that diet was acquired after a previous ant-eating life. There are special arrangements in the mouth and throat to allow the animal to bury its snout in a newly revealed mass of termites and then to swallow them while continuing to breathe. The digits (4 in hand and 5 in foot) are covered by structures sometimes referred to as compressed nails, sometimes as hoofs. The head is very long and the brain small and of an extremely primitive type, with extensive olfactory regions and very small neopallium. The olfactory turbinals are better developed than in any other mammal. The uterus is paired and the placenta of a zonary type, somewhat like that of carnivores, but with a very large allantois. *Orycteropus* occurs as fossils back to the Pliocene, but its earlier history is unknown. The animal obviously retains many characters present in the earliest eutherians, the fact that it is placed by some as an edentate or insectivore and by others close to the base of the ungulate stock suggests that it has diverged relatively little from the ancestor of all eutherians.

XXIX

ELEPHANTS AND RELATED FORMS

1. 'Near-ungulates', superorder Paenungulata

From the Palaeocene ungulate stock, when it was yet hardly differentiated from that of other mammals, there diverged several lines of herbivorous animals which rapidly increased and became diversified in the Eocene, many of them becoming very large. Most of these lines declined in the Oligocene and only the huge elephants and tiny conies remain to-day to show approximately the structure of a range of Eocene pantodonts, dinocerates, and other forms. The highly specialized Sirenia (sea-cows) were also an early offshoot of this type of animal. These various lines diverged so very long ago that we should hardly expect to find that they have much in common that they do not share with other ungulates, or indeed with all mammals, but it has long been recognized that there is a loose grouping of orders around the elephants and conies. Simpson suggests the name Paenungulata ('near ungulates') for these forms that are all slightly, but not much, beyond the protoungulate level. The legs of all of them remain rather primitive, with several digits and without well-marked hoofs. The incisors and canines often become reduced to single pairs of large tusks in each jaw and the molars are specialized for grinding, with the development of cross-ridges.

2. Classification

Superorder 3. Paenungulata

Order 1. Hyracoidea. Oligocene–Recent. Palearctic, Africa
Procavia (= *Hyrax*), coney; Africa, Asia

Order 2. Proboscidea. Eocene–Recent

*Family 1. Moeritheriidae. Eocene–Oligocene. Africa
*Moeritherium

*Family 2. Deinotheriidae. Miocene–Pleistocene. Eurasia, Africa
*Deinotherium

*Family 3. Gomphotheriidae. Oligocene–Pleistocene. Holarctic, S. America, Africa

Superorder 3. Paenungulata. Family 3 (*cont.*)

Palaeomastodon, Lower Oligocene, Africa; *Phiomia*, Oligocene, Africa; *Gomphotherium* (= *Trilophodon*), Miocene–Pliocene, Holarctic, Africa; *Serridentinus*, Miocene–Pliocene, Holarctic; *Anancus* (= *Pentalophodon*), Pliocene–Pleistocene, Eurasia; *Stegomastodon*, Pliocene–Pleistocene, N. and S. America

*Family 4. Mammutidae. Miocene–Pleistocene. Holarctic
Mammut (= *Mastodon* = *Zygolophodon* = *Turicius*)

Family 5. Elephantidae. Pliocene–Recent. Holarctic, Africa
Stegolophodon, Miocene–Pleistocene, Eurasia; *Stegodon*, Pliocene–Pleistocene, Asia; *Mammuthus* (= *Mammonteus* = *Archidiskodon*), mammoth, Pleistocene, Holarctic, Africa, S. America; *Loxodonta*, African elephant, Pleistocene–Recent; *Elephas*, Indian elephant, Pleistocene–Recent

*Order 3. Pantodonta. Palaeocene–Eocene. Holarctic
Pantolambda. Palaeocene; *Coryphodon*, Palaeocene–Eocene

*Order 4. Dinocerata. Palaeocene–Eocene. Holarctic
Uintatherium, Eocene

*Order 5. Pyrotheria. Palaeocene–Oligocene. S. America
Pyrotherium, Oligocene

*Order 6. Embrithopoda. Oligocene. Africa
Arsinoitherium

Order 7. Sirenia. Sea-cows. Eocene–Recent
Protosiren, Eocene; *Dugong* (= *Halicore*), sea-cow; Indian Ocean and Pacific; *Trichechus*, manatee, Atlantic

3. Order Hyracoidea, conies

The conies (Fig. 454) are animals that live in Africa and neighbouring regions and have persisted throughout the Tertiary as small herbivorous creatures, occupying the same niche as rabbits, which they resemble superficially in many ways. Fossils are known back to the Oligocene and probably the group existed before that time and therefore shows us something of the appearance of smaller Eocene and Oligocene ungulates. The gait is plantigrade, with four anterior and three posterior digits, carrying somewhat hoof-like nails or claws, except for a sharp claw, used for toilet purposes, on the inner hind toe (Fig. 455). There is a single pair of continually growing incisors in the upper and two in the lower jaw, the latter being comb-like. There is a diastema and a large number of lophodont premolars and molars. The lower jaw is very deep, for the attachment of the masseter muscle, and, as is usual in ungulates, the post-orbital bar is nearly or quite complete. There is a centrale in the carpus, an unusually primitive feature for an ungulate. There are paired caeca on the

FIG. 454. *Procavia*, coney. (From life.)

FIG. 455. Skeleton of *Procavia*.

large intestine, in addition to the usual caecum. The brain is of macrosmatic type. As in the elephants, the testis fails to descend and remains close to the kidney, there being no sign of a scrotum or inguinal canal. The uterus is paired, and the placenta of a peculiar zonary type, not superficially like that of other ungulates.

Various species of *Procavia* are common throughout Africa (not Madagascar), Arabia, Palestine, and Syria, living either on the ground or partly in trees.

4. Elephants. Order Proboscidea

The late Henry Fairfield Osborn, one of the greatest zoologists of his time, devoted a great part of a long working life and the large resources available to him at the American Museum of Natural History to the study of the evolution of elephants. It cannot be said that he was able as a result of all this study to draw conclusions that have revolutionized biology, and this failure is in a sense a measure of the immaturity of our science. The elephants have shown great and relatively rapid changes in recent geological times and have left abundant remains, especially of their large and hard teeth. We may therefore take knowledge about evolution of elephants as a fair example of the most that can be known of the evolutionary processes in large mammals; if the study of this great mass of material leaves us in a state of confusion rather than of certainty we shall be warned to suspect the apparent clarity of other alleged evolutionary sequences, and to distrust dogmatic statements about the 'causes' of evolutionary change.

The two existing types of elephant, referred to distinct genera, live still in considerable numbers in Africa (*Loxodonta*) and Asia (*Elephas*). They are survivors of a much larger population, reaching its greatest variety in Pliocene times. The essential feature of the type is the great size ($11\frac{1}{2}$ ft. high in *Loxodonta*) and the presence of a special food-collecting system able to gather enough raw material to support such a large living mass. Of the various factors influencing the optimum size for a given animal type, all those favouring increase must be present in the ingredients of elephant life. Elephants are larger than any other land animals, living or extinct, except perhaps the huge *Oligocene* rhinoceros *Baluchitherium* and some of the largest dinosaurs (if these were indeed terrestrial).

The basal metabolism of a mammal increases only with about the two-thirds power of its weight, so that larger animals need, on this account, relatively less food. But, as Watson (1946) has pointed out, the output of energy by the muscles is proportional to the weight of the muscle; the total intake needed is therefore proportional to some power between two-thirds and the first power of the weight of the whole, being 'larger the greater and more continuous the activity of the animal'. Elephants, as he further comments, are very active when wild, their playfulness and strength are proverbial, and often a nuisance to man. They manage to collect their food with sufficient economy of energy, though to do this they must eat throughout a large part of the day, perhaps for as much as 18 hours. Here another factor has to be considered, namely, the area of tooth available for grinding the food. This will vary approximately as the two-thirds power of the total weight; as the animals become larger the tooth surface needs therefore to be relatively increased.

With these factors in mind we shall recognize that the significant features in the organization of elephants are that they are very large animals, with an efficient nervous organization for finding the food, efficient means of collecting it, and large surfaces for grinding it.

The trunk is the main means of collection—an enormously elongated nose and upper lip, with appropriate muscles and sensitive grasping tip. The muscles have been developed chiefly from the parts of the

FIG. 456. Section of tooth of elephant. The front part of the crown (on the left) is already worn away. Notice the upstanding enamel lamellae, which reach to the base of the tooth. Dentine is shown dotted, cement by lines (from Weber).

facial musculature that are responsible for moving the sides of the nose. The trunk probably developed rather quickly, in late Miocene times, perhaps 10–15 million years ago; the earlier elephants of the Miocene possessed very long lower jaws, which then became shortened as the trunk developed. Any tall animal must have means of reaching the ground and the trunk is probably superior even to a very long neck for this purpose, because it can reach upwards and sideways as well as downwards. Only one pair of continually growing incisors remains in modern elephants, forming the two enormous upcurved tusks, up to 11½ ft. long in *Loxodonta*, composed of solid dentine except for a temporary cap of enamel at the tip. This mass of ivory is no doubt useful for defence and perhaps in food collection, but it seems to be a considerable waste of calcium and phosphorus, not to mention of the energy necessary to carry the 350 lbs. weight. This weight is balanced against that of the body, about the pillar-like front legs, and it is perhaps not fantastic to suggest that the tusks serve partly as counterweights, for purposes of balance (see p. 716), extravagant though such an arrangement may be. The tusks are smaller in females and in the Indian than in the African elephant; in the female Indian elephant they do not project beyond the lips. This difference may be connected with the relatively small size of these females.

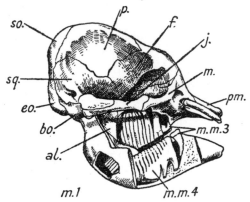

FIG. 457. Skull of young Indian elephant. The roots of the teeth have been exposed.

al. alisphenoid; *bo.* basioccipital; *eo.* exoccipital; *f.* frontal; *j.* jugal; *m.* maxillary; *m.1.* first molar; *m.m. 3* and *4.* third and fourth milk molars; *p.* parietal; *pm.* premaxillary; *so.* supraoccipital; *sq.* squamosal. (After Reynolds, *The Vertebrate Skeleton*, Cambridge University Press.)

The essential features of the grinding apparatus are the immensely large molars (Fig. 456), with numerous sharp transverse ridges, by which all sorts of plants, including hard grasses, are chopped into small fragments. There are three small premolars, which are soon shed, and the three molars are then developed in a series and used one after the other. By a special arrangement of the palate (Fig. 457) the teeth are allowed to form high up in the skull, so that each tooth has a very great area, made up by the fusion of as many as twenty-seven separate 'plates', which develop as separate cones of dentine and enamel, each with its own pulp cavity, the cones being finally joined together by cement. The teeth are placed just above the ascending ramus of the mandible, so that the large jaw-muscles work at maximum advantage. For their attachment the skull becomes extremely short and high, with the development of large air spaces between its tables. This shape also allows a large occipital region for the muscles that hold up the head.

With this head structure the elephants have been able to grow to a size which must approach the limit possible for a fully terrestrial animal. The backbone (Fig. 458) is based on a 'single girder' plan, with as many as twenty ribs, and high thoracic neural spines, forming together a huge beam that carries the weight of the abdomen and balances it on the fore-legs against the weight of the head, the hind-legs acting as propellents. The ilium is nearly vertical and expanded

FIG. 458. Skeleton of an Indian elephant. (From Owen, *The Anatomy of Vertebrates*, Longmans, Green & Co.)

transversely for the attachment of the large gluteus, iliacus, abdominal and sacrospinalis muscles. The acetabulum faces downwards.

As in other heavy animals the legs are enormous pillars, with long upper segments and no great extension of the lower. The ulna and fibula are complete and bear part of the weight, the ulna and radius being held permanently crossed in a fixed position of pronation. Walking is of a modified digitigrade type; all three of the short phalanges of each digit reach the ground, but the greater part of the weight is taken by a special pad of elastic tissue at the back of the foot. There are five digits in each foot, united by a web to make a firm basis, and having small, flat, somewhat hoof-like nails at the tips. The ribs carry so much weight that respiration is almost wholly dia-phragmatic and the lungs are fused to the walls of the thoracic cavity.

The soft parts of elephants show some features retained unmodified from their early ungulate ancestry. Thus the cerebral hemispheres are relatively rather small and leave the cerebellum uncovered. In

FIG. 459. Chart of the evolution of the paenungulate orders. The animals are shown reconstructed following Andrews, Osborn, and others and their size is indicated approximately. The stages in development of the molar teeth are also shown.

other respects the brain is well developed, it has a greater absolute weight than that of any other land mammal, and one may guess that the tactile centres of the cortex connected with the trunk are well developed. The temporal lobe is very large. In spite of the specialization of the head for a herbivorous diet, the stomach and intestine remain very simple and there is no special large fermentative chamber, presumably the intestine is large and long enough already!

The testes are remarkable in that, as in other paenungulates, they lie close to the kidneys, and have made no movement of descent into a scrotum. The two horns of the uterus remain separate, though united externally. Only one young is born at a time, after a gestation of twenty-two months. The placenta has at least a superficial similarity to the zonary arrangement of carnivores.

The earliest-known member of the elephant line, *Moeritherium*, from the Upper Eocene of Egypt, was only 2 ft. high and probably had a short snout (Fig. 459). The skull was elongated and small tusks were present, but the dentition nearly complete, $\dfrac{3.1.3.3}{3.0.3.3}$. The molars were bunodont and carried only two cross lophs, a condition easily derived from that of a condylarth quadritubercular tooth. From some such animal arose ultimately so great a collection of types that Osborn in his study of the group recognized 350 species, only two living at the present day. *Moeritherium* survived into the Lower Oligocene, where there is found also a more advanced type *Phiomia*, about twice as large. Both upper and lower jaws of this animal carried tusks and the whole front of the head was greatly elongated, with formation of a long diastema. The wear of the lower incisors shows that they were used for digging. The molars carried three low ridges and were all used together, not successively. The similar *Palaeomastodon* lived at the same time and was about 6 ft. high.

After this period there is a gap, probably covering 10 million years or more, in our knowledge of elephant evolution, but it is clear that throughout this long period the stock must have continued with little change, as a race of animals with very long digging tusks and rather mobile face and lips, becoming gradually larger and elongating the face more and more to enable the ground to be reached. In the Miocene is found a considerable variety of these long-jawed animals, the various species of the genus *Gomphotherium* (= *Trilophodon*). The teeth of the earliest of these long-faced elephants were used all at once, not in series; later the premolar teeth tended to be reduced and the molars became covered with an increasing number of cusps, arranged to make a number of cross-ridges, seldom, however, more than five. From the low cusps they are known loosely as 'mastodonts', but the colloquial terms for description of elephants are used in senses almost as varied as the 'scientific' names; as in other branches of knowledge, great abundance of information has led to confusion of terminology.

From this Miocene stage onwards the study of proboscidean evolution becomes a desperate attempt to sort out huge numbers of fossil specimens (often, however, only molar teeth) into truly phylogenetic lines. Osborn made an heroic effort to recognize only fully documented sequences, but even with the wealth of material available it is rarely possible to say with complete certainty that one type has evolved into another. The interpretations of the sequences and their expression in classificatory terms vary considerably even in the hands of the most careful interpreters of Osborn's work. However, it is probable that in this mass of material there can be seen several distinct lines, in which evolution proceeded in a parallel manner. From the end of Miocene times onwards the very elongated jaws began to shorten, and it was presumably at this time that the trunk became long and the typical elephant-like habit was adopted. Certainly not all animals having elephant-like appearance belong to the 'main' elephant line, and the shortening of the lower jaw took place at different times in the various stocks. Thus the members of the Pliocene and Pleistocene genus *Anancus, though extremely like elephants in general shape, had bunomastodont molars. This line retained little cusps between the main ridges, such as were present in the Miocene gomphotheres. *Stegomastodon was a related animal that lived on in South America until as late as A.D. 200.

The species of *Serridentinus represent another line, and in this case there were no little cusps on the teeth, but the grinding area was increased by extra 'serrate' ridges. This type retained the long lower tusks into the Pliocene, but then tended to shorten them, though never to the full elephant condition. The line which produced the modern elephants can first be recognized in the Lower Miocene, by the fact that the cusps are united into sharp ridges. This condition presumably marks the transition to feeding on hard grasses, which have to be cut, rather than on softer stalks, which can be ground. Some members of this 'zygolophodont' stock retained few ridges, and presumably a browsing diet, even into the Pleistocene, although they acquired short lower jaws like those of the elephants. These animals are therefore 'mastodons', and it is unfortunate that the rules of priority require that they shall be called *Mammut (= *Zygolophodon). In *Stegolophodon and *Stegodon of the Upper Pliocene and Pleistocene, however, the lower jaw was already short and the arrangement of the skull elephant-like, with huge curved upper tusks. From some such form the two modern elephants (Loxodonta and Elephas) and the mammoths (*Mammuthus) have been derived, but the details of the evolutionary sequence become here even more involved. We possess such great numbers of teeth, showing all sorts of detailed

differences, that to arrange them in evolutionary sequences is mostly
a matter of guesswork. Osborn preferred not to deal with individual
teeth but only with the fifty or so complete skulls which have been
found, and these fall into three groups. The mammoths, *Mammuthus* (= *Archidiskodon* = *Mammonteus*) have very long curved tusks,
turned upwards at the tips. There were several 'species', including
such forms as *M. primigenius*, the woolly mammoth, common in
Europe during the Pleistocene and surviving until recently in Alaska
and Siberia, where carcasses have been found preserved in glaciers.

Loxodonta, the African elephant, has straighter tusks and the surface of the molars wears to a diamond-shaped pattern. In *Elephas*
the tusks are also nearly straight and the molar ridges are parallel.
There are, of course, numerous other differences between the two
modern elephants and it is not possible to trace out in detail the
ancestry of the two types and of the mammoths. In fact one lesson
to be learned from the study of elephant evolution is that mammalian
fossil remains are seldom sufficiently abundant to allow study of the
details of evolutionary history. There is usually some doubt about
the exact relationship of the bones and teeth which are found. Phyletic
lines are constructed by careful comparison of the characters of the
fossils, there is seldom direct evidence of the genetic relationship of
any two types. In the present instance it is very probable that from
the gomphotheres of Miocene times onwards the lower jaw began to
shorten and the skull to achieve an elephant-like form in at least four
separate stocks (probably far more). *Anancus* and the true elephan-
tines evolved faster in this direction than *Serridentinus* and *Mammut*,
both of which retained the 'mastodont' characters associated with
browsing even into the Pleistocene. The existence of parallel evolution may be regarded as established beyond reasonable doubt in this
case; evidently there was some feature either in environmental change
or internal 'tendency', or in both, leading all these stocks to change in
similar ways, though at different times and rates.

Deinotherium was a distinct type of elephant, separate from all
others from Miocene times or earlier. There were down-turned lower
tusks and probably also a trunk. There were several molars in the
tooth row and the full elephant specializations did not develop. The
animals remained similar in structure for a very long period, but
became very large before they disappeared in the Pleistocene. This
is a good example of the development of different variants of a type;
deinotheres had the trunks but not the molars of elephants.

5. *Order Pantodonta (Amblypoda)

During the Palaeocene and Eocene the ungulate stock produced various large herbivores and these may be referred to the paenungulate group. The relationships of the numerous types discovered are still obscure and classification is probably not yet final. The animals here placed (following Simpson) in the order *Pantodonta were formerly, with others, known as amblypods ('blunt feet'). The Palaeocene *Pantolambda* was about 3–4 ft. long, with a long face and tricuspid molars. The limbs were short and broad, hence it is presumed that the animals moved slowly.

Later members of the group, such as *Coryphodon* (Fig. 460), were over 8 ft. long and very heavily built, with some formation of ridges on the teeth, and feet with five digits; some had simple hoofs, others claws. The brain was very small and evidently these were clumsy creatures, successful for a time, but unable to compete with later herbivores.

6. *Order Dinocerata

These were even larger animals, of the same general build as the Pantodonta, and were previously classed with the latter as Amblypoda. The two pairs of horns and very large dagger-like canines provided weapons of defence. The molars showed folds and ridges and provided a reasonably efficient grinding battery. *Uintatherium* (Fig. 460) was a typical Eocene form; even though the brain was small and the gait clumsy, the animals were evidently successful at the time, and reached a size as great as that achieved by any other land mammals except the elephants.

7. *Order Pyrotheria

Pyrotherium and its allies (Fig. 460) were Eocene and Oligocene South American ungulates and they are usually classed with Notoungulata, but more for geographical than phylogenetic reasons. They were remarkably similar to elephants, for instance in their large size and in the dorsal nostril, suggesting the presence of a trunk. The incisors were developed into tusks and the molar teeth carried two transverse rows of cusps, as in bilophodont early proboscidians. The similarities of the two groups are striking, but they probably indicate only common early ungulate derivation and provide another instance of convergence.

Pyrotherium

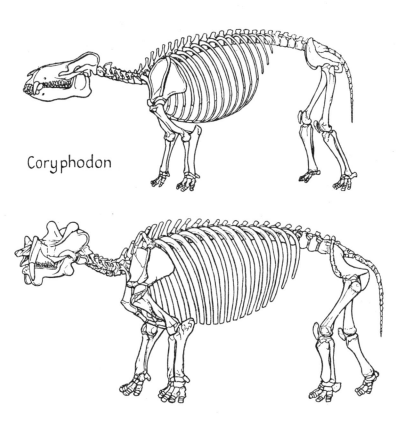

Coryphodon

Uintatherium

FIG. 460. Skeletons of a pantodont, a dinocerate, and a pyrothere.
(After Woodward, *Outlines of Vertebrate Palaeontology*, Cambridge
University Press. Flower and Lydekker, *Mammals*, A. & C. Black, Ltd.,
and Romer, *Vertebrate Paleontology* University of Chicago Press.)

8. *Order Embrithopoda

Arsinoitherium from the Lower Oligocene of Egypt was another large creature that may be placed here, since it possesses the usual paenungulate features of large size and limbs with five digits; the most striking feature was the enormous paired horn near the mid-line. There was a regular tooth row, with no enlargement of the incisors or canines, but the molars showed marked hypsodont conditions.

FIG. 461. Manatee, *Manatus*. (From photographs.)

9. Order Sirenia

The sea-cows are herbivorous creatures, living along the coasts and in rivers, and very highly adapted to aquatic life. There is little doubt, however, that they have reached this condition by modification of a basic ungulate type of organization, probably not very different from that of the early proboscidians. The two modern forms, the manatee of the Atlantic (Fig. 461) and dugong of the Pacific and Indian oceans, are different in many respects and represent lines that have been separate for a long time, probably since the Eocene. Both have a 'streamlined' body-form, with very few hairs and thick 'blubber'. The hind-limbs do not show externally, and only traces of the pelvic girdle remain, but the fore-limbs are well-developed paddles, with a full pentadactyl structure and no hyperphalangy or hyperdactyly. The caudal vertebrae are well developed and swimming is effected by the body and tail, the latter carrying a terminal horizontal fin. The vertebrae articulate with each other by flat surfaces, as in other aquatic forms, but there are zygapophyses, and the whole column is not quite reduced to the condition of a simple compression strut. The bones have a characteristic structure (pachyostosis), probably produced by lack of stressing. The manatee has only six cervical vertebrae. The ribs are round and the diaphragm is oblique, as in elephants and whales, allowing the lungs to reach far back. Respiration is probably mainly by means of the barrel-like ribs. The blood system shows retia mirabilia in the brain and elsewhere, as in other aquatic mammals (p. 632). The brain is small and the sense of smell not completely absent as it is in whales. The neopallium is smaller and less folded than in almost any other mammal of comparable size; the behaviour is probably very simple. The ear resembles that of whales in the large size of the ossicles and in reduction of cochlea and of semi-circular canals. The eyes are small and are protected by very muscular lids.

The teeth of the manatee are continually replaced from the hind end and carry two transverse ridges. In the dugong the teeth are much reduced and the lower jaw carries a horny pad, the upper a pair of tusks in the male, the pre-maxillae being very large. The lips are used to crop vegetation, which is digested in a stomach that is complex but not like that either of the whales or other ungulates. The intestine is very long.

The reproductive system shows such primitive features as abdominal testes (with no signs that there was a descent in the ancestors) and a bicornuate uterus. The young are born in the water and nursed at pectoral teats, which habit, with other features, has produced some of the legends of mermaids.

Eocene fossils are known (*Protosiren*) which, while definitely sirenians, show distinct similarity to the ungulates of those times. The nostrils were directed dorsally as in modern forms, but the tooth-row was complete and a small hind-limb was present.

XXX

PERISSODACTYLS

1. Perissodactyl characteristics

The protungulate and paenungulate herbivorous types achieved their chief radiation and greatest numbers early in the Tertiary period. Their organization was not profoundly different from that of the original eutherians and although a few of them, such as the elephants, have persisted to the present day, most have been supplanted by ungulates that appeared by later modification of the original type. Very roughly we may say that the protungulate is the chief Palaeocene mammalian herbivorous type, and the paenungulate that of the Eocene. The Perissodactyla, including horses, rhinoceroses, tapirs, and certain early extinct types, then represent a third or Oligocene–Miocene development, supplanting the paenungulates and itself then largely replaced in Pliocene, Pleistocene, and Recent times by the Artiodactyla. This analysis must of course be taken only as a very rough approximation, especially as it is given unsupported by the quantitive data which it evidently requires. It is subject to many exceptions, for example the very large development of the elephants in post-Miocene times.

The early perissodactyls were much like all other early ungulates and it is not easy to characterize the group as a whole. The limb structure developed the mesaxonic condition, with the digits arranged around the third as the main weight-bearing member, the others being reduced. With the power of fast movement the lower part of the limbs became elongated and the upper segments shortened, with reduction of the ulna and fibula, but these are characters found also in artiodactyls. A distinctive feature of the perissodactyls was the plan of the carpus and tarsus (Fig. 449). One distal carpal, the capitate (magnum), became enlarged and interlocked with the proximal carpals, while in the foot the ectocuneiform developed into a large flat bone, transmitting the thrust through a flat navicular to the talus, which has a flat under-surface, not a pulley-like one as in Artiodactyla. Modifications of the backbone for carrying great weight or for running were similar to those of other orders (elephants, Dinocerata), including increase in the number of ribs and the vertical position of the ilium (p. 671).

The feeding mechanism, which has been the basis of the success of the perissodactyls, is in several ways less specialized than that of artiodactyls. The incisors are preserved and used for cropping, having a pit on the free surface, so that sharp edges are presented as the tooth wears away (incidentally allowing the age of the animal to be determined). The canine may be reduced or absent, and there is often a diastema. The molars of many of the earlier types remained bunodont and low-crowned, but those of the later rhinoceroses and horses developed an elaborate grinding surface. This was achieved by formation of a longitudinal ectoloph along the outer edge of the upper molar and parallel transverse ridges, the protoloph and metaloph (Fig. 448). Even with the secondary complications of the latest forms these teeth remain recognizably of quadritubercular pattern, and the same might be said of the lower molars. The premolars come to resemble the molars, giving a long battery of teeth. The gut shows less specialization than in artiodactyls, the stomach being undivided, but in horses there is a large cardiac area of non-glandular, oesophageal structure. Digestion of cellulose takes place in the caecum and large intestine, which may be greatly developed. The brain of Perissodactyla is relatively small, especially in the earlier forms, such as the tapirs. It is of macrosmatic type and the sensory portion of the nose is very highly developed.

The reproductive system also shows primitive features. The uterus is bicornuate and the placenta of the diffuse epitheliochorial type, with a large allantoic sac. The yolk sac grows to a large size and forms a yolk-sac placenta during the early part of the development.

2. Classification

Superorder 4. Mesaxonia
  Order Perissodactyla
    Suborder 1. Hippomorpha
        *Family 1. Palaeotheriidae. Eocene–Oligocene. Eurasia
        Palaeotherium
      Family 2. Equidae. Horses. Eocene–Recent
        Hyracotherium(= *Eohippus*), Lower Eocene, Holarctic; *Orohippus*, Eocene, N. America; *Epihippus*, Upper Eocene, N. America; *Mesohippus*, Oligocene, N. America; *Miohippus*, Oligocene–Miocene, N. America; *Anchitherium*, Miocene, Holarctic; *Parahippus*, Miocene, N. America; *Merychippus*, Miocene, N. America; *Hipparion*, Pliocene, Holarctic,

Superorder 4. Mesaxonia. Family 2 (*contd.*)
          Africa; *Pliohippus*, Pliocene, N. America; *Hip-
          pidion*, Pleistocene, S. America; *Equus*, Pliocene–
          Recent, horses, asses, zebras, world-wide
      *Family 3. Brontotheriidae (= *Titanotheridae). Eocene–
          Oligocene. Holarctic
          Lambdotherium, Eocene; *Palaeosyops*, Eocene; *Bron-
          tops*, Oligocene
      Family 4. Chalicotheriidae. Eocene–Pliocene. Holarctic
          Eomoropus, Eocene; *Chalicotherium*, Pliocene
  Suborder 2. Ceratomorpha
      Superfamily 1. Tapiroidea. Tapirs. Eocene–Recent
          Homogalax, Eocene; *Tapirus*, tapir, Miocene–Recent,
          Asia, S. America
      Superfamily 2. Rhinocerotoidea. Rhinoceroses. Eocene–
          Recent
      *Family Hyrachyidae. Eocene. Holarctic
          Hyrachyus. Eocene
      *Family Hyracodontidae. Eocene–Oligocene. Holarctic
          Hyracodon, Oligocene
      *Family Amynodontidae. Eocene–Miocene, Holarctic
          Amynodon, Eocene
      Family Rhinocerotidae. Oligocene–Recent
          Aceratherium, Oligocene–Pliocene; *Baluchitherium*,
          Oligocene–Miocene, Asia; *Rhinoceros*, Indian and
          Javan rhinoceros, Pliocene–Recent, Asia; *Diceros*,
          black African rhinoceros, Pleistocene–Recent, Africa

3. Perissodactyl radiation

The fossil history of animals with the perissodactyl structure is
perhaps better known than that of any other mammals; the type
reached its peak during a period from which many fossils have been
preserved and we have therefore a better opportunity to study the
development, flowering, and decay of the group than in the case of
forms whose maximum development occurred either earlier or later.
Here if anywhere we should be able to learn lessons about the nature
of the evolutionary process and to study the forces that produce
change in animal form. Because of the very abundance of the fossils
it is necessary, however, to be cautious in interpretation and to
recognize exactly what can be proved from the evidence.

The known types of horses are divided into 350 species, but only

Hyracotherium

Brontops

Palaeotherium   Moropus

FIG. 462. Skeletons of some early perissodactyls. (After Woodward, *Palaeontology*, Cambridge, Osborn, Abel, and Scott, *Land Mammals*, The Macmillan Company.)

a small proportion of these can be confidently placed close to the direct line of evolution to *Equus*. Abundant though the material is, we have not, therefore, anything like a complete series of fossils to show every shade and grade of change of the populations throughout the 50 million years or so of their evolution. Our knowledge is based on a small sample of individuals, preserved at random at scattered intervals. The remains often suggest evolutionary sequences and

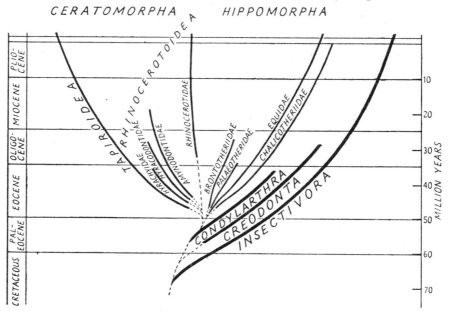

Fig. 463. Chart of the evolution of the perissodactyls.

many accounts speak confidently of changes and trends. We shall try, even in this brief account, to describe the actual discoveries and to indicate clearly what evidence is available for evolutionary speculation. With all the mass of information we possess it must yet be realized that the study of the details of perissodactyl evolution has hardly been begun, for example we have almost no quantitative information about the variability of the characters concerned.

The earliest perissodactyls had departed but little from condylarth conditions. *Hyracotherium* (= *Eohippus*) from the Eocene of Europe and North America (Fig. 462) was the size of a dog and very like the condylarth *Phenacodus*. The tooth-row was complete, with square bunodont molars. Besides the four main upper molar cusps an anterior protoconule and posterior metaconule are suggested, and between these and their neighbours the dentine is partly built up to form two transverse ridges. The premolars were tritubercular. The gait was digitigrade, with rather long metapodials and with hoofs, the front leg having four and the hind-leg three toes, the central ones the longest. These animals were already distinctly horse-like, in spite of their small size, and they probably lived in forests, browsing on the leaves.

From a population of animals of this type there evolved a varied

Fig. 464. Malayan tapir, *Tapirus*. (From photographs.)

Fig. 465. Skull of the tapir. (After Reynolds, *The Vertebrate Skeleton*, Cambridge.)

host of herbivores (Fig. 463), which may be divided into six main types: the tapirs, remaining with little change; the rhinoceroses, becoming large and heavy-bodied; brontotheres (titanotheres), also becoming large; palaeotheres, an early horse-like line; chalicotheres, which secondarily acquired digging claws, and finally the horses themselves. Of course each of these lines had many subdivisions and branches, producing a most complex evolutionary bush.

4. Suborder Ceratomorpha, tapirs and rhinoceroses

The modern tapirs of Central and South America, Malaya, and the East Indies (Fig. 464) are nocturnal creatures, mostly living in forests on damp, soft ground; they have retained many of the conditions of the ancestors of all Perissodactyla. There are four digits in the fore-foot and three in the hind; the ulna and fibula are complete and distinct. The tooth-row is complete (42 teeth in tapirs), but the pre-molars are molariform, though of a simple square pattern with low crowns (Fig. 465). The nose has developed into a short trunk, with characteristic shortening of the nasal bones. Fossil tapirs, very similar to modern forms, are found back to the Oligocene, and somewhat more primitive Eocene related forms (*Homogalax*), with triangular molars, might have been close to the ancestors of *Hyraco-therium*. We may say therefore with some confidence that the modern

Fig. 466. Indian rhinoceros (*Rhinoceros*).

tapirs show us with little change the condition of the perissodactyl stock in late Eocene or Oligocene times, perhaps 35 million years ago. Fossils almost exactly similar to the existing genus occur back to the Miocene, say, 20 million years ago, and the tapirs were then of wide-spread distribution. We may notice once again the important fact that, given suitable environments, types persist with little change even when their relatives, moving into other conditions, become greatly changed.

5. Rhinoceroses

The rhinoceroses (Fig. 466) are the only surviving large perissodac-tyls; they show the graviportal type of body form adopted by many of the extinct forms (brontotheres, &c.) and also by many other large eutherians. Dinocerates, elephants, hippopotamuses, and rhinoceroses all show the same type of skeleton. The vertebral column (Fig. 467) has long neural spines above the fore-legs, there are many ribs, reach-ing back nearly to the pelvis. The whole column thus makes a girder balanced on the fore-legs, and the head, being very heavy, counter-balances the body weight. The hind-legs provide the main locomotor thrust. It is characteristic of this 'single-girder' type of backbone that the ilia are wide and vertically placed. The feet are basically similar in all these groups in that many digits (usually four in rhinoceros) are preserved, making supports of large area.

The earliest members of the rhinoceros group, such as *Hyrachyus*

FIG. 467. *Above:* Skeleton of the Indian rhinoceros. (From Owen.) *Below:* Skull and teeth of a young Indian rhinoceros. The grinding surface is made up of four milk premolars and one adult molar on each jaw. The remaining permanent teeth have not erupted.

f. frontal; *j.* jugal; *na.* nasal; *pa.* parietal; *sq.* squamosal. (After Reynolds, *The Vertebrate Skeleton*, Cambridge.)

of the Eocene, were very like other primitive perissodactyls, mostly small and with a complete tooth-row, the molars already showing an ectoloph and the parallel transverse lophs characteristic of the group. The *Hyracodonts were an Eocene and Oligocene line specialized for swifter movement ('running rhinoceroses') with long legs and three toes in each foot, much as in the earlier horses. The members of another line, the *Amynodonts, were larger, probably semi-aquatic forms. The true rhinoceroses appear in the Oligocene, already as large creatures, fully terrestrial and hence with stout limbs and a good grinding battery, with molarized premolars. *Baluchitherium* became of enormous size, as much as 18 ft. high. Rhinoceroses became numerous in the Miocene and Pliocene (*Aceratherium*). Various types persisted through the Pliocene and Pleistocene, and the modern single-horned *Rhinoceros* of Asia and two-horned *Dicerorhinus* of the East Indies and *Diceros* of Africa are derived from some of these. Extinct types such as the woolly rhinoceros are known from Palaeolithic drawings and partly embalmed specimens. Modern rhinoceroses all have a very thick, almost hairless skin, with characteristic folds. The tendency to very active keratin development also produces the horns, either one or two median outgrowths on the head, which can be compared to clumped masses of hairs.

6. *Brontotheres (*Titanotheres)

These were early heavily built ungulates, reaching large size in the later Eocene and Oligocene, in fact preceding the rhinoceroses as large herbivores. The fully developed forms, such as *Brontops* (Fig. 462) of the Lower Oligocene, were of typical graviportal type, up to 8 ft. high, with high thoracic spines, numerous ribs, vertical and laterally expanded ilia, and rather short legs, with four digits in front and three behind. The tooth-row was complete and the molars large but low-crowned, with a ridge along the outer side, but isolated cusps on the inner (hence 'bunolophodont'). A single pair of large horns was carried on the front of the skull.

The earliest fossils that can be referred to this type, *Lambdotherium* of the Lower Eocene, were much smaller, and without horns; they could very well have been derived from *Hyracotherium*. *Palaeosyops* from the Middle Eocene was larger, but still hornless (Fig. 452); it is widely believed that from some such stage numerous lines have diverged, each becoming larger and independently acquiring horns. For obvious reasons it is difficult to obtain a proper idea of the evolution of such large fossil animals and, as Simpson points out, genera and perhaps even subfamilies have probably been created on a basis of differences that may be only sexual or individual. It is impossible to make a thorough study of the skeletons of large numbers of such giants and little reliance can be placed on the details of the various evolutionary lines proposed. The brontotheres were numerous in Eocene and Oligocene times, and it is not unreasonable to suppose that they became extinct because of the inadequacy of the grinding mechanism.

7. *Chalicotheres (= *Ancylopoda)

One remarkable side-line of perissodactyl evolution, while becoming large and horse-like in some ways, acquired structures resembling claws instead of hoofs (Fig. 468). These chalicotheres, all rather alike, existed from the Eocene to the Pleistocene and were therefore a successful group. The most probable suggestion is that their strange feet were used in digging for roots. The terminal phalanges of the three toes of each foot were cleft and undoubtedly carried a nail or claw of some sort, though not necessarily one like that of true unguiculates.

Fig. 468. Feet of a chalicothere. (After Romer, *Vertebrate Paleontology*, University of Chicago Press.)

There is no doubt that in a sense this is a case of reversal of evolution, but we cannot assert much about its possible genetic implications unless we can find details of the nails.

When chalicothere digits were first discovered in 1823 Cuvier applied his 'law of correlation' and suggested that this was the remains of an ant-eater, 'un Pangolin gigantesque', while teeth and other bones found near by he referred to an ungulate. It was only when skeletons were found in such a position that the association of the bones could not be denied that the danger of this attempt to apply deductive principles in biology was exposed. The other parts of the skeleton are unambiguously perissodactyl (Fig. 462), the teeth rather like those of brontotheres. There may have been a short proboscis and the neck vertebrae of some forms show very strong zygapophyses, perhaps suggesting that the whole head and snout were also used in digging for roots. Other chalicotheres had very long front legs, and since these animals are found in association with forest dwellers they may perhaps have used their claws to drag down branches. The attraction of speculating about these creatures has not diminished with the demonstration of its dangers.

8. *Palaeotheres

These animals were an early offshoot that acquired horse-like characters in the later Eocene and early Oligocene, long before the true horses showed such features. Though they were large they were not so heavily built as the graviportal brontotheres and rhinoceroses (Fig. 462). There were three digits in each foot, the lateral ones sometimes very slim. The teeth developed ridges on the same plan as in horses, but with different details. Probably more than one line of descent is included in the group and they serve to warn us against some easy generalizations. If the horse form developed in the Eocene as well as in the Miocene we cannot assume that suitable conditions only appeared for the first time in the latter epoch. Certainly the palaeotheres are very close to the true horses, both being derived from a *Hyracotherium-like stock.

9. Horses

The horse, besides its special interest as one of our oldest and most useful commensals, has provided a rather complete and convincing record of its origin. We shall therefore first describe its present structure and then analyse the fossil record to discover exactly what can be demonstrated about the evolution. Existing horses, asses, and zebras, all referred to the genus Equus (Figs. 469–71), are large, swiftly moving, long-legged animals, with only the third digits developed and covered with hoofs. The metapodials of digits II and IV are present as small splint-bones. There is a callosity on the inner side of the fore-limb in all species (also on the hind-limbs in E. caballus, the domestic horse), and this may be a vestigial scent gland. There are three incisors in each jaw, usually one small canine (the 'tush', absent in females). The first premolar is vestigial in each jaw ('wolf-tooth'); the remaining three resemble the three molars. All the cheek teeth are hypsodont, square in cross-section, with ectoloph and transverse protoloph and metaloph, joined by longitudinal ridges that give the tooth a certain resemblance to the selenodont molars of artiodactyls, hence 'selenolophodont'. The skull is modified to allow space for the deep, continually growing teeth and for the large jaw-muscles, and there is a complete post-orbital bar.

The hair is long all over the body and tends to show the pattern of vertical stripes which is so marked in zebras, often clear in asses, and occasionally present in horses. The tail is long, its hairs beginning close to the base in horses, half-way along in the others.

FIG. 469. Zebra (*Equus*). (From photographs.)

FIG. 470. Racehorse (*Equus*). (From a photograph.)

FIG. 471. Shire horse (*Equus*). (From a photograph.)

　　All horses in the native state live in herds, as do so many plains-dwelling herbivores.　The brain is large, and although the organs of

FIG. 472. Table to show the evolution of horses. (Based on Stirton.) The approximate condition of the limbs and teeth at each epoch are shown to the left and right.

smell are well developed the eyes are also large and the neopallium is very extensive.　Besides the keen senses common to many herbivores the horse, with its large brain, also has considerable powers of learning and ability to vary and restrain its behaviour.　In these respects horses and elephants, and perhaps also modern artiodactyls, are very different from the small-brained herbivores of the Eocene.

Modern horses show considerable genetical diversity (Figs. 470 and 471), but none of the 'species' are mutually sterile, though the F 1 resulting from the cross may be nearly so, as in the case of the mule, produced from the horse–ass cross. Evidently the population is in process of divergence. The domestic horse *E. caballus* is not found truly wild, but *E. przewalskii* of central Asia may be. There are several species of wild asses, such as *E. onager* of Asia and *E. asinus* of Africa. Several species of zebra live in Africa, one of them being *E. zebra*.

Between the modern *Equus* and the lower Eocene **Hyracotherium* a great number of fossil stages can be recognized (Fig. 472). The chief changes that can be followed may be listed as (1) increase of size, (2) lengthening of the distal portion of the legs, (3) reduction of lateral digits, (4) increase in the relative length of the front part of the skull, (5) increase of depth (hypsodonty) and of the grinding lophs of molars, (6) approximation of premolars to molar structure, (7) completion of post-orbital bar. No doubt there has been change also in many other characteristics, for instance the brain and behaviour; these are difficult to follow in a fossil series, but study of cranial casts suggests a rapid increase in size and folding of the cerebrum relatively early in the evolution.

The fossil remains are not usually available in long series of layered beds, such that we can be sure that one population has evolved into the next. However, the dating of the fossils can often be done with considerable accuracy by means of the associated animals, and a series can thus be produced such as would be expected in the progress from **Hyracotherium* to *Equus*. There are, however, many fossils which show special developments, and cannot be fitted into the direct series. These are presumed to be divergent lines: it must be emphasized that this is an arbitrary though probably justified procedure. These 'sidelines' are so numerous that they immediately throw doubt on the idea that there has been any single uniform 'trend' in horse evolution. At least twelve types sufficiently marked to be classified as genera are known, in addition to the types directly on the line leading to *Equus*; of course there is a much larger number of shorter, independent, evolutionary lines within these genera. We have enough evidence to glimpse the extraordinary complexity that would be revealed by the complete evolutionary 'bush', even in this single family. A further complication is produced by migrations. It is at present believed that the main course of horse evolution went on in North America, with migration at various times to the Old World and South America. Certainly a more continuous series of forms has been revealed in

North America than elsewhere, but it must be remembered that they have been looked for intensively, and brilliantly studied. It is not impossible that further study of Old World horses will produce still greater complications by revealing sequences of evolution within that area.

Throughout the Eocene epoch the horses all possessed four toes in each limb. The fossils classed as *Orohippus* and *Epihippus* from the Middle and Upper North American Eocene are little different from *Hyracotherium*, except for molarization of the hinder premolars. The size remains small.

The Oligocene horses, *Mesohippus* and *Miohippus*, walked with three toes on the ground, and all the premolars were molarized. The ectoloph was well formed but the inner cusps still separate, and the teeth low-crowned. Some horses of this type (*Anchitherium* and its descendant *Hypohippus*) persisted into the Miocene, presumably surviving as browsers in forests, while other descendants took to the plains. These browsing horses migrated to the Old World in the Miocene, then died out there, as they did also in North America.

Parahippus of the American Lower Miocene shows the beginning of the adaptation for life on the plains. The lateral digits II and IV still carried hoofs, but since the central proximal phalanx was much the longest and strongest, it is probable that the lateral ones touched the ground only to maintain balance over uneven surfaces, or in soft conditions. The teeth were still rather low, but were beginning to be elongated and to show cement on the crowns. The protoloph and metaloph were connected by a narrow bridge. There was a partial post-orbital bar.

Merychippus comes from later Miocene beds and could have been directly derived from *Parahippus* by increase in the depth of the teeth and reduction of the lateral digits to short stumps, still three-jointed and carrying hoofs, but vestigial in the sense of never touching the ground. The presumption is that this type of structure was found advantageous for life on large grassy plains produced by the arid Miocene conditions, the high-crowned teeth being needed to grind the tough siliceous grasses.

Apparently the type was very successful and in the Pliocene it produced various populations. *Hipparion*, with the two lateral toes remaining as vestiges, spread through Eurasia in the Pliocene. *Nannippus* was a small form that remained in America. *Pliohippus* was another American descendant from *Merychippus*, and here the lateral digits were lost altogether in the Pliocene, the metapodials remaining as long thin vestiges. When the land connexion with South America became open this type of horse migrated there and produced a special development, *Hippidion* of the Pleistocene, with rather short legs, perhaps correlated with a mountain habit.

Meanwhile in the late Pliocene or early Pleistocene the *Pliohippus* stock of North America finally reduced the lateral metapodials to short splint bones and produced the *Equus* type, which spread thence over all the available land-masses, becoming then extinct in North and South America until reintroduced by man.

10. Allometry in the evolution of horses

Although *Equus* is certainly a very different creature from *Hyracotherium*, we are fortunate in that many of the differences are due to measurable changes in proportions. A beginning has been made with attempts to esti-

FIG. 473. Relative rates of growth in horses. The lines show regression of log skull length on log face length; in A, the line of horse phylogeny; B, the ontogeny of *Equus*; C, various races of *Equus* of different sizes; D, $y = 0.25\ x^{1.23}$. (After Simpson from the data of Robb.)

mate the rate of evolutionary change, as a preliminary to study of the factors that influence it. Some of the changes in proportion seen during horse evolution are a consequence of the increase in size. If an organ grows relatively faster or slower than the body as a whole it is obvious that its proportions will differ in animals of differing adult size. The size of an organ, y, in relation to that of the body, x, is often expressed as $y = bx^k$, where the constant k describes the relative growth rate. If $k > 1$ the organ becomes larger in larger animals and is said to be positively allometric (J. S. Huxley). The demonstration that growth actually follows this law in particular cases is not easy, and the underlying assumptions have been questioned. It is probably true, however, that organs do sometimes differ in relative growth rates, and the method provides a means of investigation of the proportions of an organ not only at one stage but throughout the growth period, and indeed also between adults throughout an evolutionary sequence. Thus Robb (Fig. 473) shows that the length of a horse's face increases between embryo and adult along a line similar to that found in the series *Hyracotherium* to *Equus*, and that adult horses of different sizes vary similarly in face proportion. A nearly fitting line gives constants $b = 0.25$ and $k = 1.23$. Other methods of plotting, for instance face length against cranium length, give somewhat different results and it cannot be considered certain that no new genetic factors have been involved in the increase of face-length throughout the whole evolutionary sequence.

Again, reduction of the lateral digits of the toes is perhaps not based on any steady genetic change except that related to size. However, in this case there was probably one relatively sudden change in the constant b (which may be said to express the body size at which the toe begins to form). Thus in the three-toed horses the length (y) of the side toes is related to that of the cannon bone of the central digit (x) by the equation

$$y = 1.5\ x^{0.97}.$$

In the one-toed horses from *Pliohippus* onwards

$$y = 0.8\ x^{0.99}.$$

There has therefore been little change in the relative growth rate, which is negatively allometric in all horses, so that the lateral toes are relatively smaller in the larger animals.

11. Rate of evolution of horses

Study in the same way of other horse characters, for instance those involved in hypsodonty, shows that special genetic changes may be involved and that genetic change does not go on at a constant rate.

Estimates of rate of evolution for the whole animal have also been made by Matthew, Simpson, and others. Assuming that the genus is assessed as a comparable entity throughout (a large assumption, this!) and dividing the eight genera (excluding *Equus*) on the direct line into the time involved between *Hyracotherium* and *Pliohippus* (50 million years), we should have 6.3 million years per genus. However, there is reason to suppose that individual genera lasted for very different times, *Miohippus*, for instance, less than a third of the time of *Merychippus*. Therefore if the criterion of a genus is constant, the rate of evolution must vary.

Sufficient fossil horse material is available to allow consideration whether known rates of mutation are likely to be adequate to account for the observed evolutionary changes. Simpson calculates that from

Hyracotherium to *Equus* there must have been at least 15 million generations, which, with a population in North America of 100,000 (a low estimate), gives a total of 1.5×10^{12} individuals in the 'real and potential ancestry of the modern horse'. One in a million is a moderate rate for large mutations at any locus in *Drosophila*, and this would give 1.5 million such mutations for a single locus in the horse ancestry. It would be safe to assume that one-fifth of these (300,000) were in the direction favoured by selection and that one-tenth of all such genes affect a structural change, such as ectoloph length. The actual increase in this length between *Hyracotherium* and *Equus* was from 8 to 40 mm. which, divided into 300 steps, gives an increase per mutation of only 0.1 mm. This is a very reasonable figure, and such calculations suggest that observed mutation rates are quite adequate to account for the evolutionary changes, even neglecting possible multiple actions and interactions of genes, by which the speed of evolution could be further increased.

12. Conclusions from the study of the evolution of horses

Careful consideration of the fossil horse material therefore shows reason to suppose that evolution has proceeded by gradual change. As more and more evidence becomes available the series becomes more and more complete, and incidentally the nomenclature increasingly confusing. Incompleteness of material may give an impression of evolution by jumps and saltation, especially when, as in the Old World horses, there have been successive migrations into one region from another. The European palaeontologists, finding *Hyracotherium*, *Anchitherium*, *Hipparion*, and *Equus*, without intermediate forms, interpreted the evidence as showing evolution by saltation. This was indeed a reasonable deduction from the facts, but was not the only possible one, and was therefore unwise, as has since been shown by the discovery of the much fuller sequence in North America. It is probable that there are many equally unjustified conclusions in our current beliefs about evolution.

The outstanding conclusion from a study of horse evolution is that it is very difficult to describe the change as occurring in a single direction, as supposed by believers in 'orthogenesis'. Apart from the fact that many 'side-lines' can be detected beside the line that happens to have survived, it is very important to remember that not every line evolves in the same direction. Thus in at least two genera of horses size became progressively *smaller* (*Nannippus* and *Archaeohippus*). However, it is certainly true that in some lines evolution may proceed for long periods in one direction. We have no clear evidence why this should be so, but it is reasonable to suppose that it is due to 'orthoselection', that is to say, the survival of animals that adopt a particular method of life for which they are suited by a particular make-up. The effect of this would be gradually to select all those genetic factors that make for success in one environment (say, grazing on grassy plains) and hence to produce evolutionary change in one direction.

XXXI

ARTIODACTYLS

1. Characteristics of artiodactyls

The even-toed ungulates, though they can be traced as a distinct line back to the Eocene, may be considered as the latest mammalian herbivores, having radiated out chiefly in the Miocene and attained then a dominance which has persisted to the present day. Except for man and the horse all the large mammals really well established and successful at the present time are artiodactyls. Any attempt to be dogmatic about the reasons for the success of a group of animals is apt to be superficial, but it is not unreasonable to suggest that in this case the result is due to swiftness of foot, combined with keenness of sense and brain, efficient cropping and grinding mechanisms, and especially a complex stomach, allowing the digestion of cellulose by symbionts. Two families of artiodactyls survive without these special features, the pigs and hippopotamuses, water- and forest-living remnants that show us approximately the condition of the group in the Eocene.

The characters of artiodactyls show a fascinating 'similarity with a difference' to those of perissodactyls. The common origin of the two groups (p. 639) was little above the insectivore stage and nearly every feature has been evolved independently; the general structural similarities and detailed differences therefore show the effect produced by similar ways of life on slightly differing populations. For example, a postorbital bar developed in both groups, for attachment of the large masseter muscle, but whereas in the horses it is formed wholly of a process of the frontal bone, in ruminants there is a union of processes of the jugal and frontal. Many such similarities and differences are seen throughout the body, and especially in the limbs.

The skull of later artiodactyls shows changes of shape to accommodate the very deep molars and to support the horns that are commonly found. It becomes very high (as in horses), and there is a sharp kink between the basisphenoid and presphenoid, so that the face slopes steeply downward. The facial bones become large and the parietals restricted to the vertical posterior face of the skull, to which the powerful neck-muscles are attached.

The vertebral column shows the characteristics of other large mammals in the development of high thoracic spines. Some of the heavier types have a long rib series and graviportal 'single girder' structure, but the tendency has been to retain and develop the break in structure of the vertebral column behind the thoracic region, giving a long lumbar region with forwardly directed transverse processes. In rabbits and other mammals this division of the column is associated with the jumping habit, and this is also found, though in a different form, in ruminants. Associated with this method of progress is a fore-and-aft elongation of the pelvic girdle, the ischium being well developed for the attachment of the retractor muscles of the thigh. In making the jumping movements, which are common in all artiodactyls and are especially used by the mountain-loving types, the extensor muscles of the back (sacrospinalis and multifidus) work with the retractors of the two hind limbs to give a powerful thrust.

The characteristic of the limbs is, of course, the equal development of digits III and IV, with reduction of the rest. The gait was at first plantigrade, then digitigrade; hoofs, differing from those of perissodactyls, have developed on the toes. The elongation of the lower segments of the limbs and shortening of the upper has been similar to that of perissodactyls, but the long metapodials have become united in later forms to make the 'cannon bone'. The ulna and fibula become reduced, as in horses. The presence of two digits has led to the retention of two bones in the distal rows of carpals, the hamate and fused magnum-trapezoid, and these articulate in interlocking fashion with the three proximal carpals (Fig. 449). Similarly in the foot the two lateral cuneiforms are fused to thrust upon the third digit, while the fourth sends its thrusts to the cuboid and the latter is fused with the navicular. Between this compound bone and the talus there is a very characteristic joint, the under surface of the talus being grooved like its upper surface. These joints of the carpus and tarsus are evidently an important part of the apparatus of locomotion; probably in both limbs they serve to take strain when the animal is moving over uneven ground, and in the leg they are also the seat of a considerable propulsive thrust from the calf-muscles. In walking the limb of artiodactyls is moved as a whole at the shoulder and hip, by action of the upper muscles. The wrist and ankle joints bend just enough to raise the feet off the ground, and the elbow and knee joints, lying so high as to be hardly visible externally, also bend little. The essence of artiodactyl locomotion is the use of the upper limb muscles; indeed the hinder part of the vertebral column has almost become part of the limb!

The dentition of artiodactyls is highly specialized. The upper incisors are lost in later types, which crop by means of their gums. The canines may form tusks. Premolars are not molarized, but an efficient grinding battery is often provided by the very elongated,

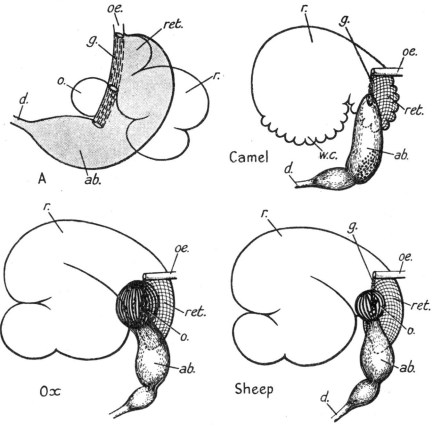

FIG. 474. Stomach of camels and ruminants.

A shows the relationship of the normal mammalian stomach (stippled) to that of ruminants. The rumen (*r.*) represents the cardiac region, the reticulum (*ret.*) the body. The oesophageal groove (*g.*) and omasum (*o.*) are derived from the lesser curvature as far as the incisura angularis and the abomasum (*ab.*) represents the pyloric antrum; *d.* duodenum; *oe.* oesphagus.

The omasum and abomasum are shown as if pulled downwards. In the camel *w.c.* are the water cells, which are lined with stratified squamous epithelium as is most of the abosum; fundic glands are found only in the dotted area. (Material for figure kindly supplied by Dr. A. T. Phillipson, partly after Pemkopf.)

hypsodont molars. These acquire a grinding surface by the development of each cusp into a longitudinal ridge—the selenodont ('moontooth') condition (Fig. 448). The effect is similar to that arrived at, by very different means, in horses, and the enamel, dentine, and cement, wearing at differing rates, provide a continually roughened surface.

The tongue is very large and is an important part of the cropping and grinding mechanism; it is very mobile, protrusible and pointed, and the papillae covering it are often horny. Elaboration of the stomach is common to all artiodactyls except the pigs and hippopotamuses, where the only sign of it is that the left (cardiac) side of the stomach secretes only mucus, pepsin being produced on the right side. In the fully developed ruminant stomach there are four chambers (Fig. 474), rumen, reticulum, omasum (= psalterium or manyplies), and abomasum. The rumen and reticulum receive the food when it is first swallowed, the omasum and abomasum after it has been returned to the mouth for the chewing of the cud. The rumen and reticulum are lined by an epithelium of oesophageal type, prolonged into low villous processes (a network of ridges in the reticulum). In these chambers the food is mixed with mucus and acted upon by a fauna of bacteria and ciliates whose enzymes rapidly break up the cellulose chemically and hence reduce the whole to pulp. In this process organic acids, from acetic acid upwards, are produced and absorbed into the circulation, providing a considerable part of the calories used.

After regurgitation from the rumen to the mouth the food is prevented from passing back into the rumen by the closure of a groove along the side of the reticulum, making a tube that leads the liquid into the omasum. This latter also has á wall of oesophageal structure, folded into long and very muscular ridges, by which the mixture is further broken up and the liquid part pressed into the abomasum, the 'true' stomach, with peptic glands. This elaborate digestive mechanism has no doubt contributed largely to the success of the artiodactyls, allowing them to eat their food rapidly and then retire to digest it in security. The efficient cellulose-splitting system also enables them to make use of hard grasses and other unpromising sources of nutriment. The bacteria are of further value to the ruminant in that they can make use of non-protein nitrogen, such as that contained in urea and amides, to build up their own microbial protein. It is probable that the ruminant later digests the microbial protein in its abomasum and intestine, and large amounts of material are thus made available for synthesis of the proteins that the animal requires.

The brain is moderately well developed in later artiodactyls, but even here the cerebral hemispheres only partly cover the cerebellum, and in the earlier forms the brain was relatively very small, as to-day in hippopotamuses and pigs. The olfactory organ and related parts of the brain are well developed and most artiodactyls also have large eyes, an acute sense of hearing, and long ears.

The reproductive system remains rather close to the presumed original eutherian condition. The uterus is bicornuate and in pigs the placenta is of the diffuse epitheliochorial type. In ruminants there is a cotyledonary placenta, but the contact between maternal and foetal tissues is never very close (syndesmo-chorial) and the allantois is usually large.

2. Classification

Superorder 5. Paraxonia
   Order Artiodactyla
      Suborder 1. Suiformes
         Infraorder 1. Palaeodonta. Pigs and peccaries. Eocene–Recent
               Diacodexis, Lower Eocene, N. America; *Homacodon*, Middle Eocene, N. America; *Entelodon*, Lower Oligocene, Holarctic; *Sus*, pigs, Lower Pliocene–Recent, Eurasia (then world-wide); *Phacochoerus*, wart-hog, Pleistocene–Recent, Africa; *Tayassu*, peccary, Pleistocene–Recent, Central and S. America; *Potamochoerus*, water-hog, Pleistocene–Recent, Africa
         Infraorder 2. Ancodonta. Hippopotamuses. Oligocene–Recent
               Anthracotherium, Oligocene–Pliocene; *Hippopotamus*, Pliocene–Recent, Eurasia, Africa
         *Infraorder 3. Oreodonta. Eocene–Pliocene. N. America
               Merycoidodon (= *Oreodon*), Oligocene; *Agriochoerus*, Oligocene–Miocene
      Suborder 2. Tylopoda. Camels. Eocene–Recent
            Protylopus, Eocene, N. America; *Poebrotherium*, Oligocene, N. America; *Procamelus*, Miocene–Pliocene, N. America; *Alticamelus*, Miocene–Pliocene, N. America; *Lama*, alpaca, Pleistocene–Recent, S. America; *Camelus*, camel, dromedary, Pleistocene–Recent, Asia
      Suborder 3. Ruminantia. Eocene–Recent
         Infraorder 1. Tragulina. Eocene–Recent. Holarctic, Africa
               Archaeomeryx, Eocene. Asia; *Tragulus*, chevrotain, Pliocene–Recent, Asia; *Hyemoschus*, water chevrotain. Pleistocene–Recent, Africa

Suborder 3. Ruminantia (*cont.*)

Infraorder 2. Pecora. Oligocene–Recent. Holarctic, Africa, S. America

Family 1. Cervidae. Oligocene–Recent. Holarctic, S. America

Blastomeryx, Miocene–Pliocene, N. America; *Palaeomeryx*, Miocene, Europe; *Moschus*, musk-deer, Pliocene–Recent, Asia; *Cervus*, red deer, American elk, &c., Pliocene–Recent, Holarctic; *Dama*, fallow deer, Pleistocene–Recent, Eurasia; *Rangifer*, reindeer, Pleistocene–Recent, Holarctic; *Capreolus*, roe deer, Pliocene–Recent, Eurasia; *Alce*, moose, European elk, Pleistocene–Recent, Holarctic

Family 2. Giraffidae. Miocene–Recent. Eurasia, Africa

Giraffa, giraffe, Pliocene–Pleistocene, Asia; Recent, Africa; *Okapia*, okapi, Recent, Africa; *Palaeotragus*, Miocene–Pliocene, Eurasia; *Sivatherium*, Pleistocene, Asia

Family 3. Antilocapridae. Miocene–Recent. N. America

Merycodus, Miocene–Pliocene; *Antilocapra*, prongbuck, Pleistocene–Recent

Family Bovidae. Miocene–Recent

Eotragus, Miocene, Europe, Africa; *Gazella*, gazelles, Pliocene–Recent, Eurasia, Africa; *Taurotragus*, eland, Pleistocene–Recent, Africa; *Aepyceros*, impala, Recent, Africa; *Bos*, cattle, yak, Pleistocene–Recent, Eurasia and N. America, now world-wide; *Bison*, buffalo, Pleistocene–Recent, Holarctic; *Capra*, goat, Pleistocene–Recent, Eurasia, Africa (now world-wide); *Ovis*, sheep, Pliocene–Recent, Holarctic, Africa (now world-wide).

3. The evolution of artiodactyls

Although abundant fossil material is available, the lines of evolution within the artiodactyls are not altogether clear, and numerous classificatory arrangements have been suggested. We shall, as usual, follow that of Simpson, who recognizes three suborders. The suborder Suiformes contains the ancestral Eocene forms and some of their little-modified descendants; it is represented to-day by the pigs and hippopotamuses. Probably no members of this group developed the ruminating habit, and they are sometimes called 'non ruminantia'.

The suborder Tylopoda is for the rather isolated camels, and the third suborder, Ruminantia, includes all the other modern forms of artiodactyl.

The earliest artiodactyls (Fig. 475), included in the Suiformes, were very close to the ancestral stock of all placentals. In *Diacodexis* from the North American Lower Eocene there were tritubercular molars

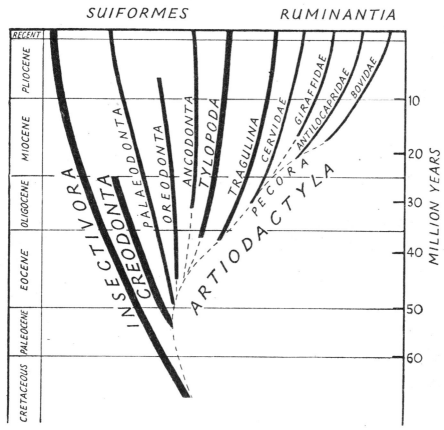

FIG. 475. Chart of the evolution of the artiodactyla.

and it was probably a small, running, omnivorous form, with four toes on both feet. These animals could indeed almost equally well be classified as insectivores or creodonts, and the only reason for placing them as artiodactyls is that the talus had the typical pulley-like lower surface. Later Eocene and early Oligocene forms developed a bunodont condition, with sometimes six cusps in the upper molars, protocone, paracone, metacone, hypocone, protoconule, and metaconule. In the later forms these cusps begin to show the selenodont condition.

4. Pigs and hippopotamuses

The pigs have remained essentially in this Eocene condition; Simpson recognizes this by classifying them with the Eocene forms in one infraorder Palaeodonta, distinct from the amphibious Ancodonta (hippopotamuses and anthracotheres) and the *Oreodonta.

FIG. 476. Above, skull of the oreodont *Merycoidodon* (after Scott); below, skeleton of *Entelodon*. (After Woodward, *Palaeontology*, Cambridge University Press.)

Undoubted pigs are found from the Eocene, with bunodont molars, carrying five cusps, the hypocone being lost, as in most artiodactyls. Several lines can be recognized, including the entelodonts, giant pigs of the Oligocene, over 5 ft. high and 12 ft. long and of graviportal structure (Fig. 476). The modern pigs (Fig. 477) show a nearly complete dentition, with persistently growing canine tusks, used for defence and for digging roots. They have been common since the Oligocene in the Old World, and with their four toes, only two reaching the ground, they represent a survival from very ancient times. *Sus*

is mainly an Asiatic genus, with some members in Malaya and in
Europe. It was represented in Great Britain by the wild boar, com-
mon until the sixteenth century. The African wart-hog (*Phacochoerus*)
(Fig. 478) is not very dissimilar. *Potamochoerus* is the red river-hog of
Africa. The peccaries, *Tayassu* (Fig. 479), of Central and S. America

FIG. 477. Skeleton of the pig. (Modified after Ellenberger from Sisson
and Grossman, *Anatomy of Domestic Animals*, 3rd edition 1938, published
by W. B. Saunders Company, Philadelphia.)

FIG. 478. The wart-hog, *Phacochoerus*. (From photographs.)

are similar to the pigs, but have been distinct since the Oligocene.
There are two small lateral digits in the fore-foot and one in the hind.
     An offshoot of the palaeodont line in the Eocene led to the develop-
ment of a race of large amphibious forms, the anthracotheres and
hippopotamuses (Figs. 480 and 481), classed together as an infraorder
Ancodonta of the Suiformes. They have short, relatively thin legs
with four digits, and a complete dentition with low-crowned bunodont
molars, wearing to a foliate pattern; the animals feed mainly on soft
water plants, though in captivity they readily eat hay. The stomach

is very large and partly divided. Modern hippopotamuses are found only in Africa, but they have been widespread through the Old World until recent times.

5. *Oreodonts

During the late Eocene, Oligocene, and Miocene of North America there existed various artiodactyls whose exact relationship to other forms is uncertain, and they must be left as a separate infraorder of the Suiformes. These oreodonts, such as *Merycoidodon* (Fig. 476), had long bodies and short legs and perhaps somewhat resembled the pigs. There were four functional digits in each foot, and a complete tooth-row, including molars whose cusps were selenodont and in some later forms quite high-crowned. There was a complete post-orbital bar.

Although Eocene intermediate forms have not been found, it may be presumed that the oreodonts arose from a basal palaeodont ancestor. There has been much discussion as to whether they are related to either the camels or ruminants. They were certainly a most successful group and remains are very numerous in the Oligocene and Miocene of North America. Probably they pursued an independent evolution there while the ruminants were evolving in the Old World, but unlike the ruminants they were at a disadvantage in the changed world of the Pliocene and then died out.

Agriochoerus and its relatives were oreodonts that acquired claws and therefore represent a parallel to ancylopod perissodactyls, with which they were for a long time confused. It can be guessed that the claws were used for digging roots.

6. Camels

All other artiodactyls chew the cud and are often included in a single group Ruminantia. However, the camels have been a separate stock since the Eocene and are so distinct from the remainder that it is convenient to keep them in a separate sub-order Tylopoda. They have been common animals since the late Eocene, flourishing especially in North America, although, like the horses, they died out there very recently and survive to-day only as remnants which migrated from North America in the Pleistocene, the camels to the Old World and the llamas to South America. The bactrian camel of the Gobi Desert in central Asia is perhaps a wild form, all others being commensals of man. The llamas (Fig. 482), though similar in basic structure to the camels, differ in the smaller size, long hair, and lack

FIG. 479. The collared peccary, *Tayassu*. (From photographs.)

FIG. 480. Hippopotamus, *Hippopotamus*. (From photographs.)

FIG. 481. Skeleton of the hippopotamus. (From Owen, *The Anatomy of Vertebrates*, Longmans, Green & Co.)

of hump. When wild they are mainly mountain-dwellers. The spitting of the llama is a well-developed protective device, the whole contents of the stomach being thrown at the attacker!

The Tylopoda show some features retained from the Eocene condition, some developments parallel to those found in the Ruminantia, and various special features of their own, the latter mainly in characters that suit them for life in sandy desert conditions. In the limbs (Fig. 483) there has been complete loss of the lateral digits and of some

FIG. 482. Llama, *Lama*. (From photographs.)

carpals and tarsals, but no fusion of navicular and cuboid so characteristic of the Pecora. A specialized feature is the loss of the hoofs, present in early camels but replaced in modern forms by a nail and large pad. The toes thus spread sideways and enable the animals to walk on soft or sandy ground. Other specializations for desert life are the presence of water-pockets with sphincters in the rumen, and the large hump of fat on the back, which provides water as well as calories when metabolized. The ruminating mechanism is different from that of the Pecora and simpler, there being no omasum (Fig. 474).

In the head there are many features of similarity to the Pecora. Cropping is by means of procumbent lower incisors, working against specialized premaxillary gums; an upper incisor and canine are still present, however (three incisors in the young). The molars have a typical selenodont pattern, and the structure of the skull shows the developments so commonly seen as a result of herbivorous life, such as closure of the post-orbital bar. A peculiar feature of camels is that the red blood corpuscles are oval, as in no other mammal. The placenta is of a diffuse (non-cotyledonary) syndesmochorial type.

There is no doubt that many of these features have developed independently in camels and Pecora; the Eocene camel-ancestors did not show them. At the stage of *Protylopus* the camels were small and had short limbs, with separate radius and ulna and four digits in the manus. Indeed, these animals were so like oreodonts that many would classify them together. Throughout the Oligocene many primitive features still remained. *Poebrotherium* was about 3 ft. high, with

FIG. 483. Skeleton of dromedary. (From Owen, *The Anatomy of Vertebrates*, Longmans, Green & Co.)

a complete dentition, and orbit only partly closed behind. However, the lateral toes had been lost and the digits began to diverge distally, though probably still carrying hoofs. The remaining increase of size, and the development of other special camel features can be traced slowly through such types as *Procamelus* of the Miocene and Pliocene. During the dry Miocene times the type was very successful in North America and developed various lines, such as *Alticamelus*, the giraffe-camels, with very long necks.

7. Ruminants

The most successful modern artiodactyls, the deer (Cervidae) and cattle, sheep, and antelopes (Bovidae), have flourished only since the Miocene and are hence the most recent ungulate group (p. 680), largely replacing the tylopods, oreodonts, perissodactyls, and still earlier protungulate and paenungulate types. They have always been largely an Old World group and this remains their headquarters, though some have reached other parts of the world. The early ancestors of the ruminants can be traced to Oligocene and late Eocene forms very like the early camels, oreodonts, and other primitive artio-dactyls; the modern chevrotains (*Tragulus*) retain some of the features of this early stage.

The characteristic features of the ruminants are the full develop-ment of the feeding system described on p. 702, with loss of the upper incisors and often also of the canines, development of selenodont

FIG. 484. Chevrotain, *Tragulus*. (After Beddard, *Cambridge Nat. Hist.*, Macmillan & Co.)

molars, and of a four-chambered stomach. In the legs only two digits are functional, though traces of others may remain. Besides loss of the extra carpal and tarsal bones there is fusion of those that remain and in particular of the navicular and cuboid. Protection is afforded mainly by swift running and keen senses, but in nearly all ruminants also by antlers or horns on the head.

This definition will not quite cover all members of the groups. The chevrotains keep so many primitive features that although they are certainly related to the ancestors of the other ruminants it would be almost as easy to class them with the camels. This is another case where it is difficult to decide whether to make horizontal or vertical classificatory divisions; any system is bound to be arbitrary.

8. Chevrotains

The deerlets or mouse-deer of Africa and Asia (Fig. 484) are peculiar little creatures, with more external resemblance to a rodent than to modern deer. In some features they show suggestive similarity to the pigs. There are no horns, but the upper canines are large and tusk-like. The upper incisors have been lost and the molars are selenodont, but the stomach has only three chambers. The feet show very primitive conditions in the retention of four, hoofed digits in each limb, and although the two main metatarsals are fused to form a cannon bone the metacarpals are still partly separate. The navicular, cuboid, and external cuneiform make a single bone, this being a 'diagnostic' ruminant character. The placenta is diffuse, as in camels.

In many of these characteristics the chevrotains show signs of retention of a very ancient organization, and fossil forms very like the modern *Tragulus* are found back to the Pliocene. Animals not very different (**Archaeomeryx*) are found back to the Eocene and were then very like the early camels or palaeodonts; they may well be close to the ancestry of all ruminants. Several not very different types and lines can be recognized. Evidently the group represents a population persisting with rather little change since the Eocene, and this status is represented by recognizing an infraorder Tragulina of the Ruminantia, contrasting with the Pecora, which includes all the higher ruminants.

FIG. 485. Musk-deer, *Moschus*. (After Beddard, *Cambridge Natural History*, Macmillan & Co.)

9. Pecora

The true ruminants show the full development of artiodactyl characteristics. They have been an actively expanding group since the Miocene and are now the most successful of the ungulates, existing in vast herds in Africa and to a lesser extent in Asia and North America, though strangely enough hardly penetrating to South America. The modern and fossil forms are of three types. The deer (Cervidae), browsing creatures with bony deciduous antlers, are closest to the central stock, from which have been derived on the one hand the giraffes and on the other the great groups of grazing ruminants or Bovidae, including the primitive prong-buck and the host of sheep, goats, cattle, and antelopes.

10. Cervidae

The ancestral population from which these forms arose must have been quite similar to the Eocene traguline **Archaeomeryx*, but the group does not become distinctly recognizable until the Oligocene. The early members either had large canines and no antlers, as in **Blastomeryx* of the Miocene of North America, or, as in **Palaeomeryx* of the Miocene of Europe, they possessed a bony outgrowth covered with skin and not shed. *Moschus*, the musk-deer (Fig. 485) of central Asia, also has large permanently growing canines and no

FIG. 486. Growth of the antlers of a mule deer. The bony outgrowth is covered with very vascular skin (velvet) which is shed when growth is complete. (From *American Mammals*, by W. J. Hamilton, McGraw Hill Book Company.)

antlers and is probably a survivor of this Miocene stage of evolution. The true deer, Cervidae, have developed antlers in the males (Fig. 486), bony growths shed each year and forming progressively more branches as the animal grows older (Fig. 487). In the reindeer the females also have antlers. A sign of the rather primitive nature of the deer is the retention of definite rudiments of the first two phalanges of the lateral digits. The deer (Fig. 488) have been very common since the Pliocene, as browsing animals of the Holarctic region and South America, but not found in Africa. They live in herds, with an elaborate social organization, based on the supremacy of a leading male, maintained by a succession of 'fights' with his rivals. These fights are very fierce, but do not necessarily result in death, and indeed the complicated horns interlock in such a way as to mitigate their danger to the challenger. Red deer (*Cervus elaphus*) are still wild in Britain in Scotland, the Lake District, Devonshire, and the New Forest. The antlers have six or more points. Roe deer (*Capreolus*) have smaller antlers (three points). They are also indigenous in Great Britain; fallow deer (*Dama*) have been introduced, and are usually spotted, with palmate antlers.

FIG. 487. Series of antlers in the British Museum (Natural History) showing the increasing number of tines in successive years. (After Romanes.)

11. Giraffidae

The giraffes (Fig. 489), like the Cervidae, from which they diverged in the Miocene, are browsing animals, now restricted to tropical Africa. The teeth are low-crowned and the head bears simple skin-covered horns, probably showing the condition found in cervids in the Miocene. There may be one or two pairs, as well as a median horn. The lateral digits are completely absent and the legs are very long; the whole structure is specialized to carry the great bulk on the fore-legs, the head and neck balancing the weight of the body and the hind-legs being used mainly for propulsion. In walking the fore- and hind-legs of one side move together; since the weight is balanced on the fore-legs there is no use of the tripodal method of movement which is usual in quadrupeds. This is an extreme development of the type of vertebral organization in which the weight-carrying beam ends in the middle of the back, there being a small number of ribs, so that the

FIG. 488. Deer, *Cervus*. (From life.)

hinder part of the column functions as an upper segment of the hind limbs and the extensor muscles of the back aid in propulsion. Generally speaking this organization is not used by large animals, but in the giraffes the long neck makes it possible to balance great weight on the fore-legs. The immensely long neck (giraffes reach 18 ft. tall) is of use not only for reaching high branches but also as a look-out among the long grasses. The rare *Okapia* (Fig. 490), discovered in 1900 in the Belgian Congo, is a form with shorter legs and neck, very similar to **Palaeotragus* and other Pliocene animals, all possessing small horns. Other lines (**Sivatherium*) acquired a pair of large non-deciduous horns, a course of evolution parallel to that found in Cervidae.

FIG. 489. Giraffe (*Giraffa*). (From photographs.)

FIG. 490. Okapi, *Okapia*. (From photographs.)

12. Antilocapridae and Bovidae

The remaining Pecora are all rather alike and are often placed in a single family, Bovidae. However, the prong-buck, *Antilocapra* (Fig. 491) of the North American west, and its numerous fossil allies, all

New World forms, have been distinct since before the Miocene from the true bovids, evolving in the Old World. The origin of the two groups is very obscure and we have no Eocene or Oligocene fossils that are certainly on the bovid line of evolution. As already mentioned *Archaeomeryx* and other Eocene tragulines show us a type of population from which the Pecora could all have been evolved, but the stages of the transformation have not been found.

FIG. 491. Prong-buck, *Antilocapra*. (From a photograph.)

Antilocaprids and bovids are alike in their grazing habits, with which are associated deeply hypsodont molars. The side toes have been almost or completely lost, a development occurring parallel to that of the cervids, since the common ancestry almost certainly possessed lateral toes, which are indeed present in rudimentary form in some bovids. In *Antilocapra* (Fig. 491) the horns are two-branched and have a bony core and rather soft keratinous covering, the latter but not the former being shed. This therefore suggests how a skin-covered antler, such as that of the Cervidae, may have become converted into the bovid horn. In earlier antilocaprids, such as the Miocene *Merycodus*, the horns were more elaborately branched; evidently the group has developed a horn structure parallel to that of the Cervidae. In all true bovids the horns are permanent coverings for the bony core. They are unbranched, though curved and twisted in various geometrically interesting ways. Moreover, they are usually borne in both sexes (though often larger in the male) and their function is definitely defensive, as well as social and sexual. Correspondingly the social organization is often into large herds, rather than into the small family groups under a dominant stag, such as are found among Cervidae. Grazing on open plains and mountains has presumably led to the formation of the larger herds, smaller and more closely knit groups being more suitable for forest life. Bovids have mostly lost all but the vestiges of the lateral toes, and another distinction from cervids is the presence of a cotyledonary placenta.

The Bovidae, with more than 100 genera, is much the largest ungulate family. The original centre of evolution of the family was in Eurasia, where they are now less common, whereas in Africa they are particularly successful at present. A few types, such as the bison, reached North America, but none entered South America until man showed that they can flourish there, and indeed also in Australia. The fact that we possess numerous fossil remains and that the group is still at the height of its development makes classification very difficult. This is the situation that we should expect, remembering that evolution consists in the slow change of the characteristics of populations. At first thought it may seem paradoxical that in a group so recently evolved and of which we know so much it should be exceptionally difficult to trace affinities and lines of descent. The fact is that the numerous remains of fossil bovids from the Pliocene and Miocene are still quite insufficient to enable us to reconstruct the changes in the populations. It is not really to be expected that the relatively few specimens of these large animals that can be collected and studied should show us the detailed changes, extending over 20 million years or more, by which a population of some million small sheep-like creatures of the late Miocene developed into the present bovid population of, say, a thousand million creatures, divisible into hundreds of non-interbreeding populations ranging in structure and habits from the gazelle to the bison. An imaginative look at the details of evolutionary change reveals a terrifyingly complicated system which we can hardly hope to follow in detail. The geological information can surely never be sufficient to show us the necessary facts about the variation of such great populations, and their gradual changes, at least in the case of animals as large and rarely preserved as Bovidae. We know hardly anything about variation and heredity in our own cattle, how can we hope to follow the genetics of their ancestors? Yet nothing less than a full view of the gradual population changes will show us how the evolution of a group has proceeded.

Following types of organization over long geological periods gives a deceptively simplified idea of the stages traversed. We recognize the 'stages' because, fortunately for us, only tiny remnants of the populations have been preserved, and perhaps some 'primitive' types remain to the present day. Thus in the long history of the perissodactyls we can refer all our modern and fossil forms to some 160 genera; the tapirs are there to show us a very ancient condition, and we know just enough fossil horses to arrange them in a number of series with side branches, so that we feel that we can imagine the whole evolution of the group.

It is interesting that the sequence of evolution used as a type-specimen for students is so often that of the horses and not of the bovids, although we have very much more material for the latter, at least in the later stages. It would be wise to study the two together and to learn

from the difficulty of recognizing clear-cut boundaries among the millions in the herds of intergrading sheep, goats, oxen, and antelopes that the most important result of the discovery of evolutionary change was the realization that our logic and use of words can no longer depend, as the ancients thought and many backward-lookers still wish to-day, on the recognition of a certain number of 'species', to one of which every individual can be referred.

In trying to classify the Bovidae we may perhaps recognize a central group of 'antelopes', but the term is vague and certainly includes several diverse lines; it is not even possible to find criteria for saying 'this is an antelope,

FIG. 492. Impala antelope, *Aepyceros*. (From life.)

that a cow, and this other a sheep'. 'Typical' antelopes (Fig. 492) live in Eurasia and Africa, especially the latter. They are rather tall and slender, with smooth hair and backward-curving horns, living mostly on warm or tropical plains. The gazelles may be taken as an example among many. The oxen are heavier animals, often almost of gravi-portal structure, with very high thoracic spines; they live in cooler conditions on more northern plains and have more and shaggier hair. Their horns curve forwards and are not twisted; their home is in Eurasia. The domestic cattle and yaks, *Bos* (Fig. 493), are good examples, and the *Bison* (Fig. 494) are related creatures, now almost restricted to North America. There are animals, however, that, with the criteria used, cannot be classed as either 'antelopes' or 'oxen'; for instance, the elands (*Taurotragus*) (Fig. 495) of Africa are large and cow-like, but have backwardly directed and twisted horns. Similarly the ovine (sheep and goat) section of the family is not clearly marked off from the antelopine. The goats (*Capra*) are characteristically mountain-living animals of the Holarctic region, with backwardly curved but not twisted horns, and the sheep, *Ovis* (Fig. 496), are very closely

FIG. 493. Central Asian Yak, *Bos*. (From photographs.)

FIG. 494. American bison, *Bos*. (From photographs.)

FIG. 495. Eland, *Taurotragus*. (From photographs.)

related, but addicted to less mountainous country and with a slight spiral on the horns. The beard and scent glands of the male are signs that there are great differences in social and sexual organization between sheep and goat life, in spite of the similarity in structure.

Thus there is very great variety of life and structure in the modern bovids, and the most striking evolutionary conclusion about the group is that the specialists have not yet succeeded in finding even a partly agreed system of classification. More important perhaps than these problems is the fact that with their fine cropping mechanism, grinding battery, and stomach the bovids provide the only satisfactory intermediary by which grass can be used as a contributor to human life. This, with their peaceful and gregarious disposition, has made them become our most important commensal. If there were no Bovidae there would be fewer human beings in the world, and our social organization would be very different. The obverse is also true; it is probable that their lives and ours will continue to evolve together and mutually to modify each other.

FIG. 496. Barbary sheep, *Ovis*. (From life.)

XXXII

CONCLUSION. EVOLUTIONARY CHANGES OF THE LIFE OF VERTEBRATES

1. The life of the earliest chordates

We set out to try to define the features that are characteristic of vertebrate life, hoping then to show how these features have changed during evolutionary history. We may now summarize the evidence collected and see how far it is possible to make general statements about vertebrate life and the factors that effect its changes.

The vertebrate type of organization has proved capable of supporting life under a wide variety of circumstances; most of its modern forms operate under conditions very different from those in which the type first appeared. According to the most probable theory (p. 72) chordate life began at the sea surface as the ciliated larvae of some creatures rather like graptolites or sessile echinoderms. The first fish-like animals, with the characteristic chordate organization, appeared when such larvae acquired powers of rhythmic metachronal muscular movement, in order to allow support of a large weight. We can still see approximately this stage to-day in *Amphioxus*. It is not possible to summarize the nature of this organization in any brief general statement. The science of morphology is still young and ill equipped with general principles; it does not allow us to define the varieties of living organization with precision and completeness. At present we cannot give a full description such as we might wish for, specifying the chemical nature and energy-balance of the activities of an organism and in particular those of its germ-cells. We can only describe some of the methods by which the system maintains itself, for example its means of nutrition, respiration, and reproduction.

The earliest chordates showed a rather low level of metazoan organization, with only a small number of distinct cell types and few special organs. Nitrogen and other raw materials were obtained in the form of minute plants, collected by ciliary action of the pharynx and gill-slits. The food was broken down by a system of enzymes working in alkaline solution, and absorbed through the walls of a simple intestine. There was probably no specialization of cells of the walls of the gut to produce enzymes or to perform special operations of conversion or storage; at least no special liver, pancreas, or other organs were present for these purposes. There were no special respiratory surfaces and the oxygen was carried to the tissues in simple solution in colourless blood. The circulatory system perhaps at first involved little more than an irregular set of spaces among the cells, but quite early there must have appeared the distinct contractile vessels, containing a blood with composition distinct from that of the surrounding lymphatic or tissue spaces. The method of excretion of the earliest chordates is not clearly known; it perhaps involved no highly specialized cells, but occurred all over the body surface. Since the animals were marine there were no serious osmotic problems. Movement was by the metachronal contraction of a series of blocks of longitudinally arranged muscle-fibres and this serial repetition of the muscles and their attendant nerves and blood-vessels has left a very large mark on the chordate plan of life.

The nervous organization was at first based on a system of nerve-cells and fibres lying spread out below the epidermis, but then became concentrated dorsally in the walls of a neural tube. The special receptor organs were probably simple and lay either in the skin or within the tube, perhaps along its whole length, with little concentration at the front end and no definite anterior enlargement or brain. The system functioned as a series of more or less separate reflex arcs, activation coming from the stimulation of receptor organs by changes in the world around. There were no large masses of nervous tissue and little possibility of sustained independent action by the creatures, which probably showed little flexibility of behaviour or variation of action with experience. The only endocrine influences were the effects of cell by-products on neighbouring tissues; there were no specialized glands of internal secretion.

Reproduction was presumably sexual (perhaps also by budding) and development followed the pattern of radial (indeterminate) cleavage and gastrulation by invagination, with chordo-mesoderm separating from the endoderm. The young were provided with yolk for their development, but were probably not otherwise cared for by their parents.

This gives a rough picture of chordate organization in the Cambrian period when it probably first arose, 500 million years ago, after the paedomorphic change by which a previously larval creature became sexually mature. It is an organization that has already proceeded far from the aggregation of similar cells that presumably characterized the first metazoans. Its embryological processes were already sufficiently elaborate to produce a creature with well-marked organ systems, though these did not have the numerous cell types and anatomically separate parts that are found later.

2. Comparison of the life of early chordates with that of mammals

Such an early chordate is immensely complicated when considered as a chemical system, yet it lacks the specializations that later became so characteristic of vertebrates. The difference appears very clearly if we contrast the organization and life of some such simple, *Amphioxus*-like chordate with those of a mammal. In almost every part of the body of the latter we find cell types and organs that are not yet differentiated in the former. For illustration of this difference we can look at almost any part, say the skin, the blood, the gut, or the brain. In a mammal the skin contains far more types of cell than are present in the skin of *Amphioxus*; there are hairs and these are different in various parts of the body; there are several types of gland and of receptor organ. The blood, again, circulates with great rapidity in two circuits, is delicately adjusted in composition so as to allow rapid flow of materials to the tissues, contains haemoglobin in special corpuscles. In addition there is a number of types of cell able to be used for defence and a system of antibodies for the same purpose that is almost certainly also far beyond anything found in the earlier creature. Digestion in a mammal involves an elaborate arrangement of mouth, oesophagus, stomach, and intestine, each with a controlled pH and special masses of cells aggregated into groups, such as the salivary glands, pancreas, and liver, the latter a most elaborate chemical workshop. Finally the nervous system possesses an enormous number of cells and very elaborate receptor organs. It gives the power to react to many aspects of environmental change that cannot be discriminated by the simpler organism. Nervous conduction is rapid, allowing these large creatures to be well co-ordinated. The nervous system, working through the many contractile parts provided by the muscular system, enables the performance of most elaborate acts, helpful in obtaining food, escaping enemies, and perhaps particularly in providing for the care of young, which is another very characteristic mammalian feature. The pattern of behaviour does not always follow one single course, but is adaptable and suited to the conditions likely in view of past experience to be encountered. There is an elaborate system of chemical co-ordination and many endocrine glands specialized to produce stimulants.

No doubt this greater complexity found in mammalian organs reflects a similar complication of the metabolic processes throughout the body, though as yet we have little information about this. Moreover, an organism with so many diverse parts presumably depends for its propagation on a genetical system that is very elaborate. There is evidence that the genetic mechanism is more complicated in the more elaborately organized later animals. In reptiles, birds, and mammals each individual has a genetic constitution so specific that a piece of tissue grafted from one individual to another of the same species (a homograft) nearly always sets up an immunity reaction and is ultimately destroyed. However, in urodeles such homografts are successful, presumably because the genetic mechanism is less specific. In the anurans homografting is unsuccessful; as in the amniotes there is an elaborate genetic organization acquired as the whole system of life became more complicated.

3. The increasing complexity and variety of vertebrates

The above comparison is not intended to be a complete analysis of the organization of early and late chordates, but only an indication that the difference between the two is in the greater number of diverse parts found in the later type. It was suggested in the first chapter that this greater complexity of the higher animals enables their life to be carried on under conditions that would have been impossible for the simpler ancestors. The survey of the evolution of chordates has certainly shown that since the Cambrian our type of organization has invaded situations very different from the sea surface in which the chordates probably arose. It would not be profitable now to recapitulate all the stages of this change—they have already been described throughout the book. If we consider ecological niches in detail the number of fresh situations invaded by vertebrate life is almost as great as that of the species in the group. Among the earlier changes were the transfer from the sea surface to other waters and to the sea bottom. The entrance into fresh water must have called into play many special mechanisms of adjustment. Development of jaws, perhaps 350 million years ago, probably from the anterior branchial arches, gave the possibility not only of eating new types of food (including fellow fishes) but also of performing simple acts of 'handling' of the environment. The better defence that the mouth provided enabled the heavy armament of the early types to be given up. The body form was then greatly improved from a hydrodynamic point of view and with development of the air-bladder into a hydrostatic organ the fishes achieved their full mastery of the water.

Meanwhile other fishes left the water, probably in the Devonian period rather less than 300 million years ago. At first they operated by simple adaptation of the method of life they had used in the water, but they later developed all sorts of devices to meet the new conditions, the earlier types dying out as the later developed. This process has been going on ever since, to produce the modern amphibia, reptiles, birds, and mammals, inhabiting a very great variety of situations.

In the water tetrapods are found at all levels, including great depths and in perpetually dark caverns. They live in the most varied situations on the land and also by burrowing beneath its surface. Not a few are able to move in the air, some even to feed there. It is hardly possible to overestimate the great variety of vertebrate life; at each new examination of any phase one is amazed at the extraordinary number of special modes of life that are adopted by variants of each type.

There are no sure means of telling the number of types or of individuals constituting the biomass present in past times, but it is probable that by means of the above special devices the vertebrate stock has increased and colonized new regions, though not perhaps continuously or at a uniform rate. It is not unlikely that to-day there are more and more varied vertebrates than at any previous period. Moreover, as Lotka has pointed out, the total energy flux through the system has probably also been enlarged. It would not be easy to demonstrate these conclusions rigorously with our present knowledge: it is difficult to believe that they are true of all populations. We should return from these speculations to reconsider the nature of the evidence about evolutionary change, to discover the changes that we are sure have taken place since the vertebrate organization first appeared.

4. The variety of evidence of evolutionary change

At various points throughout the book attention has been called to the conclusions that the evidence allows us to draw, and it is important to notice that they vary considerably from group to group within the chordates. For example, we can draw from morphology some conclusions about the changes that produced the original fish-like vertebrate, but these conclusions are unsupported by fossil evidence. The fossils available for study of evolution of the earliest gnathostomes are too few to allow us a detailed view of the change from ostracoderm to placoderm and from this to other fish organization. At the other end of the scale, there are so many fossil elephant's teeth to be studied that only an obscure picture of parallel lines of evolution has emerged. Again, in some groups, for instance birds, palaeontology is only of limited help in studying evolutionary change, but nevertheless we have a considerable knowledge about the course of evolution from study of the existing forms, because the birds are conspicuous, well known, and varied (p. 499).

A proper appraisal of the nature of evolutionary change demands an understanding of the fact that evidence about it comes from very different sources and varies in different animal groups. We may therefore profitably extract from the results of various parts of our study such simple propositions as are strictly justified by the evidence and provide us with a sure foundation of knowledge about the subject.

5. Persistence of change among vertebrates

The most outstanding fact that emerges is that the populations of vertebrates are continually changing their character. This is not a very revolutionary proposition to discover, nearly one hundred years after Darwin's work, but it is satisfactory that it remains unchallenged after careful examination of the evidence, made without the excitement that sometimes produced incautious judgements in the early years of evolutionary study. The picture of evolutionary change that emerges is now much more precise than was formerly possible and probably it differs from that commonly held by zoologists. In particular we now see that change of animal form is not exceptional or occasional but is the common rule. Our evidence is far from complete, either about long-term or short-term changes, but it suggests that animal populations very seldom remain unchanged even for a few thousand years. Perhaps the greatest of all advances in our understanding of the process of evolution has been the realization that we must direct our attention to the change of populations rather than to individuals. Evolution might be defined as the change of the genetic composition of a population. The attention given to individuals, and perhaps especially to individual fossils, obscured this point of view, whose establishment by the work of Haldane and others has provided a great clarification.

Looking first at the long-term evidence, provided by the study of fossils, where the units are millions of years, we find that among vertebrates very few stay the same for long periods. *Neoceratodus* has a good claim to be considered the 'oldest' living vertebrate; it is very similar to fossils found in the Trias, nearly 200 million years ago. Even in this case, however, there have been slight changes and the Triassic form is placed in a distinct genus *Ceratodus*.

Heterodontus, the Port Jackson shark, is another very ancient fish; it is closely similar to fossils found in the Trias; indeed, the sharks are quite like their Palaeozoic ancestors. *Sphenodon* has changed little since Permian times and hardly at all since the Jurassic, perhaps 140 million years ago. Among mammals, the opossums and hedgehogs are quite similar to those of Cretaceous times, nearly 100 million years ago, and there are several mammals that have survived with little change for the 50 million years since the Eocene, for instance dogs, pigs, and lemurs. In none of these cases, however, has a form survived absolutely without change; they are examples of the persistence of a type of organization rather than of superficial details.

6. Vertebrates that have disappeared

Set against these few examples of relative constancy of organization there are the wholesale extinctions that we deduce from study of the rocks. The ostracoderms, osteolepids, stegocephalians, dinosaurs, and pterodactyls (to mention only a few) became completely extinct or changed into some very different type of animal. Looking at any of the evolutionary trees in this book, which represent, as it were, the summary of the evidence about the populations, one notices at once how frequently types common in earlier periods become extinct or are replaced by their own descendants. Occasionally some line is recorded as continuing over a long period, but the common picture is of change, each type disappearing after a span of years.

7. Speed of evolutionary changes in vertebrates

Although gradual modification of living organization is almost universal it is clear that the change is often extremely slow. The transition from an osteolepid fish, say *Sauripterus*, through stages like *Eogyrinus* to *Seymouria* took nearly 90 million years. The change of the horses from *Hyracotherium* to *Equus* is not very profound, considering that it took at least 50 million years. Unfortunately there is rather little accurate information about these rates of evolutionary change (see p. 696). Probably few populations stay the same for long periods, but there may well be marked differences in rate of change in groups not otherwise dissimilar. Thus some lines of elephant shortened the lower jaw earlier and faster than others (p. 674); whereas the majority of elephant populations changed greatly between the Oligocene and the Pliocene, the deinotheres remained almost the same throughout this long period.

8. Successive replacement among aquatic vertebrates

Does the examination of the sequences of types enable us to say anything about the nature of these evolutionary changes? Can we record any sense in which it represents a 'progress' or 'advance'? One striking feature that we have noticed is that in many cases one type of organism seems to replace another. There is always a difficulty in establishing that this has occurred, because the fossil record does not leave us sufficient information to show for certain that the two types occupied identical 'niches'. However, if we take broad 'habitats', and particularly those that change relatively little, such as the waters, we cannot but be impressed with the succession of tenants that appears, each replacing the one before (p. 227). Thus, among fish-like vertebrates we can recognize ostracoderms, placoderms, crossopterygians, palaeoniscids, holosteans, and teleosteans, each almost completely replacing the one before.

Again, there has been an astonishing series of tetrapods returning from the land to water, developing characters suitable for aquatic life and then becoming extinct, apparently displaced by later migrants, also returning from the land. To name only a few of these returners we have among amphibians the phyllospondyls, lepospondyls, branchiosaurs, and some urodeles; among reptiles the phytosaurs, crocodiles, plesiosaurs, ichthyosaurs, mesosaurs, mosasaurs, aigialosaurs, dolichosaurs, and snakes. Finally of the mammals there are the basilosaurs, modern whales, seals, and sea-cows, as well as some less completely aquatic types.

However much we make allowance for the fact that the sea itself may be changing, it is difficult not to find in these facts a suggestion that the later types are replacing the earlier by their greater 'efficiency' in some respects. The case of these returned aquatics is especially interesting because each type when it first re-enters the water seems to be not very well suited to that medium—because of its shape for instance—and would therefore be expected to be at a disadvantage in relation to the 'stream-lined' creatures that are already there.

9. Successive replacement among land vertebrates

It is equally easy to trace out successions of types occupying habitats on land, though here it is even more difficult to be sure that the successive animals are occupying identical niches. There has been a long series of large land herbivores, including the labyrinthodonts, pareiasaurs, herbivorous synapsids, various dinosaurs, multituberculates, condylarths, dinocerates, pantodonts, brontotheres, horses, pigs, rhinoceroses, elephants, and artiodactyls. Clearly not all of these lived in similar surroundings (and there were, of course, other herbivores), but the succession is impressive. As in the case of the aquatic animals we have the curious phenomenon that the earlier members of each group seem to be clumsy creatures, no better fitted for their life than those they are replacing. The early mammalian herbivores, with their large limbs and small brains, do not seem greatly superior to the stegosaurs and ceratopsians of the Cretaceous. It is, of course, exceedingly difficult to know enough to settle such questions—in this case, for instance, to assess the value of warm-bloodedness.

If we look at other ecological niches we see the same picture of continued replacement. Thus there has been a succession of land carnivores, first synapsid reptiles, then archosaurian reptiles, followed in the Tertiary period by the creodonts, which were replaced by modern carnivores and carnivorous birds.

10. Is successive replacement due to climatic change?

A very careful analysis is needed before we can venture to say much about the nature of this successive replacement of types. We have several times noticed how easy and dangerous it is to find superficial 'causes' for evolutionary change. The periods of time involved are so long that a stern discipline is needed to prevent oneself from using analogies that are really only applicable to much shorter periods (p. 549). We have to try to imagine vast communities of animals of various sorts, interacting with each other in such ways as to produce fluctuating populations, all living in climatic conditions that vary from year to year and also, very slowly, through the centuries. Only if we can hold such a picture in mind can we begin to answer questions about whether the stimulus to evolutionary change comes from the changing environment.

In the past it has been usual to try to find rather simple correlations of this sort. We are told that emergence of land vertebrates was due to drying up of large areas of sea during the Devonian, that the mammals emerged because of the colder conditions at the end of the Cretaceous, or the horses because of the appearance of wide plains in the Miocene. For the reasons already given we must regard such suggestions with suspicion, especially when they relate to conditions extending over a long period of time. There are, however, certainly some cases in which valid correlations of climatic and faunistic changes can be made, especially in relatively recent periods. Thus the finding in Britain of woolly mammoths, cave bears, and other animals to be expected in a cold climate may reasonably be associated with an advance of the ice cap (p. 15). Indeed, in this case we have evidence of the climatic change independent of the animal remains. No doubt change of climate has been one of the variable factors that has led to the continual change of vertebrate life, which we are seeking to understand. It is probable, however, that animal populations change their character independently of any climatic change. It is not easy to find critical situations to test this belief, but cases such as the faunas of the Galapagos and other islands (p. 500) suggest that diversity can arise as animals explore the possibilities of their environment, especially if there are factors that divide up a population into a number of nearly isolated units.

We have seen a great number of cases in which a population has undergone an 'adaptive radiation', branching out to form a number of types, each suited for a particular environment or niche. The phenomenon is so widespread that it suggests a type of evolution common at least to many populations. The conception of adaptive radiation originally put forward by Osborn was that each 'stem form' (of mammals) diverged in five directions, giving cursorial, fossorial, scansorial, volant, and aquatic types, but these are, of course, only particular aspects of the radiation. When we examine a case like that of the Galapagos finches, or the marsupials, we obtain the strong impression that members of a particular animal population seek out a variety of new habits, and gradually become suited for them, until a range of new types is thus produced. This is the history of each of the groups of vertebrates, they radiate into many different types and then disappear.

11. Convergent and parallel evolution

A remarkable fact that has appeared many times in our survey is that during these radiations similar features repeatedly appear in distinct lines. It is as if the vertebrate organization produced time after time slightly different variations on a series of themes. Thus animals that feed on fishes acquire long jaws and numerous teeth. We have examples of these characteristics among the fishes themselves (garpike, *Belone*) and in the crocodiles, phytosaurs, ichthyosaurs, plesiosaurs, birds, and mammals. Perhaps even more remarkable are the 'duck-bills' of animals that sift small invertebrates from mud. There is a distinct similarity in the structures used for this purpose by *Polyodon*, the ducks themselves, and the platypus. One could continue with endless examples of the same sort, for instance, the large mouth of insect-eating animals—the frogs, swallows, swifts, and bats. The five sorts of ant-eater found among mammals provide another remarkable example of this 'convergence'; all have an elongated snout, long sticky tongue, large salivary glands, and other features. The hands of the moles show how a similar result may be arrived at by various slightly differing means (Fig. 497).

There can be no doubt that vertebrates adopting a given mode of life tend to acquire a particular structure. There is also evidence of

FIG. 497. Skeleton of the hand in various mole-like mammals.
A, *Talpa*, B, *Chrysochloris*, C, *Notoryctes* (palmar view), D, dorsal view of the same. *r*. radius; *rs*. radial sesamoid; *u*. ulna. (From Lull, *Organic Evolution*, copyright 1917, 1929 by The Macmillan Company and used with their permission.)

what we might call the converse, namely, that animals with a particular form tend to develop in certain directions. The elasmobranch fishes maintain equilibrium in the horizontal plane by a heterocercal tail, driving the head downwards, and horizontal pectoral fins and flattened front end of the body, having the opposite effect (p. 180). From this type of organization creatures of ray-like type have several times developed, markedly flattened dorso-ventrally and obtaining their propulsive thrust from the pectoral fins. Conversely among teleosts, where the compression is in a transverse plane, the bottom-living types are flattened laterally, as in the sole or plaice. Where the swim-bladder has been lost there may be dorso-ventral flattening.

The more closely we examine the evolution of populations the more signs of these similar tendencies in evolution appear. Haas and Simpson have pointed out that the distinction between convergent and parallel evolution should preserve the geometrical analogy, and therefore be based on whether or not similarity increases with evolution. Thus the acquisition of a prismatic, cement-crowned molar in several ruminants, pigs, horses, one rhinoceros (*Elasmotherium*), elephants, rodents, and others is an example of parallelism. The teeth in question have features in common but retain characteristics of the groups to which the animals belong. Cases of convergence are better known among invertebrates, especially ammonoids, than in vertebrates; they may be expected to appear especially in closely related lines as revealed by study of the detail of evolutionary sequences, whether by close examination of series of fossils, where this is possible, as among elephants, or by examination of the variety of existing animal types. The effect is so marked that such close study nearly always produces a confused taxonomy. Investigators are unable to distinguish populations that are convergent developments from those truly descended from each other. Examples we have noticed from study of modern populations are the various types of tree-living and burrowing anurans (p. 344). The 'tree-frog' and 'burrowing' conditions have been evolved both from true frogs and from toads, probably several times in each case. Again, the habit of burrowing underground, with loss of the limbs, has appeared in a number of squamate reptiles; the slow-worms, amphisbaenas, and subterranean skinks are certainly distinct lines, possibly each contains more than one, and the snakes are probably derived from another group that went underground.

12. Some tendencies in vertebrate evolution

These are only a few scattered examples, but they already suggest that the evolutionary changes of vertebrate populations follow certain patterns. Although in the history of each type there is no doubt that much is unique, yet most types tend to follow along certain lines, according to the situations they have reached. It is not possible yet for the systematic morphologist to make any complete classification or analysis of these tendencies. He can only point to a few of them, already so familiar as to be almost banal. Thus vertebrates that move in the water tend to have the fish form, with stream-lined body, vertebrae with flat articulations and paddle-like limbs. We are so used to this that perhaps its interest is often overlooked, especially the fact that the pectoral limb may revert from an elongated pentadactyl structure to a paddle, sometimes with increased number of digits and of phalanges. Evidently this form of limb is suitable for the uses demanded in the water and tends to be developed again when needed.

Similar cases that can be called in a sense a reversal of evolution are interesting not only from genetic and embryological points of view, but especially because they show strikingly that under given conditions all vertebrate populations tend to react alike, giving us the possibility of developing a reasonable science of morphology. Thus vertebrates that take to the air develop light and thin bones, those that burrow underground often lose their limbs (but among mammals these are often the main digging agents). Similar general evolutionary principles could probably be developed for each organ system. Thus the eyes develop cone-like structures in diurnal, rod-like in nocturnal species, and they become buried under the skin or lost altogether in populations that live in the dark.

13. Evolution of the whole organization

For such an analysis to be satisfactory it would have to deal not only with the evolution of isolated parts but with that of the whole organization of the activities of the population. In our present ignorance of the morphogenetic processes it is very difficult for us to provide descriptions of the nature of the whole organization that will be satisfactory. We know enough of the underlying hereditary material and the way it produces the chemical action system and organs of the body to be able to say that there are some genetic factors that affect almost the entire organization, but that sometimes individual parts change separately. Changes in the activities inherited through the egg and sperm may affect a single process, such as the deposition of pigment in the skin, but usually they influence a wide range of activities and the form of many organs. Conversely each gene is usually influenced in its action by several, perhaps many, others, and the consequent wide range of expression of each character provides the basis of variability on which natural selection can act.

There are indications that during evolution sets of characters tend to evolve together. For instance, the various features of the mammal-like organization appeared several times during the Mesozoic—the teeth, jaw and skull bones, and limbs apparently evolving together. On the other hand differing combinations are also undoubtedly possible; to take one example, the notoungulate *Thoatherium* developed the limbs but not the teeth of a horse. Genetics has made considerable advances towards providing the knowledge necessary to understand the varieties of evolutionary change, but there is still a long way to go before we can say with certainty which factors determine the direction of change.

14. Summary of evidence about evolution of vertebrates

The evidence about the history of vertebrates may be said, then, to show us the following facts: (1) In all or nearly all populations the organization of life-processes changes, though often only slowly. (2) The later types of organization usually replace the earlier in any one environment. (3) Evolutionary change is not always obviously associated with environmental change, though it may be so. (4) When different populations adopt the same habit of life they often develop similar but not identical organizations. This may not seem to be a very impressive list of discoveries, but it must be remembered that we have tried to confine ourselves to statements that can be rigidly demonstrated by the evidence produced by study of vertebrate organization. We can now combine these proved facts with our knowledge of genetics and shall find that this provides a not unsatisfactory view of the process of evolution and the factors influencing it.

Probably no population is stable either in numbers or in genetic or phenotypic characteristics. The evidence suggests that in most populations evolution is going on now and all the time. Studies such as those of mammalian populations described in Chapter XXV have shown that the number of animals in a population is seldom if ever constant. Probably the genetic and phenotypic characters of the members of the population also vary with time, perhaps actually in correlation with the fluctuations of number.

We have, therefore, a picture of an animal species as a set of individuals similar but not all identical, interbreeding with each other, though perhaps with degrees of difficulty that vary with genetical and geographical differences (themselves probably correlated). The characteristic features of such a population are given, as we have seen in Chapter I, by its power and ability to produce later populations, both like and unlike itself. Unfortunately, we know very little about these powers in vertebrates, or indeed other organisms; the present study has not dealt with them fully. They are presumably influenced by such variables as the frequency of reproduction, number of off-spring produced, and the viability of these in the face of various climatic and biotic factors, availability of food, persistence of predators, and so on. It has been pointed out by Haldane that these factors may lead to the development of various distinct sorts of organization. If the death-rate is low the productivity will also be low and those members of the population will be selected whose characters allow for a long life—for example, hypsodont molars will develop. In populations with a high death-rate due to predators or disease, however, selection will choose those individuals with high productivity and rapid development, incidentally perhaps also allowing greater variability, by which the predators and pathogens may be avoided.

Evidently the particular characteristics of a population (including its productivity) will depend on the influences to which it is subjected. Many of these variables act with an intensity that depends on the activity of the adult organisms and the energy and ingenuity with which these find situations suitable for the life of themselves and their offspring. Since this adult activity is itself influenced by hereditary and by environmental factors it is clear that the productivity and increase of a population depend on a very complicated system of interconnected variables. J. B. S. Haldane, R. A. Fisher, Sewall Wright, and others have made some progress towards analysing this situation into its elements by mathematical reasoning, but we have at present estimates for only few of the parameters involved and no approach to an exact solution. The analysis at least carries us to the point where we can visualize an approximate model of an evolving population and the factors that influence fluctuations of numbers and variability. Probably it is variation in the actions of these factors that produces the changes of the characteristics of the population that we call evolution.

15. Conservative and radical influences in evolution

In such a system we have factors that tend to keep the population the same and others that tend to make it vary; according to the preponderance of one or the other the characters of the populations will either stay steady about a mean or tend continually to change, that is to say, to evolve. We cannot make any very precise list of the factors in the two classes. Those tending to reduce evolutionary change presumably include (1) The copying or reproductive tendency that makes like produce like. Here we may include the restraints imposed by the fact that development is a highly integrated process, so that any wide departures from normality are liable to interfere with it. (2) Anything that reduces the productivity in terms of number of offspring. (3) Prevalence of predators, if these act so as to prohibit minor deviations from the previous mode of life. (4) Absence of geographical barriers. (5) Existence of stable external climatic and other physical factors. (6) Characteristics within the population tending to keep the animals in their existing conditions, rather than to seek new ones; 'adventurousness' is essential if the individuals are to enter new conditions; it corresponds to the adaptations for dispersal that are found among plants (Salisbury, 1942).

The contrary circumstances, those that encourage evolutionary development, are presumably (1) High rate of mutation, that is to say, failure of the tendency to copy. Spurway has pointed out that the extent to which change in the hereditary and developmental pattern can be varied probably differs in different populations. In some almost any change is lethal and the population appears immutable, whereas other organizations can stand considerable variations, allowing the possibility of rapid evolution. (2) High productivity, if it leads to high intra-specific competition and hence pressure to find new conditions for life. (3) Absence of predators, if this makes new adventures possible. (4) Presence of geographical barriers, which allow separation into various races that do not interbreed (or only seldom do so) and hence become more and more distinct. (5) Change in external conditions. (6) Presence of a high power of adaptibility and 'adventurousness' in the various action systems of the animals. (7) Haldane has suggested that the influence of pathogens also puts a premium on variation. The disease organism, being small, can usually evolve more rapidly than the host, and it is therefore an advantage for a member of the host population to be different from the majority, to which the pathogen is adapted.

During the present study there has been little progress towards demonstrating that these are the factors influencing evolution, though there are clear signs that some of them are at work, for instance, geographical isolation. They are treated in detail by such works as those of Huxley (1942) and Simpson (1947) and there properly discussed. These questions are raised here only as a reminder that they will have to be further considered if any satisfactory general evolutionary theory is to emerge and to be applicable to the vertebrates.

16. The direction of evolutionary change

Since we cannot closely specify the factors influencing evolution we can hardly expect to go far towards the solution of the still more difficult problem of the direction of evolutionary change. The facts of importance that have emerged from the evidence about vertebrates

are (1) That populations tend to be replaced by others of different
form, often themselves descended from the first. (2) That the later
populations often have more complicated organizations than the
earlier ones; we can hardly be said to have established this last clearly
as a rule in vertebrates, but it has repeatedly been suggested that
the evidence supports some such thesis. (3) Some later populations
invade habitats not previously occupied by vertebrates (e.g. the land).

Facts of this sort have led us repeatedly to the suspicion that the
later types are often in some way better able to carry on the self-
maintenance of life than their predecessors, and that vertebrate life
is continually invading new situations. With this goes the suspicion
that the total biomass of vertebrate life (perhaps of all life) has been
increasing and the energy flux becoming more rapid, though we have
no exact estimates to verify this.

For organizing our knowledge about the evolution of vertebrates
or other animals the above three facts about the progress or direction
of change are of very great value. The invasion of new habitats is of
particular interest, because it is usually made possible by the increase
of complexity, this provides a system of elaborate adjustments that
maintains the internal conditions nearly constant in face of fluctuations in the environment. This internal constancy or homeostasis is,
of course, only a development of the general tendency to self-maintenance, which characterizes all living organisms; but it is carried to its
extreme in the higher vertebrates, giving them the power to maintain
life under varied and unpropitious conditions.

17. The influences controlling evolutionary progress

Our analysis of the factors affecting evolution gives us clues about
the influences that have produced this increase of complexity. Excess
productivity and intra-specific competition force sections of the population to try new habits. Those with the ability to do so may, if they
can tolerate new external conditions, find situations in which they can
flourish. So a new type becomes developed, only to meet later the
competition of its own descendants or other invaders and hence be
driven to extinction or to the colonization of still other fields.

If we have interpreted the situation correctly there can be said to
be an evolutionary path that is progressive, in the sense of enabling
life to be lived effectively under wider and wider conditions. Lotka
has suggested that it is possible to recognize a 'basic principle defining
the direction of organic evolution', namely, that the collective effects
of organisms 'tend to maximize, on the one hand, the energy intake

of organic nature from the sun, and on the other, the outgo of free energy by dissipative processes in living and in decaying dead organisms'. During the present study we have not been able to show rigorously that all evolution follows such a principle, but the data are not inconsistent with it. It may be that vertebrates have proceeded farther along the path suggested by Lotka's principle than any other animals. The birds and mammals probably turn over energy faster than other vertebrates. The point that must not be overlooked is that they do this in order to provide the means by which they can remain constant, in spite of fluctuations in the external conditions of an environment that is different in composition from the living system.

We cannot at present discern with certainty the principles that determine the change of animal form, but we can see something of the influences that have modified the original vertebrate type to produce the great variety of creatures that has existed and remains to-day. We cannot give tables of numbers to show how the variables have operated to keep *Ceratodus* nearly constant for 200 million years while related descendants have gone on to produce the whole variety of tetrapod life. But we can suggest that it is worth while pursuing the study as a means of building a truly general science of zoology. We begin to see signs of the principles according to which the vast populations of animals interact with each other, with the plants, and with the inorganic world. The changes that these interactions produce seem to be, if not constantly in one direction, at least often such as to allow the appearance of more varied and complicated forms of life, ever more able to maintain themselves constant and apart from the environment, and hence to exist in a wider range of conditions. The effect of this evolutionary change has probably been to increase the amount of material organized into living things, while the total energy flux through the system has also been enlarged.

This finding is not a mere rehabilitation of the complacent anthropocentric prejudices of the nineteenth century. The conclusion that there is a sense in which the mammals and man are among the highest animals should be based on objective analysis of the behaviour of the populations of vertebrates and the energy flux through them. However, it has been repeatedly emphasized that we still have a long way to go before we have the information necessary to understand these very slow changes. It has only been possible in this volume to suggest certain principles that may one day make possible a satisfactory systematic study of the life of vertebrates.

REFERENCES

GENERAL WORKS ON EVOLUTIONARY THEORY

BURTON, M. 1949. *The Story of Animal Life*. London.
FISHER, R. A. 1929. *The Genetical Theory of Natural Selection*. Cambridge.
FORD, E. B. 1938. *Mendelism and Evolution*. London.
GOODRICH, E. S. 1936. *Evolution*. Essays dedicated to Professor Goodrich, ed. G. R. de Beer. Oxford.
HAAS, O., and SIMPSON, G. G. 1946. 'Analysis of some Phylogenetic Terms.' *Proc. Amer. Philos. Soc.* **90**, 319.
HALDANE, J. B. S. 1933. *The Causes of Evolution*. London.
—— 1949. *La ricercha scientifica*. **19**.
HUXLEY, J. S. 1942. *Evolution, the Modern Synthesis*. London.
LAMARCK, J. B. 1809. *Zoological Philosophy*, translated by H. Elliot, 1914. London.
LOTKA, A. J. 1945. 'The Law of Evolution as a Maximal Principle.' *Human Biology*, **17**, 167.
LULL, R. S. 1940. *Organic Evolution*. New York.
MAYR, E. 1942. *Systematics and the Origin of Species*. New York.
MULLER, H. J. 1939. 'Reversibility in Evolution from the Standpoint of Genetics.' *Biol. Rev.* **14**, 261.
OSBORN, H. F. 1918. *The Origin and Evolution of Life*. London.
SALISBURY, E. J. 1942. *The Reproductive Capacity of Plants*. London.
SCHOENHEIMER, R. 1942. 'The Dynamic State of Body Constituents.' Cambridge, Mass.
SIMPSON, G. G. 1944. *Tempo and Mode in Evolution*. New York.
SPURWAY, H. 1949. *La ricercha scientifica*. **19**.
THOMPSON, D'ARCY, W. 1942. *On Growth and Form*. 2nd edition. Cambridge.

GENERAL WORKS ON VERTEBRATE ZOOLOGY

BALDWIN, E. H. F. 1937. *Comparative Biochemistry*. Cambridge.
BARCROFT, J. 1936. *Features in the Architecture of Physiological Function*. Cambridge.
BERG, L. S. 1926. *Nomogenesis*. London.
BOLK, L., GOPPERT, E., KALLIUS, E., and LUBOSCH, W. 1931–9. *Handbuch der vergleichenden Anatomie der Wirbeltiere*. Berlin.
BRACHET, A. 1935. *Traité d'embryologie des vertébrés*. 2nd edition. Paris.
BREHM, A. E. 1876. *Thierleben*. 2nd edition. Leipzig.
COTT, H. B. 1940. *Adaptive Coloration in Animals*. London.
DE BEER, G. R. 1935. *Vertebrate Zoology*. London.
—— 1937. *The Development of the Vertebrate Skull*. Oxford.
GEGENBAUR, C. 1859. *Grundzüge der vergleichenden Anatomie*. Leipzig.
GOODRICH, E. S. 1930. *Studies on the Structure and Development of Vertebrates*. London.
GRAHAM KERR, J. G. 1919. *Text-book of Embryology*, vol. ii. *Vertebrata*.
HUXLEY, J. S., and DE BEER, G. R. 1934. *The Elements of Experimental Embryology*. Cambridge.
HUXLEY, T. H. 1871. *The Anatomy of the Vertebrate Animals*. London.
HYMAN, L. H. 1942. *Comparative Vertebrate Anatomy*. Philadelphia.
IHLE, J. F. W. and others. 1927. *Vergleichende Anatomie der Wirbeltiere*. Berlin.
JOHNSTON, J. B. 1906. *The Nervous System of Vertebrates*.

KAPPERS, C. U. A. 1929. *The Evolution of the Nervous System in Invertebrates, Vertebrates, and Man.* Haarlem.
—— HUBER, G. C., and CROSBY, E. 1936. *The Comparative Anatomy of the Nervous System of Vertebrates.* New York.
KINGSLEY, J. S. 1912. *Comparative Anatomy of Vertebrates.* London.
KORSCHELT, E., and HEIDER, K. 1936. *Vergleichende Entwicklungsgeschichte der Tiere.* 2 vols. Jena.
NEAL, H. V., and RAND, H. W. 1936. *Comparative Anatomy.* Philadelphia.
—— —— 1939. *Chordate Anatomy.* London.
OWEN, R. 1866. *On the Anatomy of Vertebrates.* London.
PARKER, T. J., and HASWELL, W. A. 1940. *A Text-book of Zoology.* 6th edition, revised by C. Foster Cooper. London.
PLATE, L. 1922. *Allgemeine Zoologie und Abstammungslehre.* Jena.
RANVIER, L. 1878. *Leçons sur l'histologie du système nerveux.* Paris.
REYNOLDS, S. H. 1913. *The Vertebrate Skeleton.* Cambridge.
SANDERS, J. T., and MANTON, S. M. 1949. *A Manual of Practical Vertebrate Morphology.* 2nd edition. London.
SHERBORN, C. D. 1931. *Index Animalium.* London.
WALLS, G. L. 1942. *The Vertebrate Eye.* Michigan.
WEISS, P. 1939. *Principles of Development.* New York.
WIEDERSHEIM, R. 1883. *Lehrbuch der vergleichenden Anatomie der Wirbelthiere.* Jena.
—— 1886. *Elements of the Comparative Anatomy of Vertebrates.* Translated by W. N. Parker (with additions).
WINTERSTEIN, H. 1910–25. *Handbuch der vergleichenden Physiologie.* Jena.
YOUNG, J. Z. 1936. 'The Evolution of the Nervous System and of the Relationship of Organism and Environment.' In *Evolution,* essays presented to E. S. Goodrich. Oxford.

GENERAL WORKS ON GEOLOGY AND PALAEONTOLOGY

ABEL, O. 1909. *Die Stämme der Wirbeltiere.* Berlin.
BULLARD, E. C. 1943. 'Geological Time.' *Mem. Manchester Lit. Philos. Soc.* **86,** 55.
EDINGER, T. 1929. *Die fossilen Gehirne.* Berlin.
—— 1948. 'Evolution of the Horse Brain.' *Mem. Geol. Soc. Amer.* **25.**
GOODMAN, C., and EVANS, R. D. 1941. 'Age Measurements by Radioactivity.' *Bull. Geol. Soc. Amer.,* **52,** 491.
HOLMES, A. 1944. *Principles of Physical Geology.* London.
—— 1947. 'The Construction of a Geological Time Scale'. *Trans. Geol. Soc. Glasgow,* **21,** 117.
KNOPF, J. 1949. 'Time in Earth History.' *Genetics, Palaeontology and Evolution.* Edited by G. L. Jepson and others, Princeton.
ROMER, A. S. 1941. *Man and the Vertebrates.* 3rd edition. Chicago.
—— 1945. *Vertebrate Palaeontology.* 2nd edition. Chicago.
SCHUCHERT, C., and DUNBAR, C. O. 1933. *Text-book of Geology,* Pt. 2. 3rd edition. New York.
WOODWARD, A. S. 1898. *Vertebrate Palaeontology.* Cambridge.
ZEUNER, F. E. 1946. *Dating the Past.* London.
ZITTEL, K. A. v. 1925 and 1932. *Text-book of Palaeontology.* 2 vols. Revised by A. Smith Woodward. London.

CHAPTER II. *AMPHIOXUS*

BARRINGTON, E. J. W. 1937. 'The Digestive System of *Amphioxus.*' *Phil. Trans. Roy. Soc.* **228,** 269.

GRASSÉ, P. P. 1948. *Traité de Zoologie*. Paris.

PIETSCHMANN, V. 1929. 'Acrania.' In Kükenthal, *Handbuch der Zoologie*. Berlin.

WILLEY, A. 1894. *Amphioxus and the Ancestry of Vertebrates*.

CHAPTER III. EARLY CHORDATES

BARRINGTON, E. J. W. 1940. 'Feeding and Digestion in *Glossobalanus*.' *Quart. J. Micr. Sci.* **82,** 227.

BERRILL, N. J. 1936. 'The Evolution and Classification of Ascidians.' *Phil. Trans. Roy. Soc., Lond.* **226,** 43.

GARSTANG, S. and W. 1928. 'On the Development of Botrylloides and Its Bearing on Some Morphological Problems.' *Quart. J. Micr. Sci.* **72,** 1.

GARSTANG, W. 1928. 'The Morphology of Tunicata.' *Quart. J. Micr. Sci.* **72,** 51.

GASKELL, W. H. 1908. *The Origin of Vertebrates*. London.

HARMER, S. F. 1910. 'Hemichordata', in *Cambridge Natural History*. London.

HERDMAN, W. A. 1910. 'Ascidians and Amphioxus', ibid.

HORST, C. J. VAN DER. 1927–36. 'Hemichordata.' Bronn's *Klassen u. Ordnungen des Tierreichs*, vol. iv, Abt. 4, Buch 2, Teil 2.

—— 1932. 'Enteropneusta.' Kükenthal, *Handbuch der Zoologie*, vol. iii, Abt. 2.

LOHMANN, H., HUUS, J., and IHLE, I. F. W. 1933. 'Tunicata.' Kükenthal, *Handbuch der Zoologie*, vol. v, Abt. 2.

PATTEN, W. 1912. *The Evolution of Vertebrates and their Kin*. Philadelphia.

CHAPTER IV. AGNATHA

BARRINGTON, E. J. W. 1936. 'Proteolytic Digestion and the Problem of the Pancreas in *Lampetra*.' *Proc. Roy. Soc. Lond.*, B, **121,** 221; also 1942, *J. Exp. Biol.* **19,** 45.

GAGE, S. H. 1929. 'Lampreys and Their Ways.' *Scientific Monthly*, **27,** 401.

HUBBS, C. 1925. 'The Life Cycle and Growth of Lampreys.' *Papers Michigan Acad. Sci.* **4,** 587.

KNOWLES, F. G. W. 1941. 'The Duration of Larval Life in Ammocoetes.' *Proc. Zool. Soc., A,* **III,** 101.

PIETSCHMANN, V. 1933. In Kükenthal's *Handbuch der Zoologie*, vol. vi. Berlin.

SCHULTZ, L. P. 1930. 'The Life History of *Lampetra planeri*.' *Occ. Pap. Mus. Zool. Univ. Michigan*, **221,** 1.

STENSIÖ, E. 1925. *Downtonian and Devonian Vertebrates of Spitzbergen*. Oslo.

—— 1932. *The Cephalaspids of Great Britain*. British Museum of Natural History. London.

WHITE, E. I. 1935. 'On the Ostracoderm *Pteraspis*, and the relationships of the Agnathous Vertebrates.' *Phil. Trans. Roy. Soc.*, **225,** 381.

CHAPTERS V–X. FISHES

BERG, L. S. 1940. *Classification of Fishes, Both Recent and Fossil*. Moscow (with English translation). Also American edition, 1947.

BRIDGE, T. W., and BOULANGER, G. A. 1904. *Cambridge Natural History*, vol. vii. London.

CALDERWOOD, W. L. 1907. *The Life of the Salmon*. London.

DEAN, B. 1895. *Fishes, Living and Fossil*. New York.

GOODRICH, E. S. 1909. In Lankester's *Treatise on Zoology*, vol. ix. London.

GRAY, J. 1933, &c. 'Studies in Animal Locomotion.' *Proc. Roy. Soc. Lond.*, B, **113,** and *J. Exp. Biol.* **10,** 386 and **13,** 170.

HARRIS, J. E. 1936. 'The Role of the Fins in the Equilibrium of the Swimming Fish.' *J. Exp. Biol.* **13,** 476 and **15,** 32.

JORDAN, D. S. 1905. *A Guide to the Study of Fishes*. London.

MALLOCH, P. D. 1910. *Life History and Habits of the Salmon, Sea Trout, Trout, and other Freshwater Fish*. London.

MOY-THOMAS, J. A. 1939. *Palaeozoic Fishes*. London.

NORMAN, J. R. 1931. *A History of Fishes*. London.

REGAN, C. T. 1932. *Guide to the British Freshwater Fishes*. British Museum. London.

ROMER, A. S. 1946. 'The Early Evolution of Fishes.' *Quart. Rev. Biol.* **21**, 33.

SMITH, J. L. B. 1940. 'A Living Coelacanthid Fish from South Africa.' *Trans. Roy. Soc. South Africa*, **28**.

WATSON, D. M. S. 1937. 'The Acanthodian Fishes.' *Phil. Trans. Roy. Soc. Lond.*, **228**.

WESTOLL, T. S. 1944. 'The Haplolepidae—A Study in Taxonomy and Evolution.' *Bull. Am. Mus. Nat. Hist.* **83**, 1.

—— 1945. 'A New Cephalaspid Fish.' *Trans. Roy. Soc. Edinb.* **61**, 341.

—— 1945. 'The Paired Fins of Placoderms.' Ibid. **61**, 381.

—— 1949. 'On the Evolution of the Dipnoi.' *Genetics, Palaeontology and Evolution*. Edited by G. L. Jepson and others. Princeton.

WHITE, E. I. 1946. '*Jamoytius kerwoodi*, a New Chordate from the Silurian of Lanarkshire.' *Geological Magazine*, **83**, 89.

CHAPTER XI. FISHERIES

DAVIS, F. M. 1937. *An Account of the Fishing Gear of England and Wales*. Min. Agr. Fish., Fishery Investigations, Ser. 2, vol. 15.

GRAHAM, M. 1943. *The Fish Gate*. London.

GROSS, F., and others. 1946. 'Application of Fertilizers to an Open Sea Loch.' *Nature*, **158**, 187.

—— 1949. 'Further Observations on Fish Growth in a Fertilized Sea Loch.' *J. Mar. Biol. Assoc.* **28**, 1.

HICKLING, C. F. 1935. *The Hake*, London.

OMMANEY, F. D. 1949. *The Ocean*. Oxford.

RUSSELL, E. S. 1942. *The Overfishing Problem*. Cambridge.

THOMPSON, W. F. 1935. 'Conservation of the Pacific Halibut.' *Rep. Smithsonian Inst.*, p. 361.

CHAPTERS XII, XIII. AMPHIBIA

CASE, E. C. 1946. 'A Census of Determinable Genera of Stegocephalia.' *Trans. Amer. Phil. Soc.* **35**, 325.

EVANS, F. G. 1946. 'Anatomy and Function of the Foreleg in Salamander Locomotion.' *Anat. Rec.* **95**, 257–81.

FRANCIS, E. T. B. 1934. *The Anatomy of the Salamander*. London.

GADOW, H. 1909. *Amphibia and Reptiles*. Cambridge Natural History. London.

GAUPP, E. 1901. *Anatomie des Frosches*. Braunschweig.

GRAY, J., and LISSMAN, H. W. 1946. 'The Co-ordination of Limb Movements in the Amphibia.' *J. Exp. Biol.* **23**, 133.

GREGORY, W. K., and RAVEN, H. C. 1941. 'The Origin and Early Evolution of Paired Fins and Limbs.' *Ann. N.Y. Acad. Sci.* **42**, 273.

MARSHALL, A. M. 1920. *The Frog*, 11th edition, edited by F. W. Gamble. London.

NOBLE, G. K. 1931. *Biology of the Amphibia*. New York.

ROMER, A. S. 1947. 'A Review of Labyrinthodonts.' *Bull. Mus. Comp. Zool.*, Harvard, **99**, 368.

WATSON, D. M. S. 1919 and 1925. 'Evolution and Origin of Amphibia.' *Phil. Trans. Roy. Soc.* **209** and **214.**
—— 1939. 'The Origin of Frogs.' *Trans. Roy. Soc. Edinb.* **60,** 195.
WESTOLL, T. S. 1943. 'The Origin of Tetrapods.' *Biol. Rev.* **18,** 78, and *Proc. Roy. Soc.,* B, **131,** 373.

CHAPTERS XIV, XV. REPTILES

COPE, E. D. *The Crocodiles, Lizards, and Snakes of North America.*
DITMARS, R. J. 1936. *The Reptiles of North America.*
GADOW, H. 1909. 'Amphibia and Reptiles.' *Cambridge Natural History.* London.
GRAY, J. 1946. 'The Mechanism of Locomotion in Snakes.' *J. Exp. Biol.* **23,** 101.
LEIGHTON, G. R. 1901. *British Serpents.* Edinburgh.
—— 1903. *The Life History of British Lizards.* Edinburgh.
OWEN, R. 1849–84. *A History of British Fossil Reptiles.* London.
POPE, C. H. 1937. *Snakes Alive and How They Live.*
SWINTON, W. E. 1934. *The Dinosaurs.* London.
WATSON, D. M. S. 1919. '*Seymouria.*' *Proc. Zool. Soc. Lond.*
WHITE, T. E. 1939. 'The Osteology of *Seymouria.*' *Bull. Mus. Comp. Zool. Harvard,* **85.**
WILLISTON, S. W. 1925. *The Osteology of the Reptiles.* Cambridge, Mass.

CHAPTERS XVI–XVIII. BIRDS

ALLEN, C. M. 1926. *Birds and their Attributes.* London.
AYMAR, G. C. 1936. *Bird Flight.* London.
BEDDARD, F. E. 1898. *The Structure and Classification of Birds.* London.
BRADLEY, O. C. 1938. *The Structure of the Fowl.* 2nd edition. London.
EVANS, A. H. 1900. 'Birds.' *Cambridge Natural History,* vol. ix. London.
FISHER, J. 1939. *Birds as Animals.* London.
HEILMANN, G. 1926. *The Origin of Birds.* London.
HORTON-SMITH, C. 1926. *The Flight of Birds.* London.
HUXLEY, J. S. 1914. 'Courtship of the Great Crested Grebe.' *Proc. Zool. Soc. London,* p. 491.
LACK, D. 1947. *Darwin's Finches.* Cambridge.
LILLIE, F. R., and JUHN, M. 1932 and 1938. 'The Physiology of the Development of Feathers.' *Physiol. Zool.* **5** and **11.**
PETERS, J. L. 1931 (onwards). *Check List of Birds of the World.* Harvard.
PYCRAFT, W. P. 1910. *A History of Birds.* London.
STORER, J. H. 1948. *The Flight of Birds.* Michigan.
STRESEMAN, E. 1934. In E. Kükenthal, *Handbuch der Zoologie,* vol. vii, 2.
THOMSON, J. A. 1923. *The Biology of Birds.* London.
TINBERGEN, N. 1948. 'Social Releasers.' *The Wilson Bulletin,* **60,** 6.
WETMORE, A. 1930. 'A Systematic Classification for the Birds of the World.' *Proc. U.S. National Mus.* **76,** 1–8.

CHAPTERS XIX–XXXI. MAMMALS

BAUM, H., and PEITSCHMANN, O. 1938. *Handbuch der Anatomie des Hundes.*
BEDDARD, F. E. 1909. 'Mammalia.' *Cambridge Natural History.* London.
—— 1902. *A Text-book of Zoogeography.* Cambridge.
BENSLEY, R. A. 1938. *Anatomy of the Rabbit.* 6th edition. Toronto.
BRADLEY, O. C. 1927. *Topographical Anatomy of the Dog.* Edinburgh.
—— 1920. *Topographical Anatomy of the Horse.* Edinburgh.

BRONN, H. G. 1859 (onwards). *Die Klassen und Ordnungen des Thier-Reichs*, vols. i–v. *Mammalia*.

BROOM, R. 1932. *The Mammal-like Reptiles of South Africa*. London.

BURRELL, H. 1927. *The Platypus*. Sydney.

CLARK, W. E. Le Gros. 1949. *History of the Primates*. Brit. Mus. Nat. Hist.

—— 1934. *Early Forerunners of Man*. London.

CUNNINGHAM, D. J. 1943. *Text-book of Anatomy*. London.

DAVISON, A. 1937. *Mammalian Anatomy, with Special Reference to the Cat*.

FLOWER, W. H. 1885. *Introduction to the Osteology of the Mammalia*. London.

—— and LYDEKKER, R. 1891. *An Introduction to the Study of Mammals, Living and Extinct*. London.

GERHARDT, U. 1909. *Das Kaninchen*. Leipzig.

GRAY, H. 1946. *Gray's Anatomy*. 29th edition. London.

GREENE, E. C. 1935. 'Anatomy of the Rat.' *Trans. Amer. Phil. Soc.* **27**. Philadelphia.

GREGORY, W. K. 1922. *The Origin and Evolution of the Human Dentition*. Baltimore.

—— 1934. 'A Half Century of Trituberculy.' *Proc. Amer. Phil. Soc.* **37**, 169–317.

HAMILTON, W. J. 1939. *American Mammals*. New York.

HARTMAN, C. G., and STRAUS, W. L. 1933. *The Anatomy of the Rhesus Monkey*. London.

HENDERSON, J., and CRAIG, E. C. 1932. *Economic Mammalogy*. London.

HOWELL, A. B. 1930. *Aquatic Mammals*. Springfield.

LYDEKKER, R. 1896. *A Geographical History of Mammals*. Cambridge.

OSBORN, H. F. 1929. *Titanotheres*. Washington.

REEVE, E. C. R. 1940. 'Relative Growth in the Snout of Anteaters.' *Proc. Zool. Soc.* **110**, 47.

REIGHARD, J. E., and JENNINGS, H. S. 1901. *Anatomy of the Cat*. 2nd edition. New York.

ROMER, A. S., and PRICE, L. W. 1940. *Review of the Pelycosauria*. Geol. Soc. Amer., Special Paper No. 28.

SCOTT, W. B. 1913. *A History of Land Mammals in the Western Hemisphere*. New York.

SIMPSON, G. G. 1929. *American Mesozoic Mammalia*. Mem. Peabody. Mus. Nat. Hist. Pt. I. New Haven and London.

—— 1945. 'The Principles of Classification and a Classification of the Mammals.' *Bull. Amer. Mus. Nat. Hist.* **85**.

SISSON, S., and GROSSMAN, J. D. 1938. *The Anatomy of the Domestic Animal*. 3rd edition. Philadelphia and London.

WEBER, M. 1927–8. *Die Säugetiere*. II. Auflage. Unter Mitwirkung von O. Abel und H. M. de Burlet.

WOOD JONES, F. 1916. *Arboreal Man*. London.

—— 1929. *Man's Place among the Mammals*. London.

—— 1941. *The Principles of Anatomy as seen in the Hand*. London.

—— 1944. *Structure and Function as seen in the Foot*. London.

—— 1948. *Hallmarks of Mankind*. London.

INDEX

Page references in italic are to illustrations on those pages

3 C

PRINTED IN
GREAT BRITAIN
AT THE
UNIVERSITY PRESS
OXFORD
BY
CHARLES BATEY
PRINTER
TO THE
UNIVERSITY